The Diversity of Life

interactive
SCIENCE

PEARSON

Boston, Massachusetts
Chandler, Arizona
Glenview, Illinois
Upper Saddle River, New Jersey

AUTHORS

You're an author!

As you write in this science book, your answers and personal discoveries will be recorded for you to keep, making this book unique to you. That is why you are one of the primary authors of this book.

✏️ **In the space below, print your name, school, town, and state. Then write a short autobiography that includes your interests and accomplishments.**

YOUR NAME
_____

SCHOOL
_____

TOWN, STATE
_____

AUTOBIOGRAPHY
_____

_____

_____

_____

_____

_____

_____

_____

Your Photo

Acknowledgments appear on page 307, which constitute an extension of this copyright page.

ISBN-13: 978-0-13-369367-6
ISBN-10: 0-13-369367-8
1 2 3 4 5 6 7 8 9 10 V003 14 13 12 11 10

ON THE COVER
A Hidden Defense
The nudibranchs pictured on the cover are sea slugs—snails without shells. Most sea slugs are tiny, only about 1.27 cm long. Sea slugs can't move very fast. So why don't faster animals target them as an easy meal? The sea slugs store poison from animals they eat. If other animals eat the sea slugs, they get a mouthful of poison.

Program Authors

DON BUCKLEY, M.Sc.
*Information and Communications Technology Director,
The School at Columbia University, New York, New York*
Mr. Buckley has been at the forefront of K–12 educational technology for nearly two decades. A founder of New York City Independent School Technologists (NYCIST) and long-time chair of New York Association of Independent Schools' annual IT conference, he has taught students on two continents and created multimedia and Internet-based instructional systems for schools worldwide.

ZIPPORAH MILLER, M.A.Ed.
Associate Executive Director for Professional Programs and Conferences, National Science Teachers Association, Arlington, Virginia
Associate executive director for professional programs and conferences at NSTA, Ms. Zipporah Miller is a former K–12 science supervisor and STEM coordinator for the Prince George's County Public School District in Maryland. She is a science education consultant who has overseen curriculum development and staff training for more than 150 district science coordinators.

MICHAEL J. PADILLA, Ph.D.
Associate Dean and Director, Eugene P. Moore School of Education, Clemson University, Clemson, South Carolina
A former middle school teacher and a leader in middle school science education, Dr. Michael Padilla has served as president of the National Science Teachers Association and as a writer of the National Science Education Standards. He is professor of science education at Clemson University. As lead author of the *Science Explorer* series, Dr. Padilla has inspired the team in developing a program that promotes student inquiry and meets the needs of today's students.

KATHRYN THORNTON, Ph.D.
Professor and Associate Dean, School of Engineering and Applied Science, University of Virginia, Charlottesville, Virginia
Selected by NASA in May 1984, Dr. Kathryn Thornton is a veteran of four space flights. She has logged over 975 hours in space, including more than 21 hours of extravehicular activity. As an author on the *Scott Foresman Science* series, Dr. Thornton's enthusiasm for science has inspired teachers around the globe.

MICHAEL E. WYSESSION, Ph.D.
Associate Professor of Earth and Planetary Science, Washington University, St. Louis, Missouri
An author on more than 50 scientific publications, Dr. Wysession was awarded the prestigious Packard Foundation Fellowship and Presidential Faculty Fellowship for his research in geophysics. Dr. Wysession is an expert on Earth's inner structure and has mapped various regions of Earth using seismic tomography. He is known internationally for his work in geoscience education and outreach.

Understanding by Design Author

GRANT WIGGINS, Ed.D.
President, Authentic Education, Hopewell, New Jersey
Dr. Wiggins is coauthor of *Understanding by Design®* (UbD), a philosophy of instructional design. UbD is a disciplined way of thinking about curriculum design, assessment, and instruction that moves teaching from covering the content to ensuring understanding. Dr. Wiggins is one of today's most influential educational reformers, and consults with schools, districts, and state education departments.

Planet Diary Author

JACK HANKIN
Science/Mathematics Teacher, The Hilldale School, Daly City, California Founder, Planet Diary Web site
Mr. Hankin is the creator and writer of Planet Diary, a science current events Web site. Mr. Hankin is passionate about bringing science news and environmental awareness into classrooms. He's offered numerous Planet Diary workshops at NSTA and other events to train middle school and high school teachers.

ELL Consultant

JIM CUMMINS, Ph.D.
Professor and Canada Research Chair, Curriculum, Teaching and Learning department at the University of Toronto
Dr. Cummins's research focuses on literacy development in multilingual schools and the role of technology in promoting student learning across the curriculum. The *Interactive Science* program incorporates essential research-based principles for integrating language with the teaching of academic content based on Dr. Cummins's instructional framework.

Reading Consultant

HARVEY DANIELS, Ph.D.
Professor of Secondary Education, University of New Mexico, Albuquerque, New Mexico
Dr. Daniels serves as an international consultant to schools, districts, and educational agencies. Dr. Daniels has authored or coauthored 13 books on language, literacy, and education. His most recent works include *Comprehension and Collaboration: Inquiry Circles in Action* and *Subjects Matter: Every Teacher's Guide to Content-Area Reading.*

REVIEWERS

Contributing Writers

Edward Aguado, Ph.D.
Professor, Department of
   Geography
San Diego State University
San Diego, California

Elizabeth Coolidge-Stolz, M.D.
Medical Writer
North Reading, Massachusetts

Donald L. Cronkite, Ph.D.
Professor of Biology
Hope College
Holland, Michigan

Jan Jenner, Ph.D.
Science Writer
Talladega, Alabama

Linda Cronin Jones, Ph.D.
Associate Professor of Science and
   Environmental Education
University of Florida
Gainesville, Florida

T. Griffith Jones, Ph.D.
Clinical Associate Professor
   of Science Education
College of Education
University of Florida
Gainesville, Florida

Andrew C. Kemp, Ph.D.
Teacher
Jefferson County Public Schools
Louisville, Kentucky

Matthew Stoneking, Ph.D.
Associate Professor of Physics
Lawrence University
Appleton, Wisconsin

R. Bruce Ward, Ed.D.
Senior Research Associate
Science Education Department
Harvard-Smithsonian Center for
   Astrophysics
Cambridge, Massachusetts

Content Reviewers

Paul D. Beale, Ph.D.
Department of Physics
University of Colorado at Boulder
Boulder, Colorado

Jeff R. Bodart, Ph.D.
Professor of Physical Sciences
Chipola College
Marianna, Florida

Joy Branlund, Ph.D.
Department of Earth Science
Southwestern Illinois College
Granite City, Illinois

Marguerite Brickman, Ph.D.
Division of Biological Sciences
University of Georgia
Athens, Georgia

Bonnie J. Brunkhorst, Ph.D.
Science Education and Geological
   Sciences
California State University
San Bernardino, California

Michael Castellani, Ph.D.
Department of Chemistry
Marshall University
Huntington, West Virginia

Charles C. Curtis, Ph.D.
Research Associate Professor
   of Physics
University of Arizona
Tucson, Arizona

Diane I. Doser, Ph.D.
Department of Geological
   Sciences
University of Texas
El Paso, Texas

Rick Duhrkopf, Ph.D.
Department of Biology
Baylor University
Waco, Texas

Alice K. Hankla, Ph.D.
The Galloway School
Atlanta, Georgia

Mark Henriksen, Ph.D.
Physics Department
University of Maryland
Baltimore, Maryland

Chad Hershock, Ph.D.
Center for Research on Learning
   and Teaching
University of Michigan
Ann Arbor, Michigan

Jeremiah N. Jarrett, Ph.D.
Department of Biology
Central Connecticut State
   University
New Britain, Connecticut

Scott L. Kight, Ph.D.
Department of Biology
Montclair State University
Montclair, New Jersey

Jennifer O. Liang, Ph.D.
Department of Biology
University of Minnesota–Duluth
Duluth, Minnesota

Candace Lutzow-Felling, Ph.D.
Director of Education
The State Arboretum of Virginia
University of Virginia
Boyce, Virginia

Cortney V. Martin, Ph.D.
Virginia Polytechnic Institute
Blacksburg, Virginia

Joseph F. McCullough, Ph.D.
Physics Program Chair
Cabrillo College
Aptos, California

Heather Mernitz, Ph.D.
Department of Physical Science
Alverno College
Milwaukee, Wisconsin

Sadredin C. Moosavi, Ph.D.
Department of Earth and
   Environmental Sciences
Tulane University
New Orleans, Louisiana

David L. Reid, Ph.D.
Department of Biology
Blackburn College
Carlinville, Illinois

Scott M. Rochette, Ph.D.
Department of the Earth Sciences
SUNY College at Brockport
Brockport, New York

Karyn L. Rogers, Ph.D.
Department of Geological
   Sciences
University of Missouri
Columbia, Missouri

Laurence Rosenhein, Ph.D.
Department of Chemistry
Indiana State University
Terre Haute, Indiana

Sara Seager, Ph.D.
Department of Planetary Sciences
   and Physics
Massachusetts Institute of
   Technology
Cambridge, Massachusetts

Tom Shoberg, Ph.D.
Missouri University of Science
   and Technology
Rolla, Missouri

Patricia Simmons, Ph.D.
North Carolina State University
Raleigh, North Carolina

William H. Steinecker, Ph.D.
Research Scholar
Miami University
Oxford, Ohio

Paul R. Stoddard, Ph.D.
Department of Geology and
   Environmental Geosciences
Northern Illinois University
DeKalb, Illinois

John R. Villarreal, Ph.D.
Department of Chemistry
The University of Texas–Pan
   American
Edinburg, Texas

John R. Wagner, Ph.D.
Department of Geology
Clemson University
Clemson, South Carolina

Jerry Waldvogel, Ph.D.
Department of Biological Sciences
Clemson University
Clemson, South Carolina

Donna L. Witter, Ph.D.
Department of Geology
Kent State University
Kent, Ohio

Edward J. Zalisko, Ph.D.
Department of Biology
Blackburn College
Carlinville, Illinois

Museum of Science.

Special thanks to the Museum of Science,
Boston, Massachusetts, and Ioannis Miaoulis,
the Museum's president and director, for
serving as content advisors for the technology
and design strand in this program.

CONTENTS

 Enter the Lab zone for hands-on inquiry.

Chapter Lab Investigation:
• Directed Inquiry: Please Pass the Bread
• Open Inquiry: Please Pass the Bread

Inquiry Warm-Ups: • Is It Living or Nonliving? • Can You Organize a Junk Drawer? • What Organism Goes Where? • Observing Similarities

Quick Labs: • React! • Compare Broth Samples • Classifying Seeds • Make a Classification Chart • Living Mysteries • Staining Leaves • Common Ancestors

my science online .com

Go to MyScienceOnline.com to interact with this chapter's content. Keyword: Introduction to Living Things

UNTAMED SCIENCE
• What Can You Explore in a Swamp?

PLANET DIARY
• Introduction to Living Things

INTERACTIVE ART
• Redi's and Pasteur's Experiments
• Taxonomic Key

ART IN MOTION
• Finding a Common Ancestor

VIRTUAL LAB
• Classifying Life

CHAPTER 2

Viruses, Bacteria, Protists, and Fungi

 Enter the Lab zone for hands-on inquiry.

Chapter Lab Investigation:
• Directed Inquiry: Comparing Disinfectants
• Open Inquiry: Comparing Disinfectants

Inquiry Warm-Ups: • Which Lock Does the Key Fit? • How Quickly Can Bacteria Multiply? • What Lives in a Drop of Pond Water? • There's a Fungus Among Us

Quick Labs: • How Many Viruses Fit on a Pin? • How Viruses Spread • Classifying Bacteria • Drawing Conclusions • Observing Pseudopod Movement • Predicting • Observing Slime Mold • Do All Molds Look Alike? • Considering Fungi as Decomposers

my science ONLINE.com

Go to MyScienceOnline.com to interact with this chapter's content. **Keyword: Viruses, Bacteria, Protists, and Fungi**

> **UNTAMED SCIENCE**
• What Good Are Mushrooms?

> **PLANET DIARY**
• Viruses, Bacteria, Protists, and Fungi

> **INTERACTIVE ART**
• Virus Reproduction • Exploring Protozoans

> **ART IN MOTION**
• The Benefits of Bacteria

> **REAL-WORLD INQUIRY**
• Using Organisms in the Environment

CONTENTS

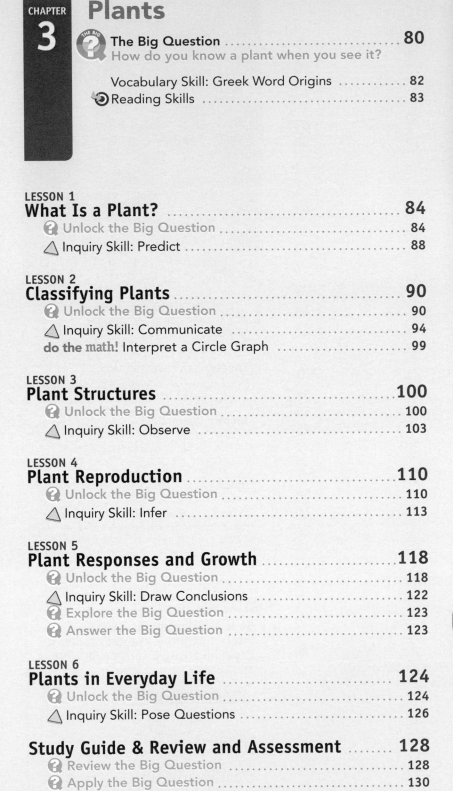

Lab zone Enter the Lab zone for hands-on inquiry.

Chapter Lab Investigation:
• Directed Inquiry: Investigating Stomata
• Open Inquiry: Investigating Stomata

Inquiry Warm-Ups: • What Do Leaves Reveal About Plants? • Will Mosses Absorb Water? • Which Plant Part Is It? • Make the Pollen Stick • Can a Plant Respond To Touch? • Feeding the World

Quick Labs: • Algae and Other Plants • Local Plant Diversity • Masses of Mosses • Examining a Fern • Common Characteristics • The In-Seed Story • Modeling Flowers • Plant Life Cycles • Where Are the Seeds? • Watching Roots Grow • Seasonal Changes • Everyday Plants

my science online.com

Go to MyScienceOnline.com to interact with this chapter's content.
Keyword: Plants

▷ **PLANET DIARY**
• Plants

▷ **INTERACTIVE ART**
• Plant Cell Structures • The Structure of a Flower • Seed Dispersal

▷ **ART IN MOTION**
• Plant Tropisms

▷ **VIRTUAL LAB**
• Classifying Plants

Introduction to Animals

CHAPTER **4**

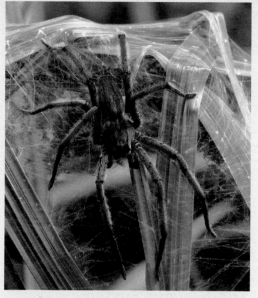

Enter the Lab zone for hands-on inquiry.

Chapter Lab Investigation:
• Directed Inquiry: Earthworm Responses
• Open Inquiry: Earthworm Responses

Inquiry Warm-Ups: • Is It an Animal? • How Many Ways Can You Fold It? • How Do Natural and Synthetic Sponges Compare? • How Is an Umbrella Like a Skeleton? • Exploring Vertebrates

Quick Labs: • Get Moving • Classifying Animals • Organizing Animal Bodies • Front-End Advantages • Characteristics of Vertebrates • Keeping Warm • It's Plane to See

my science online.com

Go to MyScienceOnline.com to interact with this chapter's content. Keyword: Introduction to Animals

> **UNTAMED SCIENCE**
• Eating Like an Animal

> **PLANET DIARY**
• Introduction to Animals

> **INTERACTIVE ART**
• Structure of a Sponge • Where Could They Live?

> **ART IN MOTION**
• Invertebrate Diversity

> **VIRTUAL LAB**
• Classifying Animals

CONTENTS

 Lab® zone Enter the Lab zone
for hands-on inquiry.

Chapter Lab Investigation:
   • Directed Inquiry: A Snail's Pace
   • Open Inquiry: A Snail's Pace

Inquiry Warm-Ups: • Will It Bend and
Move? • Sending Signals • Hydra Doing?

Quick Labs: • Comparing Bone and
Cartilage • What Do Muscles Do? • Design a
Nervous System • Compare Nervous Systems
• Webbing Along

my science online .com

Go to MyScienceOnline.com to
interact with this chapter's content.
Keyword: Getting Around

> **UNTAMED SCIENCE**
   • Science in a Bat Cave

> **PLANET DIARY**
   • Getting Around

> **INTERACTIVE ART**
   • Water Vascular System • Adaptations for
Movement • Types of Skeletons

> **ART IN MOTION**
   • Nervous Systems at Work

> **REAL-WORLD INQUIRY**
   • Responding to the Environment

Lab zone® **Enter the Lab zone for hands-on inquiry.**

Chapter Lab Investigation:
• Directed Inquiry: Looking at an Owl's Leftovers
• Open Inquiry: Looking at an Owl's Leftovers

Inquiry Warm-Ups: • How Do Snakes Feed? • How Does Water Flow Over a Fish's Gills? • Getting Oxygen

Quick Labs: • Planarian Feeding Behavior • How Do Animals Get Oxygen? • Comparing Respiratory Systems • Comparing Circulatory Systems • Double-Loop Circulation • Modeling a Kidney

my science online.com

**Go to MyScienceOnline.com to interact with this chapter's content.
Keyword: Obtaining Energy**

▷ UNTAMED SCIENCE
• Cephalic Feeding Is Soo Much Fun

▷ PLANET DIARY
• Obtaining Energy

▷ INTERACTIVE ART
• Vertebrate Circulatory Systems • Alien Mouth Match-Up

▷ ART IN MOTION
• Respiratory Structures at Work

▷ REAL-WORLD INQUIRY
• Frog Fill-Up

CONTENTS

Enter the Lab zone for hands-on inquiry.

Chapter Lab Investigation:
• Directed Inquiry: One for All
• Open Inquiry: One for All

Inquiry Warm-Ups: • Making More
• "Eggs-amination" • What Behaviors Can You Observe? • Communicating Without Words

Quick Labs: • Types of Reproduction • Types of Fertilization • "Eggs-tra "Protection • Cycles of Life • To Care or Not to Care • Animal Behavior • Become a Learning Detective • Modeling Animal Communication • Behavior Cycles

my science online

Go to MyScienceOnline.com to interact with this chapter's content.
Keyword: **Animal Reproduction and Behavior**

> UNTAMED SCIENCE
• Is That Dance Just for Me?

> PLANET DIARY
• Animal Reproduction and Behavior

> INTERACTIVE ART
• Build a Life Cycle

> ART IN MOTION
• Animal Learning

> REAL-WORLD INQUIRY
• Predicting Animal Behavior

Untamed Science™

Video Series: Chapter Adventures

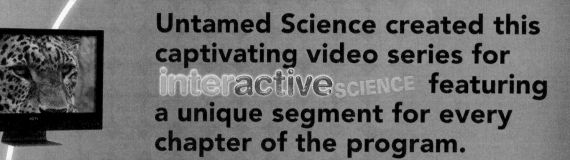

Untamed Science created this captivating video series for interactive SCIENCE featuring a unique segment for every chapter of the program.

Featuring videos such as

Chapter 1
What Can You Explore in a Swamp? Follow the crew as they sort out living and nonliving things in a cypress swamp and in a forest.

Chapter 2
What Good Are Mushrooms? See the surprising roles mushrooms play in the environment.

Chapter 3
Amazing Plant Defenses Take a closer look at how plants fend off hungry insects and other animals looking for a meal.

Chapter 4
Eating Like an Animal Follow the Untamed Science crew as they investigate how people explain what they think an animal is.

Chapter 5
Science in a Bat Cave The crew sees how animal movements relate to where and how animals live.

Chapter 6
Cephalic Feeding is Soo Much Fun Explore some of the unusual ways that animals get their food.

Chapter 7
Is That Dance Just for Me? See how a talent for dancing helps some birds find a mate.

INQUIRY IN THE SCIENCE CLASSROOM

Program Author of
Interactive Science

Associate Dean and Director of

Eugena P. Moore School of Education
Clemson University
Clemson, South Carolina

Michael J. Padilla, Ph.D.

"If students are busy doing lots of hands-on-activities, are they using inquiry skills? What is inquiry, anyway? If you are confused, you're not alone. Inquiry is the heart and soul of science education, with most of us in continuous pursuit of achieving it with our students."

What Is Inquiry?

Simply put, inquiry is thinking like a scientist —being inquisitive, asking why, and searching for answers. It's the process of taking a close examination of something in the quest for information.

Minds-on Inquiry

Students are naturally inquisitive; they want to learn, and they are always asking "Why?" They need practice and support to find answers for themselves. That's why they need experiences that are carefully scaffolded to guide them. We built that scaffolding right into this program.

Scaffolded Learning

The framework below illustrates a series of skill levels developed by educational psychologist Benjamin Bloom in the 1950s, later modified in the 1990s to reflect relevance to 21st century work. Look for the skills questions and tasks throughout the student book, scaffolded just right to provide students with the guidance and intellectual challenge they need.

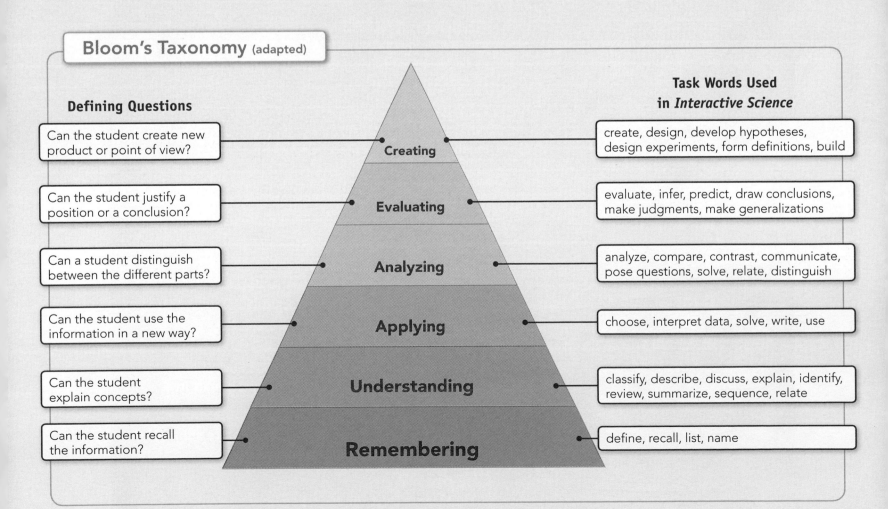

Bloom's Taxonomy (adapted)

Defining Questions

Can the student create new product or point of view? — **Creating**

Can the student justify a position or a conclusion? — **Evaluating**

Can a student distinguish between the different parts? — **Analyzing**

Can the student use the information in a new way? — **Applying**

Can the student explain concepts? — **Understanding**

Can the student recall the information? — **Remembering**

Task Words Used in *Interactive Science*

Creating — create, design, develop hypotheses, design experiments, form definitions, build

Evaluating — evaluate, infer, predict, draw conclusions, make judgments, make generalizations

Analyzing — analyze, compare, contrast, communicate, pose questions, solve, relate, distinguish

Applying — choose, interpret data, solve, write, use

Understanding — classify, describe, discuss, explain, identify, review, summarize, sequence, relate

Remembering — define, recall, list, name

Student Interactivity

Science is the study of the world around us. Studies show that students learn science best through posing questions, investigating, and communicating and collaborating about what they've learned. That's why *Interactive Science* gets students involved in their learning each day, on every page. Because the student edition is consumable, it provides students with unique opportunities to become totally engaged in their learning. Students interact with every page, whether it's marking the text, completing an illustration or a chart, summarizing relationships through Venn diagrams and other graphic devices, or recording ideas and findings about scientific concepts.

Apply It! *Students combine new content understandings with their knowledge of scientific process and experimentation.*

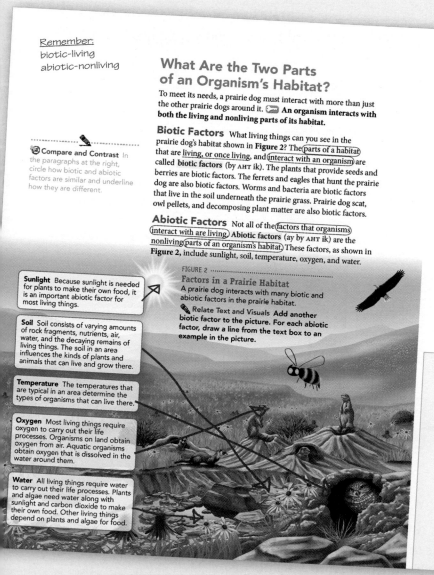

Remember:
biotic-living
abiotic-nonliving

What Are the Two Parts of an Organism's Habitat?

To meet its needs, a prairie dog must interact with more than just the other prairie dogs around it. **An organism interacts with both the living and nonliving parts of its habitat.**

Compare and Contrast In the paragraphs at the right, circle how biotic and abiotic factors are similar and underline how they are different.

Biotic Factors What living things can you see in the prairie dog's habitat shown in **Figure 2**? The (parts of a habitat) that are living, or once living, and (interact with an organism) are called **biotic factors** (by AHT ik). The plants that provide seeds and berries are biotic factors. The ferrets and eagles that hunt the prairie dog are also biotic factors. Worms and bacteria are biotic factors that live in the soil underneath the prairie grass. Prairie dog scat, owl pellets, and decomposing plant matter are also biotic factors.

Abiotic Factors Not all of the (factors that organisms interact with are living.) Abiotic factors (ay by AHT ik) are the nonliving (parts of an organism's habitat.) These factors, as shown in **Figure 2**, include sunlight, soil, temperature, oxygen, and water.

Sunlight Because sunlight is needed for plants to make their own food, it is an important abiotic factor for most living things.

Soil Soil consists of varying amounts of rock fragments, nutrients, air, water, and the decaying remains of living things. The soil in an area influences the kinds of plants and animals that can live and grow there.

Temperature The temperatures that are typical in an area determine the types of organisms that can live there.

Oxygen Most living things require oxygen to carry out their life processes. Organisms on land obtain oxygen from air. Aquatic organisms obtain oxygen that is dissolved in the water around them.

Water All living things require water to carry out their life processes. Plants and algae need water along with sunlight and carbon dioxide to make their own food. Other living things depend on plants and algae for food.

FIGURE 2
Factors in a Prairie Habitat
A prairie dog interacts with many biotic and abiotic factors in the prairie habitat.

Relate Text and Visuals Add another biotic factor to the picture. For each abiotic factor, draw a line from the text box to an example in the picture.

MY SCIENCE online | Biotic and Abiotic Factors | APPLY IT | MY SCIENCE COACH

apply it!

Salt is an abiotic factor found in some environments. To see how the amount of salt affects the hatching of brine shrimp eggs, varying amounts of salt were added to four different 500-mL beakers.

❶ Observe In which beaker(s) did the eggs, shown as purple circles, hatch? _B, C, D_

❷ Infer The manipulated variable was _the amount of salt._

❸ Infer The responding variable was _the number of hatching shrimp._

❹ **CHALLENGE** Beaker _A_ was the control.

❺ Draw Conclusions What can you conclude about the amount of salt in the shrimps' natural habitat?

It is similar to the amount in Beaker B, since that is where the most eggs hatched.

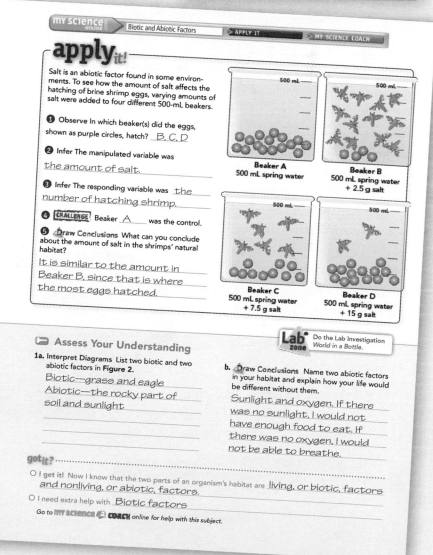

Beaker A
500 mL spring water

Beaker B
500 mL spring water + 2.5 g salt

Beaker C
500 mL spring water + 7.5 g salt

Beaker D
500 mL spring water + 15 g salt

Assess Your Understanding

Lab zone Do the Lab Investigation World in a Bottle.

1a. Interpret Diagrams List two biotic and two abiotic factors in **Figure 2**.
Biotic—grass and eagle
Abiotic—the rocky part of soil and sunlight

b. Draw Conclusions Name two abiotic factors in your habitat and explain how your life would be different without them.
Sunlight and oxygen. If there was no sunlight, I would not have enough food to eat. If there was no oxygen, I would not be able to breathe.

got it? ....

O I get it! Now I know that the two parts of an organism's habitat are _living, or biotic, factors_ and nonliving, or abiotic, factors.

O I need extra help with _Biotic factors_

Go to **MY SCIENCE COACH** online for help with this subject.

Students demonstrate critical connections between text and illustration.

Hands-on Inquiry

We know that it is through student engagement and discovery that students really learn to think like scientists. Hands-on inquiry lab activities are built into the program; there are multiple activities per lesson.

Teacher's Lab Resource

Because there are so many labs, you will want to select which ones are best for your students and your class time. That is why the labs are organized in print as blackline masters in the *Teacher's Lab Resource*. Just photocopy the lab activities you want, when you want them. Or access them in your teacher center at MyScienceOnline.com. There you can download and even edit the labs to more closely align them with a student's needs.

Lab activities vary from both directed to open-ended, and quick and simple to more complex.

1. **Inquiry Warm-Ups.** One per lesson, as a lesson starter

2. **Quick Labs.** One per lesson objective

3. **Lab Investigations.** One full-blown lab per chapter, either as a directed lab or through an in-depth inquiry approach. You choose which approach is best for your students.

Using the Labs

The yellow LabZone symbols in the student edition indicate the lab activities that support your instruction. Look for the LabZone symbol. To find your lab, look for its name in the *Teacher's Lab Resource* books or online in the teacher center.

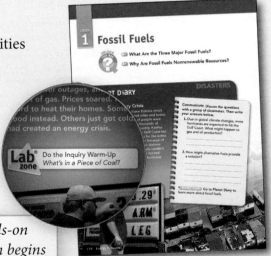

Quick Labs or Lab Investigation
Hands-on reinforcement of each lesson's key concept

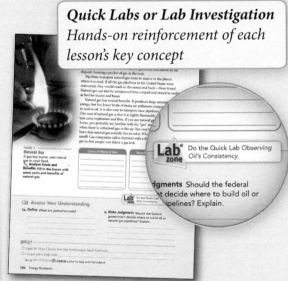

Inquiry Warm-Ups *Hands-on experience before the lesson begins*

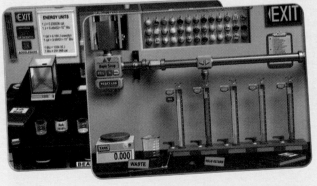

Online Labs and Simulations

Don't have time to dedicate to lab work today? For lab experiences without materials, you'll love the Online Virtual Labs. They're realistic, time efficient, and great when meeting in a laboratory is not possible. Have students use them individually, with a partner, or as a class activity to stimulate discussion or shared learning.

Inquiry Skill-Building Outside the Student Books

There are many forms of inquiry learning in *Interactive Science*, with lots of options to enrich your students' experiences. All components are in print or online for easy downloading.

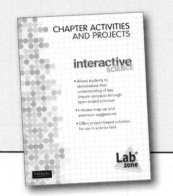

Allow students to demonstrate their understanding of chapter concepts in longer term projects.

Provide students with opportunities to apply the science they have learned to other subject areas.

Stretch students with real-life problem solving—perfect for challenging the advanced students.

Even more minds-on/hands-on activities, each targeting specific science process skills.

Interactive Science—Inquiry Learning at Its Best

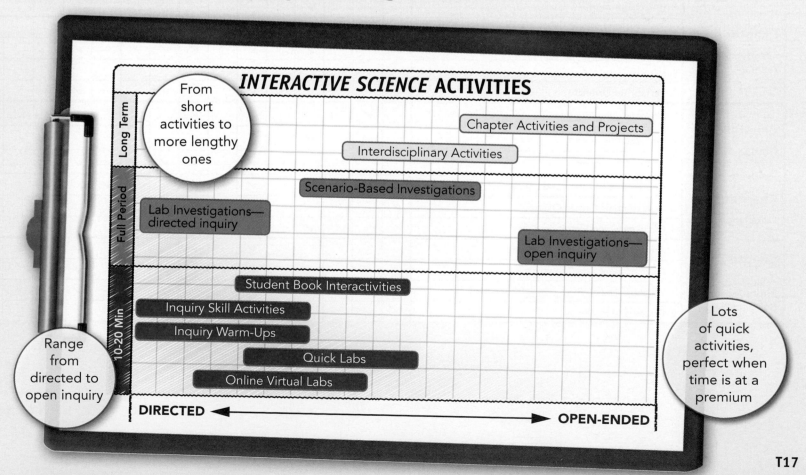

INQUIRY AND...

MODULE 8		Observe	Infer	Predict	Classify	Make Models	Calculate	Graph	Create Data Tables	Communicate	Measure	Develop Hypotheses	Interpret Data	Draw Conclusions	Control Variables	Pose Questions
	Lesson															
Chapter 1 Introduction to Living Things	1. What Is Life?		✔									✔		✔	✔	
	2. Classifying Life	✔	✔				✔	✔					✔	✔		
	3. Domains and Kingdoms				✔											
	4. Evolution and Classification		✔											✔		
Chapter 2 Viruses, Bacteria, Protists, and Fungi	1. Viruses		✔		✔	✔	✔				✔			✔		
	2. Bacteria		✔	✔	✔			✔	✔	✔			✔	✔		
	3. Protists		✔	✔	✔	✔		✔	✔	✔			✔	✔		
	4. Fungi	✔	✔	✔						✔						
Chapter 3 Plants	1. What Is a Plant?		✔							✔			✔	✔		
	2. Classifiying Plants		✔				✔		✔	✔		✔	✔	✔		
	3. Plant Structures	✔	✔				✔									
	4. Plant Reproduction		✔													
	5. Plant Responses and Growth		✔	✔						✔		✔	✔	✔		
	6. Plants in Everyday Life									✔						✔
Chapter 4 Introduction to Animals	1. What Is an Animal?				✔											
	2. Animal Body Plans		✔			✔										
	3. Introduction to Invertebrates	✔			✔		✔		✔	✔			✔			
	4. Introduction to Vertebrates													✔		
	5. Vertebrate Diversity						✔			✔			✔	✔		
Chapter 5 Getting Around	1. Skeletons and Muscles		✔							✔			✔			
	2. The Nervous System		✔		✔					✔			✔			
	3. Animal Movement						✔			✔	✔		✔			
Chapter 6 Obtaining Energy	1. How Animals Obtain and Digest Food		✔		✔		✔			✔		✔		✔		
	2. How Animals Obtain Oxygen	✔		✔						✔						
	3. Circulation and Excretion				✔									✔		
Chapter 7 Animal Reproduction and Behavior	1. Animal Reproduction and Fertilization						✔			✔				✔	✔	
	2. Development and Growth		✔				✔	✔	✔	✔			✔			
	3. What Is Behavior?		✔	✔			✔						✔			
	4. Patterns of Behavior		✔							✔				✔		

Critical Thinking Skills

Define	Identify	Name	Review	List	Describe	Explain	Sequence	Interpret Diagrams, Photos, Maps, Tables	Read Graphs	Relate Diagrams and Photos	Apply Concepts	Make Generalizations	Make Judgments	Relate Text and Visuals	Summarize	Relate Cause and Effect	Compare and Contrast	Design Experiments	Analyze Sources of Error	Estimate	Relate Evidence and Explanation
	✓		✓		✓	✓					✓	✓	✓					✓	✓		
✓	✓				✓			✓	✓			✓								✓	
✓				✓													✓				
	✓							✓			✓										
✓								✓								✓					
	✓	✓	✓	✓		✓	✓	✓			✓				✓	✓					
		✓	✓	✓	✓		✓	✓	✓		✓						✓				
✓		✓	✓		✓	✓	✓	✓													
✓			✓		✓			✓			✓										
✓	✓	✓	✓		✓			✓		✓	✓						✓				
✓		✓	✓	✓	✓			✓			✓			✓							
	✓		✓	✓	✓	✓	✓	✓			✓			✓		✓					
✓			✓			✓			✓		✓										
	✓	✓		✓	✓								✓								
✓	✓							✓									✓				
	✓			✓	✓	✓		✓			✓						✓				
	✓				✓		✓	✓	✓						✓		✓				
✓	✓													✓		✓					
		✓	✓					✓				✓			✓	✓					
✓								✓							✓						
	✓	✓		✓							✓										
	✓			✓	✓	✓					✓		✓		✓		✓				
	✓		✓	✓		✓	✓	✓							✓		✓				✓
	✓		✓		✓						✓	✓		✓	✓	✓					
	✓			✓	✓			✓			✓						✓				
✓	✓		✓		✓		✓					✓		✓	✓						
✓	✓	✓		✓	✓	✓	✓				✓			✓			✓				
✓					✓		✓	✓	✓		✓						✓				
	✓		✓	✓	✓		✓				✓						✓				

READING, VOCABULARY, MATH SKILLS

MODULE 8	Lesson	Compare, Contrast	Relate Cause, Effect	Relate Text Visuals	Outline	Ask Questions	Identify the Main Idea	Identify Supporting Evidence	Summarize	Greek Word Origins	Prefixes	Suffixes	High-Use Academic Words	Use Context to Determine Meaning	Identify Multiple Meanings	Interpret Bar Graph	Interpret Line Graph	Calculate	Draw Bar Garph	Draw Circle Graph	Draw Line Graph	Interpret Circle Graph
Chapter 1 Introduction to Living Things	1. What Is Life?	✔								✔												
	2. Classifying Life					✔												✔		✔		✔
	3. Domains and Kingdoms						✔															
	4. Evolution and Classification								✔													
Chapter 2 Viruses, Bacteria, Protists, and Fungi	1. Viruses						✔											✔				
	2. Bacteria	✔																			✔	
	3. Protists								✔		✔					✔						
	4. Fungi							✔														
Chapter 3 Plants	1. What Is a Plant?	✔															✔					
	2. Classifiying Plants				✔					✔								✔				✔
	3. Plant Structures		✔							✔								✔				
	4. Plant Reproduction								✔													
	5. Plant Responses and Growth			✔													✔					
	6. Plants in Everyday Life					✔																
Chapter 4 Introduction to Animals	1. What Is an Animal?			✔																		
	2. Animal Body Plans		✔																			
	3. Introduction to Invertebrates						✔											✔				✔
	4. Introduction to Vertebrates								✔		✔											
	5. Vertebrate Diversity	✔																✔				
Chapter 5 Getting Around	1. Skeletons and Muscles	✔												✔								
	2. The Nervous System						✔															
	3. Animal Movement			✔											✔			✔				
Chapter 6 Obtaining Energy	1. How Animals Obtain and Digest Food						✔											✔				
	2. How Animals Obtain Oxygen	✔																				
	3. Circulation and Excretion								✔				✔									
Chapter 7 Animal Reproduction and Behavior	1. Animal Reproduction and Fertilization	✔															✔	✔				
	2. Development and Growth								✔								✔	✔	✔			
	3. What Is Behavior?		✔										✔				✔	✔				
	4. Patterns of Behavior						✔															

PACING GUIDE

CHAPTER	Lesson	Periods (days)	Blocks
Chapter 1 Introduction to Living Things	1. What Is Life?	1–2	½–1
	2. Classifying Life	2–3	1–1½
	3. Domains and Kingdoms	1–2	½–1
	4. Evolution and Classification	1–2	½–1
	Chapter Review and Assessment	1	½
	Chapter 1 Total	6–10	3–5
Chapter 2 Viruses, Bacteria, Protists, and Fungi	1. Viruses	1–2	½–1
	2. Bacteria	2–3	1–1½
	3. Protists	2–3	1–1½
	4. Fungi	2–3	1–1½
	Chapter Review and Assessment	1	½
	Chapter 2 Total	8–12	4–6
Chapter 3 Plants	1. What Is a Plant?	1–2	½–1
	2. Classifiying Plants	2–3	1–1½
	3. Plant Structures	2–3	1–1½
	4. Plant Reproduction	2–3	1–1½
	5. Plant Responses and Growth	1–2	½–1
	6. Plants in Everyday Life	1–2	½–1
	Chapter Review and Assessment	1	½
	Chapter 3 Total	10–16	5–8
Chapter 4 Introduction to Animals	1. What Is an Animal?	1–2	½–1
	2. Animal Body Plans	1–2	½–1
	3. Introduction to Invertebrates	1–2	½–1
	4. Introduction to Vertebrates	2–3	1–1½
	5. Vertebrate Diversity	1–2	½–1
	Chapter Review and Assessment	1	½
	Chapter 4 Total	7–12	3½–6
Chapter 5 Getting Around	1. Skeletons and Muscles	1–2	½–1
	2. The Nervous System	2–3	1–1½
	3. Animal Movement	2–3	1–1½
	Chapter Review and Assessment	1	½
	Chapter 5 Total	6–9	3–4½
Chapter 6 Obtaining Energy	1. How Animals Obtain and Digest Food	2–3	1–1½
	2. How Animals Obtain Oxygen	2–3	1–1½
	3. Circulation and Excretion	2–3	1–1½
	Chapter Review and Assessment	1	½
	Chapter 6 Total	7–10	3½–5
Chapter 7 Animal Reproduction and Behavior	1. Animal Reproduction and Fertilization	2–3	1–1½
	2. Development and Growth	3–4	1½–2
	3. What Is Behavior?	1–2	½–1
	4. Patterns of Behavior	1–2	½–1
	Chapter Review and Assessment	1	½
	Chapter 7 Total	8–12	4–6
	Module 8 Total	52–81	26–40½

interactive SCIENCE

Dear Family Member,

As your child's science teacher, I am looking forward to helping your child learn about science. Because I know that you want your child to be successful, I offer these suggestions so that you can help your child gain proficiency in science.

- Your child's textbook is very different from most—it's meant for students to write in it. Therefore, it is a record of learning. Look through lessons your child has completed recently, and be sure to ask lots of questions. One of the best ways for students to check on their learning is to explain it to someone else.

- Ask your child about homework assignments and check that he or she has completed them.

- Help your child collect materials and information for school activities.

- Encourage computer literacy. Advise your child to use computers in school or at the library. If you have a home computer, help your child do research online.

In this unit of study, your child will be introduced to living things, their likenesses and differences, their structures and how they get and use energy, grow, change and reproduce. Your child will also learn about plants and animals, how animals move, get and use energy, survive, and reproduce. In the following weeks of study, the unit will provide your child with a deepening of understanding about the diversity of life.

I encourage you to stay involved in your child's learning. By all means, visit the classroom during open house or make an appointment with me if you have questions.

Cordially,

_____

Science Teacher

To learn more about *Interactive Science* and to see how your student is progressing through the program, go to **www.interactivescience.com**.

Estimados familiares:

Como maestro de ciencias de su hijo, me es un placer ayudarlo a descubrir las ciencias. Como sé que ustedes quieren que su hijo tenga un buen desempeño académico, les ofrezco estas sugerencias para que ayuden a su hijo a dominar las ciencias.

- El libro de texto de su hijo es muy diferente de los demás: tiene como objetivo que su hijo escriba en el libro. Por esa razón, es un registro de aprendizaje. Fíjense en las lecciones que su hijo ha terminado recientemente y asegúrense de hacerle muchas preguntas. Para los estudiantes, una de las mejores formas de repasar lo que han aprendido es explicándoselo a otras personas.

- Pregúntenle a su hijo sobre la tarea que se le asigna y asegúrense de que la complete.

- Ayúdenlo a reunir materiales e información relacionados con las actividades escolares.

- Anímenlo a adquirir destrezas con la computadora, y a usar computadoras en la escuela o en la biblioteca. Si tienen una computadora en casa, ayúdenlo a hacer investigaciones en Internet.

En esta unidad del curso, su hijo aprenderá sobre los seres vivos, sus semejanzas y diferencias, sus estructuras, y cómo obtienen y usan energía, crecen, cambian y se reproducen. Su hijo también aprenderá sobre las plantas y los animales, y cómo los animales, se mueven, obtienen y usan energía, sobreviven y se reproducen. En las semanas que siguen, la unidad ayudará a su hijo a comprender mejor la diversidad de la vida.

Los animo a que participen en el proceso de aprendizaje de su hijo. Los invito a visitar el salón de clases durante las horas de visita o a que hagan una cita para reunirse conmigo si tienen dudas.

Cordialmente,

_____

Maestro de Ciencias

Para más información sobre *Ciencias interactivas* y para ver cómo está progresando en el programa su hijo, visiten **www.interactivescience.com**.

Big Ideas of Science

According to Grant Wiggins' Understanding by Design framework, students reveal their understanding most effectively when provided with complex, authentic opportunities to explain, interpret, apply, shift perspective, empathize, and self-assess. Each chapter in the student edition uses a Big Question to focus students' attention on the content of the chapter. Related Big Questions are organized under one or more Big Ideas. A Big Idea is a concept, theory, principle, or theme that helps learners make sense of a subject.

Students will explore the Big Idea before they read a chapter, writing about what they already know and what they want to know about the topic. After completing the chapter, students will return to these pages in order to record what they have learned and how their thoughts have changed during that learning process.

? BIG IDEAS OF SCIENC

Have you ever worked on a jigsaw puzzle? Usually a puzzle has a theme that leads you to group the pieces by what they have in common. But until you put all the pieces together you can't solve the puzzle. Studyin science is similar to solving a puzzle. The big ideas of science are like p themes. To understand big ideas, scientists ask questions. The answers those questions are like pieces of a puzzle. Each chapter in this book as a big question to help you think about a big idea of science. By answer the big questions, you will get closer to understanding the big idea.

✏ **Before you read each chapter, write about what you know and what more you'd like to know.**

Grant Wiggins, coauthor of *Understanding by Design*

BIGIDEA
Living things are alike yet different.

Grasses and wildflowers look different, but they all grow in soil and need sunlight and water.

What do you already know about how all living things are alike yet different? ✏ **What more would you like to know?**

_____

_____

_____

Big Questions:

❓ How are living things alike yet different? Chapter 1

❓ How are living things other than plants and animals important to Earth? Chapter 2

❓ How do you know a plant when you see it? Chapter 3

❓ How do you know an animal when you see it? Chapter 4

✏ **After reading the chapters, write what you have learned about the Big Idea.**

_____

BIGIDEA
Structures in living things are related to their functions.

Using its wings, a hawk flies through the air and coasts to a landing.

What do you already know about how animal move in water, on land, or in air? ✏ **What m would you like to know?**

_____

_____

_____

Big Question:

❓ How do animals move? Chapter 5

✏ **After reading the chapter, write what yc have learned about the Big Idea.**

_____

_____

Living things get and use energy.

A salmon lunch provides energy for this hungry bear.

What do you already know about how animals get and eat food? ✎ **What more would you like to know?**

_____

_____

_____

Big Question:

❓ How do animals get and use energy? Chapter 6

✎ **After reading the chapter, write what you have learned about the Big Idea.**

_____

_____

_____

_____

Living things grow, change, and reproduce during their lifetimes.

Tadpoles hatch from frog eggs and grow into adults.

What do you already know about how animals survive and produce offspring? ✎ **What more would you like to know?**

_____

_____

_____

_____

Big Question:

❓ How does an animal's behavior help it survive and reproduce? Chapter 7

✎ **After reading the chapter, write what you have learned about the Big Idea.**

_____

_____

_____

_____

Connect to the Big Idea ❓

Have students form a group for each Big Idea and assign a notetaker and reporter for each group. Each group discusses what they already know, then individuals write in their student editions what else they personally would like to like to know. Individuals share their items with their group as the notetaker compiles the responses and eliminates duplicates. Each group should agree on one key item they want to learn about. Finally, each group's reporter shares their group's key item with the class and the teacher compiles these items on the board. Remember to vary the roles of group notetaker and reporter to give students a variety of experiences.

EXTENSION Select one item about which students want to learn more as an extra credit project.

Introduction to Living Things

Introduce the Big Q

Have students look at the image and read the Engaging Question and description. Ask the students to hypothesize what the two animals have in common. Have volunteers share their ideas with the class. Point out that in addition to obvious physical characteristics, these two animals have other things in common. In fact, these animals share certain traits with humans. Ask: **What other things do you think a manatee and hyrax have in common?** *(Sample: They are both living things. They live in a certain place. They are made up of cells. They move from place to place to get food. They both need oxygen to breathe. They can survive in only certain temperatures.)* **Can you name three things that you have in common with the manatee and hyrax?** *(Samples: Need for oxygen, food, water, energy; growth and development; reaction to surroundings; ability to move)* **The manatee, hyrax, and you are mammals. What are some characteristics of mammals?** *(Mammals are warm-blooded. Mammals have fur or hair. Mammals breathe with lungs.)*

Untamed Science Video

WHAT CAN YOU EXPLORE IN A SWAMP? Before viewing, invite students to discuss the different forms of life they would expect to see in and around a swamp. Then play the video. Lead a class discussion and make a list of questions that this video raises. You may wish to have students view the video again after they have completed the chapter to see if their questions have been answered.

> To access the online resources for this chapter, search on or navigate to *Introduction to Living Things.*
>
> **Untamed Science Video** shows the diversity of life in a swamp.
>
> **The Big Question** allows students to answer the Engaging Question about how the manatee and hyrax are alike.

my science online.com — Introduction to Living Things

HOW ARE THIS MANATEE AND HYRAX ALIKE?

How are living things alike yet different?

Living in Florida waters, a manatee can grow to be longer than 3 meters and weigh over 350 kilograms. A rock hyrax is a small, tailless, rodentlike animal that lives in rocky areas of Africa. While these animals appear to be very different, they are actually related.

Develop Hypotheses What could these two animals have in common?

Sample: The manatee and hyrax both have eyes, mouths, and noses. They both also have some hair.

> **UNTAMED SCIENCE** Watch the **Untamed Science** video to learn more about living things.

Professional Development Note — **From the Author**

The topic *What is life?* is a common inquiry in the biological sciences. But think of all the other ways we use the word *life*. Life is a breakfast cereal, a rock song, a musical, a film, a board game, and a nature documentary. You can talk about artificial life, city life, a life sentence, a social life, and real life. It is good to save a life, but bad to have no life. I like to have my students explore the many different ways we use common terms like the word *life,* what each of these terms means to us, and how context determines the meaning we get from words. This helps put the biological meaning in a broader context.

✏ *Michael Padilla*

Introduction to Living Things

Introduction to Living Things | UNTAMED SCIENCE | THE BIG QUESTION

Chapter at a Glance

CHAPTER PACING: 6–10 periods or 3–5 blocks

INTRODUCE THE CHAPTER: Use the Engaging Question and the opening image to get students thinking about the characteristics of living things. Activate prior knowledge and preteach vocabulary using the Getting Started pages.

Lesson 1: What Is Life?

Lesson 2: Classifying Life

Lesson 3: Domains and Kingdoms

Lesson 4: Evolution and Classification

ASSESSMENT OPTIONS: Chapter Test, *ExamView®* Computer Test Generator, Performance Assessment, Progress Monitoring Assessments, SuccessTracker™

Preference Navigator, in the online Planning tools, allows you to customize *Interactive Science* to your own teaching style. You can also edit lesson plans by selecting the Lesson Planner option.

Digital Teacher's Edition allows you to access your Teacher's Edition and Resource online.

my science online.com

Differentiated Instruction

L1 Alike and Different To help students understand that living things have similarities and differences, have them make a T-Chart to compare the manatee and hyrax. Have them list all the ways they can think of in which the two animals are the same and different. Then show students a photo of a maple tree and a rabbit. Have them do the same exercise for this pair of living things.

L3 The Plight of the Manatee Manatees are listed as vulnerable to extinction by the World Conservation Union. The major threat to manatees in the United States comes from humans. Have students do research to find out how people endanger manatees. Suggest that they include information on boat accidents, ingestion of fishing gear, drowning in water-control structures, and red tide. Have students report their findings to the class.

Getting Started

Check Your Understanding

This activity assesses students' understanding of single-celled organisms. After students share their answers, point out that while single-celled organisms represent simple forms of life, they often play very important roles. Many students may think that bacteria are only harmful and may not know that many types of bacteria are beneficial.

Preteach Vocabulary Skills

Explain to students that many English words are derived from Greek. Knowing the origins of these words can help students determine the meanings of unfamiliar words. Review the information in the table with students and then have volunteers identify other words they know that contain these Greek word parts.

---

1 Getting Started

Check Your Understanding

1. **Background** Read the paragraph below and then answer the question.

You eat **microscopic** organisms all the time without realizing it! Some microscopic organisms are necessary to prepare common foods. **Yeast**, for example, is a tiny organism that is used to make bread. **Bacteria** are used to make yogurt, sauerkraut, and many other foods.

Something **microscopic** is so small that it cannot be seen without a magnifying lens or a microscope.

Yeast is a single-celled organism that has a nucleus.

Bacteria are single-celled organisms that do not have nuclei.

• What is one kind of food that bacteria are used to make?

Yogurt or sauerkraut

> **MY READING WEB** If you had trouble completing the question above, visit My Reading Web and type in *Introduction to Living Things.*

Vocabulary Skill

Greek Word Origins Many science words come from ancient Greek words. Learning the word parts that have Greek origins can help you understand some of the vocabulary in this chapter.

Greek Word Part	Meaning	Example
autos	self	autotroph, *n.* an organism that makes its own food
taxis	order, arrangement	taxonomy, *n.* the scientific study of how living things are classified
homos	similar, same	homeostasis, *n.* the maintenance of stable internal conditions

2. **Quick Check** Circle the part of the word *taxonomy* that lets you know that the word's meaning has something to do with ordering or classifying things.

My Reading Web offers leveled readings that offer a foundation for the chapter content.

Vocab Flash Cards offer extra practice with the chapter vocabulary words.

Digital Lesson

• Assign the *Check Your Understanding* activity online and have students submit their work to you.

• Assign the *Vocabulary Skill* activity online and have students submit their work to you.

my science online.com | Introduction to Living Things

organism

species

eukaryote

branching tree diagram

Chapter Preview

LESSON 1
- organism
- cell
- unicellular
- multicellular
- metabolism
- stimulus
- response
- development
- asexual reproduction
- sexual reproduction
- spontaneous generation
- controlled experiment
- autotroph
- heterotroph
- homeostasis
- ⊙ Compare and Contrast
- △ Control Variables

LESSON 2
- classification
- taxonomy
- binomial nomenclature
- genus
- species
- ⊙ Ask Questions
- △ Observe

LESSON 3
- prokaryote
- nucleus
- eukaryote
- ⊙ Identify the Main Idea
- △ Classify

LESSON 4
- evolution
- branching tree diagram
- shared derived characteristic
- convergent evolution
- ⊙ Summarize
- △ Infer

> VOCAB FLASH CARDS For extra help with vocabulary, visit **Vocab Flash Cards** and type in *Introduction to Living Things.*

3

Preview Vocabulary Terms

Have students work together to create a word wall to display the vocabulary terms for the chapter. Be sure to discuss and analyze each term before posting it on the wall. As the class progresses through the chapter, the words can be sorted and categorized in different ways. A list of Academic Vocabulary for each lesson can be found in the Support All Readers box at the start of the lesson.

L1 Have students look at the images on this page as you pronounce the vocabulary word. Have students repeat the word after you. Then read the definition. Use the sample sentence in italics to clarify the meaning of the term.

organism *(AWR guh niz um)* A living thing. *The beetle in the image is an example of an* organism.

species *(SPEE sheez)* A group of similar organisms that can mate with each other and produce offspring that can also mate and reproduce. *All house cats, regardless of size or color, belong to the same* species.

eukaryote *(yoo KA ree oht)* Organisms with cells that contain nuclei. *A* eukaryote *can be a protist, fungus (such as the one shown in the image), plant, or animal.*

branching tree diagram *(BRANCH ing tree DY uh gram)* A visual representation of the probable evolutionary relationships among organisms and the order in which specific characteristics may have evolved. *The organisms on a* branching tree diagram *are grouped according to their shared characteristics.*

CHAPTER 1

ⒺⓁⓁ Support

Have students work together to sort and categorize the words on the word wall. As the class progresses through the chapter and new words are introduced, be sure to say each word aloud and have students repeat it.

Beginning
LOW/HIGH Have students add definitions for the words in their native languages.

Intermediate
LOW/HIGH Have students write down words for you to define and post.

Advanced
LOW/HIGH Challenge students to come up with new categories to classify the words.

What Is Life?

 How are living things alike yet different?

Lesson Pacing: 1–2 periods or $\frac{1}{2}$–1 block

⏱ **SHORT ON TIME?** To do this lesson in approximately half the time, do the Activate Prior Knowledge activity on page 4. A discussion of the Key Concepts on pages 5, 8, and 11 will familiarize students with the lesson content. Have students do the Quick Labs. The rest of the lesson can be completed by students independently.

> **Preference Navigator,** in the online Planning tools, allows you to customize *Interactive Science* to your own teaching style. You can also edit lesson plans by selecting the Lesson Planner option.
>
> **Digital Teacher's Edition** allows you to access your Teacher's Edition and Resource materials online.

my science online.com

Lesson Vocabulary

- organism • cell • unicellular • multicellular • metabolism
- stimulus • response • development • asexual reproduction
- sexual reproduction • spontaneous generation
- controlled experiment • autotroph • heterotroph • homeostasis

 Content Refresher

Comparing Growth and Development Growth is an increase in the size of an organism or its parts as a result of ongoing mitotic division, which increases the number of cells. Development, which also results from cell division, involves changes in the structures and functions of cells.

In plants and animals, development is a complex process that starts with a fertilized egg and ends with the emergence of an adult organism. The steps in development include fertilization, rapid cell division, and cell differentiation. During differentiation, groups of similar cells begin to differ in appearance from other such groups. The result is the formation of tissue and organ precursors—the first signs of an emerging plant or animal form.

While it is natural to think of cell division as occurring when an organism is formed, cell division also regularly occurs in adults. When skin tissue is damaged or dying the adult stem cells divide and replenish tissue cells as necessary. Since adult stem cells can divide indefinitely, scientists are studying if it is feasible for a few cells to redevelop an organ.

LESSON OBJECTIVES

- List the characteristics all living things share.
- Explain where living things come from.
- Identify what all living things need to survive.

Blended Path
Active learning using Student Edition, Inquiry Path, and Digital Path

ENGAGE AND EXPLORE

Teach this lesson using a variety of resources. Begin by reading **My Planet Diary** as a class. Have students share ideas about how Kismet is similar to yet different from humans. Then have students do the **Inquiry Warm-Up activity.** Students will cite characteristics that indicate whether a wind-up toy is living or nonliving. Discuss the evidence that the toy is alive. The **After the Inquiry Warm-Up worksheet** sets up a discussion about which characteristic of the toy is most likely to make others believe it is living. Have volunteers share their answers to question 4.

EXPLAIN AND ELABORATE

Teach Key Concepts by explaining that all living organisms share several important characteristics. Use **Figure 1** to identify living organisms. **Lead a Discussion** about cells and some of their important functions. Look at the images in **Figure 2** while discussing asexual and sexual reproduction.

Continue to **Teach Key Concepts** by explaining why, years ago, people believed that living things could arise from nonliving things; then explain how Redi's experiment disproved this idea. **Lead a Discussion** about why, even today, people might believe that living things can arise from nonliving things. Then have students practice the inquiry skill in the **Apply It activity.**

Teach Key Concepts by asking students to list the four basic needs that must be satisfied for all living things to survive. **Lead a Discussion** about how autotrophs and heterotrophs get the food they need to survive. **Lead a Discussion** about the fact that all the functions cells perform require water. **Support the Big Q** by explaining that living space provides a living thing with all that it needs to survive. **Lead a Discussion** about how organisms maintain homeostasis. Hand out the **Key Concept Summaries** as a review of each part of the lesson. Students can also use the online **Vocab Flash Cards** to review key terms.

EVALUATE

Have students take the **Lesson Quiz.** For an alternate assessment, see the *ExamView®* Computer Test Generator, Progress Monitoring Assessments, or SuccessTracker™.

ELL Support

1 Content and Language

Write the words *unicellular* and *multicellular* on the board. Underline the prefix in each word. Tell students that *uni-* means "one" and *multi-* means "many." A *unicellular* organism has one cell, while a *multicellular* organism has many cells.

DIFFERENTIATED INSTRUCTION KEY
L1 Struggling Students or Special Needs
L2 On-Level Students **L3** Advanced Students

LESSON PLANNER 1.1

Inquiry Path
Lab zone — Hands-on learning in the Lab zone

ENGAGE AND EXPLORE

To teach this lesson with an emphasis on inquiry, begin with the **Inquiry Warm-Up activity.** Students will investigate characteristics of living and nonliving things. Discuss the evidence students collected about the toy. Have students do the **After the Inquiry Warm-Up worksheet.** Talk about the characteristics of the toy that will most likely convince someone that it is alive. Have volunteers share their answers to question 4.

EXPLAIN AND ELABORATE

Focus on the **Inquiry Skill** for the lesson. Point out that when you control variables, you have only one factor that changes in a controlled experiment; all the other factors remain the same. Based on the **Inquiry Warm-Up activity,** if all living things move, then what is one condition, or controlled variable, that could be used to test this theory without winding up the toy? (*Control the slant of the surface. The toy will not move if it is on a flat surface.*) Use the **Teacher Demo** to review the idea that nonliving things can have some characteristics of living things, yet they must have all the characteristics to be considered living. Have students do the **Quick Lab** to classify the stimulus and response in various activities and then share their results.

Do the **Teacher Demo** to model a controlled experiment. Review the concept of a controlled experiment and the definitions of the two types of variables before beginning the **Apply It activity. Build Inquiry** by creating a poster to show how Redi's and Pasteur's experiments helped disprove the idea of spontaneous generation. Do the **Quick Lab** to reinforce understanding of Pasteur's experiment.

Use the **Support the Big Q** to explain what all living things need to get from their living space. **Build Inquiry** by doing an experiment to determine a property of water that characterizes why it is necessary for life. Do the **Lab Investigation** to allow students to explore the factors necessary for bread mold to grow. Students can use the online **Vocab Flash Cards** to review key terms.

EVALUATE

Have students take the **Lesson Quiz.** For an alternate assessment, see the *ExamView®* Computer Test Generator, Progress Monitoring Assessments, or SuccessTracker™.

Digital Path
Online learning at my science online.com

ENGAGE AND EXPLORE

Teach this lesson using digital resources. Begin by having students explore real-world connections to the origin, characteristics, and needs of all living things at **My Planet Diary** online. Have them access the Chapter Resources to find the **Unlock the Big Question activity.** There they can answer the questions and refine their responses as they continue through the lesson. You can re-assign the activity and have students submit their work so you can track their progress.

EXPLAIN AND ELABORATE

Students reading above, at, or below the lexile measure of this lesson can access basic content readings at their level at **My Reading Web.** Have students use the online **Vocab Flash Cards** to preview key terms. Do the **Quick Lab** and then ask students to share their results.

Review the concept of a controlled experiment and the definitions of the two types of variables before assigning the online **Apply It activity.** Ask volunteers to identify the manipulated and responding variables in Redi's experiment. Have students submit their work to you. Have students explore the basic idea behind Pasteur's experiment disproving spontaneous generation in the **Quick Lab.** Have students do the online **Interactive Art activity** to explore Redi's and Pasteur's experiment.

Support the Big Q by identifying why all living organisms need living space. The **Key Concept Summaries** online allow students to read a summary and see an image associated with each part of the lesson. Online remediation is available at **My Science Coach.**

EVALUATE

Have students take the **Lesson Quiz.** For an alternate assessment, see the *ExamView®* Computer Test Generator, Progress Monitoring Assessments, or SuccessTracker™.

2 Frontload the Lesson
Preview the lesson visuals, labels, and captions. Ask students what they know about the words *stimulus* and *response.* Explain the specific meanings these words have in science.

3 Comprehensible Input
Have students study the visuals and their captions on pages 6, 7, 9, 10, 11, 12, and 13 to support the Key Concepts of the lesson.

4 Language Production
Pair or group students with varied language abilities to complete labs collaboratively for language practice. Have each student copy the completed written lab for personal reference.

5 Assess Understanding
Make true or false statements using lesson content and have students indicate if they agree or disagree with a thumbs up or thumbs down gesture to check whole-class comprehension.

Lexile Measure = 950L

What Is Life?

Establish Learning Objectives

After this lesson, students will be able to:

- List the characteristics all living things share.
- Explain where living things come from.
- Identify what all living things need to survive.

Engage

Activate Prior Knowledge

MY PLANET DIARY Read *It's Kismet!* with the class. Tell students that Kismet has 21 motors, 4 cameras, and 9 computers for vision alone. Kismet can relate to people through three modalities: tone of voice, facial expression, and body posture. Ask: **How is this robot like a living thing?** *(It can move, sense its surroundings, and respond to its surroundings.)*

BIG IDEAS OF SCIENCE REFERENCE LIBRARY Have students look up the following topic: Survival.

Explore

Lab Resource: Inquiry Warm-Up

L1 **IS IT LIVING OR NONLIVING?** Students will form an operational definition of living thing by identifying the living and nonliving characteristics of a windup toy.

What Is Life?

- What Are the Characteristics of All Living Things?
- Where Do Living Things Come From?
- What Do Living Things Need to Survive?

my planet Diary   **TECHNOLOGY**

It's Kismet!

If you hear a loud noise, do you turn toward the sound to see what caused it? When someone smiles at you, do you smile back? If somebody shook something in front of your face, would you back away? Most people react in these ways, and so does Kismet, a humanlike robot! Scientists developed Kismet to interact with, cooperate with, and learn from humans. Kismet can understand information that it sees and hears as if it were a young child. When responding to information, Kismet's face changes so that it seems interested, happy, or frightened. Kismet's expressions are so convincing that it is sometimes hard to remember that Kismet isn't really alive!

Answer the questions below.

1. What does Kismet do that makes it seem human?

   <u>Sample: Kismet can respond</u>
   <u>to situations, understand</u>
   <u>information, and make faces.</u>

2. What are some things you think Kismet might not be able to do that humans can?

   <u>Sample: Kismet doesn't eat,</u>
   <u>grow, understand complex</u>
   <u>ideas, heal cuts, get sick, or</u>
   <u>have children.</u>

> **PLANET DIARY** Go to **Planet Diary** to learn more about living things.

Lab zone 'Do the Inquiry Warm-Up *Is It Living or Nonliving?*

4   Introduction to Living Things

SUPPORT ALL READERS

Lexile Measure = 950L   Lexile Word Count = 2106

Prior Exposure to Content: Many students may have misconceptions on this topic

Academic Vocabulary: *compare, contrast, variables*

Science Vocabulary: *organism, cell, autotroph, heterotroph*

Concept Level: Generally appropriate for most students in this grade

Preteach With: My Planet Diary "It's Kismet!" and Figure 2 activity

Go to **My Reading Web** to access leveled readings that provide a foundation for the content.

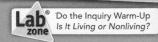

Vocabulary

- organism • cell • unicellular • multicellular • metabolism
- stimulus • response • development • asexual reproduction
- sexual reproduction • spontaneous generation
- controlled experiment • autotroph • heterotroph • homeostasis

Skills

- Reading: Compare and Contrast
- Inquiry: Control Variables

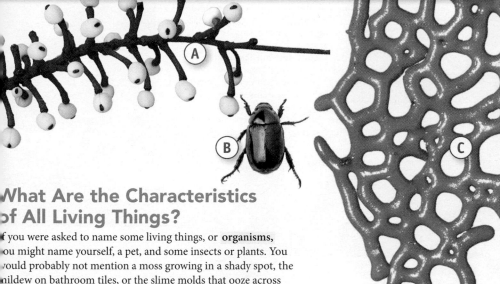

What Are the Characteristics of All Living Things?

If you were asked to name some living things, or **organisms,** you might name yourself, a pet, and some insects or plants. You would probably not mention a moss growing in a shady spot, the mildew on bathroom tiles, or the slime molds that ooze across lawns. But all of these things are organisms that share several important characteristics with all other living things. 🗝 **All living things have a cellular organization, contain similar chemicals, use energy, respond to their surroundings, grow and develop, and reproduce.**

FIGURE 1 ·····························

It's Alive . . . or Is It?
✏️ Look at the photos. Then answer the questions.

1. **Identify** List the letter of the photo(s) that you think show living thing(s). A, B, C, D

2. **Describe** What characteristics helped you decide whether or not the things shown were living or nonliving?

   Accept all
   reasonable
   answers.

5

E L L Support

1 Content and Language
Write the terms *unicellular* and *multicellular* on the board. Explain that the Latin root *uni-* means "one" and the prefix *multi-* means "many" or "multiple." So, a *unicellular* organism has one cell, whereas a *multicellular* organism has multiple cells.

2 Frontload the Lesson
Invite students to name a wide range of living things, and write these terms

on the board. Then, ask students to reflect on characteristics that are shared by living things. Encourage student volunteers to identify any of the basic characteristics present in all living things.

3 Comprehensible Input
Have students use a variety of materials, images, and text in a collage that illustrates the four basic needs shared by all living things—food, water, living space, and stable internal conditions.

Explain

Introduce Vocabulary

To help students understand the terms *autotroph* and *heterotroph*, point to the root word *-troph* and explain that it refers to nutrition. The prefix *auto-* means "self," so an autotroph gets its food by itself; it makes its own food. The prefix *hetero-* means "other," so a heterotroph gets its food from another source.

Teach Key Concepts 🗝

Explain to students that all living things share certain important characteristics: they are made up of one or more cells, they contain certain similar chemicals, they use energy, they respond to their surroundings, they grow and develop, and they produce offspring. Ask: **Do nonliving things have some of these characteristics? Explain.** *(Yes; some nonliving things use energy and/or contain chemicals.)* **Do nonliving things have all of these characteristics? Explain.** *(No; nonliving things do not develop or reproduce.)*

Teach With Visuals

Tell students to look at **Figure 1.** Ask: **Which of these images can you identify?** *(It is likely that the only image familiar to students is the beetle.)* Tell students about the other images: (A) the fruit of the White Baneberry plant, *Actaea alba,* sometimes called "Doll's eyes"; (B) beetle, *Anomala albopilosa;* (C) pretzel slime mold, *Hemitrichia serpula;* (D) stone flower, *Lithops sp.*

Address Misconceptions

L1 PLANTS ARE LIVING THINGS, TOO Some students may not realize that plants are organisms, just as animals are. This misconception may arise from the fact that students do not understand how plants respond to their environment, grow and develop, and reproduce. Also, plant movement is not like animal movement and thus not always obvious. Ask: **What characteristics make plants living things?** *(Plants are made of cells, contain chemicals, use energy, respond to their surroundings, grow and develop, and reproduce.)*

My Planet Diary provides an opportunity for students to explore real-world connections to the origin, characteristics, and needs of all living things.

my science online.com | Describing Living Things

Explain

Lead a Discussion

THE BASIC UNIT OF LIVING THINGS Students are probably familiar with the concept of the cell. Have a discussion about what students know about cells. Ask: **How would you define a cell?** *(Samples: A cell is the basic unit of structure and function of all living things. A cell is the building block of life.)* **Are all cells alike? Explain.** *(Sample: No; cells can be large or small, have a well-defined shape or no shape, and be that of a plant or an animal.)* Explain to students that organisms, whether they are unicellular or multicellular, could not survive if the cell did not perform those functions that characterize something as living. Ask: **How does an organism get and use energy?** *(In the cell, materials are broken down and built up through the processes of metabolism.)* **How does an organism grow and develop?** *(Cells divide and specialize.)* **How does an organism reproduce?** *(In asexual reproduction, cells divide to form two new identical cells. In sexual reproduction, special cells from two parents combine to produce a new organism different from both parents.)*

Teach With Visuals

Tell students to look at **Figure 2** and read the information about reproduction. Tell students that some plants reproduce asexually, such as tubers and bulbs. Ask: **How do most plants reproduce?** *(By sexual reproduction)* **What is necessary for sexual reproduction?** *(Two parents)* **What ways have you seen plants reproduce asexually, or with only one parent?** *(Students may be familiar with various forms of vegetative propagation, including rhizomes, bulbs, corms, tubers, and root propagation.)*

21st Century Learning

CRITICAL THINKING Have students reread the descriptions of the six characteristics of living things in **Figure 2.** Tell them that one characteristic is not necessary for the survival of an organism. Have them conclude which characteristic that is. *(Reproduction)*

Cellular Organization

All organisms are made of small building blocks called cells. A **cell,** like the one shown here, is the basic unit of structure and function in an organism. Organisms may be composed of only one cell or of many cells.

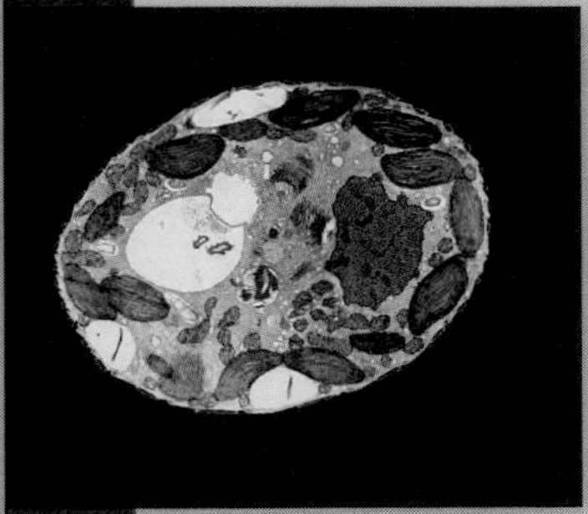

Single-celled organisms, like bacteria (bak TIHR ee uh), are **unicellular** organisms. The single cell is responsible for carrying out all of the functions necessary to stay alive. Organisms that are composed of many cells are **multicellular.** For example, you are made of trillions of cells. In many multicellular organisms, the cells are specialized to do certain tasks. Specialized cells in your body, such as muscle and nerve cells, work together to keep you alive. Nerve cells carry messages to your muscle cells, making your body move.

 Characteristics of Living Things

The Chemicals of Life

The cells of living things are made of chemicals. The most abundant chemical in cells is water. Other chemicals, called carbohydrates (kahr boh HY drayts) are a cell's main energy source. Two other chemicals, proteins and lipids, are the building materials of cells, much as wood and bricks are the building materials of houses. Finally, nucleic (noo KLEE ik) acids are the genetic material of cells—the chemical instructions that cells need to carry out the functions of life.

Energy Use

Organisms get energy from taking in and breaking down materials. The combination of chemical reactions throug[h] which an organism builds up or breaks down materials is called **metabolism.** The cells of organisms use energy to do what living things must do, such as grow and repair injured parts. An organism's cells ar[e] always hard at work. For example, as you read these words, not only are your eye and brain cells busy, but most of your othe[r] cells are working, too. Young sooty terns, like the one shown above, need lots of energy to fly. These birds can fly four to fi[ve] years without ever setting foot on land!

FIGURE 2 ··································
Living Things
All living things share the same characteristics.

✎ **Make Judgments** Which characteristic on these two pages do you think best identifies an object as a living thing? Explain your choice.

Sample: Reproduction; some nonliving things are also made of chemicals, use energy, or respond to their surroundings, but they cannot reproduce.

6 Introduction to Living Things

Response to Surroundings

If you've ever seen a plant in a sunny window, you may have observed that the plant's stems have bent so that the leaves face the sun. Like a plant bending toward the light, all organisms react to changes in their environment. A change in an organism's surroundings that causes the organism to react is called a **stimulus** (plural *stimuli*). Stimuli include changes in light, sound, and other factors.

An organism reacts to a stimulus with a **response**—an action or a change in behavior. For example, has someone ever knocked over a glass of water by accident during dinner, causing you to jump? The sudden spilling of water was the stimulus that caused your startled response.

Growth and Development

All living things grow and develop. Growth is the process of becoming larger. **Development** is the process of change that occurs during an organism's life, producing a more complex organism. As they develop and grow, organisms use energy and make new cells.

Reproduction

Another characteristic of organisms is the ability to reproduce, or produce offspring that are similar to the parents. Organisms reproduce in different ways. **Asexual reproduction** involves only one parent and produces offspring that are identical to the parent. **Sexual reproduction** involves two parents and combines their genetic material to produce a new organism that differs from both parents. Mammals, birds, and most plants sexually reproduce. Penguins lay eggs that develop into young penguins that closely resemble their parents.

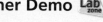 Do the Quick Lab React!

🔲 Assess Your Understanding

1a. Review A change in an organism's surroundings is a (stimulus/response).

b. Infer A bird sitting in a tree flies away as you walk by. Which of the life characteristics explains the bird's behavior?

Response to surroundings

c. CHALLENGE Trees do not move like birds do, but they are living things. Why?

Sample: They have all of the characteristics of life. Although many living things move, movement is not a characteristic of life.

got it?

○ I get it! Now I know that all living things have a cellular organization, contain similar chemicals, use energy, respond to their surroundings, grow and develop, and reproduce.

○ I need extra help with See TE note.

Go to **MY SCIENCE COACH** online for help with this subject.

7

Elaborate

Teacher Demo 🧪

L2 **A CRYSTAL GARDEN**

Materials crystal garden kit

Time 3 days

Review with students the difference between living and nonliving things. Construct a class crystal garden and have students observe crystal growth each day. (If you do cannot find a kit, instructions for growing a crystal garden are available on the Internet) Have them record their observations and list the six characteristics of living things. At the end of the three days, have students determine whether the crystals have each characteristic. Have students write a short paragraph to support their conclusions.

Ask: **Are the crystals alive?** *(No)* **What characteristics of life are the crystals missing?** *(Cellular organization, reproduction)* **What characteristics of life do the crystals appear to have?** *(Chemical composition, energy use, response to surroundings, growth and development)* **Can you list other objects that have some but not all of the characteristics of living things?** *(Samples: Fire, snowflake)*

Lab Resource: Quick Lab 🧪

L1 **REACT!** Students will explore the nature of a stimulus and its response by performing three simple activities and classifying the stimulus and the response in each.

Evaluate

Assess Your Understanding

After students answer the questions, have them evaluate their understanding by completing the appropriate sentence.

R T I Response to Intervention

1a., b. If students cannot distinguish between a stimulus and a response, **then** have them reread the definitions of these terms and the example provided.

c. If students have trouble applying the characteristics of living things to a tree, **then** have students review **Figure 2**.

MY SCIENCE COACH Have students go online for help in understanding characteristics of living things.

Differentiated Instruction

L1 **Demonstrating a Tropism** Have students reread the material in **Figure 2** about the response of a plant to sunlight. Tell them that this response is called a *phototropism*. Have students work in groups to design an experiment to demonstrate phototropism. Encourage them to include a hypothesis and follow the scientific method.

L3 **All About Tropisms** The responses of plants to stimuli in their surroundings are called *tropisms*. Have students find out more about tropisms, including the different types and the chemical processes involved. Students might want to summarize their findings in a poster.

Explain

Teach Key Concepts 🔑

Explain to students that all living things arise from other living things through reproduction. Ask: **What idea suggested that living things could arise from nonliving things?** *(Spontaneous generation)* **Who disproved this idea?** *(Francesco Redi)* **In addition to disproving the idea, what other contribution to science did Redi make?** *(He designed one of the first controlled experiments.)*

Lead a Discussion

Students may have made observations that seem to support the idea of spontaneous generation. Discuss some of those observations and try to elicit explanations that disprove the idea. Ask: **If you have ever observed mold growing on bread or cheese, where do you think it came from?** *(Sample: It did not arise from the bread or cheese. Microscopic mold spores carried in the air landed on the food and found the right conditions for growth.)* **What are some other examples that might lead you to think living things can arise from nonliving things?** *(Samples: mushrooms popping up from the soil, mildew forming on bathroom tiles or shower curtain, moss growing on a rock)*

21st Century Learning

CRITICAL THINKING Have students study **Figure 4** and reread the material about Redi's experiment. Remind students that a hypothesis is a possible explanation for an observation. Ask students to think about what Redi's hypothesis might have been. Then ask them to conclude how his hypothesis related the manipulated variable to the responding variable? *(His hypothesis described whether he thought maggots would appear based on whether the jars were uncovered or covered.)*

Make Analogies

L1 **VARIABLE TERMINOLOGY** To help students understand and differentiate between a manipulated variable and a responding variable, explain that some scientists use the terms *independent variable* and *dependent variable* instead. Discuss what the words *independent* and *dependent* mean. *(Independent: Free from control and does not rely on other factors; Dependent: Relies on another factor)* Ask: **What is another term for a manipulated variable?** *(Independent variable)* **What is another term for a responding variable?** *(Dependent variable)*

Where Do Living Things Come From?

Today, when people see weeds poking out of cracks in sidewalks or find mice in their cabinet, as shown in **Figure 3**, they know that these organisms are the result of reproduction. 🔑 **Living things arise from other living things through reproduction.**

Four hundred years ago, however, people believed that life could appear from nonliving material. For example, when people saw flies swarming around decaying meat, they concluded that flies were produced by rotting meat. The mistaken idea that living things can arise from nonliving sources is called **spontaneous generation**. It took hundreds of years of experiments to convince people that spontaneous generation does not occur.

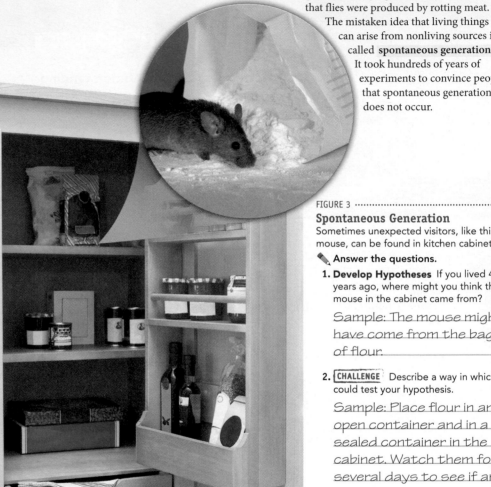

8 Introduction to Living Things

FIGURE 3 ·······
Spontaneous Generation
Sometimes unexpected visitors, like this mouse, can be found in kitchen cabinets.

✏️ **Answer the questions.**

1. **Develop Hypotheses** If you lived 400 years ago, where might you think the mouse in the cabinet came from?

   Sample: The mouse might have come from the bag of flour.

2. [CHALLENGE] Describe a way in which you could test your hypothesis.

   Sample: Place flour in an open container and in a sealed container in the cabinet. Watch them for several days to see if any mice appear.

Digital Lesson: Assign the *Apply It* activity online and have students submit their work to you.

my science online.com ▸ **Reproduction of Living Things**

Redi's Experiment In the 1600s, an Italian doctor named Francesco Redi helped to disprove spontaneous generation. Redi designed a controlled experiment to show that maggots, or young flies, do not arise from decaying meat. In a **controlled experiment**, a scientist carries out a series of tests that are identical in every respect except for one factor. The one factor that a scientist changes in an experiment is called the manipulated variable. The factor that changes as a result of changes to the manipulated variable is called the responding variable. Redi's experiment is shown in **Figure 4**.

FIGURE 4 ···········

Redi's Experiment
Francesco Redi designed one of the first controlled experiments. Redi showed that flies do not spontaneously arise from decaying meat. Here's how he did it:

Uncovered jar   Covered jar

STEP ① Redi placed meat in two identical jars. He left one jar uncovered. He covered the other jar with a cloth that let in air.

STEP ② After a few days, Redi saw maggots (young flies) on the decaying meat in the open jar. There were no maggots on the meat in the covered jar.

STEP ③ Redi reasoned that flies had laid eggs on the meat in the open jar. The eggs hatched into maggots. Because flies could not lay eggs on the meat in the covered jar, there were no maggots there. Redi concluded that decaying meat did not produce maggots.

apply it!

Use **Figure 4** to answer the following questions about Redi's experiment.

❶ Control Variables What is the manipulated variable in this experiment?

Whether or not the jar was covered

❷ Control Variables What is the responding variable?

Whether or not maggots appeared

❸ Analyze Sources of Error Name two factors that would need to be kept constant in this experiment to avoid causing error. Why?

Sample: Location and temperature; any difference in locations and temperatures could influence whether flies would be present.

9

Differentiated Instruction

L1 Redi's Experiment Redi's experiment actually involved another jar, which was tightly sealed. Have students create a diagram similar to **Figure 4** in which they include this jar. Tell them to clearly identify what happened to the meat in this jar.

L3 Pasteurization The experiments that Pasteur did to disprove spontaneous generation led to the development of pasteurization. Have students do research on pasteurization: its history, its link to Pasteur's experiments, its steps, its impact on society, and improvements that have been made through the years. Have students summarize their findings in a chart, poster, or multimedia presentation.

Elaborate

Teacher Demo 🔬 Lab zone

L1 REDI'S EXPERIMENT

Materials 2 wide-mouthed jars, 2 half-dollar-sized pieces of raw meat, cheesecloth, rubber band

Time 15 minutes with observations every 24 hours for the next 3 to 5 days

With students watching, place a piece of raw meat in each wide-mouthed jar. Cover one jar with two thicknesses of cheesecloth, using a rubber band to hold the cloth in place. Leave the other jar uncovered. With students accompanying you, put the two jars outdoors in a warm, sunny place where they will remain undisturbed and can easily be observed. Do not put the jars on a windowsill in the classroom. Have students observe the jars everyday for a period of three to five days. Have students record their observations.

Ask: **In which jar did maggots appear?** *(In the uncovered jar)* **Were there any maggots or flies in or on the other jar?** *(There were flies on or around the jar covered with cheesecloth.)* **What does this demonstrate about spontaneous generation?** *(Maggots come from eggs deposited by flies and do not appear spontaneously. If spontaneous generation were true, there would be maggots in both jars.)*

Apply It!

L1 Review the concept of a controlled experiment and the definitions of the two types of variables before beginning the activity.

△ **Control Variables** Make sure that students understand that a controlled experiment has only one factor that changes; all other factors remain the same. The factor that changes, the manipulated variable, is the variable the experimenter is testing.

21st Century Learning

INTERPERSONAL SKILLS Have students work in groups of two to develop a "recipe" for creating life from nonliving material, similar to those that supported the idea of spontaneous generation. Have student pairs exchange their recipes and challenge one another to design an experiment disproving them. Have the original recipe-writing pair determine the acceptability and validity of the proposed experiment.

Elaborate

Build Inquiry

L2 DESIGN A POSTER

Materials markers, poster board

Time 30 minutes

Tell students that they will design posters to show how Redi's and Pasteur's experiments helped disprove the idea of spontaneous generation. Divide the class into small groups for this purpose. Have students review the two experiments and choose one to illustrate. Encourage students to brainstorm how they will represent the experiment. Suggest that they consider flowcharts, a comic strip, or an illustrated story, for example. Have students present their posters to the class and then display them around the classroom.

Ask: **Which variable in Redi's experiment was the manipulated variable? In Pasteur's experiment?** *(Redi's: whether or not there was a cover; Pasteur's: exposure to bacteria-containing dust in the air)* **Which variable in Redi's experiment was the responding variable? In Pasteur's experiment?** *(Redi's: whether or not there were maggots on the meat; Pasteur's: whether or not the broth was cloudy)*

Lab Resource: Quick Lab

L2 COMPARE BROTH SAMPLES Students will explore the basic idea behind Pasteur's experiment disproving spontaneous generation.

Evaluate

Assess Your Understanding

After students answer the questions, have them evaluate their understanding by completing the appropriate sentence.

RTI Response to Intervention

2a. If students cannot identify the variables in a controlled experiment, **then** have them review the descriptions of the variables in Redi's controlled experiment.

b. If students need help explaining why the idea of spontaneous generation is incorrect, **then** review with them the information in **Figure 4** and **Figure 5**.

MY SCIENCE COACH Have students go online for help in understanding where living things come from.

Pasteur's Experiment Even after Redi's experiment, many people continued to believe in spontaneous generation. In the mid-1800s, Louis Pasteur, a French chemist, designed another experiment to test spontaneous generation. That experiment, shown in **Figure 5**, along with Redi's work, finally disproved spontaneous generation.

FIGURE 5

> INTERACTIVE ART **Pasteur's Experiment**
Louis Pasteur's carefully controlled experiment demonstrated that bacteria arise only from existing bacteria. **Design Experiments** Read each step of the experiment below. Why do you think flasks with curved necks were important?

Sample: Curved necks would prevent bacteria from accidentally getting into the flasks from the air

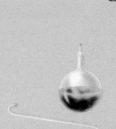

STEP 1

Boiled broth

Pasteur put clear broth into two flasks with curved necks. The necks let in air but kept out bacteria. Pasteur boiled the broth in one flask to kill any bacteria.

Unboiled broth

The broth in the other flask was not boiled.

STEP 2

A few days later, the boiled broth remained clear. Pasteur concluded that bacteria do not arise from the broth, that they appear only when living bacteria are already present.

The unboiled broth became cloudy, showing that new bacteria were growing.

STEP 3

Pasteur took the flask with the clear broth and broke its curved neck. Air carrying bacteria could now enter the flask. In a few days, the broth became cloudy. This evidence confirmed that new bacteria arise only from existing bacteria.

Lab Do the Quick Lab *Compare Broth Samples.*

Assess Your Understanding

2a. Identify A _manipulated variable_ is the one factor that changes in a controlled experiment.

b. Explain Why is the idea of spontaneous generation incorrect?

Living things can only come from other living things.

got it?

○ I get it! Now I know that living things come from _other living things through reproduction._

○ I need extra help with _____
See TE note.

Go to **MY SCIENCE COACH** online for help with this subject.

Interactive Art allows students to explore Redi's and Pasteur's experiments.

MY SCIENCE online.com | **Reproduction of Living Things**

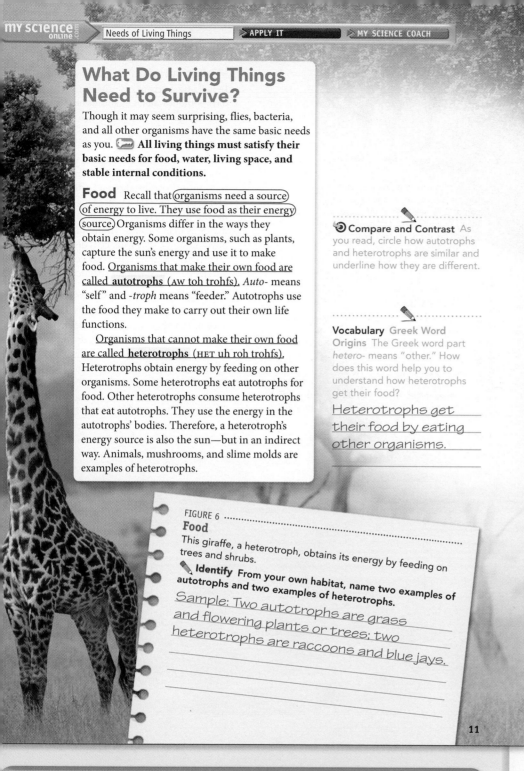

What Do Living Things Need to Survive?

Though it may seem surprising, flies, bacteria, and all other organisms have the same basic needs as you. **All living things must satisfy their basic needs for food, water, living space, and stable internal conditions.**

Food Recall that (organisms need a source) (of energy to live. They use food as their energy) (source.) Organisms differ in the ways they obtain energy. Some organisms, such as plants, capture the sun's energy and use it to make food. Organisms that make their own food are called **autotrophs** (AW toh trohfs). *Auto-* means "self" and *-troph* means "feeder." Autotrophs use the food they make to carry out their own life functions.

Organisms that cannot make their own food are called **heterotrophs** (HET uh roh trohfs). Heterotrophs obtain energy by feeding on other organisms. Some heterotrophs eat autotrophs for food. Other heterotrophs consume heterotrophs that eat autotrophs. They use the energy in the autotrophs' bodies. Therefore, a heterotroph's energy source is also the sun—but in an indirect way. Animals, mushrooms, and slime molds are examples of heterotrophs.

🖉 **Compare and Contrast** As you read, circle how autotrophs and heterotrophs are similar and underline how they are different.

🖉 **Vocabulary** Greek Word Origins The Greek word part *hetero-* means "other." How does this word help you to understand how heterotrophs get their food?

Heterotrophs get their food by eating other organisms.

FIGURE 6
Food
This giraffe, a heterotroph, obtains its energy by feeding on trees and shrubs.

🖉 **Identify** From your own habitat, name two examples of autotrophs and two examples of heterotrophs.

Sample: Two autotrophs are grass and flowering plants or trees; two heterotrophs are raccoons and blue jays.

11

Differentiated Instruction

L1 Needs of Living Things Have students reread the Key Concept statement. Then have them draw or find pictures that illustrate each need of a living thing. Suggest that they display and label the pictures in poster form. Encourage students to exchange posters with a classmate and have the classmate critique the poster.

L3 Food Chains and Energy Pyramids Autotrophs make their own food, and heterotrophs eat autotrophs or other heterotrophs to obtain food for energy. A food chain represents the flow of energy in food molecules from one organism to the next. At each level of the food chain, energy is lost. That loss can be represented by an energy pyramid. Have students find out more about food chains and energy pyramids. Tell them to illustrate one representative food chain and its accompanying energy pyramid.

Explain

Teach Key Concepts 📖

Explain to students that all living things have four basic needs that must be satisfied if they are to survive. The needs are food, water, living space, and stable internal conditions. Ask: **Why do all living things need food?** *(Food is a source of energy.)* **What is meant by living space?** *(A place to get food and water and living space)*

Lead a Discussion

AUTOTROPHS AND HETEROTROPHS Review with students the fact that all living things need food, because food is a source of energy for organisms. Introduce the idea that living things differ in the way in which they obtain food. Some organisms capture the sun's energy and use it to produce their own food. Other organisms must consume food. Emphasize the words *produce* and *consume* as you share this information. Ask: **What are organisms that make their own food called?** *(Autotrophs)* **What are organisms that feed on other organisms called?** *(Heterotrophs)* **What type of organism could also be called a producer? A consumer?** *(An autotroph is a producer; a heterotroph is a consumer.)*

🖉 **Compare and Contrast** Explain that comparing and contrasting information shows how ideas, facts, and events are similar and different.

Address Misconceptions

L1 "PLANT FOOD" IS NOT FOOD Students may be confused by the statement that plants make their own food. They may think plants get their food from commercial "plant food." Show students the label from a plant-food package. Point out the ingredients and explain that these chemicals are nutrients.

Ask: **Why aren't these chemicals actually food?** *(They are not a source of energy.)* **What do you think these nutrients are used for?** *(They help the plant grow, develop, and make food.)* **What are some nutrients people need that do not provide energy?** *(Samples: Vitamins, minerals, water)*

21st Century Learning

CRITICAL THINKING Have students study **Figure 6** and reread the definitions of *autotroph* and *heterotroph*. Ask students to identify the source of energy for the tree and the giraffe. *(Tree: the sun; giraffe: the tree)* Then ask students to identify the ultimate source of energy for both, and to explain their answer. *(The sun's energy is used directly by the tree to make food. The giraffe eats parts of the tree and gets the sun's energy indirectly.)*

11

Explain

Lead a Discussion

WATER Students know that they need water to survive. What they may not understand is why. Ask students if they know how much of their body is made up of water. *(About 70%)* Discuss where this water is found. *(In the cells of the body)* Then discuss the various functions of cells. Ask: **Why is water necessary for the survival of living things?** *(All the functions that cells perform, such as breaking down and building up substances, dividing, growing, getting rid of wastes, transporting materials to other cells all over the body, responding to the environment, require water.)*

Support the Big Q ❓ UbD

LIVING SPACE Explain to students that what is meant by living space is a place that provides a living thing with all that it needs to survive. Emphasize that an organism's living space can be very large or extremely small. It can also be very cold, very hot, very wet, or very dry. The limited amount of space on Earth often leads to competition among living things. Ask: **What is an example of an organism that requires a large amount of space?** *(Sample: An elephant, lion, human, giraffe)* **What is an example of an organism that requires a small amount of space?** *(Sample: A bacterium, ant, worm, koala)* **What is competition?** *(A struggle among living things to get the needed amount of food, water, and shelter)*

Lead a Discussion

HOMEOSTASIS Have students look at the term *homeostasis*. Remind them that the word part *homeo-* means "same." Tell students that *-stasis* comes from a Greek word meaning "stable condition or steady state." Ask: **Using the meanings of those word parts, what does *homeostasis* mean?** *(Sample: A steady state in which the internal conditions of a living thing remain the same)* **Why is it important that an organism maintain homeostasis?** *(To allow its cells to function properly)* Using the example of internal temperature, explain to students that some animals can maintain a constant body temperature regardless of the external temperature. Such animals are called *endotherms*. Ectotherms are animals that have body temperatures that fluctuate somewhat with changes in the external temperature. Ask: **Why is an endotherm sometimes referred to as *warm-blooded*?** *(An endotherm keeps its body at a constant warm temperature. Its blood—and all body tissues—would be warm.)*

did you know?

During the summer, when desert temperatures can exceed 47°C, a camel only needs to drink water every five days. At that time, a camel can drink up to 189 liters of water in just a few hours!

> FIGURE 7
> ### Desert Oasis
> You might be surprised to see so much green in the middle of a desert. In a desert oasis, there is water beneath the surface. The groundwater can bubble to the surface and create springs.
>
> ✏️ **Draw Conclusions** How can a small area in the middle of a desert provide an organism what it needs to survive?
>
> *Sample: The area is large enough to provide organisms with food, water, and space to live.*

12 Introduction to Living Things

Water All living things need water to survive. In fact, most organisms can live for only a few days without water. Organisms need water to obtain chemicals from their surroundings, break down food, grow, move substances within their bodies, and reproduce.

One property of water that is vital to living things is its ability to dissolve more chemicals than any other substance on Earth. In fact, water makes up about 90 percent of the liquid part of your blood. The food that your cells need dissolves in blood and is transported to all parts of your body. Waste from cells dissolves in blood and is carried away. Your body's cells also provide a watery environment for chemicals to dissolve.

Living Space All organisms need a place to live—a place to get food and water and find shelter. Whether an organism lives in the freezing Arctic or the scorching desert, its surroundings must provide what it needs to survive.

Because there is a limited amount of space on Earth, some organisms must compete for space. Trees in a forest, for example, compete with other trees for sunlight above ground. Below ground, their roots compete for water and minerals.

Stable Internal Conditions

Organisms must be able to keep the conditions inside their bodies stable, even when conditions in their surroundings change significantly. For example, your body temperature stays steady despite changes in the air temperature. The maintenance of stable internal conditions is called **homeostasis** (hoh mee oh STAY sis).

Homeostasis keeps internal conditions just right for cells to function. Think about your need for water after a hard workout. When water levels in your body decrease, chemicals in your body send signals to your brain, which cause you to feel thirsty.

Other organisms have different mechanisms for maintaining homeostasis. Consider barnacles, which as adults are attached to rocks at the edge of the ocean. At high tide, they are covered by water. But at low tide, the watery surroundings disappear, and barnacles are exposed to hours of sun and wind. Without a way to keep water in their cells, they would die. Fortunately, a barnacle can close up its hard outer plates, trapping some water inside. In this way, a barnacle can keep its body moist until the next high tide. Refer to **Figure 8** to see another example of how an organism maintains homeostasis.

FIGURE 8 ···

Homeostasis

During the winter months, birds rely on their feathers to maintain homeostasis. By fluffing its feathers, this bluebird is able to trap body heat to keep warm. **Make Generalizations** How do people maintain homeostasis when exposed to cold temperatures?

Sample: People shiver, they get
goosebumps, and their teeth
chatter when they are cold.

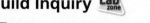 Do the Lab Investigation *Please Pass the Bread.*

🔑 Assess Your Understanding

3a. Describe Which basic need is a fox meeting by feeding on berries?

It is getting energy by
eating food.

b. Apply Concepts The arctic fox has thick, dense fur in the winter and much shorter fur in the summer. How does this help the fox maintain homeostasis?

It helps the fox keep its
internal body temperature
stable even though the
temperature of the fox's
surroundings changes.

got it? ···

○ **I get it!** Now I know that to survive, living things need _food, water, living_
space, and stable internal
conditions.

○ **I need extra help with** _See TE note._

_____

_____

Go to **MY SCIENCE** Ⓢ **COACH** online for help with this subject.

13

LESSON 1.1

INTERPERSONAL SKILLS Have students read *Survival* in the **Big Ideas of Science Reference Library** and work together in small groups to design a board game of survival. The goal of the game should involve collecting survival cards or game pieces that meet the basic needs discussed in the reading. The first player to meet all the basic needs is the winner.

Elaborate

Build Inquiry 🔬

L1 **OBSERVING ONE PROPERTY OF WATER**

Materials 2 small beakers, salt, sugar, 60 mL vegetable oil, 60 mL water, wooden stirrers

Time 10 minutes

Tell students that they will determine whether water or oil is a better solvent of salt and sugar. Ask half the class to dissolve 10 g of salt in 60 mL of water and 10 g of salt in 60 mL of oil. Instruct the other half of the class to dissolve 10 g of sugar in 60 mL of water and 10 g of sugar in 60 mL of oil. Remind students to observe all safety guidelines.

Ask: **What were the results with salt?** *(The water dissolves salt, but the oil does not.)* **What were the results with sugar?** *(Both the water and oil dissolve sugar.)* **Why is water necessary for life?** *(Water dissolves more chemicals than any other substance and provides a good environment for cells to function.)*

Lab Resource: Lab Investigation

L2 **PLEASE PASS THE BREAD** Students will explore the factors necessary for bread mold to grow.

Evaluate

Assess Your Understanding

After students answer the questions, have them evaluate their understanding by completing the appropriate sentence.

R T I Response to Intervention

3a. If students have trouble explaining why living things need food, **then** have them reread the Key Concept statement and the paragraphs about food.

b. If students need help explaining homeostasis, **then** help them review **Figure 8** and the information about stable internal conditions.

MY SCIENCE Ⓢ **COACH** Have students go online for help in understanding the basic needs of life and how living things satisfy those needs.

Differentiated Instruction

L1 **All About Living Things** Have students work in pairs to create a concept map that includes the characteristics and needs of living things.

L3 **Homeotherms and Poikilotherms** Tell students that these terms are another way of distinguishing between ectotherms and endotherms. Have students find out the definitions of these terms and then create a visual that shows how the following terms are

related: *endotherm, ectotherm, homeotherm, poikilotherm, cold-blooded, warm-blooded.*

L3 **Water in Living Things** Challenge students to design an experiment to determine what percentage of a potato's mass is water. Remind students to follow the scientific method in their design. After you have reviewed their designs, you may wish to give students time to carry out their experiments.

Lab ® **zone** **After the Inquiry Warm-Up**

What Is Life?

Inquiry Warm-Up, *Is It Living or Nonliving?*
In the Inquiry Warm-Up, you investigated what characteristics are common to all living things. Using what you learned from that activity, answer the questions below.

1. **MAKE JUDGMENTS** Think of the lists of evidence that you and your classmates shared during the lab. Name one piece of evidence that the toy is alive that you think fails to prove its point. Explain why that evidence is insufficient.

   _____

   _____

   _____

2. **MAKE JUDGMENTS** Think of the lists of evidence that you and your classmates shared during the lab. Name one piece of evidence that the toy is *not* alive that you think fails to prove its point. Explain why that evidence is insufficient.

   _____

   _____

   _____

3. **ANALYZE SOURCES OF ERROR** Think of the lists of evidence that the toy is a living thing that were shared during the lab. Which characteristic of the toy do you think is most likely to make someone believe it is alive?

   _____

   _____

4. **POSE QUESTIONS** Suppose you are trying to determine if something is living or nonliving. List one question that you think it might be helpful to ask to help you make a decision.

   _____

   _____

Name _____ Date _____ Class _____

Assess Your Understanding

What Is Life?

> ## What Are the Characteristics of All Living Things?

1a. REVIEW A change in an organism's surroundings is a (stimulus/response).

 b. INFER A bird sitting in a tree flies away as you walk by. Which of the life characteristics explains the bird's behavior? _____

_____

 c. CHALLENGE Trees do not move like birds do, but they are living things. Why?

_____

_____

_____

_____

got it? ···

○ **I get it!** Now I know that all living things _____

_____

_____

○ **I need extra help with** _____

_____

> ## Where Do Living Things Come From?

2a. IDENTIFY A _____ is the one factor that changes in a controlled experiment.

 b. EXPLAIN Why is the idea of spontaneous generation incorrect? _____

_____

got it? ···

○ **I get it!** Now I know that living things come from _____

_____

○ **I need extra help with** _____

_____

Assess Your Understanding

What Is Life?

What Do Living Things Need to Survive?

3a. DESCRIBE Which basic need is a fox meeting by feeding on berries? _____

_____

b. APPLY CONCEPTS The arctic fox has thick, dense fur in the winter and much shorter fur in the summer. How does this help the fox maintain

homeostasis? _____

_____

_____

got it? ....

○ **I get it!** Now I know that to survive, living things need _____

_____

○ **I need extra help with** _____

_____

What Is Life?

What Are the Characteristics of All Living Things?

All **organisms,** or living things, share six important characteristics. **All living things have a cellular organization, contain similar chemicals, use energy, respond to their surroundings, grow and develop, and reproduce.** All organisms are made up of cells. A **cell** is the basic unit of structure and function in an organism. Single-celled organisms, like bacteria, are **unicellular** organisms. Organisms composed of many cells are **multicellular.** The chemicals in cells include water, carbohydrates, proteins, and lipids. Nucleic acids are the genetic material of cells. The combination of reactions that break down and build up materials to provide a cell with energy is **metabolism.** A change in an organism's surroundings that causes the organism to react is called a **stimulus.** An organism reacts to a stimulus with an action or change in behavior called a **response. Development** is the process of change that occurs during an organism's life to produce a more complex organism. **Asexual reproduction** involves only one parent and produces offspring that are identical to the parent. **Sexual reproduction** involves two parents and combines their genetic material to produce a new organism that differs from both parents.

Where Do Living Things Come From?

Living things arise from other living things through reproduction. The idea that living things could arise from nonliving things, or **spontaneous generation,** was proved incorrect by the **controlled experiments** of Francesco Redi and Louis Pasteur, which were series of identical tests in which only one factor was a variable.

What Do Living Things Need to Survive?

Regardless of size, all living things have the same basic needs. **All living things must satisfy their basic needs for food, water, living space, and stable internal conditions.** Organisms that make their own food are called **autotrophs.** Organisms that cannot make their own food are called **heterotrophs.** Heterotrophs eat autotrophs or other heterotrophs. The maintenance of stable internal conditions is called **homeostasis.** Homeostasis is essential to proper cell functioning.

On a separate sheet of paper, describe living things in terms of their characteristics, needs, and origin.

What Is Life?

Understanding Main Ideas
Answer the following questions on a separate sheet of paper.

1. What are six characteristics all living things share?
2. How did Redi's experiment help disprove the idea of spontaneous generation?
3. What are the four basic needs all living things must satisfy?
4. Describe the difference between growth and development.

Building Vocabulary
Fill in the blank to complete each statement.

5. A change in an organism's environment that causes the organism to react is called a(n) _____.

6. Organisms that make their own food are _____.

7. _____ organisms are composed of many cells.

8. _____ is the mistaken idea that living organisms arise from nonliving sources.

9. The _____ is the basic unit of structure and function in an organism.

10. Organisms that get energy by consuming other organisms are _____.

11. An organism reacts to a stimulus with a(n) _____.

12. In a(n) _____, a scientist carries out a series of tests that are identical in every respect except for one factor, which is the manipulated variable.

13. An organism's ability to maintain stable internal conditions is called _____.

14. To _____ is to produce offspring that are similar to the parents.

What Is Life?

Read the passage and study the diagrams below. Then use a separate sheet of paper to write a brief description of the conditions of each dish and explain why the bacteria appeared as they did.

Bacteria Counts

Many scientists grow bacteria in a laboratory for research using a specific process. A certain amount of bacteria are placed into a solution of water and nutrients the bacteria need as an energy source. After a period of a few days, a small amount of this solution is poured onto a *petri dish*, a shallow round container with a cover, made from transparent plastic. Inside the petri dish is a layer of *agar*, usually a gelatin-like material that also contains nutrients and on which bacteria can grow. The petri dishes are then put in a warm moist place for a week. At the end of a week, a scientist can place each dish under a large magnifying glass that has a grid drawn on it. She then counts the number of spots of bacteria growing on the agar in each of the squares. Each spot is actually a colony of bacteria. The scientist knows approximately how many bacteria are in a colony, so once she knows the number of colonies growing on a Petri dish, she can calculate the number of bacteria present.

The drawings below show petri dishes growing bacteria and are labeled with the conditions the bacteria were grown in.

1.
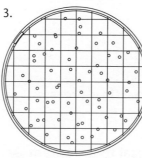

Growing conditions:
Fresh agar
37°C
moist environment
checked after 1 week

2.
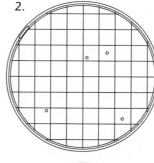

Growing conditions:
Fresh agar
0°C
moist environment
checked after 1 week

3.
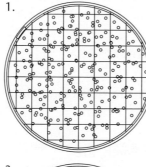

Growing conditions:
Old agar, past
expiration date
37°C
moist environment
checked after 1 week

4.
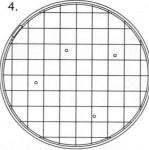

Growing conditions:
Fresh agar
37°C
moist environment
checked after 1 month

Name _____ Date _____ Class _____

What Is Life?

Write the letter of the correct answer on the line at the left.

1. ___ Which of the following terms *best* describes green plants?

   A multicellular heterotrophs

   B multicellular autotrophs

   C unicellular autotrophs

   D unicellular heterotrophs

2. ___ Which of the following is **NOT** a chemical of life?

   A mineral

   B water

   C nucleic acid

   D carbohydrate

3. ___ The one factor that a scientist changes in an experiment is called the

   A responding variable

   B hypothesis

   C controlled variable

   D manipulated variable

4. ___ A bird fluffs its feathers to trap body heat to keep warm during winter months. This is an example of

   A homeostasis

   B homeopathy

   C spontaneous generation

   D asexual reproduction

If the statement is true, write *true*. If the statement is false, change the underlined word or words to make the statement true.

5. _____ <u>Sexual</u> reproduction involves only one parent.

6. _____ The process of change during an organism's life that results in a more complex organism is called <u>growth</u>.

7. _____ Bacteria, the most numerous organisms on Earth, are <u>multicellular</u> organisms.

8. _____ Another name for living things is <u>organisms</u>.

9. _____ Organisms break down and build up materials in a process called <u>homeostasis</u>.

10. _____ In sexual reproduction, offspring are <u>identical to</u> the parent.

13G

What Is Life?

Answer Key

After the Inquiry Warm-Up

1. Answers will vary. Sample: The fact that the toy moves does not prove that it is alive. Many nonliving things move, including air, water, and machines.

2. Answers will vary. Sample: The fact that the toy does not have a heart does not prove it is not alive. Many living things do not have hearts, including plants and microscopic organisms.

3. Answers may vary. Likely answer: The toy moves.

4. Answers will vary. Samples: Does it grow or change with time? Can it reproduce?

Key Concept Summaries

All living things have a cellular organization, contain similar chemicals, use energy, respond to their surroundings, grow and develop, and reproduce. All living things must satisfy their basic needs for food, water, living space, and stable internal conditions (homeostasis). Living things arise from other living things through reproduction. They do not arise from nonliving things, the idea known as spontaneous generation.

Review and Reinforce

1. All living things have a cellular organization, contain similar chemicals, use energy, respond to their surroundings, grow and develop, and reproduce.

2. Redi's experiment showed that flies do not spontaneously arise from rotting meat but are produced from the eggs of other flies.

3. All living things must satisfy the basic needs for food, water, living space, and stable internal conditions.

4. Growth is the process of becoming larger. Development is the process of becoming more complex.

5. stimulus
6. autotrophs
7. Multicellular
8. Spontaneous generation
9. cell
10. heterotrophs
11. response
12. controlled experiment
13. homeostasis
14. reproduce

Enrich

1. The bacteria showed the best growth. They had all their basic needs satisfied: food, water, living space, and a temperature that helped maintain stable internal conditions.

2. Bacterial growth was poor because the freezing temperature did not provide stable internal conditions.

3. Only some colonies grew. Because the agar was old, it probably did not have as many nutrients available to the growing bacteria.

4. Since one month passed before the bacteria were checked, the scientists cannot be sure what happened. Perhaps the living space became overcrowded and the food source was insufficient.

Lesson Quiz

1. B
2. A
3. D
4. A
5. Asexual
6. development
7. unicellular
8. true
9. metabolism
10. different from

Classifying Life

 How are living things alike yet different?

Lesson Pacing: 2–3 periods or 1–1$\frac{1}{2}$ blocks

⏱ **SHORT ON TIME?** To do this lesson in approximately half the time, do the Activate Prior Knowledge activity on page 14. A discussion of the Key Concepts on pages 15, 18, and 20 will familiarize students with the lesson content. Have students do the Quick Labs. The rest of the lesson can be completed by students independently.

Preference Navigator, in the online Planning tools, allows you to customize *Interactive Science* to your own teaching style. You can also edit lesson plans by selecting the Lesson Planner option.

Digital Teacher's Edition allows you to access your Teacher's Edition and Resource materials online.

my science online.com

Lesson Vocabulary

- classification • taxonomy • binomial nomenclature • genus
- species

Content Refresher

Described Species To date, scientists have described around 2.5 million species of living organisms. Although the number of described species may seem large, scientists estimate that between 10 million and 100 million species actually exist. Also, millions of additional species have become extinct. Almost nothing about most of these extinct species is known because they did not leave any fossil traces.

In 2000, an international group of scientists and other individuals established All Species Foundation. Its goal is to catalog every living species within 25 years. Currently the group is identifying about 15,000 species a year, but it hopes to increase the pace to 60,000 annually. The Foundation is determined to identify these species because they feel it is important to know how humans are impacting the species on Earth. The foundation will work to set up Web-searchable databases in which detailed information about various species will be more readily available to scientists around the world—currently the tracking of species is housed in antiquated taxonomy books making it time consuming to identify, verify, and document scientists' latest discoveries.

LESSON OBJECTIVES

🔑 Explain why biologists classify organisms and how they assign scientific names.

🔑 Describe the organization of the levels of classification.

🔑 Explain how taxonomic keys are useful.

Blended Path
Active learning using Student Edition, Inquiry Path, and Digital Path

ENGAGE AND EXPLORE

Teach this lesson using a variety of resources. Begin by reading **My Planet Diary** as a class. Have students share ideas about reasons scientists classify animals. Then have students do the **Inquiry Warm-Up activity.** Students will organize objects from a desk drawer. Discuss what sorts of objects were found in the desk drawer. The **After the Inquiry Warm-Up worksheet** sets up a discussion about the main purpose of grouping the items, regardless of your method of classification. Have volunteers share their answers to question 4 about why grouping these particular items by color or shape is less useful than grouping them by function.

EXPLAIN AND ELABORATE

Teach Key Concepts by explaining the term *taxonomy* and asking students how specific objects can be classified. **Lead a Discussion** about the system originally used to name organisms.

Continue to **Teach Key Concepts** by explaining that today's classification system uses a series of many levels to classify organisms. **Lead a Discussion** about the general to specific levels of classification. Use the **Support the Big Q** to illustrate that as the levels of classification become more specific the number of organisms in each level decreases.

Teach Key Concepts by explaining that taxonomic keys are useful tools to help determine the identity of organisms. **Lead a Discussion** about the usefulness of a decision tree. Then have students go through the taxonomic key step-by-step to gather enough characteristics to identify each organism in the **Apply It activity.** Hand out the **Key Concept Summaries** as a review of each part of the lesson. Students can also use the online **Vocab Flash Cards** to review key terms.

EVALUATE

Have students take the **Lesson Quiz.** For an alternate assessment, see the *ExamView®* Computer Test Generator, Progress Monitoring Assessments, or SuccessTracker™.

ELL Support

1 Content and Language

The word classification contains the suffix *-ation* meaning "a process." *Classification* is a process scientists have developed for classifying organisms.

DIFFERENTIATED INSTRUCTION KEY
L1 Struggling Students or Special Needs
L2 On-Level Students **L3** Advanced Students

LESSON PLANNER 1.2

Lab zone Inquiry Path
Hands-on learning in the Lab zone

Digital Path
Online learning at my science online.com

ENGAGE AND EXPLORE

To teach this lesson with an emphasis on inquiry, begin with the **Inquiry Warm-Up activity.** Students will organize the objects in a junk drawer. Discuss the characteristics of the objects in the drawer. Have students do the **After the Inquiry Warm-Up worksheet.** Talk about which system of classification is more useful for organizing the junk drawer. Have volunteers share their answers to question 4 about why it is more useful to group these particular items by function rather than color or shape.

EXPLAIN AND ELABORATE

Focus on the **Inquiry Skill** for the lesson. Point out that when you observe, you use your senses to gather information. What was observed about the objects in the junk drawer in the **Inquiry Warm-Up activity?** *(Color, shape, and function)* **Build Inquiry** by naming the displayed organisms. Have students do the **Quick Lab** to develop their own classification system for seeds and then ask them to defend their systems.

Support the Big Q by using **Figure 4** to illustrate that as you move down the levels of the classification, the number of organisms in each level becomes less. Continue to **Build Inquiry** by having students develop a classification system for shoes. Do the **Quick Lab** and have students explore a leveled classification system.

Review the steps in the taxonomic key in **Figure 5** before beginning the **Apply It activity.** Ask volunteers to share how they identified each organism. Have students do the **Quick Lab** to create a taxonomic key to help identify tree leaves. Students can use the online **Vocab Flash Cards** to review key terms.

EVALUATE

Have students take the **Lesson Quiz.** For an alternate assessment, see the *ExamView®* Computer Test Generator, Progress Monitoring Assessments, or SuccessTracker™.

ENGAGE AND EXPLORE

Teach this lesson using digital resources. Begin by having students explore real-world connections to the classification of living things at **My Planet Diary** online. Have them access the Chapter Resources to find the **Unlock the Big Question activity.** There they can answer the questions and refine their responses as they continue through the lesson. You can re-assign the activity and have students submit their work so you can track their progress.

EXPLAIN AND ELABORATE

Students reading above, at, or below the lexile measure of this lesson can access basic content readings at their level at **My Reading Web.** Have students use the online **Vocab Flash Cards** to preview key terms. Assign the **Do the Math activity** online and have students submit their work to you. Have students do the **Quick Lab** to classify seeds using their own system of classification.

Have students do the online **Virtual Lab** to classify different species. **Support the Big Q** by using **Figure 4** to show students that as you move down the levels of classification, the number of organisms decreases. Do the **Quick Lab** and have students share their classification charts.

Have students do the online **Interactive Art activity** to explore how a taxonomic key can be used to classify organisms. Review the steps in the taxonomic key before assigning the online **Apply It activity.** Ask volunteers to share how they identified each organism. Have students submit their work to you. Do the **Quick Lab** to reinforce understanding of how the taxonomic key can help to identify tree leaves. The **Key Concept Summaries** online allow students to read a summary and see an image associated with each part of the lesson. Online remediation is available at **My Science Coach.**

EVALUATE

Have students take the **Lesson Quiz.** For an alternate assessment, see the *ExamView®* Computer Test Generator, Progress Monitoring Assessments, or SuccessTracker™.

2 Frontload the Lesson
Preview the lesson questions (blue heads). Ask students if there are any words they do not understand. Explain the specific meanings these words have in science.

3 Comprehensible Input
Have students make a step-by-step set of instructions to teach someone how to classify an organism.

4 Language Production
Pair or group students with varied language abilities to complete labs collaboratively for language practice. Have each student copy the completed written lab for personal reference.

5 Assess Understanding
Have students keep a content area log for this lesson using a two-column format with the headings "What I Understand" and "What I Don't Understand." Follow up so that students can move items from the "Don't Understand" to the "Understand" column.

LESSON 1.2

Classifying Life

Establish Learning Objectives

After this lesson, students will be able to:

- Explain why biologists classify organisms and how they assign scientific names.
- Describe the organization of the levels of classification.
- Explain how taxonomic keys are useful.

Engage

Activate Prior Knowledge

MY PLANET DIARY Read *Birds of a Feather* with the class. Tell students that Laybourne, who died in 2003 at the age of 92, classified bird feathers by carefully analyzing minute structural characteristics unique to different species. Ask: **What is the relationship between the characteristics of living things and the process of classifying living things?** *(Living things can be grouped according to their similar characteristics, or classified)*

BIG IDEAS OF SCIENCE REFERENCE LIBRARY 📖
Have students look up the following topics: Family Tree, Naming.

Explore

Lab Resource: Inquiry Warm-Up 🧪

L1 **CAN YOU ORGANIZE A JUNK DRAWER?**
Students will use the features of objects from a desk drawer to classify the objects into three groups.

UNLOCK THE BIG ?

- Why Do Biologists Classify Organisms?
- What Are the Levels of Classification?
- How Are Taxonomic Keys Useful?

MY PLANET DiARY

CAREER

Birds of a Feather

When people first began to travel in airplanes, birds often caused crashes. In 1960, 62 people were killed when birds flew into an airplane's engine. Something had to be done, but no one knew what kinds of birds were causing the crashes. Usually only a tiny, burnt piece of feather remained. Engineers didn't know how big or heavy the birds were, so they couldn't design planes to keep birds out of the engines. Then a scientist named Roxie Laybourne invented a way to classify birds using a tiny piece of feather. She identified the birds from many crashes. Her work helped engineers design engines to reduce bird collisions. She also helped develop bird management programs for major airports. Roxie's work has saved passengers' lives!

Answer the questions below.

1. What did Roxie Laybourne invent?
   Roxie Laybourne invented a new way to identify birds from their feathers.

2. Why was her invention so important?
   Sample: By identifying the birds that caused the crashes, engineers could take steps to prevent birds from running into planes and causing accidents.

> **PLANET DIARY** Go to **Planet Diary** to learn more about classification.

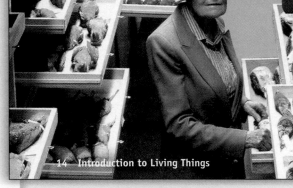

 Lab zone Do the Inquiry Warm-Up *Can You Organize a Junk Drawer?*

SUPPORT ALL READERS

Lexile Measure = 880L   Lexile Word Count = 1331

Prior Exposure to Content: Many students may have misconceptions on this topic

Academic Vocabulary: *observe, questions, infer, interpret*

Science Vocabulary: *classification, taxonomy, genus, species*

Concept Level: Generally appropriate for most students in this grade

Preteach With: My Planet Diary "Birds of a Feather" and Figure 4 activity

Go to **My Reading Web** to access leveled readings that provide a foundation for the content.

MY SCIENCE online.com

Vocabulary

- classification • taxonomy • binomial nomenclature
- genus • species

Skills

- Reading: Ask Questions
- Inquiry: Observe

Why Do Biologists Classify Organisms?

So far, scientists have identified more than one million kinds of organisms on Earth. That's a large number, and it keeps growing as scientists discover new organisms. Imagine how difficult it would be to find information about one particular organism if you had no idea even where to begin. It would be a lot easier if similar organisms were placed into groups.

Organizing living things into groups is exactly what biologists have done. Biologists group organisms based on similarities, just as grocers group milk with dairy products and tomatoes with other produce. **Classification** is the process of grouping things based on their similarities, as shown in **Figure 1.**

Biologists use classification to organize living things into groups so that the organisms are easier to study. The scientific study of how organisms are classified is called **taxonomy** (tak SAHN uh mee). Taxonomy is useful because once an organism is classified, a scientist knows a lot of information about that organism. For example, if you know that a crow is classified as a bird, then you know that a crow has wings, feathers, and a beak.

Ask Questions Before you read, preview the headings. Ask a *what, why,* or *how* question that you would like answered. As you read, write the answer to your question.

Sample: What system did Linnaeus use to name organisms? Binomial nomenclature

FIGURE 1

Classifying Insects

These bees and wasps belong to a large insect collection in a natural history museum. They have been classified according to the characteristics they share.

Observe What characteristics do you think may have been used to group these insects?

Sample: size, color, wing shape, leg length

15

ELL Support

1 Content and Language

Write the term *binomial nomenclature* on the board. Explain that the word *nomenclature* means "a system of naming." Point out that the prefix *bi-* means "two" and that *nomial* comes from another Latin word for "name." So, *binomial nomenclature* literally means "two-name naming system."

2 Frontload the Lesson

Ask students to think about the word *species.* Then, ask: **What is the name of our species?** *(Homo sapiens).* Tell students that *Homo sapiens* is from Latin, meaning "wise (or knowing) man".

3 Comprehensible Input

Invite students to create a mnemonic device to memorize the eight levels of classification in order. For example, sentences using words that begin with *d, k, p, c, o, f, g, s.*

Explain

Introduce Vocabulary

Point out the term *binomial nomenclature.* Tell students that the word *binomial* means "two names," and the word *nomenclature* means "naming." Introduce binomial nomenclature as a system of naming living things using two names.

Teach Key Concepts 🔑

Explain to students that biologists classify, or organize, living things into groups based on their similarities. Ask: **What is the scientific study of how animals are classified called?** *(Taxonomy)* **Why is classification useful?** *(By knowing how an organism is classified, you know a good deal of information about the organism.)* **How might you classify a sunflower, a robin, a lizard, a blue jay, and a tree?** *(Sample: Sunflower and tree as plants; robin, lizard, and blue jay as animals; robin and blue jay as birds)*

Ask Questions Tell students that asking questions is an excellent way to focus on and remember new information that they read or hear. Questions can guide them to identify the important information.

Address Misconceptions

L1 **NOT ALWAYS A "RIGHT" CLASSIFICATION SYSTEM** As students explore the ways in which they classify things in their daily lives and the classification systems used in other fields, they may assume that there is always a "correct" way of classifying things. Explain to students that as long as the groups are based on similar characteristics, there can be many acceptable ways to classify the same objects. Ask: **What do you think are the qualities of a good classification system?** *(It should be useful, meaningful, easily understood, and readily communicated among people.)* Have students look at **Figure 1** and choose a characteristic they would use to divide these insects into two groups. If students say "bees and wasps," point out that classification is about characteristics, not names.

Observe Relate the skill of observation to the lesson by explaining that no matter what is being classified, a classification system is always based on observable characteristics that a group of things share.

My Planet Diary provides an opportunity for students to explore real-world connections to the classification of living things.

MY SCIENCE online.com | Classifying Organisms

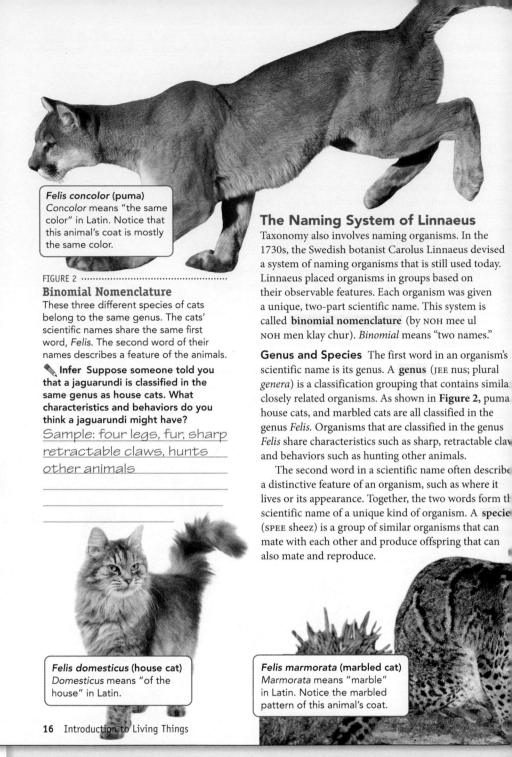

Explain

Lead a Discussion

SCIENTIFIC NAMES Many students may be familiar with the term *Homo sapiens*. Tell students that this is the scientific name for humans. Write the name on the board. Ask: **In this name, *homo* comes from the Latin meaning "man." Does anyone know what the derivation and meaning of the word *sapiens* are?** *(It is Latin for "wise.")* Write these scientific names on the board: *Perognathus californicus, Perognathus nelsoni, Perognathus spinatus.* Explain that these animals are North American field pocket mice. Also, take this opportunity to tell students that sometimes the genus is abbreviated as a letter followed by a period. Ask: **What genus/genera do these animals belong to?** *(Perognathus)* **What are the species of these mice?** *(Perognathus californicus, Perognathus nelsoni and Perognathus spinatus)* **What can you infer about these animals from their names?** *(Samples: They are different species, but all belong to the same genus. Therefore, they are closely related organisms and share many characteristics. However, mating among them would not produce fertile offspring. Students might infer that* P. nelsoni *was discovered by someone named Nelson,* P. californicus *is found in California, and* P. spinatus *has prickly fur.)*

Make Analogies

L1 BINOMIAL NOMENCLATURE The idea of giving each kind of organism a unique, two-part scientific name may be easier for students to understand if you liken it to their names. Tell students that the genus name is like their family (last) name, or surname. The species name is like their first name, or given name. Ask: **What is the most specific way of identifying yourself by name?** *(By using the two-part name, the first name and the last name.)* Students might find it interesting to know that the real name of Swedish botanist Carolus Linnaeus is Carl von Linné. He was so enthusiastic about his new system of binomial nomenclature that he decided to change his own name to a Latin version.

Felis concolor **(puma)**
Concolor means "the same color" in Latin. Notice that this animal's coat is mostly the same color.

FIGURE 2

Binomial Nomenclature
These three different species of cats belong to the same genus. The cats' scientific names share the same first word, *Felis.* The second word of their names describes a feature of the animals.

✎ **Infer** Suppose someone told you that a jaguarundi is classified in the same genus as house cats. What characteristics and behaviors do you think a jaguarundi might have?

<u>Sample: four legs, fur, sharp</u>
<u>retractable claws, hunts</u>
<u>other animals</u>

Felis domesticus **(house cat)**
Domesticus means "of the house" in Latin.

Felis marmorata **(marbled cat)**
Marmorata means "marble" in Latin. Notice the marbled pattern of this animal's coat.

The Naming System of Linnaeus

Taxonomy also involves naming organisms. In the 1730s, the Swedish botanist Carolus Linnaeus devised a system of naming organisms that is still used today. Linnaeus placed organisms in groups based on their observable features. Each organism was given a unique, two-part scientific name. This system is called **binomial nomenclature** (by NOH mee ul NOH men klay chur). *Binomial* means "two names."

Genus and Species The first word in an organism's scientific name is its genus. A **genus** (JEE nus; plural *genera*) is a classification grouping that contains similar, closely related organisms. As shown in **Figure 2**, puma, house cats, and marbled cats are all classified in the genus *Felis.* Organisms that are classified in the genus *Felis* share characteristics such as sharp, retractable claws and behaviors such as hunting other animals.

The second word in a scientific name often describes a distinctive feature of an organism, such as where it lives or its appearance. Together, the two words form the scientific name of a unique kind of organism. A **species** (SPEE sheez) is a group of similar organisms that can mate with each other and produce offspring that can also mate and reproduce.

16 Introduction to Living Things

Digital Lesson: Assign the *Do the Math* activity online and have students submit their work to you.

my science online.com **Classifying Organisms**

sing Binomial Nomenclature A complete
cientific name is written in italics. Only the first
tter of the first word in a scientific name is
apitalized. Notice that scientific names contain
atin words. Linnaeus used Latin words in his
aming system because Latin was the language
at scientists used during that time.

Binomial nomenclature makes it easy for
cientists to communicate about an organism
ecause everyone uses the same scientific name
r the same organism. Using different names or
ommon names for the same organism can get
ery confusing, as **Figure 3** describes.

FIGURE 3 ....

What Are You Talking About?

Is this animal a groundhog, a woodchuck, a marmot, or a whistlepig? Depending on where you live, all of these names are correct. Luckily, this animal has only one scientific name, *Marmota monax*.

✎ **Describe** How is a scientific name written?

In italics, with the genus name capitalized

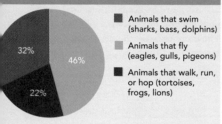

Do the math!

Aristotle and Classification

Aristotle, an ancient Greek scholar, also developed a classification system for animals.

Animals With Blood

- 46% ■ Animals that swim (sharks, bass, dolphins)
- 32% ■ Animals that fly (eagles, gulls, pigeons)
- 22% ■ Animals that walk, run, or hop (tortoises, frogs, lions)

● **Read Graphs** Which group made up the largest percentage of animals?

Animals that fly

● **Calculate** _78_ percent of these animals either fly or swim.

● **Classify** What new categories would you use to make a graph that classifies animals that move in more than one way?

Sample: Animals that fly and walk (eagles, pigeons, gulls); animals that fly, walk, and swim (gulls); animals that hop and swim (frogs)

Lab zone — Do the Quick Lab *Classifying Seeds.*

🗝 **Assess Your Understanding**

1a. Define The scientific study of how living things is classified is called

taxonomy.

b. Make Generalizations What is the advantage of using scientific names instead of using common names, like cat or dog?

Using scientific names makes it easy for scientists to communicate about organisms because everyone uses the same name for the same organism.

got it? ....

○ **I get it!** Now I know that organisms are classified _to organize living things into groups so that they are easier to study._

○ **I need extra help with** _See TE note._

Go to **my science COACH** *online for help with this subject.*

17

Differentiated Instruction

L1 What's in a Name? Make sure students understand what binomial nomenclature is and why it is important. Write the following three names of unicellular organisms on the board and ask students which two are most closely related. Have students explain their answers. *Entamoeba histolytic, Escherichia coli, Entamoeba coli.*

L3 The Dewey Decimal System Many libraries use the Dewey Decimal System to group books according to their similarities. Have students visit the school or local library to become more familiar with this system of classification. Then have them explain why it is useful and how it resembles the system used to classify living things.

Elaborate ————

Build Inquiry **Lab** zone

L1 NAMING ORGANISMS

Materials large drawings or photos of a horse, a Florida panther, and a crayfish

Time 10 minutes

Display the three animal photos on the board or an overhead projector. Below the image of the horse, write *cheval, caballo, cavalo*. Below the image of the Florida panther, write *cougar, puma, mountain lion, catamount*. Below the image of the crayfish, write *crawdad, mudbug*. Tell students they have five minutes in which to choose the correct name of the animal in each image. Discuss students' choices, and then tell them all of the names are correct.

Ask: **What does this activity teach you about common names?** *(Sample: Because there are hundreds of languages, there can be many hundreds of common names for the same animal.)*

Do the Math!

L1 Remind students that circle graphs show how the parts of a whole are related. This graph shows how the Greek scholar Aristotle classified one of the divisions of animals in his classification system: animals with blood.

Ask: **What does the whole circle represent?** *(All the animals with blood in Aristotle's classification system)* **What does each wedge represent?** *(The percentage of animals with blood with a certain characteristic)*

See the *Math Skill and Problem-Solving Activities* for support.

Lab Resource: Quick Lab **Lab** zone

L2 CLASSIFYING SEEDS Students will develop and defend their own classification system for seeds.

Evaluate ————

Assess Your Understanding

After students answer the questions, have them evaluate their understanding by completing the appropriate sentence.

R T I Response to Intervention

1a. If students cannot identify taxonomy, **then** have them reread the Key Concept statement for this lesson and the paragraph that includes it.

b. If students have trouble explaining the importance of binomial nomenclature, **then** review with them the last paragraph on this page.

my science COACH Have students go online for help in understanding classifying organisms.

Explain ————————

Teach Key Concepts 🔑

Explain to students that the modern system of classification is hierarchical, meaning it consists of levels. There are eight levels, starting with domain, which is the largest and broadest, and ending with species, which is the smallest and most specific. Two organisms that share the most classification levels have more characteristics in common and are more closely related. Ask: **What are domains made up of?** *(Kingdoms)* **What are kingdoms made up of?** *(Phyla)* **What are the levels after phylum?** *(Class, order, family, genus, species)* Tell students that it will help them to remember the correct classification sequence from kingdom to species (largest to smallest) if they come up with a mnemonic device, or a sentence in which the first letter of each word represents a level, or taxon. Provide the following example: *Danish kings play cards on fat gold stools.* Invite students to make up their own mnemonic devices. *(Samples: Daring kids put cookies on flat green saucers. Did Ken promptly come over for great spaghetti?)*

Lead a Discussion

GENERAL AND SPECIFIC LEVELS Draw a series of eight concentric circles on the board. Label the outermost circle "Domain." Label the innermost circle "Species." Ask: **Working from the outside in, how should the other circles be labeled?** *(Kingdom, phylum, class, order, family, genus)* **Which is the most general level?** *(Domain)* **Which is the most specific level?** *(Species)* **At what level would both plants and animals be included?** *(Domain)*

Make Analogies

L1 ORGANIZING TIME Help students understand the levels of classification by inviting them to think about the organization of time using calendars and clocks. Ask: **How is the organization of time using calendars and clocks similar to the levels of classification of living things?** *(Larger units of time can be grouped into smaller and smaller units: years, months, weeks, days, hours, minutes, seconds.)*

21st Century Learning 📖 DK

CRITICAL THINKING Have students read *Family Tree* in the **Big Ideas of Science Reference Library.** Ask students to research information about the two extant subfamilies of *Felidae* (*Felinae* and *Pantherinae*) including the genera that make up these subfamilies. They can use this information to construct a family tree for *Felidae*. Encourage students to include examples each genus in their diagrams.

18 Introduction to Living Things

What Are the Levels of Classification?

The classification system that scientists use today is based on the contributions of Linnaeus. But today's classification system uses a series of many levels to classify organisms.

To help you understand the levels of classification, imagine a room filled with everybody who lives in your state. First, all of the people who live in your town raise their hands. Then those who li in your neighborhood raise their hands. Then those who live on your street raise their hands. Finally, those who live in your house raise their hands. Each time, fewer people raise their hands. The more levels you share with others, the more you have in common with them.

The Major Levels of Classification Of course, organisms are not grouped by where they live, but by their shared characteristics. Most biologists today classify organisms into the levels shown in **Figure 4.** First, an organism is placed in a broad group, which in turn is divided into more specific groups.

🔑 **A domain is the broadest level of organization. Within domain, there are kingdoms. Within kingdoms, there are phyla (FY luh; singular *phylum*). Within phyla are classes. Within classes are orders. Within orders are families. Each family contains one or more genera. Finally, each genus contains one or more species.** The more classification levels two organisms share, the more characteristics they have in common and the more closely related they are.

FIGURE 4 ···

▶ **VIRTUAL LAB** **Levels of Classification**
The figure on the facing page shows how the levels of organization apply to a great horned owl.

✎ **Answer the questions.**

1. 🔍 **Observe** List the characteristics that the organisms share at the kingdom level.
   <u>Multicellullar, heterotrophs</u>

2. 🔍 **Observe** List the characteristics that the organisms share at the class level.
   <u>Multicellular, heterotrophs, wings, feathers, a beak, feet that grip</u>

3. 🔍 **Observe** List the characteristics that the organisms share at the genus level.
   <u>Body shape, tufts of feathers, hooked beak, round face, forward-facing eyes, talons</u>

4. **Draw Conclusions** How does the number of shared characteristics on your list change at each level? <u>The closer to the species level, the longer the list of shared characteristics</u>

5. **Interpret Diagrams** Robins have more in common with (lions/ⓞwls).

18 Introduction to Living Things

Virtual Lab allows students to classify different species.

my science online.com ▶ Levels of Classification

Levels of Classification

omain Eukarya

ngdom Animalia

ylum Chordata

ass Aves

der Strigiformes

mily Strigidae

enus Bubo

ecies Bubo virginianus

> As you move down these levels of classification, the number of organisms decreases. The organisms that remain share more characteristics with one another and are more related.

Lab zone Do the Quick Lab
Make a Classification Chart.

📖 Assess Your Understanding

got it? ....

○ I get it! Now I know that the levels of classification are __domain,__ __kingdom, phylum, class,__ __order, family, genus,__ __species.__

○ I need extra help with __See TE note.__

Go to MY SCIENCE COACH online for help with this subject.

19

Differentiated Instruction

L1 The Largest and the Smallest
Ask students to explain which classification level will always have the greatest number of different kinds of organisms and which level will always have the fewest number of different kinds of organisms. A correct explanation will indicate students understand the concept of classification.

L3 Kitchen Classification Make sure students understand the concept of

levels of classification by having them do the following activity. With a family member, students should go on a "classification hunt" in the kitchen. Tell students to look in the refrigerator, cabinets, and drawers to discover what classification systems their family uses to organize items. Remind students to identify the criteria used to classify the objects.

Support the Big Q ❓ UbD

Direct students' attention to **Figure 4.** Have them look at the organisms shown in the top row and notice ways they are similar and ways they are different. Ask: **Which organisms disappear at the second level? Why?** *(The tree, mushroom, and paramecium disappear because the second level is the animal kingdom and the tree is a plant, the mushroom is a fungus, and the paramecium is a protist.)* **Which organisms disappear at the phylum level? Why?** *(The dragonfly and the worm disappear because they are not chordates.)*

🔺 **Observe** Help students understand that observing involves using one or more of the five senses to gather information about the natural world. Remind students that any observation must be an accurate report of only what the senses detect.

Elaborate ———————

Build Inquiry 🔶Lab zone

L2 CLASSIFICATION OF SHOES

Materials paper, colored pencils or markers

Time 15 minutes

Have students work in pairs or groups of four. Tell students to carefully study **Figure 4.** Then tell them to develop a similar classification system for shoes. Encourage them to include as many levels as will be helpful, with a minimum of five. Remind students that their systems must be useful, easily understood by others, and easy to use.

Ask: **What is the purpose of your system?** *(Sample: To identify a specific type of shoe by its characteristics)* **Which level will have the most shoes?** *(Domain)* **Which will have the fewest shoes?** *(Species)*

Lab Resource: Quick Lab 🔶Lab zone

L1 MAKE A CLASSIFICATION CHART Students will explore a leveled classification system.

Evaluate ———————

Assess Your Understanding

Have students evaluate their understanding by completing the appropriate sentence.

R T I Response to Intervention

If students have difficulty listing the levels of classification, **then** have them review **Figure 4** and identify the eight levels.

MY SCIENCE COACH Have students go online for help in understanding the levels of classification.

Explain

Teach Key Concepts 🔑

Explain to students that it is not always possible to know the identity of an organism. A tool known as a *taxonomic key* can help determine the identity of an organism. Tell students that another name for a taxonomic key is a *dichotomous key*. The word *dichotomous* means "two parts." A taxonomic key is made up of several pairs ("two parts") of opposing statements. Ask: **What do the paired statements describe?** *(Various physical characteristics of different organisms)* **What do you do at each step in the key?** *(Choose the statement that best describes the organism)* **Do you always need to go to the last step in the key to identify an organism? Explain.** *(No; often the organism is identified in an intermediate step. The important thing is to make sure it has the characteristics observed.)*

Lead a Discussion

DECISION TREES Ask students if they are familiar with decision trees or flow charts. Some students may have used them in mathematics, programmed instruction, or computer games that involve making decisions or following steps in a process. Ask: **What is the purpose of each step in a decision tree or a flow chart?** *(Sample: To help identify the next step to go to so that a final decision or result can be reached)*

How Are Taxonomic Keys Useful?

Why should you care about taxonomy? Suppose that you are watching television and feel something tickling your foot. Startled, you look down and see a tiny creature crawling across your toes. Although it's only the size of a small melon seed, you don't like the looks of its two claws waving at you. Then, in a flash, it's gone.

How could you find out what the creature was? You could use a field guide. Field guides are books with illustrations that highlight differences between similar-looking organisms. You could also use a taxonomic key. 🔑 **Taxonomic keys are useful tools that help determine the identity of organisms.** A taxonomic key consists of a series of paired statements that describe the various physical characteristics of different organisms. The taxonomic key shown in **Figure 5** can help you identify the mysterious organism.

FIGURE 5 ·······

▶ **INTERACTIVE ART** **Identifying Organisms**
The six paired statements in this taxonomic key describe physical characteristics of different organisms.

✎ **Identify** ___Seven___ different organisms can be identified using this key. The mysterious organism is a ___mite.___

0.4 mm

Start Here

First: For each set of statements, choose the one that best describes the organism; for example, 1a.

Second: Follow the direction to the next step

Third: Continue process until organism is identified.

Taxonomic Key

Step		Characteristics	Organism
1	1a.	Has 8 legs	Go to Step 2.
	1b.	Has more than 8 legs	Go to Step 3.
2	2a.	Has one oval-shaped body region	Go to Step 4.
	2b.	Has two body regions	Go to Step 5.
3	3a.	Has one pair of legs on each body segment	Centipede
	3b.	Has two pairs of legs on each body segment	Millipede
4	4a.	Is less than 1 millimeter long	Mite
	4b.	Is more than 1 millimeter long	Tick
5	5a.	Has clawlike pincers	Go to Step 6.
	5b.	Has no clawlike pincers	Spider
6	6a.	Has a long tail with a stinger	Scorpion
	6b.	Has no tail or stinger	Pseudoscorpion

20 Introduction to Living Things

Interactive Art allows students to explore how a taxonomic key can be used to classify organisms.

Digital Lesson: Assign the *Apply It* activity online and have students submit their work to you.

my science online.com | **Taxonomic Keys**

apply it!

Use the taxonomic key in **Figure 5** to answer the following questions.

Interpret Tables Identify each pictured organism.

5 mm
_____Tick_____

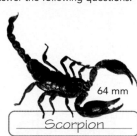
64 mm
_____Scorpion_____

40 mm
_____Spider_____

50 mm
_____Millipede_____

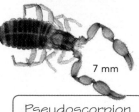
7 mm
_____Pseudoscorpion_____

25 mm
_____Centipede_____

Draw Conclusions What other information could have been helpful identifying these organisms?

Sample: organisms' colors, kinds of legs, locations of eyes
_____
_____

CHALLENGE Is this information necessary for the key in **Figure 5**? Explain your answer.

Sample: No; because the key contains all the information needed to
identify these organisms. Another key might use this information.
_____

Lab zone Do the Quick Lab
Living Mysteries.

Assess Your Understanding

Got it? ....

I get it! Now I know that taxonomic keys are used to <u>determine the identity of</u>
<u>organisms.</u>

I need extra help with <u>See TE note.</u>

Go to MY SCIENCE COACH *online for help with this subject.*

Differentiated Instruction

L1 Using a Taxonomic Key To help students understand the purpose of a taxonomic key and how to use one, have them write a short paragraph explaining how a taxonomic key is useful. Then have them create a taxonomic key to classify the utensils in the family kitchen.

L3 Make a Taxonomic Key Challenge students to create a taxonomic key for identifying the following common

beans: white northern bean, pinto bean, black bean, garbanzo bean, kidney bean. Tell students that they will have to do some research to determine the characteristics of the beans and to develop the criterion for each pair of opposing statements. Have students present their keys to the class along with pictures of the five beans. They should challenge classmates to identify each bean using the taxonomic key.

Elaborate

Apply It!

L1 Review the steps in the taxonomic key in **Figure 5** before beginning the activity. Remind students that each step consists of a pair of opposing statements that describe a characteristic of an organism. Tell students to go through the taxonomic key step by step to gather enough characteristics to identify each organism. Encourage them to match pictures with descriptions in the table.

Lab Resource: Quick Lab **Lab zone**

L2 **LIVING MYSTERIES** Students will create a taxonomic key to help identify tree leaves.

Evaluate

Assess Your Understanding

Have students evaluate their understanding by completing the appropriate sentence.

RTI Response to Intervention

If students have trouble identifying the purpose of a taxonomic key, **then** have them reread the Key Concept statement for this section.

MY SCIENCE COACH Have students go online for help in understanding taxonomic keys.

Lab® **zone** **After the Inquiry Warm-Up**

Classifying Life

> ### Inquiry Warm-Up, *Can You Organize a Junk Drawer?*
> In the Inquiry Warm-Up, you investigated different ways to group things and discussed how useful various methods are. Using what you learned from that activity, answer the questions below.

1. **MAKE GENERALIZATIONS** Besides being found in the junk drawer of a desk, what do all the items have in common?

   _____

   _____

2. **DRAW CONCLUSIONS** All of the items are supplies or tools used to do paperwork. Since they all have that general purpose in common, what system of grouping the items seems to be very useful?

   _____

   _____

   _____

   _____

3. **MAKE JUDGMENTS** How is the grouping system you suggested in question 2 *no* more useful than grouping the items by color or shape?

   _____

   _____

4. **MAKE JUDGMENTS** How is the grouping system you suggested in question 2 more useful than grouping the items by color or shape? Explain.

   _____

   _____

   _____

   _____

   _____

   _____

Assess Your Understanding

Classifying Life

Why Do Biologists Classify Organisms?

1a. DEFINE The scientific study of how living things are classified is
called _____

b. MAKE GENERALIZATIONS What is the advantage of using scientific
names instead of using common names, like cat or dog? _____

_____

_____

_____

gotit? ....

○ **I get it!** Now I know that organisms are classified _____

_____

○ **I need extra help with** _____

_____

What Are the Levels of Classification?

gotit? ....

○ **I get it!** Now I know that the levels of classification are _____

_____

_____

○ **I need extra help with** _____

_____

Assess Your Understanding

Classifying Life

How Are Taxonomic Keys Useful?

gotit? ⋅⋅

○ **I get it!** Now I know that taxonomic keys are used to _____

_____

○ **I need extra help with** _____

_____

Place the outside corner, the corner away from the dotted line, in the corner of your copy machine to copy onto letter-size paper.

Name _____ Date _____ Class _____

Key Concept Summaries

Classifying Life

Why Do Biologists Classify Organisms?

To date, scientists have identified more than one million kinds of organisms on Earth—and that number keeps growing as scientists discover new organisms. To bring order to this astonishing number of living things, scientists group organisms based on similarities, or classify them. **Classification** is the process of grouping things based on similarities. **Biologists use classification to organize living things into groups so that the organisms are easier to study.** The scientific study of how living things are classified is called **taxonomy.** Taxonomy also involves naming organisms. The system scientists use, developed by Swedish botanist Carolus Linnaeus, is called **binomial nomenclature.** Under it, each organism has a unique two-part scientific name. The first word is the **genus,** a classification grouping that contains similar, closely related organisms. The second word often describes where an organism lives or its appearance. A **species** is a group of similar organisms that can mate with each other and produce offspring that can also mate and reproduce.

What Are the Levels of Classification?

Most biologists today use a classification system that has eight levels. **A domain is the highest level of organization. Within a domain, there are kingdoms. Within kingdoms, there are phyla. Within phyla are classes. Within classes are orders. Within orders are families. Each family contains one or more genera. Finally, each genus contains one or more species.**
The more classification levels two organisms share, the more characteristics they have in common and the more closely related they are.

How Are Taxonomic Keys Useful?

Taxonomic keys are useful tools that help determine the identity of organisms. A taxonomic key consists of a series of paired statements that describe the various physical characteristics of different organisms. By choosing one statement in each pair and following its directive, the identity of an unfamiliar organism can eventually be determined.

On a separate sheet of paper, describe how a classification system works to organize living things. Then compare the classification system developed by Carolus Linnaeus with the classification system used by biologists today.

Review and Reinforce

Classifying Life

Understanding Main Ideas
Answer the following questions in the spaces provided.

1. Describe the contributions to modern classification made by Carolus Linnaeus.

   _____

   _____

   _____

2. Describe the modern system of classification.

   _____

   _____

   _____

Building Vocabulary
Match each term with its definition by writing the letter of the correct definition in the right column on the line beside the term in the left column.

3. ___ classification

4. ___ binomial nomenclature

5. ___ genus

6. ___ taxonomy

7. ___ species

a. naming system developed by Linnaeus

b. process of grouping things based on their similarities

c. a group of organisms that can mate and produce offspring that can also mate and reproduce

d. first word in an organism's scientific name

e. the scientific study of how things are classified

Enrich

Classifying Life

> Read the passage below. Then answer the questions that follow on a separate sheet of paper. Use a calculator to do the calculations.

How Many Species of Animals Are There?

There are more species of insects than any other type of animal on Earth. The majority of animals live in the tropics. If you can estimate how many species of insects there are in the tropics, you can estimate the number of species of animals on Earth.

Over the years, entomologists (scientists who study insects) have been discovering and naming new kinds (species) of insects, and now over a million kinds of insects are known. Dr. Terry Erwin, an entomologist at the Smithsonian Institution, studies beetles. Beetles make up a large percentage of insects and related animals. By estimating the number of species of beetles in the tropics, Dr. Erwin was able to estimate the total number of species of animals in the world. Dr. Erwin used the following information to arrive at his estimate:

- Dr. Erwin found 1,200 species of beetles living in *Luehea seemannii* trees.

- Of those 1,200 species of beetles, he estimated that 163 are found only in the *Luehea seemannii* tree, and not in other species of trees.

- There are about 50,000 species of trees in the tropics.

- Beetles make up about 40% of insects and related animals.

- Dr. Erwin estimate that there are about twice as many species of insects and related animals in tropical trees as there are on the ground of the forest.

1. If each kind of tree has 163 species of beetles that are found only on that type of tree but no others, how many kind of beetles are there in tropical trees?

2. Using your answer from question 1, estimate how many species of insects and related animals there are in tropical trees.

3. Using your answer from question 2, estimate how many species of insects and related animals are on the forest floor in the tropics.

4. Using your answers from questions 2 and 3, estimate how many species of insects and related animals there might be in the trees and the forest floor together in the tropics.

Lesson Quiz

Classifying Life

Fill in the blank to complete each statement.

1. Organizing rocks according to their similarities is an example of the process of _____.

2. _____ is the scientific study of how organisms are classified and named.

3. Only the _____ word in an organism's complete scientific name has its first letter capitalized.

4. The levels of classification of organisms in order are: domain, kingdom, phylum, class, order, family, genus, and species. The broadest, least specific level is _____.

5. To identify an unfamiliar organism, you could use a field guide and a(n) _____.

If the statement is true, write _true_. If the statement is false, change the underlined word or words to make the statement true.

6. _____ In Linnaeus's classification system, the smallest group was the <u>genus</u>.

7. _____ As you move down the levels of classification, from domain to species, the number of organisms in each group <u>increases</u>.

8. _____ Organisms in the same family are <u>less</u> closely related than organisms in the same order.

9. _____ Linnaeus classified organisms according to <u>similarities</u> in observable features.

10. _____ _Felis concolor_ <u>can</u> mate with _Felis domesticus_.

Classifying Life

Answer Key

After the Inquiry Warm-Up

1. They are supplies or tools used to do office work, schoolwork, or other paperwork.

2. Since all of the items are supplies or tools used for paperwork, it is useful to separate the items into groups based on the specific function of the item. For example, you might group all writing instruments together and group all types of fasteners together.

3. Whether you group the items by specific function, by color, or by shape, it should be easy to find any item you are looking for.

4. Grouping the items by specific function may make it easier to find the best tool for any job. For example, if you are looking for something to fasten several pages together and look at the group of different fasteners, you will see items such as paper clips, tape, a stapler, and glue. You should be able to see all your options and choose the best tool for the task you are doing.

Key Concept Summaries

Biologists use classification systems to organize living things into groups according to similarities so that the organisms are easier to study. The system developed by Carolus Linnaeus is called *binomial nomenclature*. In it, each organism has a unique two-part scientific name. The first word is the genus, a grouping that contains similar, closely related organisms. The second word, the species, often describes where an organism lives or its appearance. Today most biologists use a classification system that has eight levels: domain, kingdom, phylum, class, order, family, genus, and species.

Review and Reinforce

1. Carolus Linnaeus placed organisms in groups based on their observable features. He also devised a naming system called *binomial nomenclature* that indicates an organism's genus and species.

2. The modern system classifies organisms into eight levels: domain, kingdom, phylum, class, order, family, genus, and species. The scientific name given to an organism is based on binomial nomenclature. The more classification levels two organisms share, the more characteristics they have in common and the more closely related they are.

3. b   4. a   5. d

6. e   7. c

Enrich

1. $50,000 \times 163 = 8,150,000$

2. $40\% \times$ number of insects and related animals = 8,150,000; insects and related animals = 20,375,000

3. $20,375,000 \times \frac{1}{2} = 10,187,500$

4. $10,187,500 + 20,375,000 = 30,562,500$

Lesson Quiz

1. classification   2. Taxonomy

3. first   4. domain

5. taxonomic key   6. species

7. decreases   8. more

9. true   10. cannot

Domains and Kingdoms

3 How are living things alike yet different?

Lesson Pacing: 1–2 periods or $\frac{1}{2}$–1 block

🕐 **SHORT ON TIME?** To do this lesson in approximately half the time, do the Activate Prior Knowledge activity on page 22. A discussion of the Key Concept on page 23 will familiarize students with the lesson content. Have students do the Quick Lab. The rest of the lesson can be completed by students independently.

Preference Navigator, in the online Planning tools, allows you to customize *Interactive Science* to your own teaching style. You can also edit lesson plans by selecting the Lesson Planner option.

Digital Teacher's Edition allows you to access your Teacher's Edition and Resource materials online.

my science online.com

Lesson Vocabulary

- prokaryote
- nucleus
- eukaryote

Professional Development Note

Content Refresher

Classification Before 1869, most scientists classified all organisms into two kingdoms—plants and animals. Starting around 1869, a five-kingdom classification system became popular: Monera, Protista, Plantae, Fungi, Animalia. In this system, all prokaryotes were included in kingdom Monera. Later, a distinction was made between organisms with nuclei and those without—giving rise to domains Prokarya and Eukarya. This was the predominant system until around 1990, when the prokaryotes were divided into kingdoms Eubacteria and Archaebacteria, based on differences in structure, biochemistry, physiology, and evolutionary history. Because the differences between archaebacteria and eubacteria are so fundamental, prokaryotes now form two different domains. Since the study of evolution is ongoing, it is likely that the classification system used today will continue to undergo further developments and changes based on new evidence and discoveries being made by scientists.

LESSON OBJECTIVE

🔑 Explain how organisms are classified into domains and kingdoms.

Blended Path Active learning using Student Edition, Inquiry Path, and Digital Path

ENGAGE AND EXPLORE

Teach this lesson using a variety of resources. Begin by reading **My Planet Diary** as a class. Have students share ideas about why there are so many different species of bees. Then have students do the **Inquiry Warm-Up activity.** Students will investigate how scientists organize living things into kingdoms. Discuss the shared characteristics students used to place two organisms in the same kingdom. The **After the Inquiry Warm-Up worksheet** sets up a discussion about the criteria involved in a specific classification of an organism. Have volunteers share their answers to question 4 about whether or not all observations needed to classify organisms can be made in a minute or two with the unaided eye.

EXPLAIN AND ELABORATE

Teach Key Concepts by explaining the three criteria used to place organisms into domains and kingdoms. **Lead a Discussion** about the similarities and differences between domain Bacteria and domain Archaea. **Support the Big Q** by identifying the four kingdoms of the domain Eukarya. Then have students practice the inquiry skill in the **Apply It activity.** Hand out the **Key Concept Summaries** as a review of each part of the lesson. Students can also use the online **Vocab Flash Cards** to review key terms.

EVALUATE

Have students take the **Lesson Quiz.** For an alternate assessment, see the *ExamView®* Computer Test Generator, Progress Monitoring Assessments, or SuccessTracker™.

ELL Support

1 Content and Language

The word *prokaryote* contains the prefix *pro-* meaning "before."

DIFFERENTIATED INSTRUCTION KEY
L1 Struggling Students or Special Needs
L2 On-Level Students **L3** Advanced Students

Lab zone Inquiry Path
Hands-on learning in the Lab zone

ENGAGE AND EXPLORE

To teach this lesson with an emphasis on inquiry, begin with the **Inquiry Warm-Up activity.** Students will investigate how scientists organize living things into kingdoms. Discuss the shared characteristics students used to place two organisms in the same kingdom. Have students do the **After the Inquiry Warm-Up worksheet.** Talk about the shared characteristics that could place specific organisms into similar kingdoms. Have volunteers share their answers to question 4 about whether or not all observations needed to classify organisms can be made in a minute or two with the unaided eye.

EXPLAIN AND ELABORATE

Focus on the **Inquiry Skill** for the lesson. Point out that when you classify, you look for similarities among items and then you group them according to those similarities. How could the items in the **Inquiry Warm-Up activity** be classified? *(Answers will vary.)* **Support the Big Q** by asking students what the organisms in the four kingdoms of the domain Eukarya have in common. Review the characteristics of the four kingdoms of the domain Eukarya before beginning the **Apply It activity.** Ask volunteers to identify how they classified the organism. **Build Inquiry** by having groups of students classify organisms by domain. Have students do the **Quick Lab** to explore the autotrophic nature of plants and then share their results. Students can use the online **Vocab Flash Cards** to review key terms.

EVALUATE

Have students take the **Lesson Quiz.** For an alternate assessment, see the *ExamView®* Computer Test Generator, Progress Monitoring Assessments, or SuccessTracker™.

Digital Path
Online learning at my science online.com

ENGAGE AND EXPLORE

Teach this lesson using digital resources. Begin by having students explore real-world connections to domains and kingdoms at **My Planet Diary** online. Have them access the Chapter Resources to find the **Unlock the Big Question activity.** There they can answer the questions and refine their responses as they continue through the lesson. You can re-assign the activity and have students submit their work so you can track their progress.

EXPLAIN AND ELABORATE

Students reading above, at, or below the lexile measure of this lesson can access basic content readings at their level at **My Reading Web.** Have students use the online **Vocab Flash Cards** to preview key terms. **Support the Big Q** by identifying the common characteristics of organisms in the four kingdoms of the domain Eukarya. Review the characteristics of each kingdom in the domain Eukarya before assigning the online **Apply It activity.** Ask volunteers to share how they classified the organisms. Have students submit their work to you. Do the **Quick Lab** and then ask students to share their results. The **Key Concept Summaries** online allow students to read a summary and see an image associated with each part of the lesson. Online remediation is available at **My Science Coach.**

EVALUATE

Have students take the **Lesson Quiz.** For an alternate assessment, see the *ExamView®* Computer Test Generator, Progress Monitoring Assessments, or SuccessTracker™.

2 Frontload the Lesson

Preview the lesson visuals, labels, and captions. Ask students what they know about the words *prokaryote* and *eukaryote*. Explain the specific meanings these words have in science.

3 Comprehensible Input

Have students study the visuals and their captions on pages 23, 24, and 25 to support the Key Concepts of the lesson.

4 Language Production

Pair or group students with varied language abilities to complete labs collaboratively for language practice. Have each student copy the completed written lab for personal reference.

5 Assess Understanding

Have students create a portfolio of their notes and then do oral presentations of lesson content.

Domains and Kingdoms

Lexile Measure = 880L

Establish Learning Objective

After this lesson, students will be able to:

- Explain how organisms are classified into domains and kingdoms.

Engage

Activate Prior Knowledge

MY PLANET DIARY Read *Unbeelievable!* with the class. Discuss with students their reactions to learning that there are more than 19,000 species of bees. Emphasize that each species has unique characteristics. To further impress students with the abundance and diversity of life on Earth, tell them that more than 2.5 million types of organisms have been discovered, and scientists estimate that several million more will be discovered in the future.

BIG IDEAS OF SCIENCE REFERENCE LIBRARY 📖
Have students look up the following topics: DNA Connections, Naming.

Explore

Lab Resource: Inquiry Warm-Up 🧪

L1 **WHAT ORGANISM GOES WHERE?** Students will use their observations of several organisms to determine the kingdom in which the organisms are classified.

Domains and Kingdoms

🔑 How Are Organisms Classified Into Domains and Kingdoms?

my planeT DiaRy

Unbeelievable!

If you were classifying organisms, would you expect there to be more bees, more birds, or more mammals in the world? The table below shows the number of species of bees, mammals, and birds that scientists have found so far!

Number of Species		
Bees	**Mammals**	**Birds**
19,200	4,620	10,000

SCIENCE STATS

Answer the question below.

Why do you think that bee species outnumber mammal and bird species combined?

Sample: The bees reproduce faster and do not need as much food or space to stay alive.

▶ PLANET DIARY Go to **Planet Diary** to learn more about domains and kingdoms.

🧪 Lab zone Do the Inquiry Warm-Up
What Organism Goes Where?

How Are Organisms Classified Into Domains and Kingdoms?

Suppose you helped Linnaeus classify organisms. You probably would have identified organisms as either plants or animals. That's because in Linnaeus' time there were no microscopes to see the tiny organisms that are known to exist today. Microscopes helped to discover new organisms and identify differences among cells.

Today, a three-domain system of classification is commonly used. As shown in the table on the top of the next page, the three domains are Bacteria, Archaea, and Eukarya. Within the domains are kingdoms. 🔑 **Organisms are placed into domains and kingdoms based on their cell type, their ability to make food, and the number of cells in their bodies.**

SUPPORT ALL READERS
Lexile Measure = 880L   Lexile Word Count = 845

Prior Exposure to Content: Many students may have misconceptions on this topic

Academic Vocabulary: *classify, identify, main idea*

Science Vocabulary: *prokaryote, nucleus, eukaryote*

Concept Level: Generally appropriate for most students in this grade

Preteach With: My Planet Diary "Unbeelievable" and Figure 1 activity

Go to **My Reading Web** to access leveled readings that provide a foundation for the content.

my science online.com

Vocabulary
- prokaryote • nucleus
- eukaryote

Skills
🔁 Reading: Identify the Main Idea
△ Inquiry: Classify

Three Domains of Life

Bacteria	Archaea	Eukarya		
		Protists	Fungi	Plants	Animals

Domain Bacteria Although you may not know it, members of the domain Bacteria are all around you. You can find them on the surfaces you touch and inside your body. Some bacteria are autotrophs, while others are heterotrophs.

Members of the domain Bacteria are called prokaryotes (proh KA ree ohtz). **Prokaryotes** are unicellular organisms whose cells lack a nucleus. A **nucleus** (NOO klee us; plural *nuclei*) is a dense area in a cell that contains nucleic acids—the chemical instructions that direct the cell's activities. In prokaryotes, nucleic acids are not contained within a nucleus.

Domain Archaea Deep in the Pacific Ocean, hot gases and molten rock spew out from a vent in the ocean floor. It is hard to imagine that any living thing could exist in such harsh conditions. Surprisingly, a group of tiny organisms thrives in such a place. They are members of the domain Archaea (ahr KEE uh), whose name comes from the Greek word for "ancient."

Like bacteria, archaea are unicellular prokaryotes. And like bacteria, some archaea are autotrophs and others are heterotrophs. Archaea are classified in their own domain because their chemical makeup differs from that of bacteria. Bacteria and archaea also differ in the structure of their cells. The bacteria in **Figure 1** and the archaea in **Figure 2** have been stained and magnified to make them easier to see.

FIGURE 1 ·······················
Bacteria
Most bacteria, such as *Lactobacillus acidophilus*, are helpful. These bacteria help to produce yogurt and milk for people who are lactose intolerant.

FIGURE 2 ·······················
Archaea
Archaea can be found in extreme environments such as hot springs, very salty water, and the intestines of cows! Scientists think that the harsh conditions in which archaea live are similar to those of ancient Earth.

✎ **Compare and Contrast** How are archaea and bacteria similar? How are they different?

Both are microscopic, unicellular prokaryotes. They differ in structure and chemical makeup.

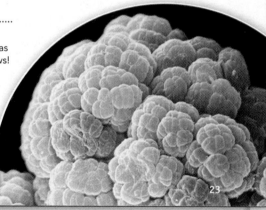

23

Explain ─────────────

Introduce Vocabulary
Have students look at the three vocabulary terms. Explain that two of the terms are related by the presence or absence of the third term, *nucleus*. Briefly review with students the functions of a cell's nucleus.

Teach Key Concepts 🗝
Explain to students that three criteria are used to place organisms into domains and kingdoms. Those criteria are cell type, ability to make food, and number of cells in the body. Ask: **What are the two types of organisms according to cell type?** *(Prokaryotes and eukaryotes)* **What are the two types of organisms according to ability to make food?** *(Autotrophs and heterotrophs)* **What are the two types of organisms according to cell number?** *(Unicellular and multicellular)*

Lead a Discussion
DOMAIN BACTERIA AND DOMAIN ARCHAEA Ask students to compare the magnified images of bacteria and archaea in **Figure 1** and **Figure 2**. Ask: **How are archaea and bacteria alike?** *(They both are prokaryotes, unicellular, and can be autotrophs or heterotrophs.)* **How are archaea and bacteria different?** *(They differ in the structure and chemical makeup of their cells.)* **Why aren't archaea and bacteria classified in the same domain as they are similar in cell type, cell number, and source of nutrition?** *(Because their chemical makeup differs significantly, it is believed they are not closely related.)*

My Planet Diary provides an opportunity for students to explore real-world connections to domains and kingdoms.

Ⓔ Ⓛ Ⓛ Support

1 Content and Language
Explain that *nucleus* comes from Latin, meaning "nut." Have students discuss how the term *nucleus* is related to its original Latin meaning.

2 Frontload the Lesson
Invite students to speculate on whether an eagle has more in common with a fungus or with bacteria. After students offer comments, explain that, though both fungi and bacteria seem utterly unlike birds, scientists classify fungi and birds as members of the same kingdom.

3 Comprehensible Input
Have students create a concept map to illustrate the three domains, major characteristics of each domain, and brief explanations or examples of each characteristic.

Explain

Support the Big Q ❓ UbD

DOMAIN EUKARYA List ten different plants, animals, protists, and fungi on the board and direct students' attention to the list. Tell students all the organisms are eukaryotes. List the kingdoms that make up domain Eukarya (Animals, Plants, Protists, Fungi). Review the main characteristics of each kingdom. Ask: **What do members of these kingdoms have in common?** *(They all are made of cells that have a nucleus.)* **How would you classify each organism on the list on the board?** *(Answers will depend on organisms selected.)* **To which domain and kingdom do you belong?** *(Domain Eukarya, kingdom Animal)*

Identify the main idea Tell students that a paragraph may include several ideas, but one idea is the most important, or biggest, idea. That is the main idea. Other information in the paragraph supports or further explains the main idea.

Address Misconceptions

L1 PROTISTS AND FUNGI Because protists and fungi are members of domain Eukarya along with plants and animals, students may assume that they are multicellular organisms. Remind students that although the majority of fungi are multicellular, a few are unicellular. **What is an example of a unicellular fungus?** *(Yeast are unicellular fungi.)*

21st Century Learning

CRITICAL THINKING Explain to students that fungi were originally classified as plants. Because of a certain characteristic, they were later classified into a separate kingdom. Ask students to identify the characteristic that differentiates fungi from plants. *(Fungi do not carry out photosynthesis. They are heterotrophs.)*

Elaborate

Apply It!

L1 Before beginning the activity, have students write the name of each kingdom of domain Eukarya on a sheet of paper. Then have them identify the characteristics of each kingdom using the terms *autotrophs, heterotrophs, unicellular, multicellular, nucleus, no nucleus.*

△ Classify Remind students that when they classify, they look for similarities among the items and group the items according to those similarities.

FIGURE 3 ·······························
Eukarya
You can encounter organisms from all four kingdoms of Eukarya on a trip to a salt marsh.

Three Domains of Life

Bacteria	Archaea	Eukarya		
		Protists	Fungi	Plants	Animals

Domain Eukarya What do seaweeds, mushrooms, tomatoes, and dogs have in common? They are all members of the domain Eukarya. Organisms in this domain are **eukaryotes** (yoo KA ree ohtz)—organisms with cells that contain nuclei. Scientists classify organisms in the domain Eukarya into one of four kingdoms: protists, fungi, plants, or animals.

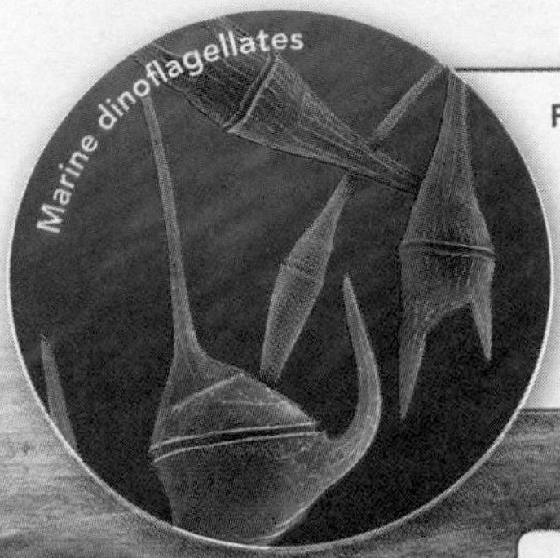

Marine dinoflagellates

Protists

A protist (PROH tist) is any eukaryotic organism that cannot be classified as a fungus, plant, or animal. Because its members are so different from one another, the protist kingdom is sometimes called the "odds and ends" kingdom. For example, some protists are autotrophs, while others are heterotrophs. Most protists are unicellular, but some, such as seaweeds, are multicellular.

Aspergillus fumigatus

Fungi

If you have eaten mushrooms, then you have eaten fungi (FUN jy). Mushrooms, molds, and mildew are all fungi. The majority of fungi are multicellular eukaryotes. A few, such as the yeast used in baking, are unicellular eukaryotes. Fungi are found almost everywhere on land, but only a few live in fresh water. All fungi are heterotrophs. Most fungi feed by absorbing nutrients from dead or decaying organisms.

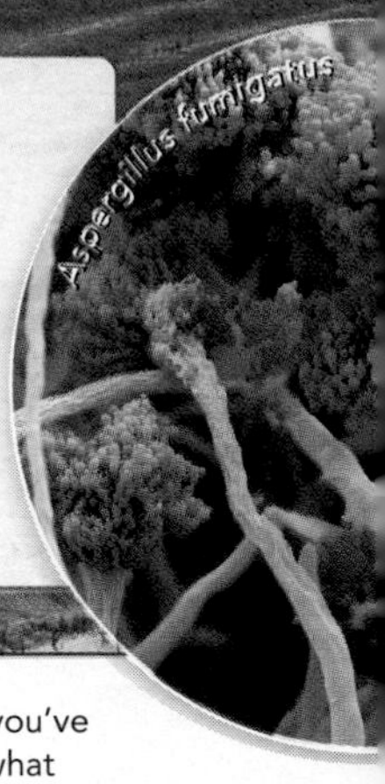

apply it!

Classify While on a walk, you find an organism that you've never seen before. You are determined to figure out what kingdom it belongs to. Starting with the first observation below, circle the kingdom(s) the organism could fit into. Using the process of elimination, determine what kingdom the organism belongs to.

1 There are nuclei present. (Protists)(Fungi)(Plants)(Animals)

2 You can count more than one cell. (Protists)(Fungi)(Plants)(Animals)

3 The organism cannot make its own food. (Protists)(Fungi)Plants(Animals)

4 The organism gets nutrients from dead organisms. (Protists/(Fungi)/Plants/(Animals)

5 Other members of this kingdom can be unicellular. (Protists/(Fungi)/Plants/Animals)

Digital Lesson: Assign the *Apply It* activity online and have students submit their work to you.

my science online.com | **Domains and Kingdoms**

Plants

Dandelions on a lawn, peas in a garden, and the marsh grass shown here are familiar members of the plant kingdom. Plants are all multicellular eukaryotes, and most live on land. Also, plants are autotrophs that make their own food. Plants provide food for most of the heterotrophs on land.

The plant kingdom includes a great variety of organisms. Some plants produce flowers, while others do not. Some plants, such as giant redwood trees, can grow very tall. Others, like mosses, never grow taller than a few centimeters.

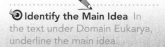 **Identify the Main Idea** In the text under Domain Eukarya, underline the main idea.

Snowy egret

Animals

A dog, a flea on the dog's ear, and a cat that the dog chases have much in common because all are animals. All animals are multicellular eukaryotes. In addition, all animals are heterotrophs. Animals have different adaptations that allow them to locate food, capture it, eat it, and digest it. Members of the animal kingdom live in diverse environments throughout Earth. Animals can be found from ocean depths to mountaintops, from hot, scalding deserts to cold, icy landscapes.

Lab zone ® Do the Quick Lab *Staining Leaves.*

Assess Your Understanding

1a. Define A cell that lacks a nucleus is called a (eukaryote/prokaryote).

b. List Two ways that the members of the two domains of prokaryotes differ are in the structure and chemical makeup of their cells.

c. CHALLENGE You learn that a dandelion is in the same kingdom as pine trees. Name three characteristics that these organisms share.
Both are multicellular, eukaryotes, and autotrophs.

got it?

○ **I get it!** Now I know that organisms are classified into domains and kingdoms based on their cell type, their ability to make food, and the number of cells they contain.

○ **I need extra help with** See TE note.

Go to **MY SCIENCE COACH** online for help with this subject.

25

LESSON 1.3

Build Inquiry **Lab zone**

L2 IDENTIFY THE DOMAIN

Materials 20 pictures of a variety of bacteria, archaea, protists, fungi, plants, and animals, each labeled and numbered; sheet of paper; pencil

Time 20 minutes

Have students work in groups of four, designating one person as group recorder. Have the recorder make a three-column chart with one column titled *Bacteria*, another *Archaea*, and the third *Eukarya*. Hand each group five of the pictures. Give students four minutes to identify the domain to which each organism belongs, placing its number in the correct column. At the end of each four-minute time period, alternate the pictures until each group has seen all of them. Discuss the classifications of the groups.

Ask: **To which domains do only prokaryotes belong?** *(Bacteria and Archaea)* **How could domain Eukarya be further divided?** *(Into the kingdoms Protists, Fungi, Plants, and Animals)* **What three characteristics can a protist share with a plant?** *(Cells contain a nucleus, are multicellular, and are autotrophs.)*

Lab Resource: Quick Lab **Lab zone**

L3 STAINING LEAVES Students will explore the autotrophic nature of plants by testing leaves for the presence of starch, which is the form in which sugar is stored.

Evaluate ─────

Assess Your Understanding

After students answer the questions, have them evaluate their understanding by completing the appropriate sentence.

RTI Response to Intervention

1a. If students cannot distinguish between prokaryotes and eukaryotes, **then** have them locate the highlighted terms and reread the definition of each term.

b. If students need help contrasting the two kinds of prokaryotes, **then** review with them the characteristics of archaea and bacteria.

c. If students have trouble listing characteristics of plants, **then** have then reread the material about plants on this page.

MY SCIENCE COACH Have students go online for help in understanding how organisms are classified into domains and kingdoms.

Differentiated Instruction

L1 Compare and Contrast Kingdoms Have students work in small groups to prepare a compare-and-contrast table that shows similarities and differences in the six main groups presented in this

lesson. Suggest that students use these column headings: *Kingdom/Domain, Cell Type, Ability to Make Food, Number of Cells, Examples.* Have students fill in information from their reading.

Lab zone **After the Inquiry Warm-Up**

Domains and Kingdoms

Inquiry Warm-Up, *Which Organism Goes Where?*

In the Inquiry Warm-Up, you investigated how scientists organize living things into kingdoms. Using what you learned from that activity, answer the questions below.

1. **POSE QUESTIONS** Think about the shared characteristics you used to place two organisms in the same kingdom. What is one question it might be helpful to ask when classifying organisms?

   _____

   _____

2. **CLASSIFY** Consider your response to question 1. Do you think humans belong to the same kingdom as the organisms you classified together in the lab? Explain.

   _____

   _____

3. **CLASSIFY** Imagine that you were told that the green plant, insect (or worm), and mushroom were all members of the same kingdom but that the remaining organism was not. What criteria do you think might result in that classification?

   _____

   _____

4. **MAKE JUDGMENTS** In the lab you were told to imagine that scientists classified organisms purely based on their ability or lack of ability to make food. Do you think all the observations needed to classify organisms can be made in a minute or two? Can they all be made with the unaided eye? Explain.

   _____

   _____

   _____

Name _____ Date _____ Class _____

Domains and Kingdoms

| How Are Organisms Classified Into Domains and Kingdoms? |

1a. DEFINE A cell that lacks a nucleus is called a (eukaryote/prokaryote).

b. LIST Two ways that the members of the two domains of prokaryotes

differ are in the _____

_____

c. CHALLENGE You learn that a dandelion is in the same kingdom as pine

trees. Name three characteristics that these organisms share. _____

_____

got it? ···

○ **I get it!** Now I know that organisms are classified into domains and kingdoms based on

their _____

_____

○ **I need extra help with** _____

_____

Domains and Kingdoms

How Are Organisms Classified Into Domains and Kingdoms?

Taxonomy has come a long way since the time of Linnaeus. Since then, microscopes have helped scientists discover tiny new organisms and identify differences among cells. The modern classification system is made up of three domains. Within the domains are kingdoms. **Organisms are placed into domains and kingdoms based on their cell type, their ability to make food, and the number of cells in their bodies.** The three domains are Bacteria, Archaea, and Eukarya.

Bacteria are all around you—on the surfaces you touch and even inside your body. Some are autotrophs, while others are heterotrophs. Members of domain Bacteria are **prokaryotes,** or organisms whose cells lack a nucleus. A **nucleus** is a dense area in a cell that contains nucleic acids, which are the chemicals that direct all of the cell's activities. In prokaryotes, nucleic acids are not contained within a nucleus.

Like bacteria, members of domain Archaea are also unicellular prokaryotes that can be autotrophs or heterotrophs. Archaea are classified in their own domain because their chemical makeup differs from that of bacteria. Bacteria and archaea also differ in the structure and chemical makeup of their cells. Archaea can be found in extreme environments.

Domain Eukarya consists of **eukaryotes,** organisms with cells that contain nuclei. Domain Eukarya is divided into four kingdoms: protists, fungi, plants, and animals. Organisms in these four kingdoms can be unicellular or multicellular. The protist kingdom is sometimes called the "odds and ends" kingdom. It includes any eukaryote that cannot be classified as an animal, plant, or fungus.

Mushrooms, molds, and mildew are all members of the fungi kingdom. Most fungi feed by absorbing nutrients from dead or decaying organisms. The plant kingdom includes a great variety of organisms, from giant redwood trees to mosses. All plants are autotrophs that make their own food. Members of the animal kingdom are all heterotrophs. Animals have different adaptations that allow them to locate food, capture it, eat it, and digest it.

On a separate sheet of paper, describe the classification of organisms into domains and kingdoms.

Domains and Kingdoms

Understanding Main Ideas

Identify the kingdom to which the following organisms belong by writing *protist*, *fungi*, *plant*, or *animal* in the spaces provided.

1. mushroom _____

2. horse _____

3. redwood tree _____

4. seaweed _____

5. yeast _____

6. dog _____

7. dandelion _____

8. human _____

Building Vocabulary

Write a definition for each of these terms on the lines below.

9. nucleus

_____

_____

10. prokaryote

_____

_____

11. eukaryote

_____

_____

Domains and Kingdoms

> Read the passage and study the diagram below. Then answer the questions that follow on a separate sheet of paper.

A New Phylum

In 1995, scientists discovered a new species of organism, which they named *Symbion pandora*. It is not unusual for new species to be identified. However, the discovery of *S. pandora* drew attention from around the world because this strange animal did not seem to belong to any of the phyla into which scientists classify organisms. As a result, a new phylum called Cycliophora was created for *S. pandora*. So far, *S. pandora* is the only species belonging to this phylum. (Contrast this with the phylum Chordata, which includes all species of reptiles, amphibians, birds, and mammals.)

S. pandora was discovered living on bristles that surround the mouths of Norway lobsters. It has a very complex life cycle with several different stages. One stage consists of a female that stays attached to the lobster's bristles. This stage is about 0.35 mm in length and is shown in the figure below. A tiny male clings to this female feeding stage. There are also stages of *S. pandora* that swim freely; these stages do not feed.

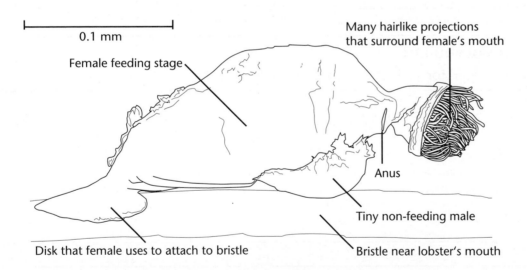

1. *S. pandora* is a member of the animal kingdom. What are three things that you can conclude about *S. pandora* from this statement?
2. Why do you think *S. pandora* was not discovered earlier?
3. What genus does *S. pandora* belong to? How many species are in this genus?
4. How do you think *S. pandora* gets food?

Name _____ Date _____ Class _____

Domains and Kingdoms

Write the letter of the correct answer on the line at the left.

1. ___ Which of the following is **NOT** true about bacteria?

   A Bacteria can be autotrophic or heterotrophic.

   B Bacteria are prokaryotes.

   C Bacteria have a cell nucleus.

   D Bacteria are unicellular.

2. ___ Which of the following is true about animals?

   A Animals are eukaryotes.

   B Animals are autotrophic.

   C Animals are unicellular.

   D Animal cells do not contain nucleic acids.

3. ___ Bacteria and archaea are placed in separate kingdoms because

   A they both are unicellular

   B their structure and chemical makeup differs

   C bacteria are autotrophs and archaea are heterotrophs

   D bacteria are prokaryotes and archaea are eukaryotes

4. ___ Organisms belonging to which kingdom are all autotrophs?

   A fungi

   B plants

   C protists

   D animals

Fill in the blank to complete each statement.

5. The dense area of a cell that contains nucleic acids is the _____.

6. In the modern system of classification, the three domains are Bacteria, Archaea, and _____.

7. An organism whose cells lack a nucleus is called a(n) _____.

8. Marine dinoflagellates and seaweed are members of the _____ kingdom.

9. Most members of the _____ kingdom feed by absorbing nutrients from dead or decaying organisms.

10. Multicellular organisms that make their own food belong to the _____ kingdom.

Domains and Kingdoms

Answer Key

After the Inquiry Warm-Up

1. Answers will vary. Sample: Is the organism able to move on its own?

2. Answers will vary. If students determined that the ability to move was a key characteristic, they will place humans in the same kingdoms as insects or worms and a sea animal.

3. Answers will vary. Sample: The green plant, insect (or worm), and mushroom are all land creatures. The other organism is from the sea.

4. Answers will vary. Sample: No, not all observations needed to classify organisms can be made in a minute or two or with the unaided eye. For example, to tell whether an organism makes its own food may require longer observation and/or the use of a microscope.

Key Concept Summary

All organisms are classified into three domains: Bacteria, Archaea, and Eukarya. Within the domains are kingdoms. Members of domain Bacteria and domain Archaea are prokaryotes, or organisms whose cells lack a nucleus. They are unicellular and can be autotrophic or heterotrophic. Archaea are classified in their own domain because their structure and chemical makeup differs from that of bacteria. Domain Eukarya consists of eukaryotes, organisms with cells that contain nuclei. Domain Eukarya is divided into four kingdoms: protists, fungi, plants, and animals.

Review and Reinforce

1. fungi
2. animal
3. plant
4. protist
5. fungi

6. animal
7. plant
8. animal
9. a dense area in a cell that contains nucleic acids
10. organisms whose cells lack nuclei and whose nucleic acids are not contained in nuclei
11. organisms with cells that have nuclei containing nucleic acids.

Enrich

1. All animals, including *S. pandora*, are multicellular, eukaryotic, and heterotrophic.

2. Answers may vary. Sample: I think it wasn't discovered earlier because it is so small.

3. Genus *Symbion*; there is only one known species, *Symbion pandora*, in this genus.

4. Answers may vary. In fact, *S. pandora* feeds by sweeping food into its mouth with its hairlike projections.

Lesson Quiz

1. C
2. A
3. B
4. B
5. nucleus
6. Eukarya
7. prokaryote
8. Protist
9. Fungi
10. Plant

Place the outside corner, the corner away from the dotted line, in the corner of your copy machine to copy onto letter-size paper.

Evolution and Classification

Lesson Pacing: 1–2 periods or $\frac{1}{2}$–1 block

🕐 **SHORT ON TIME?** To do this lesson in approximately half the time, do the Activate Prior Knowledge activity on page 26. A discussion of the Key Concept on page 27 will familiarize students with the lesson content. Use the Explore the Big Q to help students understand how living things are alike yet different. Do the Quick Lab and have students do the Art in Motion activity online. The rest of the lesson can be completed by students independently.

Preference Navigator, in the online Planning tools, allows you to customize *Interactive Science* to your own teaching style. You can also edit lesson plans by selecting the Lesson Planner option.

Digital Teacher's Edition allows you to access your Teacher's Edition and Resource materials online.

Lesson Vocabulary

- evolution
- branching tree diagram
- shared derived characteristics
- convergent evolution

Content Refresher

Classification and Cladistics The science of cladistics tries to identify each species by its significant evolutionary features. Tree diagrams, with their branching form, are used to illustrate evolutionary relationships. A branching tree diagram, or cladogram, begins with a group of organisms that share a particular trait. The branches below the starting point represent an ancestral species. All organisms on a specific branch have a single significant trait in common. Subsequent branches show both the sequence and significance of the traits that come later.

All true birds have feathers, but not all have perching feet, or beaks for tearing prey, or wings for flight. A cladogram would show the sequential nature of these changes and the relationships among them. However, when using the cladistics system to develop the sequence of evolution, no weight is given to the common trait. In cladograms, the emphasis is on the order in which characteristics developed rather than the value of the evolutionary characteristic.

LESSON OBJECTIVE

🔑 Explain the relationship between evolution and classification.

ENGAGE AND EXPLORE

Teach this lesson using a variety of resources. Begin by reading **My Planet Diary** as a class. Have students share ideas about what they know about a platypus. Then have students do the **Inquiry Warm-Up activity.** Students will investigate the connection between skeletal structures and evolutionary relationships. Discuss the similarities between the three skeletal structures. The **After the Inquiry Warm-Up worksheet** sets up a discussion about which animals are more closely related based on their skeletons. Have volunteers share their answers to question 4 about how a plant's X-ray would compare to the X-rays of these skeletal systems.

EXPLAIN AND ELABORATE

Teach Key Concepts by explaining that species with similar evolutionary histories are classified more closely together. Then have students practice the inquiry skill in the **Apply It activity. Explore the Big Q** by recording observations about new species seen on page 28. **Lead a Discussion** about how some unrelated organisms have similar characteristics because they evolved in similar environments. Use **Figure 3** to identify similarities and differences between bird and insect wings and discuss what this tells scientists about evolutionary history. To help students **Answer the Big Q** discuss how living things are alike in some ways and different in other ways. Hand out the **Key Concept Summaries** as a review of each part of the lesson. Students can also use the online **Vocab Flash Cards** to review key terms.

EVALUATE

Have students take the **Lesson Quiz.** For an alternate assessment, see the *ExamView®* Computer Test Generator, Progress Monitoring Assessments, or SuccessTracker™.

ELL Support

1 Content and Language

Evolution originates from the Latin word *evolvere* meaning "to roll out of." Ask students what rolls out of or what comes out of the study of evolution. *(The history of how specific species developed)*

DIFFERENTIATED INSTRUCTION KEY
- **L1** Struggling Students or Special Needs
- **L2** On-Level Students **L3** Advanced Students

LESSON PLANNER 1.4

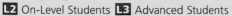

Lab zone Inquiry Path
Hands-on learning in the Lab zone

ENGAGE AND EXPLORE

To teach this lesson with an emphasis on inquiry, begin with the **Inquiry Warm-Up activity.** Students will investigate skeletal structures of different animals to identify evolutionary relationships. Discuss what students noticed that all three skeletal systems have in common. Have students do the **After the Inquiry Warm-Up worksheet.** Talk about how students' observations helped them to determine which animals they think are more closely related. Have volunteers share their answers to question 4 about how the X-rays of a plant and these three animals would compare.

EXPLAIN AND ELABORATE

Focus on the **Inquiry Skill** for the lesson. Point out that when you infer, you use what you observe and your knowledge to draw a logical conclusion. Based on the **Inquiry Warm-Up activity,** what could be inferred about the differences between plants and animals? *(Plants do not have skeletal systems, animals do.)* Review **Figure 1** and think about the complexity of organisms along the evolutionary path before beginning the **Apply It activity.** Ask volunteers to share their inferences. **Explore the Big Q** by recording your observations about new species. Have students do the **Quick Lab** to examine the shared traits among several animals in order to build a branching tree diagram and then ask students to share their diagrams. Have students **Answer the Big Q** and then share their responses. Students can use the online **Vocab Flash Cards** to review key terms.

EVALUATE

Have students take the **Lesson Quiz.** For an alternate assessment, see the *ExamView*® Computer Test Generator, Progress Monitoring Assessments, or SuccessTracker™.

Digital Path
Online learning at **my science online**.com

ENGAGE AND EXPLORE

Teach this lesson using digital resources. Begin by having students explore real-world connections to evolution and classification at **My Planet Diary** online. Have them access the Chapter Resources to find the **Unlock the Big Question activity.** There they can answer the questions and refine their responses as they continue through the lesson. You can re-assign the activity and have students submit their work so you can track their progress.

EXPLAIN AND ELABORATE

Students reading above, at, or below the lexile measure of this lesson can access basic content readings at their level at **My Reading Web.** Have students use the online **Vocab Flash Cards** to preview key terms. Have students do the online **Art in Motion activity** to trace the common ancestry of Galapagos finches. Review **Figure 1** and discuss the complexity of organisms along the evolutionary path before assigning the online **Apply It activity.** Ask volunteers to share their inferences. Have students submit their work to you. Have students **Explore the Big Q** by recording observations about the new species in field journals. Do the **Quick Lab** and then ask students to share their results. Have students **Answer the Big Q** and then invite volunteers to share their thoughts on how living things are alike yet different. The **Key Concept Summaries** online allow students to read a summary and see an image associated with each part of the lesson. Online remediation is available at **My Science Coach.**

EVALUATE

Have students take the **Lesson Quiz.** For an alternate assessment, see the *ExamView*® Computer Test Generator, Progress Monitoring Assessments, or SuccessTracker™.

2 Frontload the Lesson
Preview the lesson visuals, labels, and captions. Ask students what they know about the term *evolution.* Explain the specific meanings these words have in science.

3 Comprehensible Input
Have students study the visuals and their captions on page 27 and 29 to support the Key Concept of the lesson.

4 Language Production
Pair or group students with varied language abilities to complete labs collaboratively for language practice. Have each student copy the completed written lab for personal reference.

5 Assess Understanding
Divide the class into small groups. Have each student identify a Key Concept from the lesson to discuss in his or her group. After the discussions, have students talk about the Key Concepts as a group.

Lexile Measure = 950L

Evolution and Classification

Establish Learning Objective

After this lesson, students will be able to:

Explain the relationship between evolution and classification.

Engage

Activate Prior Knowledge

MY PLANET DIARY Read *If It Looks Like a Duck…* with the class. Review the basic characteristics of birds (have feathers, lay eggs) and mammals (have hair or fur, produce milk). A platypus usually lays from one to three eggs, which she keeps warm for the ten days it takes them to hatch. Once hatched, the young platypuses will feed on milk produced by the mother's mammary glands. Ask: **Why is the platypus not a bird?** (*Because it feeds its young on milk*)

BIG IDEAS OF SCIENCE REFERENCE LIBRARY Have students look up the following topics: Family Tree, Naming.

Explore

Lab Resource: Inquiry Warm-Up

L2 **OBSERVING SIMILARITIES** Students will observe how the skeletal structures of different animals indicate their evolutionary relationships.

Evolution and Classification

 How Are Evolution and Classification Related?

MY PLANET DIARY

DISCOVERY

If It Looks Like a Duck...

The first scientist to see the pelt of the platypus thought it was a joke. Could a four-legged, duck-billed, egg-laying mammal exist? How had it evolved? Native people from Australia believed that the first platypus was born when a water rat mated with a duck. But scientists put the platypus into a new group of egg-laying mammals. Then many years later, scientists began to argue. Had the platypus really evolved later with younger marsupials such as kangaroos? Would the platypus have to be reclassified? Scientists studied its DNA and discovered that the platypus was in the right place!

Answer the question below.
How did DNA help classify the platypus?
Sample: The DNA evidence proved that the platypus was a member of a group of very old mammals and that it hadn't evolved from the same branch as the marsupials.

▶ **PLANET DIARY** Go to **Planet Diary** to learn more about evolution and classification.

 Do the Inquiry Warm-Up *Observing Similarities.*

How Are Evolution and Classification Related?

When Linnaeus developed his classification system, people thought that species never changed. In 1859, a British naturalist named Charles Darwin published an explanation for how species could change over time. Recall that the process of change over time is called **evolution.** Darwin thought that evolution occurs by means of natural selection. Natural selection is the process by which individuals that are better adapted to their environment are more likely to survive and reproduce than other members of the same species.

SUPPORT ALL READERS
Lexile Measure = 950L   Lexile Word Count = 652

Prior Exposure to Content: Many students may have misconceptions on this topic

Academic Vocabulary: *infer, summarize, interpret*

Science Vocabulary: *shared derived characteristic, convergent evolution*

Concept Level: Generally appropriate for most students in this grade

Preteach With: My Planet Diary "If It Looks Like a Duck" and Figure 1 activity

Go to **My Reading Web** to access leveled readings that provide a foundation for the content.

my science online.com

Vocabulary

- evolution • branching tree diagram
- shared derived characteristic
- convergent evolution

Skills

- Reading: Summarize
- Inquiry: Infer

As understanding of evolution increased, biologists changed how they classify species. Scientists now understand that certain organisms may be similar because they share a common ancestor and an evolutionary history. The more similar the two groups are, the more recent the common ancestor probably is. Today's system of classification considers the history of a species. **Species with similar evolutionary histories are classified more closely together.**

Branching Tree Diagrams Two groups of organisms with similar characteristics may be descended from a common ancestor. A **branching tree diagram**, like the one in **Figure 1**, shows probable evolutionary relationships among organisms and the order in which specific characteristics may have evolved. Branching tree diagrams begin at the base with the common ancestor of all the organisms in the diagram. Organisms are grouped according to their shared derived characteristics.

Summarize Name two things that similar organisms share.

Common ancestor,
evolutionary history

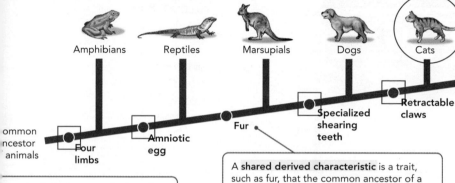

Amphibians   Reptiles   Marsupials   Dogs   Cats

Common ancestor of animals

Four limbs

Amniotic egg

Fur

Specialized shearing teeth

Retractable claws

A **shared derived characteristic** is a trait, such as fur, that the common ancestor of a group had, and passed on to its descendants. Organisms to the right of the fur label all have this shared derived characteristic.

Characteristics lower on the branching tree probably developed before characteristics higher on the tree.

FIGURE 1

ART IN MOTION **A Branching Tree**

This branching tree diagram shows how cats have evolved.

Complete the tasks.

1. **Interpret Diagrams** Put squares around the shared derived characteristics.
2. **Interpret Diagrams** Circle the animal(s) that belong to the smallest group.
3. **Apply Concepts** Cats are more closely related to (reptiles/marsupials).

27

ELL Support

1 Content and Language

Write *convergent evolution* on the board, and explain that *convergent* combines the prefix *con-* ("together") with the Latin word *vergere,* meaning "to bend." So, *convergent evolution* is the process by which characteristics of unrelated organisms "bend together."

2 Frontload the Lesson

Invite students to name species that are related to one another, such as cats and

tigers. Encourage students to speculate about which species are closely related to humans. Tell students that this lesson explains how classification is related to evolution.

3 Comprehensible Input

Explain the Big Q images and captions. Have students complete the Draw Conclusions activity, allowing them to draw or write according to their proficiency level.

Explain ——————

Introduce Vocabulary

To help students understand the terms *shared derived characteristic* and *convergent evolution,* discuss with them the meanings for the words *derived* and *convergent.*

Teach Key Concepts 🔑

Explain that the theory of evolution has changed the way organisms are classified, and today's system of classification takes into account the history of a species. Ask: **What does it mean if two species are classified closely together?** *(They have similar evolutionary histories and a recent common ancestor.)* **What is evolution?** *(The gradual change in species over time)* **Who is credited for the theory of evolution?** *(Charles Darwin)*

Summarize Tell students that when they summarize, they briefly restate the main ideas of what they have read or heard in their own words.

Address Misconceptions

L1 **THE PROCESS OF EVOLUTION** Some students may think that the changes that occur in organisms are the result of a will or desire to change. For example, because the ancestors of birds wanted to fly, over many years birds acquired wings. Ask: **According to Darwin, how does evolution take place?** *(Through natural selection, in which individuals that are better adapted to their environment are more likely to survive and reproduce than other members of the species)*

Elaborate ——————

21st Century Learning

L3 **CRITICAL THINKING** Tell students the process that Darwin called *natural selection* was based on several observations, including the following: There is variation within species of living things. Some variations are favorable. Not all offspring produced in each generation can survive. Instruct students to write a short, well-developed paragraph that explains how these three observations became the theory of natural selection.

My Planet Diary provides an opportunity for students to explore real-world connections to evolution and classification.

Art in Motion allows students to trace the common ancestry of Galapagos finches.

my science online | Evolution and Classification

Elaborate

Apply It!

L1 Before beginning the activity, have students study **Figure 1** and think about the complexity of organisms along the evolutionary path.

 **Infer** Help students understand that inferring involves interpreting observations. When they infer, or make an inference, they combine what they observe with their own experience and knowledge to reach a logical conclusion. Make sure students understand that there is a progression to the four figures, from less complex to more complex.

Ask: **If you were to draw an even more complex figure, which figure would it look most like?** *(Figure B)*

Explore the Big Q 🄌 UbD

Direct students' attention to the images of a possible new species and two known species from the same area. As a class, talk about the features of all three organisms, emphasizing similarities. Tell students that 1,068 species were discovered or newly identified in the Greater Mekong Region of Southeast Asia (Cambodia, Laos, Malaysia, Myanmar, Thailand, Vietnam, and the Yunnan Province of China) between 1997 and 2007. That averages out to two new species per week! Tell students that the Laotian rock rat was thought to be extinct 11 million years ago. Ask: **What do all three organisms have in common?** *(They all are animals, so they share the same domain and kingdom. They also live in the same area.)* **What kinds of characteristics would provide evidence that the three organisms are related? Explain.** *(Shared derived characteristics would show a common evolutionary ancestor.)* **What evidence would be conclusive proof that the unknown animal is a new species?** *(DNA evidence)* Tell students that the "new species" is actually a known animal. It is a Malayan colugo *(Cynocephalus variegates)*. It is commonly known as a flying lemur.

Digital Lesson: Assign the *Apply It* activity online and have students submit their work to you.

my science online | **Evolution and Classification**

Note the characteristics of Figures A, B, C, and D.

❶  **Infer** Which figure is the most similar to Figure B?

Figure D

❷ **CHALLENGE** Suppose these shapes are fossils of extinct organisms. Which organism do you think might be the ancestor of all the others? Why?

Sample: Figure C is the simplest, so it might be the ancestor of the others.

EXPLORE THE BIG ?

Finding a New Species

How are living things alike yet different?

FIGURE 2

While on an expedition, you photograph what you think is a new species.

✎ **Draw Conclusions** Use the camera image of the new species and the photos of organisms previously identified from the same area to record your observations in your field journal.

Laotian rock rat
Laonastes aenigmanus

Golden-crowned flying fox
Acerodon jubatus

FIELD JOURNAL

Location: Greater Mekong region of Asia

Date: _____

Organism's observable characteristics: Large eyes, small ears; brown color; membrane between limbs, and body to glide

Observed habitat(s): In the rainforest, living in the trees

Domain and kingdom: Eukarya, animalia

Additional information needed to determine if organism is a new species: Sample: diet, behavior, DNA samples

Name (assuming it's a new species): Accept all reasonable responses.

Significance/meaning of name: Accept all reasonable responses.

28 **Introduction to Living Things**

Professional Development Note | **Teacher to Teacher**

Activity One of the concepts that ties together the study of classification with evolution is adaptation. I like to do an activity I call "Adapt-A-Fish." Students are asked to invent a fish based on the descriptions I have chosen; for example, a fish that would live between rocks or on a coral reef, and would try to eat whatever swims by, moving quickly between the crevices. They draw the fish showing its special adaptations for the environment, including things that make up its environment. We can then use these pictures to discuss how living things adapt over time (evolution), and group them together to form a classification tree.

✎ *Mrs. Anne Rice*
Woodland Middle School
Gurnee, Illinois

GURE 3 ······
onvergent Evolution
rds and insects both use wings
• help them fly. However, these
vo organisms are not closely
•lated.

Determining Evolutionary Relationships How do scientists determine the evolutionary history of a species? One way is to compare the structure of organisms. Scientists can also use information about the chemical makeup of the organisms' cells.

Sometimes unrelated organisms evolve similar characteristics because they evolved in similar environments, like organisms that move through the water or eat similar foods. Because the organisms perform similar functions, their body structures may look similar. Look at **Figure 3.** The process by which unrelated organisms evolve characteristics that are similar is called **convergent evolution.**

When studying the chemical makeup of organisms, sometimes new information is discovered that results in reclassification. For example, skunks and weasels were classified in the same family for 150 years. When scientists compared nucleic acids from the cells of skunks and weasels, they found many differences. These differences suggest that the two groups are not that closely related. As a result, scientists reclassified skunks into a separate family.

> **Lab** **zone** Do the Quick Lab
> *Common Ancestors.*

🔑 Assess Your Understanding

1a. Identify Look back at **Figure 1.** What characteristics do all reptiles share?

<u>Four limbs and amniotic eggs</u>

b. How are living things alike yet different? <u>They share the</u> <u>same characteristics and</u> <u>needs, but how they meet</u> <u>their needs may be different.</u>

got it? ··········

○ I get it! Now I know that evolution and classification are related because <u>species</u> <u>with similar evolutionary</u> <u>histories are classified more</u> <u>closely together.</u>

○ I need extra help with <u>See TE note.</u>

Go to MY SCIENCE ⓢ COACH *online for help with this subject.*

Differentiated Instruction

L1 Comparing Evolutionary Relationships Have students demonstrate an understanding of how evolutionary relationships are indicated on a branching tree diagram by answering the following questions related to **Figure 1**: Which animals are most closely related? Which animals are least closely related? As the number of branches between two organisms increases, what is true about the relationship between the organisms?

L3 Vestigial Structures Another piece of evidence that supports the theory of evolution and is used by scientists to classify organisms is a vestigial structure. Have students find out what a vestigial structure is, what it indicates about evolution, and how it is used in classification. Tell students to include examples of vestigial structures.

Explain

Lead a Discussion

EVOLUTIONARY RELATIONSHIPS Review with students the ways in which scientists determine the evolutionary history of a species. Discuss homologous structures and DNA. Tell students that the forelimbs of a whale, crocodile, and bird are homologous structures. Ask: **What do the homologous structures of a whale, crocodile, and bird indicate?** *(These organisms evolved from a common ancestor.)* Tell students that the similar structures unrelated organisms share as a result of convergent evolution are called *analogous structures.* Birds and butterflies both have wings, which they use to fly, but their structures are different. Ask: **What do the structures that result from convergent evolution indicate about organisms?** *(They do not have a common ancestor.)*

Teach With Visuals

Tell students to look at **Figure 3.** Ask: **How are bird wings and insect wings alike?** *(They are similar body features that are used for the same function.)* **How are they different?** *(Their structures are different.)* **What does this tell you about their evolutionary history?** *(They do not have a common ancestor.)*

Lab Resource: Quick Lab

L2 COMMON ANCESTORS Students will examine shared traits among several animals and build a branching tree diagram.

Evaluate

Assess Your Understanding

After students answer the questions, have them evaluate their understanding by completing the appropriate sentence.

Answer the Big Q ❓ UbD

To help students focus on the Big Question, lead a class discussion about how living things are alike in some ways and different in other ways.

R T I Response to Intervention

1a. If students cannot interpret a branching tree diagram, **then** have students reread the description of a branching tree diagram and the definition of a shared derived characteristic.

b. If students need help similarities and differences among living things, **then** review with them the explanation of evolution.

MY SCIENCE ⓢ COACH Have students go online for help in understanding how evolution and classification are related.

Lab zone®   **After the Inquiry Warm-Up**

Evolution and Classification

Inquiry Warm-Up, *What's the Connection?*

In the Inquiry Warm-Up, you investigated how the skeletal structures of different animals can provide clues to their evolutionary relationships. Using what you learned from that activity, answer the questions below.

1. **COMPARE AND CONTRAST** What structures do all three skeletons appear to share?

   _____

   _____

2. **COMPARE AND CONTRAST** What structures do not appear to be shared by all three skeletons?

   _____

   _____

   _____

3. **DEVELOP HYPOTHESES** Based on your answers to questions 1 and 2, which animals do you think are more closely related, the mammal and the reptile or the mammal and the fish? Explain.

   _____

   _____

   _____

4. **PREDICT** Suppose you had an X-ray of a plant. How do you think it would compare to the X-rays of the three animals? Explain.

   _____

   _____

Assess Your Understanding

Evolution and Classification

How Are Evolution and Classification Related?

1a. **IDENTIFY** In Figure 1 on page 27 of your textbook, what characteristics do all reptiles share?

_____

_____

b. **ANSWER** How are living things alike yet different? _____

_____

_____

got it? ....

○ **I get it!** Now I know that evolution and classification are related because _____

_____

_____

○ **I need extra help with** _____

_____

Place the outside corner, the corner away from the dotted line, in the corner of your copy machine to copy onto letter-size paper.

Evolution and Classification

How Are Evolution and Classification Related?

In 1859, Charles Darwin published a theory about how species could change over time. Darwin's theory is often referred to as the theory of evolution. **Evolution** is the gradual change in a species over time. Darwin believed that evolution took place through the process of natural selection in which individuals that are better adapted to their environment are more likely to survive and reproduce than other members of the same species.

The theory of evolution has changed how biologists classify organisms. Scientists now understand that certain organisms may be similar because they share a common ancestor and an evolutionary history. The more similar the two groups are, the more recent the common ancestor probably is. Today's system of classification takes into account the history of a species. **Species with similar evolutionary histories are classified more closely together.**

Probable evolutionary relationships among groups of organisms and the order in which specific characteristics may have evolved are illustrated using a **branching tree diagram.** The base of such a diagram shows the common ancestor. Organisms are grouped according to their **shared derived characteristics,** which are usually homologous structures, or structures that have the same evolutionary origin. In addition to comparing the structures of organisms, scientists can also use information about the chemical makeup of their cells.

Unrelated organisms may have similar characteristics or body structures because they evolved in similar environments. The process by which unrelated organisms evolve characteristics that are similar is called **convergent evolution.** When studying the chemical makeup of organisms, scientists sometimes discover new information that results in reclassification.

On a separate sheet of paper, describe the role structure plays in determining evolutionary relationships between organisms.

Review and Reinforce

Evolution and Classification

Understanding Main Ideas
Answer the following questions in the spaces provided.

1. How has the theory of evolution changed how biologists classify organisms?

   _____

   _____

   _____

2. Describe how a branching tree diagram is organized.

   _____

   _____

   _____

   _____

3. On a branching tree diagram, which characteristics probably developed the earliest?

   _____

   _____

4. What are two methods scientists use to determine the evolutionary history of a species?

   _____

   _____

   _____

Building Vocabulary
On a separate sheet of paper, write a definition for each of these terms.

5. shared derived characteristic
6. convergent evolution
7. branching tree diagram

Evolution and Classification

The diagram below shows many different types of animals and connections between them. Study the diagram and then answer the questions that follow on a separate sheet of paper.

Species Relationships

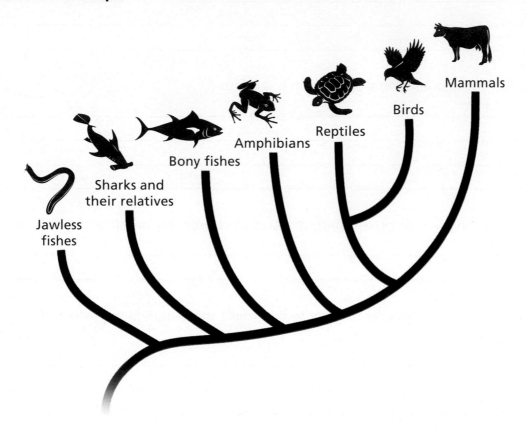

1. What is this type of diagram called, and what is the purpose of such a diagram?

2. What types of evidence did scientists use to make this diagram?

3. Did amphibians evolve from reptiles? Give evidence for your answer.

4. Are birds more closely related to mammals or reptiles? Explain your answer.

5. What could cause scientists to change the information on this diagram in the future?

Lesson Quiz

Evolution and Classification

Write the letter of the correct answer on the line at the left.

1. ___ Similar organisms that are **NOT** related is an example of

A   natural selection

B   convergent evolution

C   divergent evolution

D   common ancestor

2. ___ Two groups of organisms with similar characteristics may share

A   a common ancestor

B   an evolutionary history

C   both A and B

D   neither A nor B

3. ___ Of the following, the *best* definition of evolution is

A   a rapid change in a species over time

B   the adaptation of an organism to its environment

C   the ability of an organism to survive and reproduce

D   a gradual change in a species over time

4. ___ Which statement is true?

A   Species with similar evolutionary histories are not classified together.

B   Species with different evolutionary histories are classified more closely together.

C   Species with similar evolutionary histories are classified more closely together.

D   Species with similar evolutionary histories are classified in the same species.

Fill in the blank to complete each statement.

5. To determine whether two organisms are related, scientists may compare the _____ of their cells.

6. _____ is the process by which individuals that are better adapted to their environment are more likely to survive and reproduce.

7. A(n) _____ is usually a homologous structure that is shared by all organisms in a group.

8. The theory of evolution was proposed by _____.

9. If two species have very similar structures, they may have evolved from a(n) _____.

10. One thing a branching tree diagram shows is the _____ in which specific characteristics may have evolved.

Evolution and Classification

Answer Key

After the Inquiry Warm-Up

1. Answers will vary, depending on the X-rays used. Students will likely note that all three skeletons have a skull, backbone, and ribcage.

2. Answers will vary. Unless the reptile featured was a snake, students will likely note that, while the reptile and mammal both have limbs, the fish does not.

3. Answers will vary. Unless the reptile featured was a snake, students will likely say that the mammal and reptile are more closely related than the mammal and the fish. If so, they may refer to the presence of limbs in both the mammal and reptile as supporting their conclusion.

4. The X-ray of the plant would be very different from the X-rays of the three animals because plants do not have skeletons.

Key Concept Summary

In order to determine the evolutionary history of a species, scientists often compare the structure of organisms. Organisms are grouped according to their shared derived characteristics, which are usually homologous structures.

Review and Reinforce

1. Biologists now understand that certain organisms may be similar because they share a common ancestor and an evolutionary history. Species with similar evolutionary histories are classified more closely together.

2. The common ancestor of all the organisms in a branching tree diagram is located at its base. Organisms are grouped together according to their shared derived characteristics. For example, all organisms above the label "four limbs" have four limbs.

3. The characteristics lowest on a branching tree diagram probably developed earliest.

4. To determine the evolutionary history of a species, scientists compare the structure of organisms and study the chemical makeup of organisms' cells.

5. a characteristic exhibited by all organisms in a group

6. process by which unrelated organisms evolve similar characteristics

7. a way to show probable evolutionary relationships and the order in which specific characteristics may have developed

Enrich

1. It is a branching tree, which shows how scientists think different groups of organisms are related.

2. Evidence includes fossils as well as similarities in body structure, early development, and DNA sequences among modern-day organisms.

3. Amphibians did not evolve from reptiles; both amphibians and reptiles evolved from a common ancestor.

4. to reptiles, because the diagram shows a closer relationship between reptiles and birds

5. Any new information might cause a change, including newly discovered fossils and DNA evidence.

Lesson Quiz

1. B
2. A
3. D
4. C
5. chemical makeup
6. Natural selection
7. shared derived characteristic
8. Charles Darwin
9. common ancestor
10. order

Place the outside corner, the corner away from the dotted line, in the corner of your copy machine to copy onto letter-size paper.

Study Guide

Review the Big Q UbD

Have students complete the statement at the top of the page. These Key Concepts support their understanding of the chapter's Big Question. Have students return to the chapter opener pages. What is different about how students view the image of the manatee and hyrax now that they have completed the chapter? Thinking about this will help them prepare for the *Apply the Big Q* activity in the Review and Assessment.

Partner Review

Have partners review definitions of vocabulary terms by using the Study Guide to quiz each other. Students could read the Key Concept statements and leave out words for their partner to fill in, or change a statement so that it is false and then ask their partner to correct it.

Class Activity: Concept Map

Have students develop a concept map to show how the information in this chapter is related. Have students brainstorm to identify Key Concepts, vocabulary, details, and examples, and then write each one on a sticky note and attach it at random on chart paper or on the board. Explain that the concept map will begin at the top with Key Concepts. Ask students to use the following questions to help them organize the information on the notes:
- What are the six characteristics of all living things?
- What are the four basic needs of all living things?
- What are the levels of classification of living things and what do they indicate about similarities and differences?
- What information is used to classify organisms into domains and kingdoms?
- How is evolution related to classification?

My Science Coach allows students to complete the *Practice Test online.*

The Big Question allows students to complete the *Apply the Big Q* activity about how living things are alike yet different.

Vocab Flash Cards offer a way to review the chapter vocabulary words.

my science online.com | **Introduction to Living Things**

---

1 Study Guide

REVIEW THE BIG **?**

Living things can vary. For example, organisms may be prokaryotes or ___eukaryotes___.
Yet all living things are made of ___cells___, which grow, develop, and reproduce.

LESSON 1 What Is Life?

🔑 All living things have a cellular organization, contain similar chemicals, use energy, respond to their surroundings, grow and develop, and reproduce.

🔑 Living things arise from other living things through reproduction.

🔑 All living things must satisfy their basic needs for food, water, living space, and stable internal conditions.

Vocabulary
- organism • cell • unicellular • multicellular • metabolism • stimulus • response • development
- asexual reproduction • sexual reproduction • spontaneous generation • controlled experiment
- autotroph • heterotroph • homeostasis

LESSON 2 Classifying Life

🔑 Biologists use classification to organize living things into groups so that the organisms are easier to study.

🔑 The levels of classification are domain, kingdom, phylum, class, order, family, genus, and species.

🔑 Taxonomic keys are useful tools that help determine the identity of organisms.

Vocabulary
- classification • taxonomy • binomial nomenclature
- genus • species

LESSON 3 Domains and Kingdoms

🔑 Organisms are placed into domains and kingdoms based on their cell type, ability to make food, and the number of cells in their bodies.

Vocabulary
- prokaryote
- nucleus • eukaryote

LESSON 4 Evolution and Classification

🔑 Species with similar evolutionary histories are classified more closely together.

Vocabulary
- evolution
- branching tree diagram
- shared derived characteristic
- convergent evolution

E L L Support

4 Language Production
Arrange the class in small-group circles. Introduce a question based on the essential questions from the chapter. Then have one member of each circle give a fact or detail that helps answer the question. The student to his or her right should then provide a different fact or detail. The cycle continues until there is no new information to share and all questions have been discussed.

Beginning
LOW/HIGH Students can refer to their books or notes during the discussion.

Intermediate
LOW/HIGH Allow students extra time to share their facts and details.

Advanced
LOW/HIGH Challenge students to use vocabulary terms during the discussion.

Review and Assessment

LESSON 1 What Is Life?

1. The maintenance of stable internal conditions is called

  a. stimulus.   **b.** autotrophy.

  (c.) homeostasis.   **d.** response.

2. _Asexual reproduction_ involves only one parent and produces offspring that are identical to the parent.

3. Apply Concepts Pick an organism in your home and describe how this organism meets the four basic conditions for survival.

Accept all reasonable answers, such as a plant, pet, or person.

4. Control Variables A student is designing a controlled experiment to test whether the amount of water that a plant receives affects its growth. Which variables should the student hold constant and which variable should the student manipulate?

Plant type, pot type, soil type, location, and sun exposure should all be identical. The manipulated variable should be the amount of water.

5. **Write About It** Suppose you are searching for new life forms as part of an expedition in a remote region of Alaska. At one site you find 24 greenish-brown objects, each measuring around 1 cm³. The objects do not appear to have heads, tails, or legs, but you suspect they may be alive. Describe what you would do to determine if the objects are alive.

See TE rubric.

LESSON 2 Classifying Life

6. Which of the following is the broadest level of classification?

  a. genus   **b.** species

  (c.) domain   **d.** kingdom

7. The two-part naming system called _binomial nomenclature_ was devised by Linnaeus in the 1700s.

8. Predict The scientific name for the red maple tree is _Acer rubrum_. Another organism is called _Acer negundo_. Based on its name, what can you predict about this organism? Explain.

It is in the same genus as the red maple, so I would predict that it is a closely related tree.

9. Make Models Develop a taxonomic key that a person could use to identify each of the plants shown below.

White ash   Red oak   White oak   Pasture rose

31

Review and Assessment

Assess Understanding

Have students complete the answers to the Review and Assessment questions. Have a class discussion about what students find confusing. Write Key Concepts on the board to reinforce knowledge.

R T I Response to Intervention

3. If students cannot identify the four basic conditions for survival, **then** have them reread the third Key Concept statement.

9. If students need help with developing a taxonomic key, **then** have them review **Figure 5**.

Alternate Assessment

L3 MULTIMEDIA PRESENTATION Have students create a multimedia presentation to discuss what they have learned in this chapter about living things and how they are classified. Have students brainstorm to identify Key Concepts, vocabulary, and important details and examples. Students should give oral presentations and include visual aids, props, and videos.

CHAPTER 1

Write About It Assess student's writing using this rubric.

SCORING RUBRIC	SCORE 4	SCORE 3	SCORE 2	SCORE 1
Identify the characteristics of all living things and how objects could be tested	Student identifies all six characteristics of living things and describes how the objects could be tested for each.	Student identifies all six characteristics of living things and describes some ways the objects could be tested.	Student identifies only a few of the six characteristics of living things and does not describe how objects could be tested.	Student does not identify any characteristics of living things or how objects could be tested.

Review and Assessment, Cont.

RTI Response to Intervention

12. If students have trouble comparing and contrasting plants and fungi, **then** have them reread the information in the boxes titled *Plants* and *Fungi* and organize this information using a Venn diagram.

14. If students cannot identify the diagram, **then** have them look for the highlighted term *branching tree diagram* and restate the definition in their own words.

Apply the Big Q UbD

TRANSFER Students should be able to demonstrate understanding of how living things are alike and different by answering this question. See the scoring rubric below.

Connect to the Big Idea UbD

BIG IDEA: Living things are alike yet different.

Send students back to the Big Ideas of Science at the beginning of their student edition. Have them read what they wrote before they started the chapter. Lead a class discussion about how their thoughts have changed. If all chapters have been completed, have students fill in the bottom section for the Big Idea.

L3 **WRITING IN SCIENCE** Ask students to write an article that explains to readers how living things are alike and how they are different.

LESSON 3 Domains and Kingdoms

10. Which four kingdoms belong to the domain Eukarya?

   a. prokarya, archaea, eukarya, bacteria

   ⓑ protists, fungi, plants, animals

   c. mite, tick, scorpion, spider

   d. class, order, family, genus

11. All eukaryotes belong to domain Eukarya, while __prokaryotes__ belong to domain Bacteria or domain Archaea.

12. Compare and Contrast Both plants and fungi belong to the domain Eukarya. What is one main difference between these organisms?

   <u>Sample: Fungi are heterotrophs while plants are autotrophs.</u>

LESSON 4 Evolution and Classification

13. Which of the following factors is most important when classifying an organism?

   a. size   **b.** shape

   c. habitat   **ⓓ** evolutionary history

14. A diagram that shows probable evolutionary relationships among organisms is called a <u>branching tree diagram.</u>

15. Apply Concepts If you discovered two unrelated organisms that looked very similar, how could you explain it?

   <u>Sample: Each organism evolved in similar environments and developed similar characteristics through convergent evolution.</u>

APPLY **How are living things alike yet different?**

16. With the advances in commercial space travel, some day you may have the opportunity to visit another planet and see things you've never seen before! How would you go about identifying things on the other planet as being living or nonliving? If an object turns out to be living, what characteristics would you look for in order to classify? Use four vocabulary terms from the chapter in your answer.

<u>Sample: I would see if it had **cells**, contained similar chemicals to living things on Earth, used energy, and responded to its environment. I would also look for older, younger, bigger, or smaller versions as evidence that it could grow, develop, and reproduce. In trying to classify the **organism**, I would look to see if it was a **prokaryote** or a **eukaryote** by looking for a **nucleus**. Counting the number of cells would help to identify it as being **unicellular** or **multicellular**.</u>

See TE rubric.

THE BIG Q **How are living things alike yet different?**
Assess student's response using this rubric.

SCORING RUBRIC	SCORE 4	SCORE 3	SCORE 2	SCORE 1
Determine if an object is living or nonliving	Student identifies the characteristics of living things.	Student mostly identifies the characteristics of living things.	Student poorly identifies the characteristics of living things.	Student does not know the characteristics of living things.
Identify the basis for classifying in domains and kingdoms	Student identifies the three criteria for classifying.	Student mostly identifies the three criteria for classifying.	Student poorly identifies the three criteria for classifying.	Student does not know the three criteria for classifying.

Standardized Test Prep

Multiple Choice

Circle the letter of the best answer.

1. How many kingdoms are represented by the organisms shown below?

A 1	Ⓑ 2
C 3	D 4

2. According to the system of binomial nomenclature, which of the following is a properly written scientific name?

A Acer rubrum   B Acer Rubrum

Ⓒ *Acer rubrum*   D *acer rubrum*

3. Which of the following is an example of an autotroph?

A a lion	Ⓑ a tree
C an eagle	D a mushroom

4. Which domain does NOT contain prokaryotes?

A Archaea

B Bacteria

Ⓒ Eukarya

D None of the above. All three domains contain prokaryotes.

5. A branching tree diagram shows evolutionary relationships by _____

A grouping organisms according to their differences.

B determining the identity of organisms.

Ⓒ grouping organisms according to their shared derived characteristics.

D giving an organism a unique, two-part scientific name.

Constructed Response

Use the chart below and your knowledge of science to help you answer Question 6. Write your answer on a separate piece of paper.

Some Types of Trees

Common Name of Tree	Kingdom	Family	Species
Bird cherry	Plants	Rosaceae	*Prunus avium*
Flowering cherry	Plants	Rosaceae	*Prunus serrula*
Smooth-leaved elm	Plants	Ulmaceae	*Ultimus minor*
Whitebeam	Plants	Rosaceae	*Sorbus aria*

6. Which one of the four trees is most different from the other three? Explain your answer.

See TE note.

33

Standardized Test Prep

Test-Taking Skills

INTERPRETING ILLUSTRATIONS Tell students that when they answer questions like Question 1, where the question involves interpreting illustrations, they should make sure they understand the concept represented by the illustrations. In Question 1, students should first identify each organism and then the kingdom to which it belongs. By doing so, they can determine how many kingdoms are represented (2) and thus eliminate choices **A, C,** and **D.**

Constructed Response

6. Smooth-leaved elm is most different, because it is in the family Ulmaceae. The other three trees are all in the family Rosaceae. Species that are similar are classified more closely together.

Additional Assessment Resources

Chapter Test
ExamView® Computer Test Generator
Performance Assessment
Progress Monitoring Assessments
SuccessTracker™

Remediate If students have trouble with...

QUESTION	SEE LESSON	STANDARDS
1	3	
2	2	
3	1	
4	3	
5	4	
6	2	

Science Matters

Think Like a Scientist

Have students read *A Recipe for Success*. Explain to students that Louis Pasteur was a French chemist who was considered one of the fathers of microbiology. Tell students that Pasteur's experiments supported germ theory, or the theory that microorganisms are the cause of many diseases. Explain that the "recipe" of steps that Pasteur followed in his experiments is more commonly known as the scientific method.

Explain that Pasteur worked to prevent many diseases from being spread. He discovered that he could create a weakened form of a disease and inject it into an experimental subject. The subject's immune system would fight off that weakened form of the disease and become immune to stronger forms of it. Thus, Pasteur invented vaccines for cholera and anthrax.

Tell students that Pasteur was the first to give the rabies treatment invented by one of his colleagues to a human. A boy was attacked by a rabid dog. Pasteur decided to give him the experimental treatment, even though it had only been tested on a few animal subjects and Pasteur was not technically a doctor. Pasteur could have gotten in a lot of trouble for this, but the vaccine worked so he became a hero.

As students design their own experiments based on van Helmont's, ask them to identify other theories as to how the mice got into the barrel. Have them identify which step in the recipe was skipped.

Ask: **What was the variable in Pasteur's experiment?** *(the boiled broth)* **Why did Pasteur break the neck of the flask holding the boiled broth?** *(He expected to be able to show that bacteria entered the broth through material in the air.)*

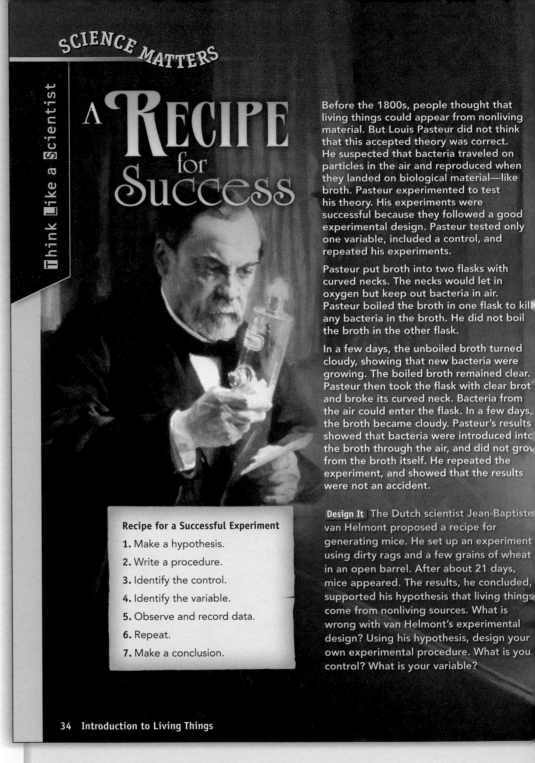

SCIENCE MATTERS

Think Like a Scientist

A RECIPE for Success

Before the 1800s, people thought that living things could appear from nonliving material. But Louis Pasteur did not think that this accepted theory was correct. He suspected that bacteria traveled on particles in the air and reproduced when they landed on biological material—like broth. Pasteur experimented to test his theory. His experiments were successful because they followed a good experimental design. Pasteur tested only one variable, included a control, and repeated his experiments.

Pasteur put broth into two flasks with curved necks. The necks would let in oxygen but keep out bacteria in air. Pasteur boiled the broth in one flask to kill any bacteria in the broth. He did not boil the broth in the other flask.

In a few days, the unboiled broth turned cloudy, showing that new bacteria were growing. The boiled broth remained clear. Pasteur then took the flask with clear broth and broke its curved neck. Bacteria from the air could enter the flask. In a few days, the broth became cloudy. Pasteur's results showed that bacteria were introduced into the broth through the air, and did not grow from the broth itself. He repeated the experiment, and showed that the results were not an accident.

Design It The Dutch scientist Jean-Baptiste van Helmont proposed a recipe for generating mice. He set up an experiment using dirty rags and a few grains of wheat in an open barrel. After about 21 days, mice appeared. The results, he concluded, supported his hypothesis that living things come from nonliving sources. What is wrong with van Helmont's experimental design? Using his hypothesis, design your own experimental procedure. What is your control? What is your variable?

Recipe for a Successful Experiment

1. Make a hypothesis.
2. Write a procedure.
3. Identify the control.
4. Identify the variable.
5. Observe and record data.
6. Repeat.
7. Make a conclusion.

34 Introduction to Living Things

Quick Facts

The best way to prevent disease from bacteria is by washing your hands. Some people believe a quick rinse will be good enough. Rinsing your hands may remove visible dirt and some bacteria, but there are still plenty of bacteria left. Even a quick wash may not eliminate most bacteria. Experts recommend washing with soap and warm water for 40 seconds to a minute to eliminate all bacteria. People whose hands become dirty a lot, such as people who work in restaurants, may use a sanitizing solution. Sanitizing solution has been shown to stop the growth of bacteria if not remove it. So restaurant workers should still wash their hands, but sanitizing solution is a quick way to stop the spread of bacteria and allow them to keep working. Have students think of other ways to prevent bacteria from spreading.

Are You Going to Eat That?

Bacteria are everywhere. Most bacteria have no effect on you. Some even help you. But bacteria in your food can be dangerous and can make you sick.

Milk and many juices are treated by a process called pasteurization. The process is named after Louis Pasteur, who invented it. Before the milk or juice reaches the grocery store, it is heated to a temperature that is high enough to kill the most harmful bacteria. Fewer bacteria means slower bacterial growth, giving you enough time to finish your milk before it spoils.

Tips for Keeping Food Safe in Homes and Restaurants

- Keep foods refrigerated until cooking them to prevent any bacteria in the foods from reproducing.

- Cook meat thoroughly, so that the meat reaches a temperature high enough to kill any bacteria that has been growing on it.

- Wash fresh foods, such as fruits and vegetables, to remove bacteria on the surface.

- Do not use the same utensils or cutting board for cutting raw meat and fresh foods, so that any bacteria in raw meat are not transferred to other foods.

Write About It Some champions of raw-food diets suggest that traditional methods of pasteurization reduce the nutritional value of milk and cause milk to spoil rather than to sour. Research the debate about raw dairy products and write a persuasive article that explains whether you support pasteurization of dairy products.

35

Everyday Science

Have students read *Are You Going To Eat That?* Explain that pasteurization is very important to keeping people healthy and most dairy products that are sold today are pasteurized. Tell students that Pasteur and a colleague originally invented pasteurization as a way to keep wine and beer from going sour quickly. Point out that pasteurization is different from sterilization, the purpose of which is to kill all bacteria.

Students may be confused by intentional heating of dairy products, because they are used to seeing them stored cold. Explain that temperatures below boiling are usually used in pasteurization to prevent the milk from curdling. In one method of pasteurization, milk is run through pipes or between metal plates that have been heated on the outside by warm water for a few seconds. In another method, the milk is heated to a very high temperature, but only for a fraction of a second.

Explain that bacteria do not reproduce in cold temperatures, which is why it is important to keep cold food cold. Point out that cooking meat thoroughly is an example of sterilization. Tell students it is important to wash all fresh produce because it is grown outdoors in the dirt and can be exposed to all kinds of bacteria. Explain that when bacteria is transferred from one kind of food to another, it is called *cross-contamination*.

Ask: **Based on the ways bacteria growth is prevented and bacteria is killed, what temperature does it probably grow best in?** *(warm temperatures)* **Pasteurization gives foods a longer "shelf life." What does this term mean?** *(Sample: Shelf-life is the length of time food can sit on a shelf without spoiling.)*

Viruses, Bacteria, Protists, and Fungi

Introduce the Big Q ? UbD

Have students look at the image and read the Engaging Question and description. Ask the students to develop hypotheses about where the mushrooms might grow. Have volunteers share some of their ideas. Point out that in addition to animals and plants, other living things are vital to the balance of all habitats on Earth. Ask: **What details in the photograph give information about where these mushrooms live?** *(Sample: The numerous dead leaves on the ground indicate that these mushrooms live in a wooded area.)* **What other words would you use to describe the environment in which these mushrooms are growing?** *(Sample: moist, damp, rotting, decomposing, waste)* **How many distinct structures do you see on each mushroom?** *(Students may indicate the white stalk, the green cap, and the lacy yellow covering.)*

Untamed Science Video

WHAT GOOD ARE MUSHROOMS? Before viewing, invite students to discuss what they know about mushrooms. Then play the video. Lead a class discussion and make a list of questions that this video raises. You may wish to have students view the video again after they have completed the chapter to see if their questions have been answered.

To access the online resources for this chapter, search on or navigate to *Viruses, Bacteria, Protists, and Fungi.*

Untamed Science Video shows what roles mushrooms play in the environment.

The Big Question allows students to answer the Engaging Question about where mushrooms grow.

my science online.com | **Viruses, Bacteria, Protists, & Fungi**

WHERE DO MUSHROOMS GROW?

? THE BIG

How are living things other than plants and animals important to Earth?

The mushrooms in this photo have a lacy, delicate covering and bright colors. But don't get too close—these mushrooms smell like rotting meat! Their beauty and powerful smell gives them the name netted stinkhorns. The rotting smell attracts flies. When a fly lands on the mushroom, tiny reproductive structures may stick to the fly's legs. These reproductive structures can then drop off when the fly lands on another rotting surface. If conditions are right, a new netted stinkhorn will begin to grow there.

Develop Hypotheses Where might mushrooms grow?

Sample: Mushrooms might grow where organisms are rotting or decomposing.

> **UNTAMED SCIENCE** Watch the **Untamed Science** video to learn more about mushrooms.

Professional Development Note | From the Author

The general opinion of bacteria is negative: the word brings to mind disease-causing organisms like *Streptococcus.* It's true that pathogenic bacteria cause diseases such as cholera and tuberculosis. Bacteria can be dangerous because they are able to grow in widely varied conditions and go dormant for long periods. But what about some good press for bacteria? Probiotics such as *lactobacillus acidophilus,* found in yogurt, can help maintain a healthy balance in the human digestive tract. Bacteria also play an important part in the cycling of nutrients in the global ecosystem. When dead organisms are decomposed by bacteria, carbon is released back into the environment.

✐ *Zipporah Miller*

Viruses, Bacteria, Protists, and Fungi

Chapter at a Glance

CHAPTER PACING: 8–12 periods or 4–6 blocks

INTRODUCE THE CHAPTER: Use the Engaging Question and the opening image to get students thinking about viruses, bacteria, protists, and fungi. Activate prior knowledge and preteach vocabulary using the Getting Started pages.

Lesson 1: Viruses

Lesson 2: Bacteria

Lesson 3: Protists

Lesson 4: Fungi

ASSESSMENT OPTIONS: Chapter Test, *ExamView®* Computer Test Generator, Performance Assessment, Progress Monitoring Assessments, SuccessTracker™

Preference Navigator, in the online Planning tools, allows you to customize *Interactive Science* to your own teaching style. You can also edit lesson plans by selecting the Lesson Planner option.

Digital Teacher's Edition allows you to access your Teacher's Edition and Resource online.

my science online.com

Differentiated Instruction

L1 Plants, Animals, and Other Living Things Have pairs or small groups of students review characteristics of animals and of plants. Make sure that students understand that animals are living things that move by themselves, have sense organs, and do not make their own food, whereas plants are living things that cannot move by themselves, have no sense organs, and usually make their own food. Invite students to analyze the photograph and discuss whether these mushrooms share any traits with either animals or plants.

L3 Life on the Forest Floor Challenge students to brainstorm a list of organisms that thrive in damp forest habitats. After students have developed a significant list, encourage them to organize the organisms into groups under the headings *Animals, Plants,* and *Neither a Plant nor an Animal.*

Getting Started

Check Your Understanding

This activity assesses students' understanding of the distinctions between prokaryotes and eukaryotes. After students have shared their answers, point out that all life on Earth is composed of cells that are either prokaryotes or eukaryotes. This simple classification is true even of one-celled organisms.

Preteach Vocabulary Skills

Draw students' attention to the headings and entries of the three-column chart. Explain to students that a prefix has its own meaning. Point out that when a prefix is added to a word, the meaning of the prefix is added to or combined with the meaning of the root. Learning prefixes can make it easier to learn new vocabulary words. Also point out that the prefixes *endo-* and *pseudo-* appear in many different words, such as *endotherm, endoskeleton, endocrine, pseudonym,* and *pseudomorph.*

Check Your Understanding

1. **Background** Read the paragraph below and then answer the question.

"Yes, it is a **prokaryote**!" said Lena, pulling her head away from the microscope. "No, it's not!" said Kiera. "Stop fighting!" said their friend Isa. "Let me see." Isa looked. "It's not a prokaryote; that's for sure. First of all, it is too large. More importantly, you can clearly see its **nucleus.** It is obviously a **eukaryote.**"

> A **prokaryote** is an organism whose single cell lacks a nucleus.
>
> A **nucleus** is a large oval organelle that contains the cell's genetic material in the form of DNA and controls many of the cell's activities.
>
> A **eukaryote** is an organism with cells that contain nuclei.

- Which organisms have nuclei—prokaryotes or eukaryotes?

  Eukaryotes

> **MY READING WEB** If you had trouble completing the question above, visit **My Reading Web** and type in *Viruses, Bacteria, Protists, and Fungi.*

Vocabulary Skill

Prefixes Some words can be divided into parts. A root is the part of the word that carries the basic meaning. A prefix is a word part that is placed in front of the root to change the word's meaning. The prefixes below will help you understand some of the vocabulary in this chapter.

Prefix	Meaning	Example
endo-	inside, within	endospore, *n.* a small, rounded, thick-walled cell that forms inside of a bacterial cell
pseudo-	false	pseudopod, *n.* a "false foot"; a structure used by certain protozoans for movement

2. **Quick Check** Which part of the word *endospore* tells you it is something that forms inside a bacterial cell?

   Endo-

38 Viruses, Bacteria, Protists, and Fungi

My Reading Web offers leveled readings that offer a foundation for the chapter content.

Vocab Flash Cards offer extra practice with the chapter vocabulary words.

Digital Lesson

- Assign the *Check Your Understanding* activity online and have students submit their work to you.
- Assign the *Vocabulary Skill* activity online and have students submit their work to you.

my science online.com   Viruses, Bacteria, Protists, & Fungi

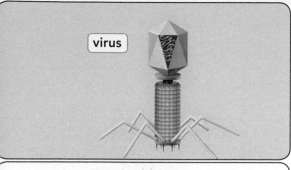

virus

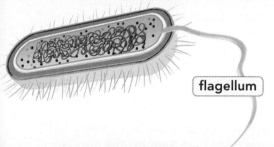

flagellum

algae

budding

Chapter Preview

LESSON 1
- virus
- host
- parasite
- vaccine
- 🔄 Identify the Main Idea
- △ Infer

LESSON 2
- bacteria
- cytoplasm
- ribosome
- flagellum
- cellular respiration
- binary fission
- conjugation
- endospore
- pasteurization
- decomposer
- 🔄 Compare and Contrast
- △ Predict

LESSON 3
- protist
- protozoan
- pseudopod
- contractile vacuole
- cilia
- algae
- pigment
- spore
- 🔄 Summarize
- △ Graph

LESSON 4
- fungus
- hyphae
- fruiting body
- budding
- lichen
- 🔄 Identify Supporting Evidence
- △ Observe

► **VOCAB FLASH CARDS** For extra help with vocabulary, visit **Vocab Flash Cards** and type in *Viruses, Bacteria, Protists, and Fungi.*

Preview Vocabulary Terms

Have students create a personalized science glossary for the vocabulary terms in this chapter. In their glossaries, students should define each term and reference the pages in the chapter that define and explain the term. Encourage students to include drawings and diagrams that help explain the meaning of the terms and concepts. A list of Academic Vocabulary for each lesson can be found in the Support All Readers box at the start of the lesson.

L1 Have students look at the images on this page as you pronounce the vocabulary word. Have students repeat the word after you. Then read the definition. Use the sample sentence in italics to clarify the meaning of the term.

virus *(VY rus)* A tiny, nonliving particle that enters and then reproduces inside a living cell. *Some viruses are shaped like robots.*

flagellum *(fluh JEL um)* A long, whiplike structure that helps a cell to move. *A flagellum helps a cell to move through water.*

algae *(AL jee)* Plant-like protists. *Algae like this one are commonly referred to as seaweed.*

budding *(BUD ing)* A form of asexual reproduction in unicellular fungi in which no spores are produced. *A new yeast cell breaks off from the parent through budding.*

ⒺⒻⓁⓁ Support

Have students complete the **Preview Vocabulary Terms** activity either alone or in pairs. Before students begin creating their science glossaries, write each word and introduce it to students by pointing and saying it aloud.

Beginning
LOW Draw a picture or other visual aid for each vocabulary term in the glossary to associate the term with its definition.

HIGH Include words and phrases in the native language to help students remember specific terms they have trouble with.

Intermediate
LOW/HIGH Include English pronunciations for each term in the glossary.

Advanced
LOW/HIGH For each vocabulary term in the glossary, write a sentence that uses the term correctly.

Viruses

Lesson Pacing: 1–2 periods or $\frac{1}{2}$–1 block

SHORT ON TIME? To do this lesson in approximately half the time, do the Activate Prior Knowledge activity on page 40. A discussion of the Key Concepts on pages 40 and 44 will familiarize students with the lesson content. Have students do the Quick Labs. The rest of the lesson can be completed by students independently.

Preference Navigator, in the online Planning tools, allows you to customize *Interactive Science* to your own teaching style. You can also edit lesson plans by selecting the Lesson Planner option.

Digital Teacher's Edition allows you to access your Teacher's Edition and Resource materials online.

Lesson Vocabulary

- virus • host • parasite • vaccine

Content Refresher

Characteristics of Viruses Viruses vary widely in size and shape. However, all viruses share a similar structure. A virus particle consists of a protein casing enclosing a nucleic acid core. Some viruses are also surrounded by a membrane envelope, which derives from its host, but also contains viral proteins.

Viruses can be classified according to the type of nucleic acid they contain. The genetic material may be double stranded DNA, single-stranded DNA, double-stranded RNA, or single-stranded RNA. Viruses are also classified according to their structure and the host organisms they infect. Viruses infect organisms from all three domains. However, because the interaction between a virus' proteins and the proteins on a host's cell is highly specific, a particular virus is able to infect only certain types of cells.

LESSON OBJECTIVES

Name and describe the characteristics of viruses and how they multiply.

Discuss both positive and negative ways that viruses affect living things.

Blended Path
Active learning using Student Edition, Inquiry Path, and Digital Path

ENGAGE AND EXPLORE

Teach this lesson using a variety of resources. Begin by reading **My Planet Diary** as a class. Have students discuss rabies and its physical symptoms. Then have students do the **Inquiry Warm-Up activity.** Students will visualize the relationship between interlocking parts in anticipation of reading about a virus's protein coat and its host cell. The **After the Inquiry Warm-Up worksheet** sets up a discussion about the concept of lock and key and how it could be incorporated into mechanisms in living things. Have volunteers share their answers to question 4 telling how a cell can protect itself from invading organisms.

EXPLAIN AND ELABORATE

Teach Key Concepts by explaining that viruses are nonliving and that they cannot reproduce on their own. **Support the Big Q** by identifying diseases that are caused by viruses. **Lead a Discussion** about the two basic structural components of every virus: a protein coat and an inner core of genetic material.

Teach Key Concepts by explaining that viruses can also be used to prevent and treat illnesses. **Lead a Discussion** about gene therapy and how it works. Have students practice the inquiry skill in the **Apply It activity.**

Hand out the **Key Concept Summaries** as a review of each part of the lesson. Students can also use the online **Vocab Flash Cards** to review key terms.

EVALUATE

Have students take the **Lesson Quiz.** For an alternate assessment, see the *ExamView®* Computer Test Generator, Progress Monitoring Assessments, or SuccessTracker™.

ELL Support

1 Content and Language

Explain to students that the term *host* has several different meanings. Have them find the term in a dictionary, read the definitions, and then use the visuals in the chapter to predict which of the meanings fits the way the term will be used in the chapter.

DIFFERENTIATED INSTRUCTION KEY
L1 Struggling Students or Special Needs
L2 On-Level Students **L3** Advanced Students

LESSON PLANNER 2.1

 **Inquiry Path** Hands-on learning in the Lab zone

ENGAGE AND EXPLORE

To teach this lesson with an emphasis on inquiry, begin with the **Inquiry Warm-Up activity.** Students will visualize the relationship between interlocking parts in anticipation of reading about a virus's protein coat and its host cell. The **After the Inquiry Warm-Up worksheet** sets up a discussion about the concept of lock and key and how it could be incorporated into mechanisms in living things. Have volunteers share their answers to question 4 telling how a cell can protect itself from invading organisms.

EXPLAIN AND ELABORATE

Focus on the **Inquiry Skill** for the lesson. Remind students that when they infer, they combine evidence with their experience and knowledge to reach a logical conclusion. Point out that an inference is not a fact. Instead, it is only one of many possible interpretations for an observation. What knowledge was used to infer why every house in the neighborhood has a different front door key in the **Inquiry Warm-Up activity?** *(Sample: People used front door locks for security, so they would want to have a different key than their neighbors.)* **Support the Big Q** by identifying diseases that are caused by viruses. **Build Inquiry** by giving students the opportunity to build models of viruses and recognize their distinct shapes. Use the next **Build Inquiry** to challenge small groups to create model viruses to attach to particular types of cells. Have students do the **Quick Lab** making a model showing a virus's size compared to the head of a pin and calculating the number of viruses that could fit on a pin's head.

Before beginning the **Apply It activity,** review details about the characteristics of viruses as well as information about how viruses multiply. Have students do the **Quick Lab** exploring how vaccines affect the spread of viral diseases. Students can use the online **Vocab Flash Cards** to review key terms.

EVALUATE

Have students take the **Lesson Quiz.** For an alternate assessment, see the *ExamView®* Computer Test Generator, Progress Monitoring Assessments, or SuccessTracker™.

Digital Path Online learning at my science online.com

ENGAGE AND EXPLORE

Teach this lesson using digital resources. Begin by having students learn more about viruses and explore real-world connections to viruses at **My Planet Diary** online. Have them access the Chapter Resources to find the **Unlock the Big Question activity.** There they can answer the questions and refine their responses as they continue through the lesson. You can re-assign the activity and have students submit their work so you can track their progress.

EXPLAIN AND ELABORATE

Students reading above, at, or below the lexile measure of this lesson can access basic content readings at their level at **My Reading Web.** Encourage students to use the online **Vocab Flash Cards** to preview key terms. **Support the Big Q** by identifying diseases that are caused by viruses. Use the **Interactive Art activity** online to show how a virus attacks a cell. Have students do the **Quick Lab** making a model showing a virus's size compared to the head of a pin and calculating the number of viruses that could fit on a pin's head.

Assign the **Apply It activity** online and have students submit their work to you. Have students do the **Quick Lab** exploring how vaccines affect the spread of viral diseases. The **Key Concept Summaries** online allow students to read a summary and see an image associated with each part of the lesson. Online remediation is available at **My Science Coach.**

EVALUATE

Have students take the **Lesson Quiz.** For an alternate assessment, see the *ExamView®* Computer Test Generator, Progress Monitoring Assessments, or SuccessTracker™.

2 Frontload the Lesson

Have students make a three-column chart to rate their knowledge of the terms, listing each in the first column. In the second column, students should indicate whether they can define and use the word, whether they have heard or seen it before, or do not know it. As they read, students should write definitions in the third column.

3 Comprehensible Input

Have students use the information from the visual on page 42 to write sentences about the relative size of virus.

4 Language Production

Pair or group students with varied language abilities to complete labs collaboratively for language practice. Have each student copy the completed written lab for personal reference.

5 Assess Understanding

Make true or false statements using lesson content and have students indicate if they agree or disagree with a thumbs up or thumbs down gesture to check whole-class comprehension.

Viruses

Establish Learning Objectives

After this lesson, students will be able to:

 Name and describe the characteristics of viruses and how they multiply.

 Discuss both positive and negative ways that viruses affect living things.

Engage

Activate Prior Knowledge

MY PLANET DIARY Read *A Mad Choice* with the class. Point out that humans and all other warm-blooded animals can be infected by rabies. Explain that rabies is transmitted through a bite. Ask: **What are some animals that are apt to be infected by rabies?** *(Samples: Bats, skunks, raccoons, foxes, dogs, cats)* **What physical symptom of rabies is visible in the photograph of the dog?** *(Frothing or foaming mouth)*

BIG IDEAS OF SCIENCE REFERENCE LIBRARY Have students look up the following topic: Common Cold.

Explore

Lab Resource: Inquiry Warm-Up

L1 **WHICH LOCK DOES THE KEY FIT?** Students will visualize the relationship between interlocking parts in anticipation of reading about a virus's protein coat and its host cell.

---

1 Viruses

 What Are the Characteristics of Viruses?

 How Do Viruses Interact With the Living World?

MY PLANET DIARY — VOICES FROM HISTORY

A Mad Choice

Have you ever seen a snarling dog on TV? Chances are this "mad dog" was supposed to have rabies. Rabies is a virus that affects the brain, causing "mad" behaviors and spasms of the throat. Infected animals avoid water, giving the disease the nickname *hydrophobia*, meaning "fear of water."

In the 1800s, if people were bitten by a mad dog, they would likely die. Then, in 1884, the scientist Louis Pasteur said he had a cure. He claimed, "Whoever gets bitten by a mad dog has only to submit to my three little inoculations, and he need not have the slightest fear of hydrophobia."

Answer the question below.

Would you try Pasteur's cure, even if it had not been tested on humans? Why or why not?

Sample: I would not want to die from rabies, so I would try the cure.

 PLANET DIARY Go to **Planet Diary** to learn more about viruses.

Lab zone Do the Inquiry Warm-Up *Which Lock Does the Key Fit?*

What Are the Characteristics of Viruses?

Have you ever noticed that when you spent time with a friend suffering from a cold, you sometimes felt sick a few days later? You were probably infected by a virus. A **virus** is a tiny, nonliving particle that enters and then reproduces inside a living cell.

 Viruses are nonliving, have a protein coat that protects an inner core of genetic material, and cannot reproduce on their own.

SUPPORT ALL READERS

Lexile Measure = 940L   Lexile Word Count = 1261

Prior Exposure to Content: May be the first time students have encountered this topic

Academic Vocabulary: *identify, infer, main idea*

Science Vocabulary: *virus, host, parasite, vaccine*

Concept Level: Generally appropriate for most students in this grade

Preteach With: My Planet Diary "A Mad Choice" and Figure 2 activity

Go to **My Reading Web** to access leveled readings that provide a foundation for the content.

my science online

Vocabulary
- virus • host
- parasite • vaccine

Skills
- Reading: Identify the Main Idea
- Inquiry: Infer

Virus Needs Why are viruses considered nonliving? They lack most of the characteristics of living things. Viruses are not cells and do not use their own energy to grow or to respond to their surroundings. Viruses also cannot make food, take in food, or produce wastes. Although viruses can multiply like organisms, they can only do so when they are inside a living cell.

The organism that a virus enters and multiplies inside of is called a **host**. A **host** is an organism that provides a source of energy for a virus or another organism. A virus acts like a **parasite** (PA ruh syt), an organism that lives on or in a host and causes it harm. Almost all viruses destroy the cells in which they multiply.

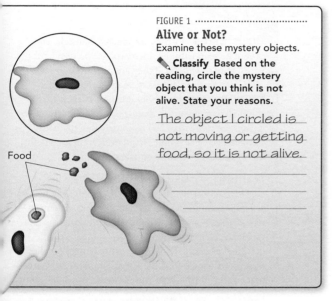

FIGURE 1 ··································
Alive or Not?
Examine these mystery objects.

✎ **Classify** Based on the reading, circle the mystery object that you think is not alive. State your reasons.

The object I circled is not moving or getting food, so it is not alive.

Food

Virus Shapes As you can see in **Figure 2**, viruses vary widely in shape. Some viruses are round, and some are rod-shaped. Other viruses are shaped like bricks, threads, or bullets. There are even viruses that have complex, robotlike shapes, such as the bacteriophage. A bacteriophage (bak TEER ee oh fayj) is a virus that infects bacteria. In fact, its name means "bacteria eater."

Influenza virus

Tobacco mosaic virus

T4 bacteriophage

FIGURE 2 ··································
Virus Shapes
The leglike structures on the bottom of the T4 bacteriophage keep the virus firmly in place as it infects a cell.

41

ⒺⓁⓁ Support

1 Content and Language
Have students write the term *parasite* in their vocabulary notebooks. Encourage them to use their own words to explain the meaning of the word. Invite students to create a graphic image, such as a diagram or cartoon, to illustrate *parasite*.

2 Frontload the Lesson
Invite students to share words and phrases that they associate with the

term *virus*. Accept responses that have to do with computers as well as with illness.

3 Comprehensible Input
Invite groups of students to act out what happens when a virus enters a host, acts like a parasite, and multiplies. Provide ample class time so that groups can assign roles, design and rehearse their skits, and share their demonstrations with the rest of the class.

Explain ——————

Introduce Vocabulary
Encourage students to think of the terms *host* and *parasite* in relation to one another, perhaps as a kind of "odd couple." Explain that despite the fact that a parasite lives on or in a host and causes it harm, the host usually continues to live and provide a source of energy for the parasite.

Teach Key Concepts 🔑
Explain to students that viruses are nonliving and that they cannot reproduce on their own. Ask: **What is a virus made up of?** (*A protein coat and an inner core of genetic material*) **What do viruses need to get energy and multiply?** (*A host*) **What effect does a virus have on its host?** (*It harms the host.*) **Where does a virus multiply?** (*Inside a living cell*) **What effect do the actions of a virus usually have on the living cell?** (*Usually a virus destroys the cell.*)

Support the Big Q ❓ UbD
IDENTIFY VIRAL DISEASES Invite students to name diseases they are familiar with. List the diseases on the board. Tell students that viruses are the cause of some diseases. Encourage them to identify any diseases on the list that they know are caused by viruses. Point out that viruses can also affect plants, which can significantly reduce crop yield.

Elaborate ——————

Build Inquiry 🧪

L1 MAKE MODELS OF VIRUS SHAPES

Materials clay (enough for each student to make one model of a virus)

Time 15 minutes

Have students work in groups of three to make models of the viruses pictured in **Figure 2.** Ask that each group member make a model of a different one of the viruses, labeling them A, B, and C. Then ask groups to look at models made by other groups and identify each virus by name.

Ask: **What are some distinct shapes of the viruses in these models?** (*Samples: round, cylindrical, robot-shaped*)

My Planet Diary provides an opportunity for students to explore real-world connections to viruses.

my science online.com | Describing Viruses

Explain

Teach With Visuals

Tell students to look at **Figure 3.** Remind students that viruses can reproduce only inside cells. Ask: **Given that viruses reproduce only inside cells, what can you conclude about the size of viruses?** (*Viruses are smaller than cells.*) Have students study **Figure 3** and compare the sizes of the five viruses. Point out that bacteria are much smaller than most body cells. Explain also that viruses are even smaller than bacteria, which are the smallest living organisms. Ask: **Why do you think the many different shapes and sizes of viruses could be significant to the bodies of their hosts?** (*Sample: It may be hard for a body to recognize and fight viruses because they are so small and so different from one another.*)

Lead a Discussion

TWO STRUCTURAL COMPONENTS Tell students that every virus has two basic structural components. Ask: **What two structural components are present in every virus?** (*A protein coat, an inner core of genetic material*) **What role do a virus's surface proteins play in the virus's relationship with the cells of its host?** (*The virus's surface proteins attach to proteins on the surface of certain host cells.*)

Make Analogies

L1 **FIT OF VIRUS AND CELL** Show students clothing snaps and other fasteners. Fasten and unfasten them several times so that students can see how the two parts of the fastener lock and unlock. Ask: **Would one of these snaps fit other types of snaps or fasteners?** (*No, it fits only the unique partner it was made to fit.*) Then direct students' attention to **Figure 4.** Ask: **How is the relationship between the two parts of a clothing snap similar to the relationship between surface proteins of a virus and the surface proteins on a host's cells?** (*The fit between the viral proteins and cell proteins is very specific, just as these kinds of snaps fit with only each other.*)

Elaborate

21st Century Learning

CRITICAL THINKING Remind students that only certain cells in the host have surface proteins with a shape that will fit a particular virus's surface proteins. Ask: **How could the fact that a virus's surface proteins can attach only to certain cells in the host help a scientist's effort to locate a virus in the body?** (*Sample: A virus for a certain disease attaches itself to a specific type of cell, often found in a specific part of the body.*)

FIGURE 3 ⋯⋯⋯⋯⋯⋯⋯⋯⋯⋯⋯⋯⋯⋯⋯⋯

Virus Sizes

The *Streptococcus* bacterium is a round organism that causes the infection strep throat.

✎ **Read the text about virus sizes and then complete each task.**

1. **Calculate** A *Streptococcus* bacterium is 10 times larger than a cold virus. Calculate the size of the bacterium.

   75 nm x 10 = 750 nm

2. **Measure** Use your calculation from Step 1 to mark and label on the scale the size of the *Streptococcus* bacterium.

3. **Make Models** Draw the bacterium to scale in the box provided.

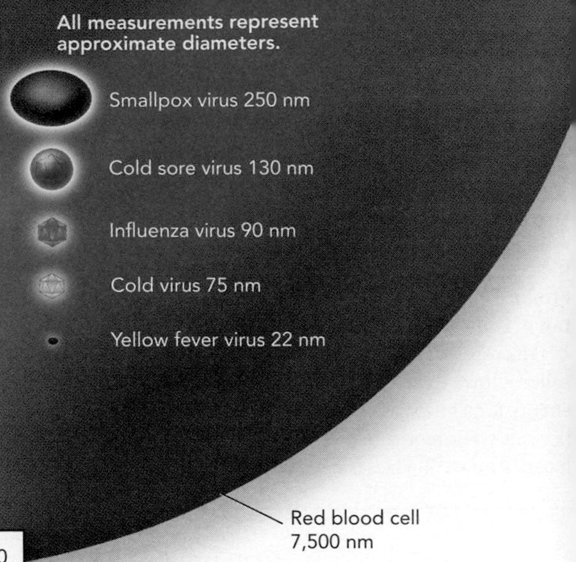

All measurements represent approximate diameters.

 Smallpox virus 250 nm

 Cold sore virus 130 nm

Influenza virus 90 nm

Cold virus 75 nm

Yellow fever virus 22 nm

Red blood cell 7,500 nm

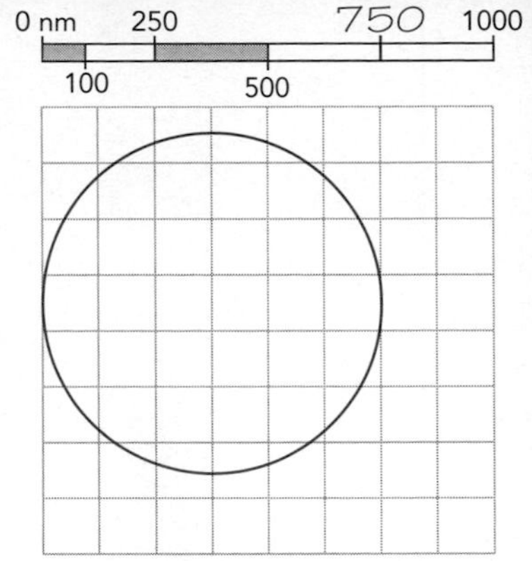

0 nm	250	750	1000
	100	500	

Streptococcus bacterium

Virus Sizes Viruses are smaller than cells and cannot be seen with the microscopes you use in school. Viruses are so small that they are measured in units called nanometers (nm). One nanometer is one billionth of a meter (m). The smallest viruses are about 20 nanometers in diameter, while the largest viruses are more than 200 nanometers in diameter. The average virus is quite small even compared with the smallest cells—those of bacteria.

Naming Viruses Because viruses are not considered organisms, scientists do not use the two-part scientific naming system to identify them. Scientists name viruses in a variety of ways. For example, some viruses, such as the poliovirus, are named after the disease they cause. Other viruses are named for the area where they were discovered. The West Nile virus is named after the place in Africa where it was first found.

How Viruses Multiply After a virus attaches to a host cell, it enters the cell. Once inside a cell, the virus's genetic material takes over many of the cell's functions. It instructs the cell to produce the virus's proteins and genetic material. These proteins and genetic material then assemble into new viruses. Some viruses take over cell functions immediately. Other viruses wait for a while.

42 Viruses, Bacteria, Protists, and Fungi

Interactive Art shows how a virus attacks a cell.

 my science online.com ▶ **Describing Viruses**

The Structure of Viruses Although viruses have many different shapes and sizes, they all have a similar structure. All viruses have two basic parts: an inner core containing genetic material and a protein coat that protects the virus. A virus's genetic material contains the instructions for making new viruses.

Each virus contains unique surface proteins. These surface proteins play an important role during the invasion of a host cell. The shape of the surface proteins allows a virus to attach only to certain cells in the host. Like keys, a virus's proteins fit only into specific "locks," or proteins, on the surface of a host's cells. So a particular virus can attach only to one or a few types of host cells. For example, most cold viruses infect cells only in the nose and throat of humans. Those cells have proteins on their surfaces that complement or fit the proteins on cold viruses. **Figure 4** shows how the lock-and-key system works.

FIGURE 4 · · · · · · · · · · · · · · · ·
> INTERACTIVE ART **Virus Structure and Invasion** Some viruses are surrounded by an outer membrane envelope.

✎ **Interpret Diagrams** For the virus on the right, draw a line from the virus surface proteins to the matching cell surface proteins. Circle any of the cell proteins that do not match.

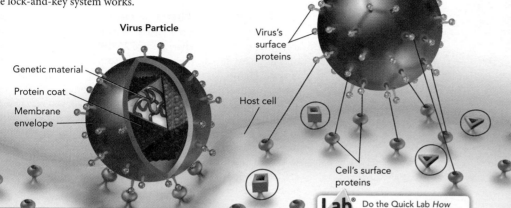

Virus Particle

Genetic material
Protein coat
Membrane envelope

Virus's surface proteins

Host cell

Cell's surface proteins

 Do the Quick Lab How Many Viruses Fit on a Pin?

⚷ Assess Your Understanding

1a. Define A virus is a (living/~~nonliving~~) particle that enters a cell and uses it to reproduce.

b. Relate Cause and Effect How do the surface proteins on a virus help it to invade a host cell?
They fit cell surface proteins and allow the virus to attach.

c. CHALLENGE Scientists hypothesize that viruses could not have existed on Earth before organisms appeared. Do you agree? Explain.
Yes; viruses need organisms for energy and reproduction.

got it? ·

○ **I get it!** Now I know that the characteristics of viruses are *that they are nonliving, have a protein coat, and cannot reproduce on their own.*

○ **I need extra help with** *See TE note.*

Go to MY SCIENCE ⓢ COACH online for help with this subject.

43

Differentiated Instruction

L1 Virus Sizes Students may find the relative sizes in different figures confusing. Make sure that students understand that illustrations of viruses are not all done to the same scale. In order to show detail, some images are enlarged more than others. Each square on the grid in **Figure 3** represents 125 nm. Have students add some of the viruses listed in **Figure 3** to the grid, using the correct scale.

L3 Create Displays Have students research viruses to choose one aspect of viruses to present to the class. Have students submit topics for approval before proceeding with the project. Try to have each student present a different aspect of viruses. You might suggest that they create posters to make their presentations more varied and informative.

Build Inquiry Lab

L2 MAKE MODELS OF VIRAL STRUCTURES

Materials construction paper of different colors, glue, poster board, scissors

Time 30 minutes

Before class, cut out four large circles to represent four different types of cells. Use scissors to notch the edges of the circles so that each circle has a distinct pattern. In class, review the basic components of viral structure with students. Then divide the class into four groups and give each group one cell model. Challenge groups to create model viruses to attach to their particular type of cell. When students have completed their models, each group can contribute to the creation of a poster showing the four cells and the four viruses.

Ask: **If each virus can attach to only one kind of cell, does that mean that each cell can be attacked by only one kind of virus?** *(Sample: No, different types of viruses can attach to the same type of cell.)*

Lab Resource: Quick Lab Lab

L2 HOW MANY VIRUSES FIT ON A PIN? Students will make a model showing a virus's size compared to the head of a pin, and calculate the number of viruses that could fit on a pin's head.

Evaluate ———————

Assess Your Understanding

After students answer the questions, have them evaluate their understanding by completing the appropriate sentence.

R T I Response to Intervention

1a. If students cannot state whether viruses are living or nonliving, **then** remind them that a virus acts like a parasite with a host because it lacks most characteristics of living things.

b. If students need help explaining the role of surface proteins in invading a host cell, **then** encourage them to study the images and labels in **Figure 4**.

c. If students have trouble making a hypothesis about the history of viruses, **then** review with them the relationship between parasites and hosts.

MY SCIENCE ⓢ COACH Have students go online for help in understanding the characteristics of viruses.

Explain

Teach Key Concepts 🔑

Explain to students that although viruses can cause disease, they can also be used to prevent and treat illnesses. Invite students to offer their ideas about how viruses might be helpful in the prevention and treatment of disease. Ask: **How serious are viral diseases, and how long do they last in the human body?** *(Some viral diseases are not serious and do not last long. Others are extremely serious and have effects on the body that last a long time.)* **What can scientists do with viruses that are weakened or dead?** *(Scientists can use such viruses to create vaccines.)* If students are surprised at the use of the word *dead* to describe something that is nonliving, explain that some vaccines use viruses that are weakened—damaged but not completely unable to cause a disease. A "dead" virus used in a vaccine has been damaged to the point that it cannot cause the disease. **How do vaccines prevent illness?** *(A vaccine has chemicals that activate the body's natural defenses so that they will be able to destroy a specific virus the next time it appears in the body.)* Explain to students that vaccines are administered in different forms—through injection, pills, or inhaled substances.

🎯 Identify the Main Idea Remind students

that the main idea is the most important idea in a paragraph or section of text. Details and other information in the text support or further explain the main idea. Point out that some main ideas are stated directly, whereas others must be identified by the reader.

Lead a Discussion

GENE THERAPY Remind students that a virus multiplies by invading a cell and causing the cell to use the virus's genetic information. By attaching a needed gene to the genetic information of a harmless virus, scientists can insert the gene into body cells. Ask: **What is gene therapy?** *(It is a medical technique where scientists can use a virus to treat certain disorders.)* **How does gene therapy work?** *(Scientists add needed genetic material to a virus and use the virus to deliver the genetic material to a patient's cells.)* Point out that gene therapy is a relatively new area of research. A disorder like cystic fibrosis, which is caused by a single faulty gene, is a good candidate for gene therapy because there is only one genetic error to correct. Other disorders are caused by more than one gene, and so scientists would have to isolate more than one gene and possibly develop more than one kind of carrier virus.

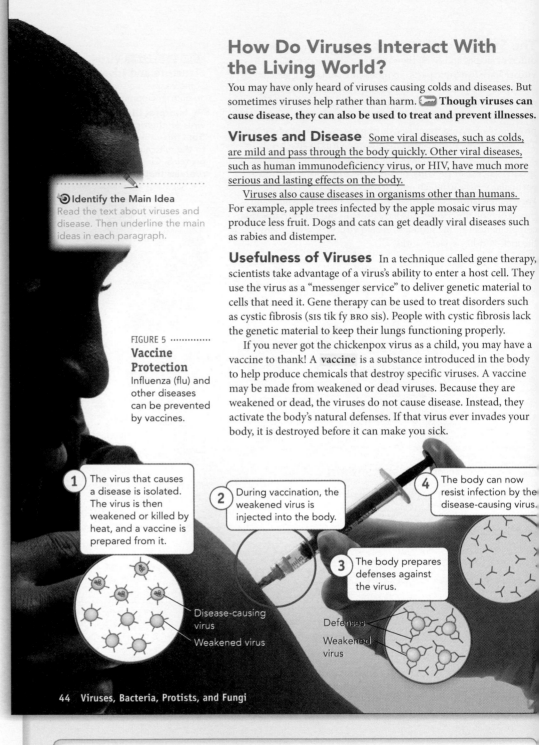

🖊 **Identify the Main Idea**
Read the text about viruses and disease. Then underline the main ideas in each paragraph.

FIGURE 5 ....
Vaccine Protection
Influenza (flu) and other diseases can be prevented by vaccines.

1. The virus that causes a disease is isolated. The virus is then weakened or killed by heat, and a vaccine is prepared from it.

2. During vaccination, the weakened virus is injected into the body.

3. The body prepares defenses against the virus.

4. The body can now resist infection by the disease-causing virus.

Disease-causing virus
Weakened virus
Defenses
Weakened virus

44 Viruses, Bacteria, Protists, and Fungi

How Do Viruses Interact With the Living World?

You may have only heard of viruses causing colds and diseases. But sometimes viruses help rather than harm. 🔑 **Though viruses can cause disease, they can also be used to treat and prevent illnesses.**

Viruses and Disease Some viral diseases, such as colds, are mild and pass through the body quickly. Other viral diseases, such as human immunodeficiency virus, or HIV, have much more serious and lasting effects on the body.

Viruses also cause diseases in organisms other than humans. For example, apple trees infected by the apple mosaic virus may produce less fruit. Dogs and cats can get deadly viral diseases such as rabies and distemper.

Usefulness of Viruses In a technique called gene therapy, scientists take advantage of a virus's ability to enter a host cell. They use the virus as a "messenger service" to deliver genetic material to cells that need it. Gene therapy can be used to treat disorders such as cystic fibrosis (SIS tik fy BRO sis). People with cystic fibrosis lack the genetic material to keep their lungs functioning properly.

If you never got the chickenpox virus as a child, you may have a vaccine to thank! A **vaccine** is a substance introduced in the body to help produce chemicals that destroy specific viruses. A vaccine may be made from weakened or dead viruses. Because they are weakened or dead, the viruses do not cause disease. Instead, they activate the body's natural defenses. If that virus ever invades your body, it is destroyed before it can make you sick.

Digital Lesson: Assign the *Apply It* activity online and have students submit their work to you.

my science online › | **Viruses and the Living World**

apply it!

Viruses can cause disease around the world. Use the world map below to answer the questions about dengue (DEN gay) fever, a viral disease.

1 Interpret Maps Which continents have outbreaks of dengue fever?

North and South America, Africa, Asia, and Australia

2 Draw Conclusions Why do you think dengue fever only occurs in warm places?

Mosquitoes cannot spread the virus below 16°C.

3 Infer Suppose people in South America are getting sick with an influenza virus. A few days earlier, there were reports of the same virus infecting people in Africa. How could the influenza virus have spread so quickly?

Sample: Maybe someone in Africa who was infected with influenza flew on a plane to South America and spread the virus.

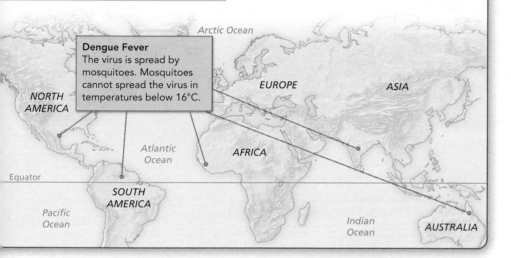

Dengue Fever
The virus is spread by mosquitoes. Mosquitoes cannot spread the virus in temperatures below 16°C.

Arctic Ocean
EUROPE
ASIA
NORTH AMERICA
Atlantic Ocean
AFRICA
Equator
SOUTH AMERICA
Pacific Ocean
Indian Ocean
AUSTRALIA

Lab zone Do the Quick Lab How Viruses Spread.

Assess Your Understanding

got it? ....

○ **I get it!** Now I know that viruses interact in the living world by both __sometimes causing diseases and sometimes helping to treat or prevent them.__

○ **I need extra help with** __See TE note.__

Go to my science COACH *online for help with this subject.*

45

Differentiated Instruction

L3 Active and Hidden Viruses
Challenge students to do research about the distinction between active viruses and hidden viruses. Encourage students to prepare an oral presentation of their findings, including examples of each type. Students might use effective graphic aids, such as a Venn diagram or a poster showing the sequential steps that occur with each type of virus.

L1 Vaccines and Diseases Invite students to brainstorm a list of vaccines—or diseases the vaccines were designed to prevent—from their own personal knowledge and experience. Students may mention diseases such as seasonal influenza, specific flus, polio, mumps, measles, rubella, tetanus, chicken pox, smallpox, and rabies.

Elaborate

Apply It!

L1 Before beginning the activity, review details about the characteristics of viruses as well as information about how viruses multiply.

Infer Remind students that when they infer, they combine evidence (the locations of viral infections in South America and Africa) with their experience and knowledge to reach a logical conclusion. Point out that an inference is not a fact. Instead, it is only one of many possible interpretations for an observation.

Lab Resource: Quick Lab **Lab zone**

L1 HOW VIRUSES SPREAD Students will explore how vaccines affect the spread of viral diseases.

Evaluate

Assess Your Understanding

Have students evaluate their understanding by completing the appropriate sentence.

RTI Response to Intervention

If students have trouble understanding that viruses both cause disease and can be used to prevent and treat illness, **then** have them study the details about vaccine production in **Figure 5**.

my science COACH Have students go online for help in understanding the relationship between viruses and diseases.

Lab zone **After the Inquiry Warm-Up**

Viruses

Inquiry Warm-Up, *Which Lock Does the Key Fit?*

In the Inquiry Warm-Up, you investigated the concept of lock and key and how it could be incorporated into mechanisms in living things. Using what you learned from that activity, answer the questions below.

1. **INFER** Would it be easier or harder to open a lock without the right key? Explain.

   _____

   _____

2. **INFER** Why doesn't every house in your neighborhood use the same key to open the front door?

   _____

   _____

3. **EXPLAIN** Would it be easier to match keys with their locks if all the keys were similar or different? Explain.

   _____

   _____

   _____

4. **PREDICT** Over time, some invading organisms change the keys they use to match the locks on cells. How can a cell protect itself when this happens?

   _____

   _____

Assess Your Understanding

Viruses

What Are the Characteristics of Viruses?

1a. **DEFINE** A virus is a (living/nonliving) particle that enters a cell and uses it to reproduce.

b. **RELATE CAUSE AND EFFECT** How do the surface proteins on a virus help it to invade a host cell?

_____

_____

c. **CHALLENGE** Scientists hypothesize that viruses could not have existed on Earth before organisms appeared. Do you agree? Explain.

_____

_____

_____

_____

gotit?**···**

○ **I get it!** Now I know that the characteristics of viruses are _____

_____

○ **I need extra help with** _____

How Do Viruses Interact With the Living World?

gotit?**···**

○ **I get it!** Now I know that viruses interact with the world by both _____

_____

○ **I need extra help with** _____

_____

Viruses

What Are the Characteristics of Viruses?

A **virus** is a tiny, nonliving particle that enters and then reproduces inside a living cell. **Viruses are nonliving, have a protein coat that protects an inner core of genetic material, and cannot reproduce on their own.** Viruses are considered nonliving because they lack most of the characteristics of living things—they are not cells, do not use their own energy to grow or to respond to their surroundings, cannot make or take in food, and cannot produce wastes. The organism that a virus enters and multiplies inside of is called a **host.** A host is an organism that provides a source of energy for a virus or another organism. A virus acts like a **parasite,** an organism that lives on or in a host and causes it harm. Almost all viruses destroy the cells in which they multiply. Viruses can be round or shaped like rods, bricks, threads, bullets, or robots. Viruses are so small that they are measured in units called nanometers. The average virus is quite small when compared with even the smallest cells. After a virus attaches to a host cell, it enters the cell and takes over many of the cell's functions. It instructs the cell to produce the virus's proteins and genetic material, and they assemble into new viruses. Although viruses have many shapes and sizes, all have a structure featuring two basic parts: an inner core containing genetic material and a protective protein coat. Each virus contains unique surface proteins, the shape of which allows the virus to attach to certain cells in the host.

How Do Viruses Interact With the Living World?

Though viruses can cause disease, they can also be used to prevent and treat illnesses. Some viral diseases pass through the body quickly, whereas others have much more serious and lasting effects on the body. Viruses also cause diseases in organisms other than humans. Dogs and cats, as well as trees, for example, can be infected with viruses. Scientists have learned how to take advantage of a virus's ability to enter a host cell. In gene therapy, a virus is used to deliver genetic material to cells that need it. A **vaccine** is a substance introduced in the body to help produce chemicals that destroy specific viruses. Because vaccines are made from dead or weakened viruses, they do not cause disease. Instead, they activate the body's natural defenses so that if that virus ever invades your body, it will be destroyed before it can cause disease.

On a separate sheet of paper, explain the basic characteristics of viruses.

Review and Reinforce

Viruses

Understanding Main Ideas
Answer the following questions on a separate sheet of paper.

1. Viruses are considered to be nonliving. How are they similar to living organisms, and how are they different?
2. How are viruses similar to parasites?
3. In the diagram below, what is the structure and function of the part labeled "A"?
4. In the diagram below, what is the structure and function of the part labeled "B"?

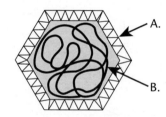

Building Vocabulary
Match each term with its definition by writing the letter of the correct definition in the right column on the line beside the term in the left column.

5. ___ virus

    a. an organism that lives on or in a host and causes it harm

6. ___ host

    b. a substance introduced in the body to help produce chemicals that destroy specific viruses

7. ___ parasite

    c. an organism that provides a source of energy for a virus or another organism

8. ___ vaccine

    d. a tiny, nonliving particle that enters and then reproduces inside a living cell

Enrich

Viruses

> Read the passage and study the graph below. Then use a separate sheet of paper to answer the questions that follow.

Viral Multiplication

Different kinds of viruses multiply at different rates. The rate at which a virus multiplies and when and how this multiplication takes place can help to identify the virus. The graph below shows the rate of growth of four groups of animal viruses, that is, viruses that infect animal cells.

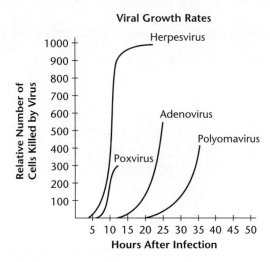

Viral Growth Rates

To collect the data for the graph above, scientists grew viruses in the laboratory. Counting viruses is very difficult because they are so small. It's much easier to measure how effective a virus is at killing cells. So in the graph, the *y*-axis of the graph shows the number of cells that have been destroyed because of viral activity. For each kind of virus, a higher number of cells killed by the virus means a higher number of virus particles.

1. Which kind of virus begins multiplying first? How soon after infection does this happen?

2. Which kind of virus begins multiplying last? How soon after infection does this happen?

3. What is similar about the four lines on the graph? What does this mean about the growth rate of the four kinds of virus groups?

4. The upper part of the line representing the growth curve of the herpesvirus is nearly horizontal. What does this mean about the rate of multiplication of the herpesvirus from 15 to 20 hours after infection?

Lesson Quiz

Viruses

If the statement is true, write *true*. If the statement is false, change the underlined word or words to make the statement true.

1. _____ Viruses are <u>living</u> and cannot reproduce on their own.

2. _____ Viruses <u>lack</u> most of the characteristics of living things.

3. _____ The average virus is quite <u>large</u> when compared with cells.

4. _____ <u>Viruses</u> can cause or help to prevent and treat disease.

5. _____ Vaccines <u>cause</u> viruses.

Fill in the blank to complete each statement.

6. A virus is a tiny particle that enters and then reproduces inside a living

    _____.

7. The organism that a virus enters and multiplies inside of is called a(n)

    _____.

8. A(n) _____ is an organism that lives on or in a host and causes it harm.

9. A(n) _____ is a substance introduced in the body to help produce chemicals that destroy specific viruses.

10. All viruses have a structure featuring an inner core and a protective

    _____ coat.

Viruses

Answer Key

After the Inquiry Warm-Up

1. It would be harder. You would have to break the lock open if you didn't have the right key.

2. Answers will vary. Sample: If every house used the same key, then anyone who had a key for one house in that neighborhood could get into every house in that neighborhood. There would be no security.

3. It would be easier to match keys to their locks if the keys are different. Similar keys might be confused with each other. Different keys are easier to tell apart.

4. Answers will vary. Sample: The cell can change the lock and the type of key used to open it.

Key Concept Summaries

Viruses are tiny, nonliving particles that enter and then reproduce inside living cells. They have a protein coat and an inner core of genetic material, and they cannot reproduce on their own. They take a variety of shapes and sizes, though all are smaller than cells. Viruses multiply by taking over the functions of a host cell, instructing the cell to produce the virus's proteins and genetic material, and having these proteins and genetic material assemble into new viruses.

Review and Reinforce

1. Viruses resemble organisms because they can multiply. They are different because they are not alive: they are not cells, they do not use their own energy to grow or respond to their surroundings.

2. A parasite is an organism that causes harm to its host. Although nonliving, a virus also destroys the invaded host cell by multiplying until the cell is destroyed.

3. Part A is the protein coat. The protein coat protects the virus and enables it to attach to a host cell by fitting into specific proteins on the host cell's surface.

4. Part B is the genetic material. The genetic material contains instructions for making new viruses. It takes over the host cell's functions and directs the cell to produce the virus's proteins and genetic material.

5. d

6. c

7. a

8. b

Enrich

1. herpesvirus; a little less than 5 hours after infection

2. polyomavirus, 20 hours

3. The first part of each line rises steeply. This means that each viral group multiplies very rapidly at first.

4. It means the virus' rate of multiplication has slowed down to the point that it is nearly zero.

Lesson Quiz

1. nonliving	2. true
3. small	4. true
5. destroy	6. cell
7. host	8. parasite
9. vaccine	10. protein

Place the outside corner, the corner away from the dotted line, in the corner of your copy machine to copy onto letter-size paper.

45H

Bacteria

 How are living things other than plants and animals important to earth?

Lesson Pacing: 2–3 periods or 1–1½ blocks

🕐 **SHORT ON TIME?** To do this lesson in approximately half the time, do the Activate Prior Knowledge activity on page 46. A discussion of the Key Concepts on pages 47, 49, and 53 will familiarize students with the lesson content. Have students do the Quick Labs. The rest of the lesson can be completed by students independently.

> **Preference Navigator,** in the online Planning tools, allows you to customize *Interactive Science* to your own teaching style. You can also edit lesson plans by selecting the Lesson Planner option.
>
> **Digital Teacher's Edition** allows you to access your Teacher's Edition and Resource materials online.

Lesson Vocabulary

- bacteria
- cytoplasm
- ribosome
- flagellum
- cellular respiration
- binary fission
- conjugation
- endospore
- pasteurization
- decomposer

Content Refresher

Professional Development Note

Bacteria in the Body Bacteria are part of the normal flora of humans. Found on the skin and in the mouth, intestines, and other sites, these bacteria are part of the mixture of microorganisms that regularly live in or on the body without causing harm. The normal flora of humans consists of more than 200 species of bacteria. In normal health, the interactions between the bacteria and the human host are thought to be mutualistic. The host provides the bacteria with a stable shelter and temperature, and a supply of nutrients. In return, the bacteria provide the host with benefits including aid in digestion, production of certain vitamins, stimulation of the immune system, and competition against pathogens.

LESSON OBJECTIVES

- Name and describe structures, shapes, and sizes of a bacterial cell.
- Explain how bacteria obtain food, obtain energy, and reproduce.
- Describe the positive roles that bacteria play in the natural world.

Blended Path
Active learning using Student Edition, Inquiry Path, and Digital Path

ENGAGE AND EXPLORE

Teach this lesson using a variety of resources. Begin by reading **My Planet Diary** as a class. Have students discuss foods that are made with bacteria that keeps our bodies healthy. Then have students do the **Inquiry Warm-Up activity.** Students will model the rapid multiplication of bacterial cells. The **After the Inquiry Warm-Up worksheet** sets up a discussion about how quickly bacteria can reproduce. Have volunteers share their answers to question 4 whether they think there are more people or more bacteria on Earth.

EXPLAIN AND ELABORATE

Teach Key Concepts by explaining the structures of a typical bacteria cell: genetic material, cytoplasm, ribosomes, cell membrane, cell wall, and flagellum.

Teach Key Concepts by explaining that bacteria get energy by making food or eating other organisms and can reproduce asexually or sexually. **Lead a Discussion** about cellular respiration. Before beginning the **Apply It activity,** review how bacteria obtain food and carry on respiration. **Lead a Discussion** about the right conditions for bacteria to reproduce. **Lead a Discussion** about the purpose of endospore formation.

Teach Key Concepts by explaining that bacteria are involved in oxygen and food production as well as health maintenance, medicine production, and environmental cleanup and recycling. Have students practice the inquiry skill in the **Apply It activity. Lead a Discussion** about the value of bacteria. **Support the Big Q** by discussing how oil-eating bacteria have become very helpful in cleaning up oil and grease in many locations, such as those with major oil spills.

Hand out the **Key Concept Summaries** as a review of each part of the lesson. Students can also use the online **Vocab Flash Cards** to review key terms.

EVALUATE

Have students take the **Lesson Quiz.** For an alternate assessment, see the *ExamView*® Computer Test Generator, Progress Monitoring Assessments, or SuccessTracker™.

ELL Support

1 Content and Language

Pronounce and define aloud vocabulary terms for students. Suggest that they create a personal set of vocabulary flash cards, with each term and its definition on one side of an index card and a visual of the term on the other side.

Lab zone Inquiry Path
Hands-on learning in the Lab zone

Digital Path
Online learning at my science online.com

ENGAGE AND EXPLORE

To teach this lesson with an emphasis on inquiry, begin with the **Inquiry Warm-Up activity.** Students will model the rapid multiplication of bacterial cells. The **After the Inquiry Warm-Up worksheet** sets up a discussion about how quickly bacteria can reproduce. Have volunteers share their answers to question 4 telling whether they think there are more people or more bacteria on Earth.

EXPLAIN AND ELABORATE

Focus on the **Inquiry Skill** for the lesson. Remind students that predicting involves making an inference about a future event based on current evidence or past experience. What predictions could be made in the **Inquiry Warm-Up activity?** *(Sample: That bacteria would be able to increase their population in a short period of time)* Have students do the **Quick Lab** to observe, sketch, and classify the three main bacterial cell shapes.

Before beginning the **Apply It activity,** review the information about how bacteria obtain food and carry on respiration. **Build Inquiry** by having students design an experiment to show the conditions that bacteria need in order to grow. Do the **Lab Investigation** having students observe how well disinfectants control the growth of bacteria.

Before beginning the **Apply It activity,** review the information about how the production of oxygen relates to the sun. **Support the Big Q** by discussing how oil-eating bacteria have become very helpful in cleaning up oil and grease in many locations, such as those with major oil spills. **Build Inquiry** by giving students the opportunity to examine some modern ways to preserve food. Have students do the **Quick Lab** investigating the role of bacteria as decomposers. Students can use the online **Vocab Flash Cards** to review key terms.

EVALUATE

Have students take the **Lesson Quiz.** For an alternate assessment, see the *ExamView®* Computer Test Generator, Progress Monitoring Assessments, or SuccessTracker™.

ENGAGE AND EXPLORE

Teach this lesson using digital resources. Begin by having students learn more about bacteria and explore real-world connections to the benefits of bacteria at **My Planet Diary** online. Have them access the Chapter Resources to find the **Unlock the Big Question activity.** There they can answer the questions and refine their responses as they continue through the lesson. You can re-assign the activity and have students submit their work so you can track their progress.

EXPLAIN AND ELABORATE

Students reading above, at, or below the lexile measure of this lesson can access basic content readings at their level at **My Reading Web.** Encourage students to use the online **Vocab Flash Cards** to preview key terms. Have students do the **Quick Lab** to observe, sketch, and classify the three main bacterial cell shapes.

Assign the **Apply It activity** online and have students submit their work to you.

Assign the second **Apply It activity** online and have students submit their work to you. **Support the Big Q** by discussing how oil-eating bacteria have become very helpful in cleaning up oil and grease in many locations, such as those with major oil spills. Have students do the **Quick Lab** investigating the role of bacteria as decomposers. The **Key Concept Summaries** online allow students to read a summary and see an image associated with each part of the lesson. Online remediation is available at **My Science Coach.**

EVALUATE

Have students take the **Lesson Quiz.** For an alternate assessment, see the *ExamView®* Computer Test Generator, Progress Monitoring Assessments, or SuccessTracker™.

2 Frontload the Lesson

Have students create a word map graphic organizer by writing the vocabulary terms in the top box. As they read the chapter, they should fill in the bottom boxes with terms, phrases, or images associated with the vocabulary term.

3 Comprehensible Input

Have students use an outline to better understand the information in this lesson. Have them use the blue and red heads to organize the information in their outlines.

4 Language Production

Pair or group students with varied language abilities to complete labs collaboratively for language practice. Have each student copy the completed written lab for personal reference.

5 Assess Understanding

Ask students to make notes about Key Concepts in the lesson and use the notes to prepare an oral presentation of the concepts. Encourage students to use the visuals in the lesson to support their presentations.

Bacteria

Establish Learning Objectives

After this lesson, students will be able to:

- Name and describe structures, shapes, and sizes of a bacterial cell.
- Explain how bacteria obtain food, obtain energy, and reproduce.
- Describe the positive roles that bacteria play in the natural world.

Engage

Activate Prior Knowledge

MY PLANET DIARY Read *"Good" Germs* with the class. Explain that foods, such as yogurt, certain cereals, and smoothies, are made with different bacteria. Ask: **Do any of these foods have a "taste" of bacteria?** *(No)* **In what way do probiotics help to keep your body healthy?** *(Sample: Probiotics work inside your body to fight off harmful bacteria.)* **What word that is similar to *probiotics* has to do with fighting disease?** *(Antibiotics)*

BIG IDEAS OF SCIENCE REFERENCE LIBRARY DK
Have students look up the following topic: Bacteria.

Explore

Lab Resource: Inquiry Warm-Up Lab

L1 HOW QUICKLY CAN BACTERIA MULTIPLY?
Students will model the rapid multiplication of bacterial cells.

Bacteria

- What Are Bacteria?
- How Do Bacteria Get Food, Get Energy, and Reproduce?
- What Is the Role of Bacteria in Nature?

my planeT DiaRY

"Good" Germs

Misconception: All bacteria are harmful.

Many bacteria are harmless or even good for you! Your intestines are full of good bacteria. Some types of helpful bacteria, often called probiotics, are found in foods like yogurt, smoothies, and even cereal! Scientists have found that eating foods containing probiotics keeps you healthy. These foods put good bacteria into your body to help fight off the harmful bacteria that can cause disease.

MISCONCEPTION

Communicate Discuss these questions with a classmate. Write your answers below.

1. Why do people often think all bacteria are bad for you?

   Sample: Many bacteria can make you sick.

2. Can you think of some products you have used at home or at school to kill harmful bacteria?

   Sample: Antibacterial soaps, cleaning products, and hand sanitizers are used to kill bacteria.

▶ PLANET DIARY Go to **Planet Diary** to learn more about bacteria.

Lab zone Do the Inquiry Warm-Up *How Quickly Can Bacteria Multiply?*

What Are Bacteria?

They thrive in your cup of yogurt. They coat your skin and swarm inside your nose. You cannot escape them because they live almost everywhere—under rocks, in the ocean, and all over your body. In fact, there are more of these organisms in your mouth than there are people on Earth! You don't notice them because they are very small. These organisms are bacteria.

SUPPORT ALL READERS

Lexile Measure = 910L   Lexile Word Count = 2042

Prior Exposure to Content: Many students may have misconceptions on this topic

Academic Vocabulary: *compare, contrast, predict*

Science Vocabulary: *bacteria, cytoplasm, ribosome, flagellum*

Concept Level: Generally appropriate for most students in this grade

Preteach With: My Planet Diary "'Good' Germs" and Figure 1 activity

Go to **My Reading Web** to access leveled readings that provide a foundation for the content.

Vocabulary

- bacteria • cytoplasm • ribosome • flagellum
- cellular respiration • binary fission • conjugation
- endospore • pasteurization • decomposer

Skills

- Reading: Compare and Contrast
- Inquiry: Predict

Cell Structures Bacteria were first discovered in the late 1600s by a Dutch merchant named Anton von Leeuwenhoek (LAY vun hook). He made microscopes as a hobby. One day, while looking at scrapings of his teeth, he noticed small wormlike organisms. If Leeuwenhoek had owned a modern high-powered microscope, he would have seen that the single-celled organisms were **bacteria** (singular *bacterium*). **Bacteria are prokaryotes. The genetic material in their cells is not contained in a nucleus.** In addition to lacking a nucleus, the cells of bacteria also lack many other structures that are found in the cells of eukaryotes. Recall that eukaryotes include protists, fungi, and animals.

Figure 1 shows the structures in a typical bacterial cell. Most bacterial cells are surrounded by a rigid (cell wall) that protects the cell. Just inside the cell wall is the (cell membrane), which controls what materials pass in and out of the cell. The region inside the cell membrane, called the (cytoplasm) (SY toh plaz um), contains a gel-like fluid that moves structures throughout the cell. Located in the cytoplasm are tiny structures called (ribosomes) (RY bo sohmz), chemical factories where proteins are produced. The cell's genetic material, which looks like a tangled string, is also found in the cytoplasm. It contains the instructions for all of the cell's functions. A bacterial cell may also have a (flagellum) (fluh JEL um; plural *flagella*), a long, whiplike structure that helps a cell to move.

Bacteria as seen through Anton von Leeuwenhoek's microscope

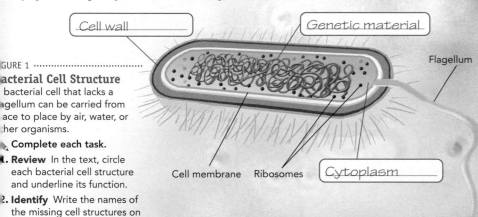

Cell wall

Genetic material

Flagellum

FIGURE 1 ....

Bacterial Cell Structure

A bacterial cell that lacks a flagellum can be carried from place to place by air, water, or other organisms.

Cell membrane   Ribosomes   Cytoplasm

▶ **Complete each task.**

1. **Review** In the text, circle each bacterial cell structure and underline its function.

2. **Identify** Write the names of the missing cell structures on the lines provided.

47

Explain

Introduce Vocabulary

To help students enrich their understanding of the term *bacteria*, tell them that this word did not enter the English language until 1884—and that its singular counterpart, *bacterium*, was coined about 1850. Point out that the relatively late arrival of these words in the English language indicate that before that time, scientists had not developed or refined their knowledge of this type of organism to the extent that they needed a word for it.

Teach Key Concepts

Explain to students that bacteria are prokaryotes. Ask: **How do prokaryotes differ from eukaryotes?** (*In eukaryotes, the genetic material in their cells is contained in a nucleus. In prokaryotes, the genetic material in their cells is not contained in a nucleus.*) **How many cells do bacteria have?** (*One*) **What surrounds a bacterial cell?** (*A cell membrane, and in most bacteria, also a cell wall*) **Where in the cell is a bacterium's genetic material?** (*In the cytoplasm*) **What happens in the tiny structures called *ribosomes*?** (*Proteins are produced there.*) **What is a flagellum?** (*A long, whiplike structure that helps a cell to move*) Point out that not all bacteria have the same structures. Some bacteria lack a cell wall, and many bacteria lack a flagellum.

My Planet Diary provides an opportunity for students to explore real-world connections to bacteria.

MY SCIENCE online.com | Describing Bacteria

E L L Support

1 Content and Language

Write *conjugation* on the board. This word comes from the Latin verb *jungere*, meaning "to join," and the prefix *con-* ("with" or "together"). So, *conjugation* is a process bacteria uses to join together to reproduce.

2 Frontload the Lesson

Ask students to recall when they spent days resting at home due to an illness such as a bacterial infection.

Tell students they will learn about positive and negative effects of bacteria.

3 Comprehensible Input

Provide students with materials such as yarn, clay, peppercorns, and small clear plastic bags, for making a model of the structure of a bacterial cell. Have them look at **Figure 1** and list appropriate materials to reflect the structures of bacterial cells.

Explain

Address Misconceptions

L1 **WHAT ARE BACTERIA?** Students who are accustomed to thinking of organisms as plants or animals may need extra help to understand that bacteria *are* organisms, but are *not* animals or plants. Ask: **What do bacteria have in common with animals?** *(They are alive; some are heterotrophs.)* **How are they different?** *(Bacteria are simple one-celled organisms; animals have many cells that are highly organized. Bacteria are prokaryotes; animals are eukaryotes.)* Tell students that, though bacteria are very small, they help sustain life on Earth.

Teach With Visuals

Tell students to look at **Figure 2.** Remind students that the three basic shapes of bacterial cells are spherical, rod-like, and spiral. Ask: **How do the three bacteria pictured fit into these basic categories?** *(Bacillus anthracis is shaped like a rod;* Leptospira interrogans *is spiral, and* Streptococcus thermophilus *is spherical.)* Students may recognize *Streptococcus* as the bacteria that cause strep throat. They may also have heard of staph infections. Explain that *Streptococcus* bacteria are spheres in a chain. *Staphylococcus* bacteria are spheres in a sheet. Make sure students understand that although both names include the word part *coccus,* they are different genera, each including many species.

Elaborate

Lab Resource: Quick Lab **Lab** zone

L1 **CLASSIFYING BACTERIA** Students will observe, sketch, and classify the three main bacterial cell shapes.

Evaluate

Assess Your Understanding

After students answer the questions, have them evaluate their understanding by completing the appropriate sentence.

RTI Response to Intervention

1a. If students have trouble identifying the cytoplasm, **then** have them review **Figure 1.**

b. If students cannot interpret the meaning of the name *Stella vacuolata,* **then** have them to review the *Key to Scientific Names* in **Figure 2.**

my science **coach** Have students go online for help in understanding the structures, shapes, and sizes of bacteria.

Cell Shapes If you were to look at bacteria under a microscope, you would notice that most bacterial cells have one of three basic shapes: spherical, rodlike, or spiral. The chemical makeup of the cell wall determines the shape of a bacterial cell. The shape of the cell helps scientists identify the type of bacteria.

Cell Sizes Bacteria vary greatly in size. The largest known bacterium is about as big as the period at the end of this sentence. An average bacterium, however, is much smaller. For example, the spherical strep throat bacteria are about 0.5 to 1 micrometer in diameter. A micrometer is one millionth of a meter.

FIGURE 2 ·····················

Bacteria Shapes and Names

Bacteria are sometimes named for their shape.

✎ **Classify** Use the key to match the scientific names in the word bank to the correct bacteria. Write your answers in the boxes.

Word Bank

Leptospira interrogans   Bacillus anthracis

Stella vacuolata   Streptococcus thermophilus

Leptospira interrogans

Streptococcus thermophilus

Key to Scientific Names

Stella: star

Spira: coil or spiral

Kokkos: sphere

Bacillus: rod

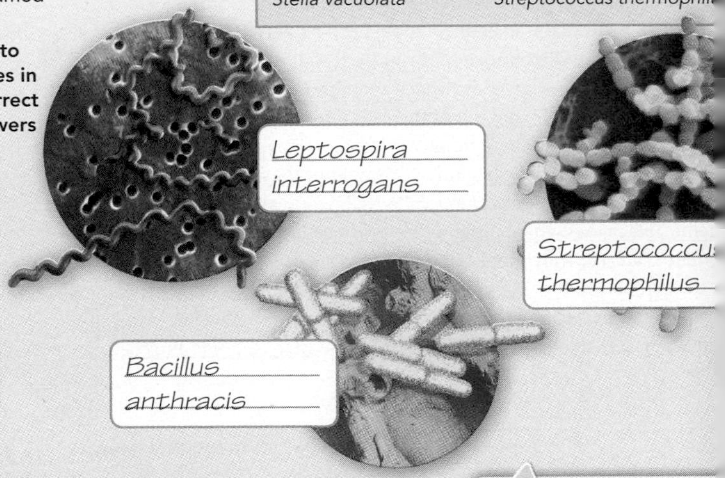

Bacillus anthracis

Lab® zone   Do the Quick Lab
Classifying Bacteria.

💬 Assess Your Understanding

1a. Identify Where is the genetic material located in a bacterial cell?

In the cytoplasm

b. Interpret Diagrams You are looking at a *Stella vacuolata* bacterium. What is its shape and how do you know?

Stella means "star" in Latin, so the bacterium is star shaped.

got it?

○ I get it! Now I know that bacteria are _____ prokaryotes that do not have genetic material in a nucleus.

○ I need extra help with See TE note.

Go to **my science** **coach** *online for help with this subject.*

How Do Bacteria Get Food, Get Energy, and Reproduce?

From the bacteria that live in soil to those that live in the pores of your skin, all bacteria need certain things to survive and reproduce. **Bacteria get energy by either making food or eating other organisms, and can reproduce asexually or sexually.**

Obtaining Food Some bacteria are autotrophs, meaning they make their own food. Some capture and use the sun's energy as plants do. Others, such as bacteria that live deep in mud, do not use the sun's energy. Instead, these bacteria use the energy from chemical substances in their environment to make their food.

Some bacteria are heterotrophs, and cannot make their own food. These bacteria must consume other organisms or the food that other organisms make. Heterotrophic bacteria consume a variety of foods—from milk and meat, which you might also eat, to decaying leaves on a forest floor.

✎

⊘ **Compare and Contrast** How do autotrophic and heterotrophic bacteria differ in the way they obtain food?

<u>Autotrophic bacteria</u>
<u>can make their own</u>
<u>food. Heterotrophic</u>
<u>bacteria consume</u>
<u>other organisms.</u>

Autotrophic bacteria

Hot springs ▲

Heterotrophic bacteria

FIGURE 3 ·····················

Obtaining Food
Autotrophic bacteria in hot springs use chemical energy to make food. Heterotrophic bacteria in compost get energy from decaying food.

Compost ▼

Explain ————

Teach Key Concepts 🔑

Explain to students that bacteria get energy by either making food or eating other organisms. Explain also that bacteria can reproduce asexually or sexually. Ask: **How do autotrophs get food?** *(They make their own food.)* **What different ways do autotrophic bacteria make their own food?** *(Capture energy from the sun, use energy from chemical substances in the environment)* **How do heterotrophs get food?** *(They eat other organisms or the food made by other organisms.)* **What are some foods that heterotrophic bacteria consume?** *(Milk, meat, decaying food, decaying leaves)*

⊘ **Compare and Contrast** Remind students that when they compare and contrast, they examine the similarities and differences between objects, processes, or events.

Elaborate ————

21st Century Learning

COMMUNICATION Have students investigate bacteria that live in hot springs like those found at Yellowstone National Park. Students should define the term *thermophile. (An organism that thrives in high temperatures, usually 45°C to 80°C.)* Challenge students to summarize the basic environmental conditions found in a hot spring. *(High temperatures, and sulfur-rich water)*

Differentiated Instruction

L1 Classify Bacteria by Shape Have students title three poster boards *spherical, rod-like,* and *spiral.* Then have them collect copies of photographs of these shapes of bacteria, and mount the images on the appropriate poster boards. Have reference books, scissors, and poster board available. Use the boards to review bacterial shapes.

L3 Research Bacteria Challenge students to research how various bacteria obtain food. Students might contrast how some autotrophs use photosynthesis to get food from the sun and give off oxygen, as plants do. Other autotrophs get their energy from chemical substances such as sulfur compounds.

Explain

Lead a Discussion

RESPIRATION Remind students that all living things need energy, and this energy is released from food in cells. Ask: **What is cellular respiration?** *(The process of breaking down food to release energy)* **In addition to food, what else do most bacteria need to carry out respiration?** *(Oxygen)* **Do all bacteria need oxygen? Explain.** *(No; for some bacteria, oxygen is poisonous.)* Tell students that bacteria that do not use oxygen for respiration do not have a substitute for oxygen. These bacteria carry out a simplified version of respiration, which produces less energy than the process carried out in the presence of oxygen. Although the lower energy yield is a disadvantage, being able to live without oxygen allows some species of bacteria to survive where their oxygen-dependent competitors cannot.

Address Misconceptions

RESPIRATION IS NOT BREATHING Because breathing is sometimes called respiration, as in *artificial respiration* or the *respiratory system*, students may confuse the two processes. Students may think that bacteria breathe because they carry out respiration. Explain that cellular respiration is a series of chemical reactions that take place in individual cells. In most organisms, this process requires oxygen. Many multicellular organisms, including humans, acquire oxygen by breathing. Unicellular organisms, such as bacteria, do not breathe. Oxygen enters the bacterial cell by diffusion, and carbon dioxide leaves the cell by diffusion.

Elaborate

Apply It!

L1 Before beginning the activity, review the information about how bacteria obtain food and carry on respiration. Encourage students to use this information as they fill in the first and second columns of the data table. Point out that students should look at the information in the first and third columns in order to draw conclusions about how to destroy each of the three types of bacteria. You might also point out that "Give oxygen" is another possible answer for how to destroy a bacterium that cannot survive in the presence of oxygen.

FIGURE 4

Bacteria Buffet
These bacteria break down pollutants in this biopile to get energy.

Respiration Like all organisms, bacteria need a constant supply of energy to carry out their functions. This energy comes from food. The process of breaking down food to release energy is called **cellular respiration.** Like many other organisms, most bacteria need oxygen to break down their food. But a few kinds of bacteria do not need oxygen for respiration. In fact, those bacteria die if oxygen is present in their surroundings. For them, oxygen is a poison that kills!

apply it!

Suppose you are a scientist studying disease-causing bacteria. You make a table that lists how the bacteria get energy and whether they need oxygen. One day, some of your data are accidentally erased.

❶ **Create Data Tables** Use what you know about bacteria to fill in the first two columns in the table.

❷ **Draw Conclusions** How would you destroy these dangerous bacteria? Use the information in the table to fill in the last column.

Food Source	Type of Bacterium	Need Oxygen?	How to Destroy
Decaying leaves	Heterotrophic	Yes	Deny oxygen
Sunlight	Autotrophic	No	Block sun
Chemicals	Autotrophic	No	Remove chemicals

Digital Lesson: Assign the *Apply It* activity online and have students submit their work to you.

my science online.com | **Bacteria Life Processes**

Reproduction One of the characteristics of living things is that they are able to reproduce, or make more copies of themselves. When bacteria have plenty of food, the right temperature, and other suitable conditions, they thrive and reproduce often. Bacteria can reproduce asexually or sexually.

FIGURE 5 ·······································

Bacterial Reproduction
Some bacteria are able to reproduce every 20 minutes.

✎ **Relate Text and Visuals** In the diagrams, label each reproductive process and answer the questions.

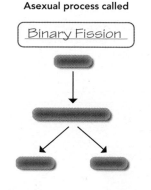
Bacteria undergoing conjugation

Asexual Reproduction
Bacteria sometimes reproduce asexually by a process called **binary fission,** in which one cell divides to form two identical cells. To prepare for binary fission, a bacterial cell grows to almost twice its size. Then it duplicates its genetic material and splits into two separate cells. Each new cell receives a complete copy of the parent's genetic material. As a result, the offspring are genetically identical to the parent. Binary fission increases the number of bacteria.

Asexual process called

Binary Fission

Why are all the bacteria the same color?

They are genetically identical.

Sexual Reproduction
Sometimes bacteria reproduce sexually by a process called **conjugation.** During conjugation, one bacterium transfers some of its genetic material into another bacterium through a thin, threadlike bridge. After the transfer, the bacteria separate. Conjugation results in bacteria with new combinations of genetic material. When the bacteria divide by binary fission, the new genetic material passes to the offspring. Conjugation does not increase the number of bacteria, as binary fission does. However, it does result in bacteria that are genetically different from the parent cells.

Sexual process called

Conjugation

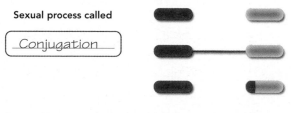

Why is the bacterium on the bottom right colored red and yellow?

It has a new combination of genetic material.

51

Lead a Discussion

THE RIGHT CONDITIONS Tell students that in order to reproduce, bacteria need suitable conditions, including sufficient food and the right temperature. Ask: **What are two types of reproduction in bacteria?** *(Asexual reproduction, sexual reproduction)* **Why does binary fission increase the number of bacteria?** *(Because each bacteria cell duplicates its genetic material and splits into two separate cells)* **How does conjugation differ from binary fission in an essential way?** *(Sample: Conjugation does not increase the number of bacteria; after conjugation, the two joined bacteria separate with new genetic composition.)*

21st Century Learning

CRITICAL THINKING Remind students that bacteria use different ways to reproduce. Ask: **What benefit is there in knowing how bacteria reproduce?** *(If we understand how bacteria reproduce, we can promote the growth of good bacteria and prevent the reproduction of harmful bacteria.)*

Teach With Visuals

Tell students to look at the diagram showing binary fission in **Figure 5.** Ask: **If you were to extend the diagram further, how many cells would appear in the next "generation"?** *(Four)* **What is a concise way to explain by how many the number of cells would increase every generation?** *(The number would double with every generation.)* Then have students look at the diagram showing conjugation. Ask: **After conjugation, does the number of bacteria change?** *(No)* **What is different about the bacteria after conjugation?** *(Their genetic makeup)* **How would this change affect offspring?** *(They would be made from the new combination of genetic material.)*

Differentiated Instruction

L1 Answer Questions Select a short passage from the text, such as *Asexual Reproduction.* Read the passage aloud to students as they follow along in their books. After reading, ask some questions about the passage. If students don't know the answers, challenge them to return to the passage to locate the relevant information.

L3 Research Reproduction Have especially capable students research different aspects of bacterial reproduction and write a report summarizing their findings. They could choose from sexual reproduction or asexual reproduction. Reports could also include some detailed information about binary fission or conjugation.

Explain

Lead a Discussion

ENDOSPORE FORMATION Remind students that conditions do not always favor the growth of bacteria. Ask: **What are some factors that can be unfavorable for bacterial growth?** *(The disappearance of sources of food, lack of water, extreme temperature changes)* **How can bacteria survive when conditions are not good enough for reproduction?** *(Endospores, which contain and protect genetic material, are produced by bacteria. Endospores can endure unfavorable conditions. Later, when conditions are favorable, endospores open up, and the bacteria can begin to grow and multiply.)*

Elaborate

Build Inquiry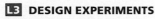

L3 DESIGN EXPERIMENTS

Materials beakers, dried beans, water

Time 20 minutes

Ask: **What do bacteria need to survive?** *(Food, energy, a favorable environment)* Tell students that they will design an experiment to show the conditions that bacteria need in order to grow. Students should formulate a hypothesis, have a control, and design a method of observing and recording results.

Lab Resource: Lab Investigation

L2 COMPARING DISINFECTANTS Students will observe how well disinfectants control the growth of bacteria.

Evaluate

Assess Your Understanding

After students answer the questions, have them evaluate their understanding by completing the appropriate sentence.

RTI Response to Intervention

2a. If students cannot name three ways bacteria get food, **then** have them reread the information about obtaining food.

b, c. If students need help explaining bacterial reproduction, **then** have them reread the section titled *Reproduction*.

MY SCIENCE COACH Have students go online for help in understanding how bacteria get food and energy and how they reproduce.

Endospore Formation Sometimes, conditions in the environment become unfavorable for the growth of bacteria. For example, food sources can disappear, water can dry up, or the temperature can fall or rise dramatically. Some bacteria can survive harsh conditions by forming endospores. An **endospore** is a small, rounded, thick-walled resting cell that forms inside a bacterial cell. It encloses the cell's genetic material and some of its cytoplasm.

Because endospores can resist freezing, heating, and drying, they can survive for many years in harsh conditions. Endospores are also light—a breeze can lift and carry them to new places. If an endospore lands in a place where conditions are suitable, it opens up. Then the bacterium can begin to grow and multiply.

FIGURE 6

Endospore Formation
The panels below illustrate endospore formation.

✎ **Sequence** Based on the reading, draw and label the last panel.

Increasing time

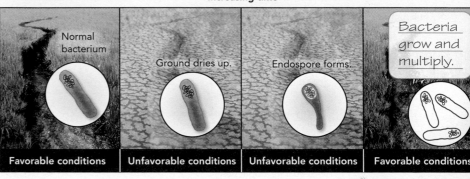

| Normal bacterium | Ground dries up. | Endospore forms. | Bacteria grow and multiply. |
| Favorable conditions | Unfavorable conditions | Unfavorable conditions | Favorable conditions |

Lab zone Do the Lab Investigation *Comparing Disinfectants.*

🔑 Assess Your Understanding

2a. Name What are three ways bacteria get food?
Make food using sunlight,
make food using chemicals,
or eat other organisms

b. Explain What are the steps of binary fission?
A bacterial cell duplicates its
genetic material and divides.

c. CHALLENGE Why might bacteria that undergo conjugation be better able to survive in unfavorable conditions?
These bacteria will contain
new combinations of genetic
material.

got it?

○ **I get it!** Now I know that bacteria get food and energy by *making food or eating other* *organisms* and reproduce *asexually or sexually.*

○ I need extra help with *See TE note.*

Go to **MY SCIENCE COACH** online for help with this subject.

52 Viruses, Bacteria, Protists, and Fungi

What Is the Role of Bacteria in Nature?

When you hear the word *bacteria*, you may think about getting sick. After all, strep throat, many ear infections, and other diseases are caused by bacteria. However, most bacteria are either harmless or helpful to people. In fact, in many ways, people depend on bacteria. **Bacteria are involved in oxygen and food production, in health maintenance and medicine production, and in environmental cleanup and recycling.**

Oxygen Production Would it surprise you to learn that the air you breathe depends in part on bacteria? As autotrophic bacteria use the sun's energy to produce food, they release oxygen into the air. Billions of years ago, Earth had very little oxygen. Scientists think that autotrophic bacteria were responsible for first adding oxygen to Earth's atmosphere. Today, the distant offspring of those bacteria help keep oxygen levels in the air stable.

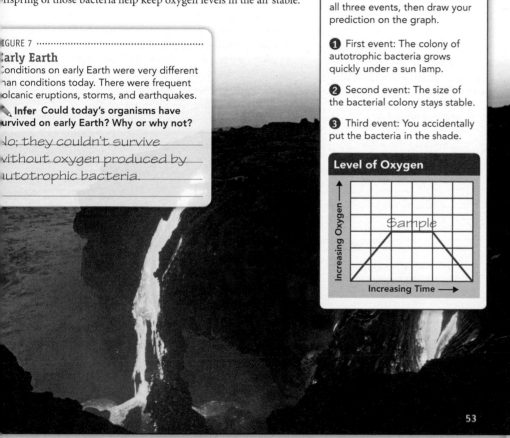

FIGURE 7 ··················

Early Earth
Conditions on early Earth were very different than conditions today. There were frequent volcanic eruptions, storms, and earthquakes.

✎ **Infer** Could today's organisms have survived on early Earth? Why or why not?

No; they couldn't survive without oxygen produced by autotrophic bacteria.

apply it!

✎ **Predict** Imagine you are growing a colony of autotrophic bacteria in the laboratory. What might happen to the level of oxygen as each of the three events listed below occurs? Read all three events, then draw your prediction on the graph.

❶ First event: The colony of autotrophic bacteria grows quickly under a sun lamp.

❷ Second event: The size of the bacterial colony stays stable.

❸ Third event: You accidentally put the bacteria in the shade.

Level of Oxygen

Increasing Oxygen →

Sample

Increasing Time →

53

Explain

Teach Key Concepts

Explain to students that bacteria are involved in oxygen and food production. Point out that they are also involved in health maintenance, medicine production, and environmental cleanup and recycling. Ask: **What kind of bacteria produce oxygen?** *(Autotrophic bacteria)* **How does this oxygen production occur?** *(During the process of using the sun's energy to produce food, autotrophic bacteria release oxygen into the environment.)* **Why might humans be grateful for the existence of autotrophic bacteria?** *(Sample: Scientists think that autotrophic bacteria were responsible for adding oxygen to Earth's atmosphere, which billions of years ago was extremely lacking in oxygen. Without such oxygen, human beings would not have been able to survive on the planet.)*

Elaborate

Apply It!

L1 Before beginning the activity, review the information about how the production of oxygen relates to the sun. Note that students may draw a version of the graph that differs from the sample answer. They may infer that in the second event, the level of oxygen will continue to climb at a similar rate as in the first event. In this case, their diagram should reflect this continuing diagonal line rather than the horizontal line of the sample. The line would begin to descend at event 3. Both this answer and the sample answer are correct, as long as students show a decrease in oxygen in the third event.

△ **Predict** Remind students that predicting involves making an inference about a future event based on current evidence or past experience.

Digital Lesson: Assign the *Apply It* activity online and have students submit their work to you.

Differentiated Instruction

L1 Cells Within Cells Help students understand the concept of endospore formation by having them look again at **Figure 6.** Encourage students to describe the differences between the bacterium in the second frame and the one in the third frame. Suggest that the phrase "a cell within a cell" is a helpful way to think of the formation of an endospore.

L3 Helpful and/or Harmful Invite pairs or small groups of students to prepare Venn diagrams that compare and contrast harmful bacteria with helpful bacteria. Encourage students to use the names of specific bacteria whenever possible, as well as words and phrases that characterize their essential effects.

Explain

Lead a Discussion

THE VALUE OF BACTERIA Remind students that bacteria can be both helpful and harmful. Ask: **What are some negative ways that bacteria can affect food?** (*Some kinds of bacteria cause food to spoil.*) **How did Louis Pasteur help to prevent harmful bacteria from growing in food?** (*Pasteur invented the process of pasteurization, heating food to a temperature high enough to kill most harmful bacteria.*) **How are bacteria beneficial as decomposers in the soil?** (*As decomposers, bacteria in soil break down dead organisms, returning small, simple chemicals to the environment for other living things to reuse.*)

Support the Big Q ? UbD

ENVIRONMENTAL CLEANUP Tell students that some oil spills are cleaned up by using a substance that contains *Ochrobactrum anthropi*, bacteria that break down oil and convert it to harmless substances. Explain that oil-eating bacteria have become very helpful in cleaning up oil and grease in many locations, such as those with major oil spills. Ask: **What are some other ways these bacteria might be useful?** (*Samples: Substances containing oil-eating or grease-eating bacteria are now sold for cleaning driveways, parking lots, and even household drains.*)

21st Century Learning 📖 DK

INFORMATION LITERACY Have students read *Bacteria* in the **Big Ideas of Science Reference Library** and work in small groups to find out more about the bacteria that live in the human digestive system. Groups can summarize their findings in short multimedia presentations.

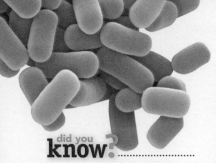

did you know?

Did you know that one to two kilograms of your body weight are bacteria in your digestive system? Up to 1,000 species of bacteria are crowded into your stomach and intestines.

FIGURE 8 ....

> ART IN MOTION **Bacteria and the Environment**
The *Deinococcus* bacteria pictured are named for their spherical shape.

✏ **Summarize** Fill in this graphic organizer to summarize the role of bacteria in nature.

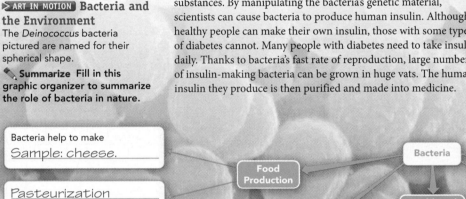

Bacteria help to make
Sample: cheese.

Pasteurization
delays spoiling in milk and juice.

Bacteria can help plants by
converting nitrogen in the air into products plants need to grow.

Food Production

Environmental Recycling

Bacteria that break down dead organisms are
decomposers.

Bacteria

Health and Medicine

Bacteria are used to make large amounts of medicine because
they reproduce quickly.

Food Production Do you like cheese, sauerkraut, or pickles? The activities of helpful bacteria produce all of these foods and more. For example, bacteria that grow in milk produce dairy products such as buttermilk, yogurt, sour cream, and cheeses.

However, some bacteria cause food to spoil when they break down the food's chemicals. Spoiled food usually smells or tastes foul and can make you very sick. Refrigerating and heating foods are two ways to slow down food spoilage. Another method, called pasteurization, is most often used to treat beverages such as milk and juice. During **pasteurization,** the food is heated to a temperature that is high enough to kill most harmful bacteria without changing the taste of the food. As you might have guessed, this process was named after Louis Pasteur, its inventor.

Health and Medicine Did you know that many of the bacteria living in your body actually keep you healthy? In your digestive system, for example, your intestines teem with bacteria. Some help you digest your food. Some make vitamins that your body needs. Others compete for space with disease-causing organisms. They prevent the harmful bacteria from attaching to your intestines and making you sick.

Scientists use certain bacteria to make medicines and other substances. By manipulating the bacteria's genetic material, scientists can cause bacteria to produce human insulin. Although healthy people can make their own insulin, those with some types of diabetes cannot. Many people with diabetes need to take insulin daily. Thanks to bacteria's fast rate of reproduction, large numbers of insulin-making bacteria can be grown in huge vats. The human insulin they produce is then purified and made into medicine.

54 Viruses, Bacteria, Protists, and Fungi

Professional Development Note — Teacher to Teacher

The Role of Bacteria An activity that illustrates the role of bacteria in environmental recycling and cleanup is a compost pile. With my students, I use a quick compost method that is finished within 3 weeks. This method requires all plants to be shredded before being composted. The proper ratio of carbon to nitrogen, adequate moisture and ventilation, along with an injection of bacteria in a few well-placed shovels of soil will encourage quick decomposition. Students are amazed that so many plants are changed by bacteria into rich, black soil in such a short time.

✏ *James Kuhl*
Central Square Middle School
Central Square, New York

Environmental Cleanup Some bacteria help to clean up Earth's land and water. Certain bacteria can convert the poisonous chemicals in oil into harmless substances. Scientists have put these bacteria to work cleaning up oil spills in oceans and gasoline leaks in the soil under gas stations.

Environmental Recycling Do you recycle? So do bacteria! Some bacteria that live in soil are **decomposers**—organisms that break down large, complex chemicals in dead organisms into small, simple chemicals.

Decomposers are "nature's recyclers." They return basic chemicals to the environment for other living things to reuse. For example, in autumn, the leaves of many trees die and drop to the ground. Decomposing bacteria spend the next months breaking down the chemicals in the dead leaves. The broken-down chemicals mix with the soil and can then be absorbed by the roots of nearby plants.

Another type of recycling bacteria, called nitrogen-fixing bacteria, help plants survive. Nitrogen-fixing bacteria live in the roots of certain plants, such as peanuts, peas, and soybeans. These helpful bacteria change nitrogen gas from the air into nitrogen products that plants need to grow. Plants are unable to make this conversion on their own. Therefore, nitrogen-fixing bacteria are vital to the plants' survival.

Bacteria are able to convert poisons into harmless substances.

Environmental cleanup

Oxygen production

Bacteria help provide oxygen for breathing.

 Do the Quick Lab
Drawing Conclusions.

Assess Your Understanding

3a. Review How can certain bacteria in food make you sick?

They cause food to spoil.

b. List A friend says that all bacteria are harmful to people. List three reasons this statement is incorrect.

Sample: Bacteria make medicine, clean up oil spills, and decompose dead organisms.

c. Relate Cause and Effect How would life on Earth change if all autotrophic bacteria died off?

Oxygen in the atmosphere would decrease, so living things might not survive.

d. Apply Concepts How can bacteria acting as decomposers help plants grow?

They break down chemicals in dead organisms that can then be absorbed by plants.

got it?

○ I get it! Now I know that the role of bacteria in nature includes _producing oxygen and food, maintaining health, producing medicine, cleaning up the environment, and recycling._

○ I need extra help with _See TE note._

Go to **MY SCIENCE COACH** online for help with this subject.

55

Differentiated Instruction

L1 Helpful Bacteria have students work in pairs or small groups to solidify their understanding of information about the positive aspects and uses of bacteria. Encourage students to list one or two facts or details relating to how bacteria are involved in the following processes: oxygen production, food production, environmental cleanup, health maintenance, and the production of medicine.

L3 Bacteria and Foods of the World Challenge students to do historical research on how some cultures have used bacteria to preserve foods. For example, ancient Egyptians made cheese after letting bacteria feed on the sugars in milk. Sourdough bread was first created using bacteria around 1850 in California.

Elaborate

Build Inquiry Lab

L3 FOOD PREPARATION AND SPOILAGE PREVENTION

Materials empty boil-in bags, bottles, cans, freezer packages, jars, and other containers from a variety of prepared foods with labels included

Time 20 minutes

Prior to the activity, ask students to bring in various clean and empty food packages. Tell students that they will examine some modern ways to preserve food. Organize students into groups, and provide each group with two or three packages.

CAUTION: *Be sure packaging materials are clean, and students wash hands after handling materials.*

Challenge students to draw conclusions about food preparation and spoilage prevention. Ask them to infer how each spoilage-prevention method inhibits the growth of bacteria. Have a reporter from each group share findings with the class.

Lab Resource: Quick Lab

L2 DRAWING CONCLUSIONS Students will investigate the role of bacteria as decomposers.

Evaluate

Assess Your Understanding

After students answer the questions, have them evaluate their understanding by completing the appropriate sentence.

RTI Response to Intervention

3a, b. If students need help explaining the effects of bacteria, **then** have them scan the sections in *What Is the Role of Bacteria in Nature?*

c. If students have difficulty explaining the effect of autotrophic bacteria dying off, **then** urge them to reread about oxygen production.

d. If students need help explaining how bacteria can aid the growth of plants, **then** help them review the information about environmental recycling.

MY SCIENCE COACH Have students go online for help in understanding the role of bacteria in nature.

Art in Motion allows students to explore some of the benefits of bacteria.

 Bacteria in Nature

Lab zone After the Inquiry Warm-Up

Bacteria

Inquiry Warm-Up, *How Quickly Can Bacteria Multiply?*
In the Inquiry Warm-Up, you investigated how quickly bacteria can reproduce. Using what you learned from that activity, answer the questions below.

1. **INFER** Why would being able to reproduce quickly be advantageous to an organism? Explain.

_____

_____

2. **INFER** How could an organism able to reproduce quickly be dangerous to other organisms? Explain.

_____

_____

3. **INFER** Would it be harder for your body to fight off an infection from an organism that reproduced quickly or one that reproduced slowly? Explain.

_____

_____

_____

4. **DRAWING CONCLUSIONS** Based on the results you observed in the lab, do you think there are more people or more bacteria on Earth? Explain.

_____

_____

_____

Assess Your Understanding

Bacteria

What Are Bacteria?

1a. IDENTIFY Where is the genetic material located in a bacterial cell?

_____

b. INTERPRET DIAGRAMS You are looking at a *Stella vacuolata* bacterium. What is its shape and how do you know?

_____

_____

got it? ···

○ **I get it!** Now I know that bacteria are _____

_____

○ **I need extra help with** _____

How Do Bacteria Get Food, Get Energy, and Reproduce?

2a. NAME What are three ways bacteria get food?

_____

_____

b. EXPLAIN What are the steps of binary fission?

_____

_____

c. CHALLENGE Why might bacteria that undergo conjugation be better able to survive in unfavorable conditions?

_____

_____

got it? ···

○ **I get it!** Now I know that bacteria get food and energy by _____

and reproduce _____

_____

○ **I need extra help with** _____

Assess Your Understanding

Bacteria

What Is the Role of Bacteria in Nature?

3a. REVIEW How can certain bacteria in food make you sick?

_____

_____

b. LIST A friend says that all bacteria are harmful to people. List three reasons why this statement is incorrect.

_____

_____

_____

_____

c. RELATE CAUSE AND EFFECT How would life on Earth change if all autotrophic bacteria died off?

_____

_____

_____

_____

d. APPLY CONCEPTS How can bacteria acting as decomposers help plants grow?

_____

_____

_____

_____

got it? ....

○ **I get it!** Now I know that the role of bacteria in nature includes _____

_____

_____

_____

○ **I need extra help with** _____

_____

Bacteria

What Are Bacteria?

Bacteria live almost everywhere—under rocks, in the ocean, in the human body. **Bacteria are prokaryotes. The genetic material in their cells is not contained in a nucleus.** The cells lack many structures found in the cells of eukaryotes. Most bacterial cells are surrounded by a cell wall. Inside the cell wall, the cell membrane controls what materials pass in and out of the cell. Inside the cell membrane, the **cytoplasm** contains a gel-like material and tiny structures called **ribosomes,** chemical factories where proteins are produced. A bacterial cell may have a **flagellum,** a long, whip-like structure that helps it move. Most bacterial cells are spherical, rod-like, or spiral. The cell wall's chemical makeup determines the bacterial cell's shape. An average bacterium is smaller than a period.

How Do Bacteria Get Food, Get Energy, and Reproduce?

Bacteria get energy by either making food or eating other organisms, and can reproduce asexually or sexually. Some bacteria make food using the sun's energy or chemicals in their environment. Some bacteria consume other organisms or the food of those organisms, such as milk, meat, or decayed leaves. The process of breaking down food to release energy is called **cellular respiration.** With plenty of food and suitable conditions, bacteria thrive and reproduce. Sometimes bacteria reproduce asexually through **binary fission,** when one cell divides to form two identical cells. Sometimes bacteria reproduce sexually through **conjugation,** when one bacterium transfers some of its genetic material into another bacterium. Some bacteria can survive harsh conditions by forming **endospores,** small, rounded, thick-walled resting cells that form inside a bacterial cell.

What Is the Role of Bacteria in Nature?

Though some infections and diseases are caused by bacteria, most bacteria are harmless or helpful to people. **Bacteria are involved in oxygen and food production, in health maintenance and medicine production, and in environmental cleanup and recycling.** Bacteria release oxygen into the air. The activities of bacteria produce a variety of foods. **Pasteurization** is a method of slowing down food spoilage by heating food to a temperature that is high enough to kill most harmful bacteria without changing the taste of the food. Bacteria inside the body help digestion and make vitamins. Scientists use bacteria to make medicines and other helpful substances. Bacteria are used to clean up Earth's land and water. Some bacteria that live in soil are **decomposers**—organisms that break down large, complex chemicals in dead organisms into small, simple chemicals.

On a separate sheet of paper, explain how bacteria can help people as well as how they can harm people.

Review and Reinforce

Bacteria

Understanding Main Ideas
Answer the following questions on a separate sheet of paper.

1. How are bacterial cells different from the cells of eukaryotes?
2. List four ways that bacteria are helpful to people.

Building Vocabulary
Match each term with its definition by writing the letter of the correct definition in the right column on the line beside the term in the left column.

3. ___ bacteria

4. ___ cytoplasm

5. ___ ribosomes

6. ___ flagellum

7. ___ cellular respiration

8. ___ binary fission

9. ___ conjugation

10. ___ endospore

11. ___ pasteurization

12. ___ decomposers

a. tiny structures that produce proteins inside bacteria

b. a process by which bacteria reproduce asexually

c. organisms that break down large, complex chemicals in dead organisms into small, simple chemicals

d. the region inside the cell membrane of a bacterium

e. a process by which bacteria reproduce sexually

f. the process of breaking down food to release energy

g. tiny single-celled organisms that live almost everywhere

h. a method of slowing down food spoilage

i. a small, rounded, thick-walled resting cell inside a bacterial cell

j. a whip-like structure that helps a bacterial cell to move

Enrich

Bacteria

> The table below shows the characteristics of some bacteria. Read the passage below and study the table. Then use a separate sheet of paper to answer the questions that follow.

Identifying Bacteria

Thousands of different kinds of bacteria inhabit Earth. Each kind can be distinguished from the others by its characteristics. In addition to shape, these characteristics include: whether it will grow in water hotter than 45°C; whether it will grow in very salty water; whether it will grow in the presence of air; whether it will grow without air; and whether it forms endospores.

Scientists who study bacteria use these and about 15 other characteristics to identify a bacterium. In the table below, a plus (+) sign means the bacterium has the characteristic. A minus (−) sign means the bacterium does not have the characteristic.

Bacterium	Rod	Sphere	Grows at 45°C	Grows in 6.5% Salt Water	Grows in Air	Grows Without Air	Endospores
1	+	−	+	unknown	+	+	+
2	+	−	+	unknown	−	+	+
3	−	+	−	+	+	+	−
4	+	−	+	−	−	+	−
5	−	+	−	−	+	+	−
6	−	+	+	−	+	+	−

1. What characteristic do all of the bacteria have in common?
2. How could you distinguish bacterium 1 from bacterium 2?
3. Which bacteria might be found in hot springs?
4. What characteristic(s) can you use to distinguish the spherical bacteria from one another?
5. Sea water is about 3.5% salt. In some places, sea water gets trapped when the tide goes out. The heat of the sun will cause some of this water to evaporate. Which bacteria are most likely to survive in such water? Explain your answer.

Lesson Quiz

Bacteria

Fill in the blank to complete each statement.

1. Some bacteria _____ other organisms or the food of those organisms.

2. Tiny structures called _____ produce proteins inside bacteria.

3. Scientists use bacteria to make _____.

4. Autotrophic bacteria release _____ into the air.

5. _____ is a method of slowing down food spoilage.

If the statement is true, write *true*. If the statement is false, change the underlined word or words to make the statement true.

6. _____ Bacteria are <u>eukaryotes</u>.

7. _____ Bacteria live almost everywhere, <u>excluding</u> in the ocean and in the human body.

8. _____ Some bacteria get <u>energy</u> by eating other organisms.

9. _____ <u>All</u> bacteria reproduce asexually.

10. _____ Most bacteria are <u>harmless or helpful</u> to people.

Bacteria

Answer Key

After the Inquiry Warm-Up

1. Answers will vary. Sample: They are able to increase their population in a short period of time.

2. Answers will vary. Sample: They can overwhelm other organisms with their numbers.

3. Answers will vary. Sample: It would be more difficult to fight off an infection from an organism that reproduced quickly because there would be more of them in a shorter period of time to fight off.

4. Answers will vary. Sample: There must be more bacteria than people on Earth because bacteria reproduce much quicker than people do.

Lesson Summaries

Some bacteria can harm people by causing infections and diseases. However, most bacteria are harmless, and many are helpful to people. Bacteria release oxygen into the air. Bacteria inside the body help digestion and make vitamins. People use the activities of bacteria to produce certain foods and medicines and to clean up Earth's land and water. Some bacteria in soil decompose large, complex chemicals in dead organisms into small, simple chemicals.

Review and Reinforce

1. Bacteria are prokaryotes. Their genetic material is not contained within nuclei. Eukaryotes have their genetic material in the nuclei.

2. Samples: Bacteria provide oxygen, food products, environmental recycling, medicines, help with human digestion and disease prevention.

3. g
4. d
5. a
6. j
7. f
8. b
9. e
10. i
11. h
12. c

Enrich

1. All can grow without air.

2. Bacterium 1 can grow in air. Bacterium 2 cannot grow in air.

3. 1, 2, 4, 6

4. growth at 45°C and growth in 6.5% salt water

5. Bacterium 3 is most likely to survive since it can grow in 6.5% salt water. Evaporation will increase the saltiness of the water to a concentration above which bacteria 4, 5, and 6 cannot survive. However, the sun might warm the water to a temperature that bacteria 3 could not tolerate.

Lesson Quiz

1. consume
2. ribosomes
3. medicines
4. oxygen
5. Pasteurization
6. prokaryotes
7. including
8. true
9. Some
10. true

Protists

How are living things other than plants and animals important to earth?

Lesson Pacing: 2–3 periods or 1–1½ blocks

🕐 **SHORT ON TIME?** To do this lesson in approximately half the time, do the Activate Prior Knowledge activity on page 56. A discussion of the Key Concepts on pages 57, 61, and 64 will familiarize students with the lesson content. Have students do the Quick Labs. The rest of the lesson can be completed by students independently.

Preference Navigator, in the online Planning tools, allows you to customize *Interactive Science* to your own teaching style. You can also edit lesson plans by selecting the Lesson Planner option.

Digital Teacher's Edition allows you to access your Teacher's Edition and Resource materials online.

MY SCIENCE online.com

Lesson Vocabulary

- protist • protozoan • pseudopod • contractile vacuole
- cilia • algae • pigment • spore

 Content Refresher

Diversity of Protists It is probably easier to describe what protists are not rather than what they are. A protist is a eukaryote that is not an animal, plant, or fungus. The traditional approach is to group these hard-to-classify organisms under one kingdom—Protista. However, protists are so incredibly varied that many taxonomists debate whether a kingdom Protista still makes sense. There are currently 30 to 40 phyla of protists recognized by most taxonomists. However, the groups are so different from one another that some biologists have proposed classifying protists into several kingdoms. This idea is supported by recent comparisons of cell physiology, DNA, and ribosomal RNA sequences. At present, there are many unanswered questions about the protists; the evolutionary history of many of the groups is unclear. Therefore, many people still adopt the traditional classification of protists as one kingdom.

An informal way to classify protists, which does not reflect their evolutionary histories, is according to the way they obtain nutrition. The three nutritional categories are animal-like protists, plant-like protists, and fungus-like protists, based on characteristics they share with animals, plants, and fungi.

LESSON OBJECTIVES

📖 Describe the characteristics of animal-like protists and give examples.

📖 Describe the characteristics of plant-like protists and give examples.

📖 Describe characteristics of fungus-like protists and give examples.

Blended Path
Active learning using Student Edition, Inquiry Path, and Digital Path

ENGAGE AND EXPLORE

Teach this lesson using a variety of resources. Begin by reading **My Planet Diary** as a class. Have students discuss the method by which malaria is spread. Then have students do the **Inquiry Warm-Up activity.** Students will draw organisms they observe in a drop of pond water under a microscope. The **After the Inquiry Warm-Up worksheet** sets up a discussion about microscopic organisms in a drop of pond water. Have volunteers share their answers to question 4 telling why it was necessary to wash their hands at the end of the lab.

EXPLAIN AND ELABORATE

Teach Key Concepts by explaining that animal-like protists are heterotrophs, and most can move to get food. **Lead a Discussion** about protists' characteristics and the three categories used to classify protists. Then **Lead a Discussion** about plasmodium. Have students practice the inquiry skill in the **Apply It activity.**

Teach Key Concepts by explaining that plant-like protists are autotrophs, can be unicellular or multicellular, and use pigments to capture the sun's energy. **Lead a Discussion** about two examples of algae: euglenoids and dinoflagellates. **Support the Big Q** by explaining the vital roles of algae.

Teach Key Concepts by explaining that fungus-like protists are heterotrophs, have cell walls, and use spores to reproduce.

Hand out the **Key Concept Summaries** as a review of each part of the lesson. Students can also use the online **Vocab Flash Cards** to review key terms.

EVALUATE

Have students take the **Lesson Quiz.** For an alternate assessment, see the *ExamView*® Computer Test Generator, Progress Monitoring Assessments, or SuccessTracker™.

ELL Support

1 Content and Language

Have students copy the vocabulary terms into a journal or personal glossary. Then ask them to find the first time the words are used in the chapter. Have them copy the definition of each vocabulary term into their journal or personal glossary.

DIFFERENTIATED INSTRUCTION KEY
L1 Struggling Students or Special Needs
L2 On-Level Students **L3** Advanced Students

LESSON PLANNER 2.3

Lab zone Inquiry Path
Hands-on learning in the Lab zone

Digital Path
Online learning at my science online.com

ENGAGE AND EXPLORE

To teach this lesson with an emphasis on inquiry, begin with the **Inquiry Warm-Up activity.** Students will draw organisms they observe in a drop of pond water under a microscope. The **After the Inquiry Warm-Up worksheet** sets up a discussion about microscopic organisms in a drop of pond water. Have volunteers share their answers to question 4 telling why it was necessary to wash their hands at the end of the lab.

EXPLAIN AND ELABORATE

Focus on the **Inquiry Skill** for the lesson. Remind students that a graph can be an effective tool for analyzing data. A graph can show trends and make it easier to make comparisons. What information from the **Inquiry Warm-Up activity** could be graphed to make it easier to understand? *(Sample: The numbers of various microscopic organisms in the drop of pond water)* Use the **Build Inquiry** to challenge small groups to design models of one protozoan from the four groups shown in **Figures 2–5.** Before beginning the **Apply It activity,** review the paragraph under the heading *Protozoans with Pseudopods.* Have students do the **Quick Lab** observing an amoeba's shape, size, and motion.

Support the Big Q by explaining the vital roles of algae. **Build Inquiry** by directing students to make a "living" model of how algae of various sizes take in food and eliminate waste. Have students do the **Quick Lab** predicting and observing the response of euglena to light.

Have students do the **Quick Lab** using a microscope to observe how slime molds react to oatmeal. Students can use the online **Vocab Flash Cards** to review key terms.

EVALUATE

Have students take the **Lesson Quiz.** For an alternate assessment, see the *ExamView®* Computer Test Generator, Progress Monitoring Assessments, or SuccessTracker™.

ENGAGE AND EXPLORE

Teach this lesson using digital resources. Begin by having students learn and explore real-world connections to protists at **My Planet Diary** online. Have them access the Chapter Resources to find the **Unlock the Big Question activity.** There they can answer the questions and refine their responses as they continue through the lesson. You can re-assign the activity and have students submit their work so you can track their progress.

EXPLAIN AND ELABORATE

Students reading above, at, or below the lexile measure of this lesson can access basic content readings at their level at **My Reading Web.** Encourage students to use the online **Vocab Flash Cards** to preview key terms. Use the **Interactive Art activity** online to allow students to explore protozoans. Assign the **Apply It activity** online and have students submit their work to you. Have students do the **Quick Lab** observing an amoeba's shape, size, and motion.

Support the Big Q by explaining the vital roles of algae. Have students do the **Quick Lab** predicting and observing the response of euglena to light.

Assign the **Do the Math activity** online and have students submit their work to you. Have students do the **Quick Lab** using a microscope to observe how slime molds react to oatmeal. The **Key Concept Summaries** online allow students to read a summary and see an image associated with each part of the lesson. Online remediation is available at **My Science Coach.**

EVALUATE

Have students take the **Lesson Quiz.** For an alternate assessment, see the *ExamView®* Computer Test Generator, Progress Monitoring Assessments, or SuccessTracker™.

2 Frontload the Lesson
Preview the lesson with students by calling attention to titles, visuals, captions, and vocabulary terms. Then, have students predict what they think the lesson will be about. Make sure that students confirm their predictions as they read the lesson.

3 Comprehensible Input
Have students create a T-chart titled Animal-Like Protists and list the characteristics of animal-like protists on the one side of the chart and examples on the other. Repeat with plant-like and fungus-like protists.

4 Language Production
Pair or group students with varied language abilities to complete labs collaboratively for language practice. Have each student copy the completed written lab for personal reference.

5 Assess Understanding
Ask students to make notes about Key Concepts in the lesson and use the notes to prepare an oral presentation of the concepts. Encourage students to use the visuals in the lesson to support their presentations.

Protists

Establish Learning Objectives

After this lesson, students will be able to:

🔑 Describe the characteristics of animal-like protists and give examples.

🔑 Describe the characteristics of plant-like protists and give examples.

🔑 Describe the characteristics of fungus-like protists and give examples.

Engage

Activate Prior Knowledge

MY PLANET DIARY Read *Dancin' for a Cause* with the class. Point out that malaria is most common in regions of tropical and subtropical climates, such as much of Africa, South and Southeast Asia, and the northern half of South America. Ask: **Why does the method by which malaria is spread make the disease especially difficult to control?** *(The movements of mosquitoes are hard to control.)*

BIG IDEAS OF SCIENCE REFERENCE LIBRARY 📖
Have students look up the following topic: Red Tide.

Explore

Lab Resource: Inquiry Warm-Up 🧪

L1 **WHAT LIVES IN A DROP OF POND WATER?**
Students will draw organisms they observe in a drop of pond water under a microscope.

---

3 Protists

🔓 UNLOCK THE BIG ❓

🔑 **What Are the Characteristics of Animal-Like Protists?**

🔑 **What Are the Characteristics of Plant-Like Protists?**

🔑 **What Are the Characteristics of Fungus-Like Protists?**

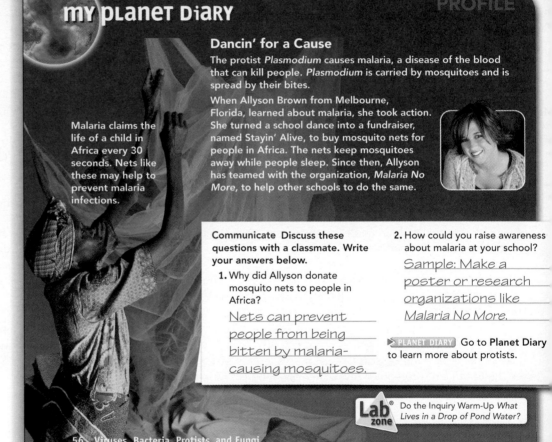

my planet DiaRy

PROFILE

Dancin' for a Cause

The protist *Plasmodium* causes malaria, a disease of the blood that can kill people. *Plasmodium* is carried by mosquitoes and is spread by their bites.

When Allyson Brown from Melbourne, Florida, learned about malaria, she took action. She turned a school dance into a fundraiser, named Stayin' Alive, to buy mosquito nets for people in Africa. The nets keep mosquitoes away while people sleep. Since then, Allyson has teamed with the organization, *Malaria No More*, to help other schools to do the same.

Malaria claims the life of a child in Africa every 30 seconds. Nets like these may help to prevent malaria infections.

Communicate Discuss these questions with a classmate. Write your answers below.

1. Why did Allyson donate mosquito nets to people in Africa?

   Nets can prevent people from being bitten by malaria-causing mosquitoes.

2. How could you raise awareness about malaria at your school?

   Sample: Make a poster or research organizations like Malaria No More.

▶ PLANET DIARY Go to **Planet Diary** to learn more about protists.

🧪 Lab zone
Do the Inquiry Warm-Up *What Lives in a Drop of Pond Water?*

56 Viruses, Bacteria, Protists, and Fungi

SUPPORT ALL READERS
Lexile Measure = 900L   **Lexile Word Count = 2066**

Prior Exposure to Content: Many students may have misconceptions on this topic

Academic Vocabulary: *graph, summarize*

Science Vocabulary: *protist, protozoan, cilia, algae, spore*

Concept Level: Generally appropriate for most students in this grade

Preteach With: My Planet Diary "Dancin' for a Cause" and Figure 1 activity

Go to **My Reading Web** to access leveled readings that provide a foundation for the content.

my science online

Vocabulary
• protist • protozoan • pseudopod
• contractile vacuole • cilia • algae
• pigment • spore

Skills
⟳ Reading: Summarize
△ Inquiry: Graph

What Are the Characteristics of Animal-Like Protists?

The beautiful and diverse organisms in **Figure 1** below are protists. **Protists** are eukaryotes that cannot be classified as animals, plants, or fungi. The word that best describes protists is *diverse.* For example, most protists are unicellular, but some are multicellular. Some are heterotrophs, some are autotrophs, and others are both. Some protists cannot move, while others zoom around their habitats. However, all protists are eukaryotes, and all protists live in moist surroundings. Recall that eukaryotes are cells in which the genetic material is contained in a nucleus.

Because protists are so different from each other, scientists divide them into three categories based on characteristics they share with organisms in other kingdoms. These categories are: animal-like protists, plant-like protists, and fungus-like protists.

What image pops into your head when you think of an animal? Most people immediately associate animals with movement. In fact, movement is often involved with an important characteristic of animals—obtaining food. All animals that obtain food by eating other organisms are heterotrophs.

⚷ **Like animals, animal-like protists are heterotrophs, and most can move to get food.** But unlike animals, animal-like protists, or **protozoans** (proh tuh ZOH unz), are unicellular.

······✎······
Vocabulary Prefixes The Greek word *proton* means "first" or "early." If the Greek word *zoia* means "animal," what do you think *protozoan* means?

<u>First animal</u>

FIGURE 1 ·····················
Diversity of Protists
Protists come in many sizes and forms. Slime molds, amoebas, and euglenoids are just some of the many types of protists.

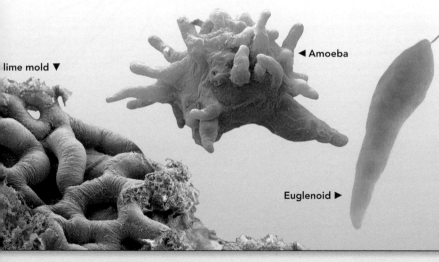

lime mold ▼

◀ Amoeba

Euglenoid ▶

57

Explain ─────────────

Explain ─────────────

Introduce Vocabulary

To help students understand the plural terms *cilia* and *algae*, have them focus on the words' plural suffixes. Explain that *cilia* identifies a group of structures and that *algae* identifies a group of organisms. Point out that these plural forms are used as much if not more than the singular forms *cilum* and *alga.*

Teach Key Concepts ⚷

Explain to students that animal-like protists are heterotrophs, and most can move to get food. Reinforce that they share these two characteristics with animals. Ask: **What are heterotrophs?** *(Organisms that consume other organisms in a food chain)* **What is one way that animals and animal-like protists are distinct?** *(Animal-like protists are unicellular, whereas animals have more than one cell.)*

Lead a Discussion

PROTISTS' CHARACTERISTICS Emphasize that protists are highly diverse, but make sure students realize that they do share some traits. Ask: **Which traits are shared by all protists?** *(They are eukaryotes; they live in moist environments.)* **What three categories are used to classify protists?** *(Animal-like, plant-like, fungus-like)* **What term is sometimes used to identify animal-like protists?** *(Protozoans)*

> **My Planet Diary** provides an opportunity for students to explore real-world connections to protists.

MY SCIENCE online.com ▶ | Animal-Like Protists

LESSON 2.3

ⒺⓁⓁ Support

1 Content and Language
Write the terms *cilia* and *algae* on the board. Point out that the singular form *cilium* is Latin for eyelash, and that the singular form *alga* is Latin for seaweed.

2 Frontload the Lesson
Use **Figure 1** to help students visualize the wide assortment of forms that protists take. Point to each protist, and invite students to suggest descriptive words and to identify other objects or living things that each resembles.

3 Comprehensible Input
Have students create a four-column table in which they compare and contrast types of protists. Use of the headings *Animal-Like Protists, Plant-Like Protists,* and *Fungus-Like Protists* for three columns. Label rows *Characteristic 1, Characteristic 2,* and so on.

Explain

Teach With Visuals

Have students scan the text on these two pages and look at **Figures 2–5**. Explain that the four groups of protozoans are sarcodines, flagellates, ciliates, and protozoans that act like parasites. Read aloud with the students the text that accompanies **Figure 2,** and have students look again at the diagram of the amoeba. Ask: **What characteristic helps amoeba move and trap food?** *(Pseudopods)* Explain to students that sarcodines move away from bright light to avoid overheating and drying. **Why can an amoeba live in fresh water?** *(The contractile vacuole allows excess water to be expelled.)* Read aloud with the students the text that accompanies **Figure 3,** and have students look again at the diagram of the *Giardia.* Ask: **How does *Giardia* get into fresh water?** *(It enters water in the wastes of wild animals.)* **How do *Giardia* get into the intestines of people?** *(If people drink water containing* Giardia, *these protozoans will attach themselves to their intestines.)*

Make Analogies

STRUCTURES FOR MOTION Ask students to look at the diagram of the boat with a single oar in **Figure 3.** Explain that the analogy of a flagellum and a single oar is apt because some flagellates have a single flagellum that whips slowly from side to side to move the organism forward. Point out that the movement of some flagella is very similar to the propeller on an outboard motor, twisting and whirling to move the organism. Have students look at the diagram of a boat with many oars in **Figure 4.** If students have ever watched a rowing team, they have seen oars all moving at the same time. Point out that cilia move in a wave, like one oar hitting the water after another, not all at the same time. Ask: **What characteristics make the paramecium suited to life in water?** *(Sample: Its two contractile vacuoles remove excess water from the cell. Its cilia move the paramecium through water and sweep food into the organism.)*

21st Century Learning

CRITICAL THINKING Have students observe **Figure 2** and **Figure 4.** Ask: **What do these two protists have in common?** *(Both have structures such as a contractile vacuole, nucleus, and a food vacuole.)* **What is different about them?** *(An amoeba has only one nucleus; a paramecium has two. An amoeba uses pseudopods to move; a paramecium uses cilia. An amoeba uses pseudopods to trap food inside the cell; a paramecium uses cilia to sweep food into the organism.)*

The Four Groups of Protozoans—How They Move and Live

Protozoans With Pseudopods

The amoeba in **Figure 2** belongs to the first group of protozoans called sarcodines. Sarcodines move and feed by forming **pseudopods** (SOO duh pahdz)—temporary bulges of the cell. The word *pseudopod* means "false foot." Pseudopods form when cytoplasm flows toward one location and the rest of the organism follows. Pseudopods enable sarcodines to move away from bright light. Sarcodines also use pseudopods to trap food by extending one on each side of a food particle. When the two pseudopods join together, the food is trapped inside the cell, as shown in **Figure 2.** Protozoans that live in fresh water have a problem. If excess water builds up inside the cell, the amoeba will burst. But amoebas have a **contractile vacuole** (kun TRAK til VAK yoo ohl), a structure that collects and expels excess water from the cell.

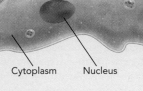

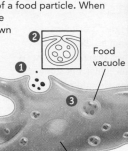

Food vacuole

FIGURE 2

Amoeba
This amoeba's pseudopods surround and trap a food particle.

✎ **Interpret Diagrams** Draw the second step of this process in the box on the left.

Cytoplasm   Nucleus

Contractile vacuole

Pseudopod

Protozoans With Flagella

The second group of protozoans are the flagellates. Flagellates (FLAJ uh lits) are protozoans that use long, whiplike flagella to move. Some live inside the bodies of other organisms. One type of flagellate lives in the intestines of termites. When the termite eats wood, the flagellate breaks it down into sugars that the termite can eat. In return, the termite protects the flagellate. Sometimes, however, a protozoan harms its host. For example, the parasite *Giardia,* shown in **Figure 3,** is deposited in fresh water in the wastes of wild animals. When people drink water containing *Giardia,* these flagellates attach to their intestines, where they feed and reproduce. The people develop an intestinal condition commonly called hiker's disease.

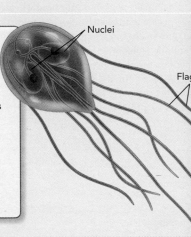

Nuclei

Flag

FIGURE 3

Giardia
Giardia has eight flagella and two nuclei.

✎ **Make Models** How is the movement of the oar on this boat similar to the movement of a flagellum?

One oar moves the boat forward, just as a flagellum moves a protozoan.

58   Viruses, Bacteria, Protists, and Fungi

Interactive Art allows students to explore protozoans.

MY SCIENCE online.com   **Animal-Like Protists**

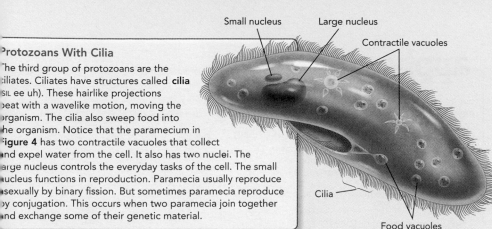

Small nucleus   Large nucleus

Contractile vacuoles

Cilia

Food vacuoles

Protozoans With Cilia

The third group of protozoans are the ciliates. Ciliates have structures called **cilia** (SIL ee uh). These hairlike projections beat with a wavelike motion, moving the organism. The cilia also sweep food into the organism. Notice that the paramecium in **Figure 4** has two contractile vacuoles that collect and expel water from the cell. It also has two nuclei. The large nucleus controls the everyday tasks of the cell. The small nucleus functions in reproduction. Paramecia usually reproduce asexually by binary fission. But sometimes paramecia reproduce by conjugation. This occurs when two paramecia join together and exchange some of their genetic material.

FIGURE 4 ....

> INTERACTIVE ART **Paramecium**

Paramecia use cilia to move through water.

✎ **Make Models** How is the movement of oars on this boat similar to the movement of cilia?

The oars move back and forth, like a wave, to push the boat forward.

Protozoans That Are Parasites

The fourth group of protozoans are characterized more by the way they live than by the way they move. They are all parasites that feed on the cells and body fluids of their hosts. These protozoans move in a variety of ways. Some have flagella, and some depend on hosts for transport. One even produces a layer of slime that allows it to slide from place to place! Many of these parasites have more than one host. *Plasmodium*, shown in **Figure 5**, is a protozoan that causes malaria, a disease of the blood. Two hosts are involved in *Plasmodium's* life cycle—humans and a species of mosquitoes found in tropical areas. The disease spreads when a mosquito bites a person with malaria, becomes infected, and then bites a healthy person. Symptoms of malaria include high fevers that alternate with severe chills. These symptoms can last for weeks, then disappear, only to reappear a few   months later. Malaria can be fatal.

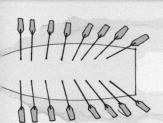

FIGURE 5 ....

Plasmodium

Plasmodium is transmitted through mosquito saliva.

✎ **Apply Concepts** If you lived in a tropical area, how could you reduce the risk of being infected with malaria?

Sample: Avoid mosquito bites by wearing repellent.

59

Differentiated Instruction

L1 Identify Protozoan Structures Provide pairs of students with a list of structures found in amoebas and structures found in paramecia, as they are shown in **Figures 2** and **4.** Also provide pairs of students with a written description of each structure. Have students match each structure with the correct description. Encourage students to study the images and labels in **Figures 2** and **4** as they work.

L3 Protozoan Research Provide books or online sources with more extensive information on ciliate and sarcodine protozoans. Have students prepare and present a visual display that highlights the features of one of the two groups: the variety of protozoans in the group, what they eat, whether any cause disease to humans, and so forth.

Lead a Discussion

PLASMODIUM Read aloud the text that accompanies **Figure 5,** and have students look at the diagram of the *Plasmodium*. Ask: **In what sense are the fourth group of protozoans easier to characterize by the way they live than by the way they move?** *(Sample: These protozoans live like parasites, feeding on the cells and body fluids of one or more hosts. Parasitic protozoans may have all these methods of locomotion—they may include members of sarcodines, flagellates, and ciliates.)* **What disease is caused by *Plasmodium*?** *(Malaria)* Point out that avoiding malaria depends on avoiding being bitten by infected mosquitoes. Any responses from students that have to do with avoiding mosquito bites are acceptable. For example, students might mention wearing clothing that covers all of the skin, avoiding being outside when mosquitoes are active, and eliminating pools of standing water where mosquitoes lay eggs.

Elaborate

Build Inquiry 🧪 Lab zone

L2 MODEL ANIMAL-LIKE PROTISTS

Materials clay, paint, string, pipe cleaners, cardboard, and other materials of students' choice

Time 30 minutes

Challenge small groups to design models of one protozoan from the four groups—sarcodines, flagellates, ciliates, and parasites—shown in **Figures 2–5.** Have students consult the illustrations and photo in the text, or locate others in reference materials. Students' models should include unique details for each organism, as well as labels. Have students compare and contrast their completed models, explaining similarities and differences. Encourage them to note the structures, shapes, and methods of movement of the various protozoans. Challenge groups to use their models to demonstrate how these organism move or feed.

21st Century Learning

COMMUNICATION Have students research ways that hikers can avoid ingesting *Giardia*. *(Samples: Carry enough uncontaminated water. Use water-purifying treatments. Boil water before using it.)* Encourage students to create posters advising other students of the dangers of drinking water that is not purified, and several ways they can avoid getting ill from it.

Elaborate

Apply It!

L1 Before beginning the activity, review the paragraph under the heading *Protozoans with Pseudopods*. Ask: **How do you think the amoebas would respond if the bright light were then turned off?** *(Samples: They might move away from one another. They might not move much.)*

Lab Resource: Quick Lab

L1 OBSERVING PSEUDOPOD MOVEMENT Students will observe an amoeba's shape, size, and motion.

Evaluate

Assess Your Understanding

After students answer the questions, have them evaluate their understanding by completing the appropriate sentence.

R T I Response to Intervention

1a. If students cannot recall the three types of movement, **then** have them review *Four Groups of Protozoans—How They Move and Live.*

  b. If students need help identifying the type of protist, **then** have them study the diagrams in **Figures 2–5.**

  c. If students have trouble explaining the importance of filtering water, **then** remind them that organisms such as *Giardia* in drinking water can cause stomach illness.

MY SCIENCE (S) COACH Have students go online for help in understanding the characteristics of animal-like protists.

---

apply it!

Suppose you fill a container with a culture of amoebas. Then you shine a bright light on one half of the container.

❶ Predict How do you think the amoebas will respond to bright light? Draw your prediction in the empty container below.

❷ Explain How were the amoebas able to respond to the light?

<u>They used pseudopods to move away from the light.</u>

❸ Infer Why do you think it is important for amoebas to respond to bright light?

<u>Sample: They could get too hot, dry up, and die in the bright light.</u>

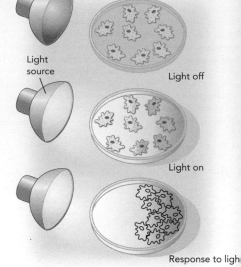

Light source

Light off

Light on

Response to light

Lab **zone** Do the Quick Lab *Observing Pseudopod Movement.*

🔑 Assess Your Understanding

1a. Review What are the three ways that animal-like protists move?

<u>Pseudopods, flagella, cilia</u>

b. Classify You observe a protist under a microscope. It moves by forming temporary bulges of the cytoplasm. What type of protist is it? Explain your answer.

<u>It is a sarcodine, because it is moving with pseudopods.</u>

c. Draw Conclusions Why should you filter water from a stream before drinking it?

<u>To avoid swallowing parasites that can be found in fresh water</u>

got it?

○ **I get it!** Now I know that the characteristics of animal-like protists are <u>that they are all heterotrophs, most can move to get food, and all are unicellular.</u>

○ I need extra help with <u>See TE note.</u>

Go to **MY SCIENCE (S) COACH** *online for help with this subject.*

60 Viruses, Bacteria, Protists, and Fungi

Digital Lesson: Assign the *Apply It* activity online and have students submit their work to you.

MY SCIENCE online.com | **Animal-Like Protists**

What Are the Characteristics of Plant-Like Protists?

Plant-like protists, which are commonly called **algae** (AL jee; singular *alga*), are extremely diverse. **Algae are autotrophs, can be unicellular or multicellular, and use pigments to capture the sun's energy.** Most are able to use the sun's energy to make their own food.

Algae play a significant role in many environments. For example, algae that live near the surface of ponds, lakes, and oceans are an important food source for other organisms. In addition, much of the oxygen in Earth's atmosphere is made by these algae.

Algae vary greatly in size and color. Some algae are unicellular, while others are multicellular. Still others are groups of unicellular organisms that live together in colonies. Algae exist in a wide variety of colors because they contain many types of **pigments**—chemicals that produce color. Depending on their pigments, algae can be green, yellow, red, brown, orange, or even black.

> ✐
> 🔁 **Summarize** Read the text about plant-like protists. Then summarize three characteristics of algae on the lines below.
>
> Algae are autotrophs, have pigments, and vary in size.

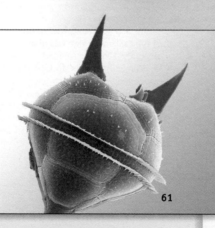

Euglenoids

Euglenoids (yoo GLEE noydz) are green, unicellular algae that are usually found in fresh water. Most euglenoids are autotrophs that produce food using the sun's energy. However, when sunlight is not available, euglenoids will act as heterotrophs and obtain food from their environment. The euglena on the right is a common euglenoid. Notice the long, whiplike flagellum that helps the organism move. Locate the red eyespot near the flagellum. The eyespot is not really an eye, but it contains pigments that are sensitive to light. It helps the euglena recognize the direction of a light source. Think how important this response is to an organism that needs light to make food.

Dinoflagellates

Dinoflagellates (dy noh FLAJ uh lits) are unicellular algae surrounded by stiff plates that look like a suit of armor. Dinoflagellates exist in a variety of colors because they have different amounts of green, orange, and other pigments. All dinoflagellates have two flagella held in grooves between their plates. When the flagella beat, the dinoflagellates twirl like toy tops as they move through the water. Many glow in the dark. They can light up an ocean's surface when disturbed by a passing boat or swimmer at night.

61

Explain

Teach Key Concepts 🔑

Explain to students that algae are autotrophs, can be unicellular or multicellular, and use pigments to capture the sun's energy. Ask: **What is the term *algae* commonly used to identify?** (*Plant-like protists*) **After they capture energy from the sun, how do algae use the energy?** (*To make their own food*) **How do algae help to sustain Earth's atmosphere?** (*They make oxygen.*) **How else do algae play an important role in their environments?** (*They serve as a source of food for other organisms near the surface of ponds, lakes, and oceans.*) **What are some ways in which algae are diverse?** (*Size, color, unicellular or multicellular, living independently or in colonies*)

🔁 **Summarize** Explain that a summary restates the main ideas and most important points in a passage. Point out that summarizing helps students distinguish main ideas from the information that supports those ideas.

Lead a Discussion

EUGLENOIDS AND DINOFLAGELLATES Point out that euglenoids and dinoflagellates are two examples of algae. Ask: **How do euglenoids obtain food?** (*They use the sun's energy to make food; if no sunlight is available, they get food from their environment.*) **How does an euglenoid know if sunlight is available?** (*An eyespot on the organism is able to detect light and its direction.*) **How are dinoflagellates similar to euglenoids?** (*Both are unicellular; both live and move in water.*) **What is unique about the appearance and movement of dinoflagellates?** (*They are surrounded by stiff plates that look like a suit of armor, and many glow in the dark; they can move through water like spinning tops.*)

Differentiated Instruction

L1 Terms of Identification Ask students to give the other names for animal-like protists (*protozoans*) and plant-like protists (*algae*). Have students practice pronounce both terms aloud. Invite students to write each pair of terms on the board as the headings of two lists. Then encourage other students to name several types of protozoans that students can list underneath the general label. Have students help each other to identify and spell correctly such terms as *sarcodines* (such as amoeba), *flagellates* (such as *Giardia*), *ciliates* (such as paramecium), and those protozoans that act like parasites (such as *Plasmodium*). Finally, have students begin a list of types of algae, such as euglenoids and dinoflagellates.

Explain

Support the Big Q ? UbD

VITAL ROLES OF ALGAE Explain that diatoms, red algae, and brown algae are three other examples of algae. Encourage students to reflect on how algae relate to their environments in important ways. Ask: **How are algae important to the environment?** *(They serve as a source of food and oxygen for many heterotrophs.)* **What common word do people use to identify red algae and brown algae?** *(Seaweeds)* **What uses have people found for red algae and brown?** *(People eat red algae and brown algae, and substances from these algae are used in the production of hair conditioner, ice cream, pudding, and other foods.)*

Address Misconceptions

L1 NOT ALL RED ALGAE ARE RED Explain that algae contain other pigments in addition to the dominant pigment. The combination of pigments creates a great variety of colors. Students may think that all red algae look red, all green algae look green, and all brown algae look brown. Help clarify that although these algae contain particular pigments in their names, they also contain other pigments, sometimes in concentrations that, for example, a red alga may actually look pink or purple. Remind students that plant leaves also contain pigments. Ask: **What is the function of the pigments in algae and in plant leaves?** *(They absorb light needed for the algae and plants to make food.)*

Elaborate

Build Inquiry Lab zone

L2 BUILD MODELS OF ALGAE

Materials none

Time 15 minutes

Direct students to make a "living" model of how algae of various sizes take in food and eliminate waste. Divide the class into three groups: unicellular algae, multicellular algae, and a colony of algae. Have each student act out the role of an individual algae cell. Give each group a deck of cards to use as a food source, and encourage the "cells" to act out how each organism accomplishes food intake and waste elimination.

Have students describe food intake and waste elimination in terms of whether they are individual or cooperative processes. *(Samples: Unicellular: individual students pick up and put down cards without interacting; multicellular: cooperative process, as one student picks up a card and passes it on, another put its down; colony: both individual and cooperative)*

Diatoms

Diatoms are unicellular protists with beautiful glasslike cell walls. Some float near the surface of lakes or oceans or attach to rocks in shallow water. Diatoms are also a source of food for heterotrophs in the water. Many diatoms can move by oozing chemicals out of slits in their cell walls and gliding in the slime. When diatoms die, their cell walls collect on the bottoms of oceans and lakes. Over time, they form layers of a coarse substance called diatomaceous (dy uh tuh MAY shus) earth. Diatomaceous earth makes a good polishing agent and is used in household scouring products. It is even used as an insecticide—the diatoms' sharp cell walls puncture the bodies of insects.

Red Algae

Almost all red algae are multicellular seaweeds. Divers have found red algae growing more than 260 meters below the ocean's surface. Their red pigments are especially good at absorbing the small amount of light that is able to reach deep ocean waters. People use red algae in a variety of ways. Substances extracted from red algae, such as carrageenan (ka ruh JEE nun) and agar, are used in products such as ice cream and hair conditioner. Red algae is a nutrient-rich food that is eaten fresh, dried, or toasted by many people in Asian cultures.

Brown Algae

Many of the organisms that are commonly called seaweeds are brown algae. In addition to their brown pigment, brown algae also contain green, yellow, and orange pigments. A typical brown alga has many plant-like structures. For example, structures called holdfasts anchor the alga to rocks much as roots do for plants. Stalks support the blades, which are the leaflike structures of the alga. Many brown algae also have gas-filled sacs called bladders that allow the algae to float upright in ocean water. Some people eat brown algae. In addition, substances called algins are extracted from brown algae and used as thickeners in puddings and other foods.

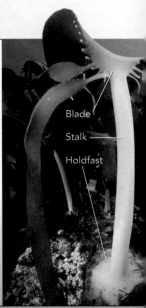

Blade

Stalk

Holdfast

FIGURE 6 ....
Functions of Algae
Algae play important roles in the environment.

✎ **Complete each task.**

1. **Classify** Label the type of algae in each of these photos.

2. **Explain** Check off the functions for each type of algae in the table below.

Red algae

Diatoms

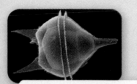
Dinoflagellates

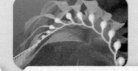
Brown algae

Euglenoids

Function	Type of Algae				
	Euglenoids	Dinoflagellates	Diatoms	Red Algae	Brown Algae
Produce oxygen	✓	✓	✓	✓	✓
Food source for other aquatic organisms	✓	✓	✓	✓	✓
Eaten by people				✓	✓
Used in insecticides			✓		
Used in polishing products			✓		
Used in hair conditioner				✓	

Lab zone
Do the Quick Lab
Predicting.

▭ **Assess Your Understanding**

a. **Review** Why is sunlight important to plant-like protists?

They use the sun's energy to produce food.

b. **Compare and Contrast** What are some ways that algae are different from each other?

Sample: size, pigment color, number of cells

c. [CHALLENGE] How are euglenoids similar to animal-like protists?

They can be heterotrophic.

got**it?**

○ **I get it!** Now I know that the characteristics of plant-like protists are that they are multicellular or unicellular, and that they produce food using the sun's energy.

○ **I need extra help with** See TE note.

Go to **my science ⑤ coach** *online for help with this subject.*

63

Elaborate

Lab Resource: Quick Lab **Lab**

L2 PREDICTING Students will predict and observe the response of euglena to light.

21st Century Learning

COMMUNICATION Have students read *Red Tide* in the **Big Ideas of Science Reference Library** and then design a poster showing what they have learned.

Evaluate

Assess Your Understanding

After students answer the questions, have them evaluate their understanding by completing the appropriate sentence.

RTI Response to Intervention

2a. If students have trouble identifying why sunlight is important to plant-like protists, **then** have them reread the first two paragraphs of the section.

b. If students need help contrasting different types of algae, **then** ask them to review the images of five types of algae, as well as the information in the table in **Figure 6**.

c. If students have trouble explaining how euglenoids are similar to protozoans, **then** have them reread the paragraph about euglenoids.

my science ⑤ coach Have students go online for help in understanding the characteristics of plant-like protists.

Differentiated Instruction

L1 Main Ideas About Plant-Like Protists Have students work together in pairs to summarize information. Remind them that summarizing will help them focus on main ideas and remember what they read. Have each pair of students read a paragraph describing one plant-like protist and summarize the material in their own words. You might wish to have pairs listen to one another's summaries, so that they can go over main ideas for all five protists.

L3 North Atlantic Food Challenge students to do research on the red alga *Palmaria palmata*, which is used as food by various North Atlantic cultures. Encourage students to include information on the variety of places where this alga is eaten, such as Canada, Iceland, Ireland, and Scotland.

Explain

Teach Key Concepts

Explain to students that fungus-like protists are heterotrophs, have cell walls, and use spores to reproduce. Ask: **In what way do fungus-like protists resemble plants?** *(Their cells have cell walls, and they use spores to reproduce.)* **In what way do fungus-like protists resemble animals?** *(They are heterotrophs, and they move at some point in their lives.)* **Where are you likely to find slime molds?** *(On a forest floor)* **How do you think they came to be called slime molds?** *(Sample: They have a jellylike mass and ooze along the ground.)* **How do slime molds differ from water molds and downy mildews in their impact on human beings?** *(Unlike slime molds, water molds and downy mildews can attack and destroy agricultural crops.)*

Elaborate

21st Century Learning

L3 CREATIVITY Challenge students to imagine that they are a fungus-like protist and to write a short story in which they recount their experiences with other microscopic life forms, such as amoebas, euglenoids, paramecia, and other protists. Encourage students to describe how these microscopic organisms behave and how the main character identified them.

What Are the Characteristics of Fungus-Like Protists?

You can think of the fungus-like protists as the "sort of like" organisms. Fungus-like protists are sort of like animals because they are heterotrophs. They are sort of like plants because their cells have cell walls. **Fungus-like protists are heterotrophs, have cell walls, and use spores to reproduce.** A **spore** is a tiny cell that is able to grow into a new organism. All fungus-like protists are able to move at some point in their lives. Three types of fungus-like protists are slime molds, water molds, and downy mildews.

Slime Molds Slime molds are often brilliantly colored. They live in moist, shady places like forest floors. They ooze along the surfaces of decaying materials, feeding on bacteria and other microorganisms. Some slime molds are so small that you need a microscope to see them. Others may span several meters!

Slime molds begin their life cycle as tiny, amoeba-like individual cells. The cells use pseudopods to feed and creep around. If food is scarce, the cells grow bigger or join together to form a giant, jellylike mass. In some species, the giant mass is multicellular. In others, the giant mass is actually one giant cell with many nuclei.

The mass oozes along as a single unit. When environmental conditions become harsh, spore-producing structures grow out of the mass, as shown in **Figure 8,** and release spores. Eventually the spores develop into a new generation of slime molds.

Water Molds and Downy Mildews Most water molds and downy mildews live in water or moist places. These organisms often grow as tiny threads that look like fuzz.

Water molds and downy mildews attack many food crops, such as potatoes, corn, and grapes. A water mold impacted history when it destroyed the Irish potato crops in 1845 and 1846. The loss of these crops led to a famine. More than 1 million people in Ireland died.

FIGURE 7 ·····

A Slime Mold

This colorful slime mold, *Diachea leucopodia,* is producing spores.

✎ Interpret Photos What conditions might have changed in the slime mold's environment to cause spore production?

Sample: The environment may now be too dry or too cold.

64 Viruses, Bacteria, Protists, and Fungi

Digital Lesson: Assign the *Do the Math* activity online and have students submit their work to you.

my science online.com | **Fungus-Like Protists**

do the math! Analyzing Data

Soybean Crop Loss

Soybean plants can be infected and ruined by a water mold called *Phytophthora sojae*. The graph shows crop loss in metric tons in the United States between 2002 and 2005.

① △ **Graph** Create a title for the graph. Then label the vertical axis.

② **Read Graphs** In which year were the most soybeans lost?

2004

③ **Read Graphs** Describe how the soybean crop loss changed between 2002 and 2005.

Soybean loss increased
between 2002 and 2004.
Then it decreased in 2005.

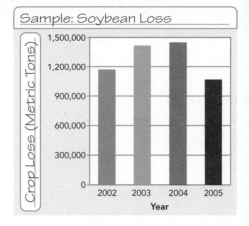

Sample: Soybean Loss

Crop Loss (Metric Tons) — Year

Do the Quick Lab
Observing Slime Mold.

⬒ Assess Your Understanding

a. List What are three types of fungus-like protists?

Slime molds, water molds, and
downy mildews

b. Describe What are two ways that fungus-like and animal-like protists are similar?

Sample: They both can move
and are heterotrophic.

c. Apply Concepts A forest loses its trees and the forest floor dries up. How would slime molds be affected?

Because there would be no
moisture left, they would form
and release spores.

got it?

◯ **I get it!** Now I know that the characteristics of fungus-like protists are that they are
heterotrophic, have cell walls, and use spores to reproduce.

◯ **I need extra help with** See TE note.

Go to MY SCIENCE COACH online for help with this subject.

65

Differentiated Instruction

L1 Identify Protists Display in stations around the room pictures of various protists, such as slime molds, paramecia, euglenoids, diatoms, and algae. Have small groups list on index cards the characteristics they observe in the pictures. Next, display three headings on the board: animal-like protists, plant-like protists, and fungus-like protists. Have students attach under the appropriate headings the index cards containing the protist traits observed in the pictures. Discuss any overlap of traits among the protist groups, and ask students if it is possible to create an operational definition of a protist.

Elaborate

Do the Math!

L1 Remind students that bar graphs show comparisons and contrasts between categories. Point out that this graph uses four bars on the horizontal axis to compare and contrast the amount of crop loss due to water mold in four different years. Have students locate the *y-axis* to learn that the unit of measurement in the graph is metric tons.

△ **Graph** Help students see that a graph can be an effective tool for analyzing data. A graph can show trends and make it easier to make comparisons. Explain that the values that fall between the horizontal lines of a graph can be approximated by determining the increments between lines and then estimating the percentage of that interval that the value takes up.

See the *Math Skill and Problem-Solving Activities* for support.

Lab Resource: Quick Lab

L3 OBSERVING SLIME MOLD Students will use a microscope to observe how slime molds react to oatmeal.

Evaluate

Assess Your Understanding

After students answer the questions, have them evaluate their understanding by completing the appropriate sentence.

RTI Response to Intervention

3a. If students have trouble naming the three types of fungus-like protists, **then** have them review the headings printed in red.

b. If students need help describing two similarities between fungus-like and animal-like protists, **then** have them reread the first paragraph of the section.

c. If students have difficulty explaining the effect on slime molds of changes in a forest, **then** urge them to study **Figure 7** and the information about slim molds.

MY SCIENCE COACH Have students go online for help in understanding the characteristics of fungus-like protists.

Lab zone **After the Inquiry Warm-Up**

Protists

Inquiry Warm-Up, *What Lives in a Drop of Pond Water?*
In the Inquiry Warm-Up, you investigated microscopic organisms in a drop of pond water. Using what you learned from that activity, answer the questions below.

1. **INFER** Why do you think it is necessary for some water to be filtered before drinking it? Explain.

   _____

   _____

2. **OBSERVE** What characteristics did you observe under the microscope that you think made seeing the organisms without the microscope difficult?

   _____

   _____

3. **INFER** Why might being microscopic be advantageous to an organism? Explain.

   _____

   _____

   _____

4. **EXPLAIN** Why was it necessary to wash your hands at the end of the lab? Explain.

   _____

   _____

Name _____ Date _____ Class _____

Protists

What Are the Characteristics of Animal-Like Protists?

1a. REVIEW What are the three ways that animal-like protists move?

_____

b. CLASSIFY You observe a protist under a microscope. It moves by forming temporary bulges of the cytoplasm. What type of protist is it? Explain your answer.

_____

_____

c. DRAW CONCLUSIONS Why should you filter water from a stream before drinking it?

_____

_____

got it? ....

○ **I get it!** Now I know that the characteristics of animal-like protists are _____

_____

_____

○ **I need extra help with** _____

_____

Protists

What Are the Characteristics of Plant-Like Protists?

2a. REVIEW Why is sunlight important to plant-like protists?

_____

b. COMPARE AND CONTRAST What are some ways that algae are different from each other?

_____

_____

c. CHALLENGE How are euglenoids similar to animal-like protists?

_____

got it?

○ **I get it!** Now I know that the characteristics of plant-like protists are _____

_____

○ **I need extra help with** _____

What Are the Characteristics of Fungus-Like Protists?

3a. LIST What are three types of fungus-like protists?

_____

b. DESCRIBE What are two ways that fungus-like and animal-like protists are similar?

_____

_____

c. APPLY CONCEPTS A forest loses its trees and the forest floor dries up. How would slime molds be affected?

_____

_____

got it?

○ **I get it!** Now I know that the characteristics of fungus-like protists are _____

_____

○ **I need extra help with** _____

Key Concept Summaries

Protists

What Are the Characteristics of Animal-Like Protists?

Protists are eukaryotes that cannot be classified as animals, plants, or fungi. Protists live in moist surroundings, and are extremely diverse. Scientists divide protists into three categories: animal-like, plant-like, and fungus-like. **Like animals, animal-like protists are heterotrophs, and most can move to get food.** Unlike animals, animal-like protists, or **protozoans** are unicellular. The four groups of protozoans are sarcodines, flagellates, ciliates, and parasites. Sarcodines move and feed by forming **pseudopods**—temporary bulges of the cell. Amoebas have a **contractile vacuole,** a structure that collects and expels excess water from the cell. Ciliates have structures called **cilia,** hair-like projections that beat with a wavelike motion, moving the organism.

What Are the Characteristics of Plant-Like Protists?

Plant-like protists, commonly called **algae,** are extremely diverse. **Algae are autotrophs, can be unicellular or multicellular, and use pigments to capture the sun's energy.** Most use the sun's energy to make their own food. Algae play a significant role in many environments. Some algae in ponds, lakes, and oceans produce much of Earth's oxygen and are an important source of food for other organisms. Algae vary in size, can be unicellular or multicellular, and exist in various colors because they contain many types of **pigments**—chemicals that produce color. Euglenoids are green, unicellular algae usually found in fresh water. Dinoflagellates are unicellular algae surrounded by stiff plates that look like a suit of armor. Diatoms are unicellular protists with beautiful glasslike cell walls. Almost all red algae are multicellular seaweeds. Many of the organisms that are commonly called seaweeds are brown algae. In addition to their brown pigment, brown algae also contain green, yellow, and orange pigments.

What Are the Characteristics of Fungus-Like Protists?

Fungus-like protists share qualities of animals and plants. **Fungus-like protists are heterotrophs, have cell walls, and use spores to reproduce.** A **spore** is a tiny cell that is able to grow into a new organism. All fungus-like protists can move at some point in their lives. Slime molds live in moist, shady places like forest floors, oozing along the surfaces of decaying materials, feeding on bacteria and other microorganisms. Most water molds and downy mildews live in water or moist places. These organisms often grow as tiny threads and look like fuzz.

On a separate sheet of paper, briefly identify some similarities and differences among the three types of protists.

Review and Reinforce

Protists

Understanding Main Ideas
Answer the following questions on a separate sheet of paper.

1. What characteristic distinguishes most animal-like protists from other protists?
2. What characteristic distinguishes plant-like protists from other protists?
3. What characteristic distinguishes fungus-like protists from other protists?
4. What characteristics are shared by all three types of protists?

Building Vocabulary
Match each term with its definition by writing the letter of the correct definition in the right column on the line beside the term in the left column.

5. ___ protist

6. ___ protozoan

7. ___ pseudopod

8. ___ contractile vacuole

9. ___ cilia

10. ___ algae

11. ___ pigment

12. ___ spore

a. plant-like protists

b. a temporary bulge of the cytoplasm used for feeding and movement

c. hair-like projections that are used to sweep in food and move

d. a tiny cell that is able to grow into a new organism

e. a eukaryote that cannot be classified as an animal, plant, or fungus

f. a chemical that produces color

g. an animal-like protist

h. a structure that collects excess water and expels it from a cell

Enrich

Protists

Read the passage and study the diagrams below. Then use a separate sheet of paper to answer the questions that follow.

Water Hazards

You learned that freshwater protists must pump excess water from their cells using a contractile vacuole. Protists that live in salt water don't have this problem. Why? The answer involves diffusion.

Small particles dissolved in water constantly move about. This movement, called *diffusion*, causes the particles to spread out evenly in the water. The particles of a substance tend to diffuse from an area of high concentration to an area of low concentration. *Concentration* is the number of particles of a substance per unit of volume. Figure 1 illustrates the diffusion of salt particles through a barrier with holes in it. Particles of water also diffuse from an area of high concentration to an area of low concentration. Figure 2 shows what happens if the holes in the barrier allow water but not salt particles to pass through it.

A protist cell, like all cells, contains salt particles as well as water particles in its cytoplasm. In addition, its cell membrane acts like the barrier in Figure 2; water particles can pass through it, but not salt particles. In the case of a saltwater protist, there are normally equal concentrations of salt particles and water particles on either side of the cell membrane. In freshwater protists, the concentration of salt particles inside the cell is much higher that the concentration of salt particles outside the cell.

Figure 1

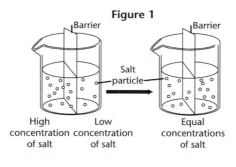

High concentration of salt / Low concentration of salt → Equal concentrations of salt

Figure 2

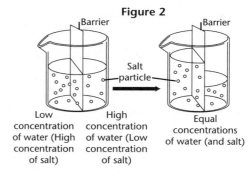

Low concentration of water (High concentration of salt) / High concentration of water (Low concentration of salt) → Equal concentrations of water (and salt)

1. A protist that lives in fresh water faces a situation similar to the one shown in Figure 2. In which direction will diffusion of water particles occur: into the cell, out of the cell, or not at all? Explain.

2. Explain why a protist living in salt water doesn't need a contractile vacuole.

3. Predict what would happen to a protests living in salt water if the number of salt particles in its cytoplasm were increased ten times.

Lesson Quiz

Protists

If the statement is true, write *true*. If the statement is false, change the underlined word or words to make the statement true.

1. _____ Protists are eukaryotes that <u>can</u> be classified as animals, plants, or fungi.

2. _____ <u>Pseudopods</u> produce oxygen and are a source of food for other organisms.

3. _____ Most <u>plant-like</u> protists can move to get food.

4. _____ <u>Algae</u> use pigments to capture the sun's energy.

5. _____ Fungus-like protists use <u>cilia</u> to reproduce.

Fill in the blank to complete each statement.

6. _____ are animal-like protists.

7. Plant-like protists are commonly called _____.

8. _____ have hair-like projections that beat with a wavelike motion to move the organism.

9. Algae contain many types of _____, or chemicals that produce color.

10. A(n) _____ is a tiny cell that is able to grow into a new organism.

Protists

Answer Key

After the Inquiry Warm-Up

1. Answers will vary. Sample: Filtering the water will remove microscopic organisms that may live in the water.

2. Answers will vary. Sample: The organisms are very tiny; many of the organisms are nearly transparent or clear.

3. Answers will vary. Sample: Being microscopic, the organism needs fewer resources to live, and more organisms can occupy a smaller volume of space.

4. Answers will vary. Sample: Some microscopic organisms can be harmful to humans, and can easily invade our bodies because they are so small.

Key Concept Summaries

All protists are eukaryotes, live in moist surroundings, and are extremely diverse. Animal-like protists are unicellular, heterotrophs, and able to move. Plant-like protists are autotrophs, can be unicellular or multicellular, and use a variety of pigments to capture the sun's energy. Most make their own food. Fungus-like protists share qualities of animals and plants. They are heterotrophs, have cell walls, and use spores to reproduce. All fungus-like protists can move at some point in their lives.

Review and Reinforce

1. Most animal-like protists move to get food.

2. Plant-like protists use a variety of pigments to capture the sun's energy.

3. Fungus-like protists use spores to reproduce.

4. All protists are eukaryotes that cannot be classified as animals, plants, or fungi, and all live in moist surroundings.

5. e
6. g
7. b
8. h
9. c
10. a
11. f
12. d

Enrich

1. The concentration of water outside the cell is greater than the concentration of water inside the cell. As a result, water particles will diffuse into the cell.

2. Water is distributed evenly inside and outside the cell. Therefore, excess water will not build up in the cell and there is no need for a contractile vacuole.

3. Water would diffuse into the cell to balance the extra number of salt particles.

Lesson Quiz

1. cannot
2. Algae
3. animal-like
4. true
5. spores
6. Protozoans
7. algae
8. Ciliates
9. pigments
10. spore

Fungi

LESSON

4 **How are living things other than plants and animals important to earth?**

Lesson Pacing: 2–3 periods or 1–1½ blocks

🕐 **SHORT ON TIME?** To do this lesson in approximately half the time, do the Activate Prior Knowledge activity on page 66. A discussion of the Key Concepts on pages 67 and 70 will familiarize students with the lesson content. Explore the Big Q using the images in Figure 6. Have students do the Read-World Inquiry activity and the Quick Labs. The rest of the lesson can be completed by students independently.

Preference Navigator, in the online Planning tools, allows you to customize *Interactive Science* to your own teaching style. You can also edit lesson plans by selecting the Lesson Planner option.

Digital Teacher's Edition allows you to access your Teacher's Edition and Resource materials online.

my science online.com

Lesson Vocabulary

- fungus
- hyphae
- fruiting body
- budding
- lichen

 Content Refresher

Molds The common black bread mold *Rhizopus stolonifer* is a zygote fungus. *Rhizopus*, like other molds, grows quickly. A growth of *Rhizopus* appears as a layer of dark fuzz. But upon closer inspection, various types of hyphae are visible, including stolons, rhizoids, and sporangiophores. Stolons are stem-like, horizontal hyphae that run along the surface of the bread. Rhizoids are root-like hyphae that anchor the fungus to the bread. They penetrate the surface of the bread, release digestive chemicals, and absorb the nutrients into the fungus. Sporangiophores are upright hyphae that develop tiny, black, pinhead-like spore cases at their tips. Within each spore case, or sporangium, are thousands of spores. These spores are dispersed through the air and grow into new fungi if they land in a favorable environment.

As well as producing spores asexually in its sporangiophores, *Rhizopus* can also produce spores sexually. During sexual reproduction, neighboring hyphae of opposite mating types come together and join to form a tough, thick-walled structure called a zygospore. Zygospores are very resistant and can survive long periods of freezing, drying, and other harsh environmental conditions. When conditions become favorable again, the zygospores germinate into sporangia. The sporangia release spores that can grow into a new generation of fungi.

LESSON OBJECTIVES

🔲 Name and describe the characteristics of fungi and how they reproduce.

🔲 Describe the roles fungi play in the natural world.

Blended Path Active learning using Student Edition, Inquiry Path, and Digital Path

ENGAGE AND EXPLORE

Teach this lesson using a variety of resources. Begin by reading **My Planet Diary** as a class. Have students discuss how leafcutter ants and the fungus benefit from their relationship. Then have students do the **Inquiry Warm-Up activity.** Students will examine the structure of a mushroom. The **After the Inquiry Warm-Up worksheet** sets up a discussion about the structure of a mushroom. Have volunteers share their answers to question 4 explaining why they think the gills were given their name.

EXPLAIN AND ELABORATE

Teach Key Concepts by explaining the characteristics of fungi. **Lead a Discussion** using **Figure 1** to explain how mushrooms grow. Then **Lead a Discussion** using **Figures 2 and 3** to explain how fungi reproduce.

Teach Key Concepts by explaining the roles of fungi in nature. **Lead a Discussion** about how to identify, treat, and avoid a fungal disease. Have students practice the inquiry skill in the **Apply It activity. Lead a Discussion** about fungus-plant root associations and lichens. **Explore the Big Q** using the images in **Figure 6. Answer the Big Q** by leading a class discussion about the importance of living things other than plants and animals.

Hand out the **Key Concept Summaries** as a review of each part of the lesson. Students can also use the online **Vocab Flash Cards** to review key terms.

EVALUATE

Have students take the **Lesson Quiz.** For an alternate assessment, see the *ExamView*® Computer Test Generator, Progress Monitoring Assessments, or SuccessTracker™.

ELL Support

1 Content and Language

Pronounce and define aloud vocabulary terms for students. Suggest that they create a personal set of vocabulary flash cards, with each term and its definition on one side of an index card and a visual of the term on the other side.

66A Viruses, Bacteria, Protists, and Fungi

 **Inquiry Path** Hands-on learning in the Lab zone

ENGAGE AND EXPLORE

To teach this lesson with an emphasis on inquiry, begin with the **Inquiry Warm-Up activity.** Students will examine the structure of a mushroom. The **After the Inquiry Warm-Up worksheet** sets up a discussion about the structure of a mushroom. Have volunteers share their answers to question 4 explaining why they think the gills were given their name.

EXPLAIN AND ELABORATE

Focus on the **Inquiry Skill** for the lesson. Remind students that when they use one or more of their five senses to gather information about the world, they are observing. Remind them that an observation must be an accurate report of what their senses detect. What sense was used to make observations in the **Inquiry Warm-Up activity** and what was observed? *(Sample: Sight; to discover the function of the gills on mushrooms)* **Build Inquiry** to give students the opportunity to observe mushroom spores. Have students do the **Quick Lab** to examine, describe, and sketch two molds.

Use the **Teacher Demo** modeling how spores spread. Before beginning the **Apply It activity,** review details relating to Alexander Fleming's observations of bacteria and fungi. **Explore the Big Q** using the images in **Figure 6.** Have students do the **Quick Lab** creating a compost pile to explore the role of decomposers in creating compost. **Answer the Big Q** by leading a class discussion about the importance of living things other than plants and animals. Students can use the online **Vocab Flash Cards** to review key terms.

EVALUATE

Have students take the **Lesson Quiz.** For an alternate assessment, see the *ExamView®* Computer Test Generator, Progress Monitoring Assessments, or SuccessTracker™.

Digital Path Online learning at my science online.com

ENGAGE AND EXPLORE

Teach this lesson using digital resources. Begin by having students learn and explore real-world connections to fungi at **My Planet Diary** online. Have them access the Chapter Resources to find the **Unlock the Big Question activity.** There they can answer the questions and refine their responses as they continue through the lesson. You can re-assign the activity and have students submit their work so you can track their progress.

EXPLAIN AND ELABORATE

Students reading above, at, or below the lexile measure of this lesson can access basic content readings at their level at **My Reading Web.** Encourage students to use the online **Vocab Flash Cards** to preview key terms. Have students do the **Quick Lab** to examine, describe, and sketch two molds.

Assign the **Apply It activity** online and have students submit their work to you. **Explore the Big Q** using the images in **Figure 6.** Use the **Interactive Art activity** online to explore the uses of viruses, bacteria, protists, and fungi. Have students do the **Quick Lab** creating a compost pile to explore the role of decomposers in creating compost. **Answer the Big Q** by leading a class discussion about the importance of living things other than plants and animals. Students can use the online **Vocab Flash Cards** to review key terms. The **Key Concept Summaries** online allow students to read a summary and see an image associated with each part of the lesson. Online remediation is available at **My Science Coach.**

EVALUATE

Have students take the **Lesson Quiz.** For an alternate assessment, see the *ExamView®* Computer Test Generator, Progress Monitoring Assessments, or SuccessTracker™.

2 Frontload the Lesson

Have students create a word map graphic organizer by writing the vocabulary terms in the top box. As they read the chapter, they should fill in the bottom boxes with terms, phrases, or images associated with the vocabulary term.

3 Comprehensible Input

Have students create a T-chart titled "What Fungi Do." Have them write the roles fungi play in the natural world on the left side of the chart and an example of each role on the right side of the chart.

4 Language Production

Pair or group students with varied language abilities to complete labs collaboratively for language practice. Have each student copy the completed written lab for personal reference.

5 Assess Understanding

Ask students to make notes about Key Concepts in the lesson and use the notes to prepare an oral presentation of the concepts. Encourage students to use the visuals in the lesson to support their presentations.

Fungi

Establish Learning Objectives

After this lesson, students will be able to:

🔑 Name and describe the characteristics of fungi and how they reproduce.

🔑 Describe the roles fungi play in the natural world.

Engage

Activate Prior Knowledge

MY PLANET DIARY Read *Fungus Farmers* with the class. Point out that leafcutter ants work in groups as large as a thousand ants to transport tiny leaf pieces to underground nests that contain as many as 1,000 chambers and millions of ants. Ask: **What benefits do the ants receive from bringing leaf fragments back to underground nests?** *(Samples: They can grow a valuable food source; their food source is located close to a group of ants rather than spread out.)*

BIG IDEAS OF SCIENCE REFERENCE LIBRARY 📖
Have students look up the following topic: Fungi.

Explore

Lab Resource: Inquiry Warm-Up

L1 **THERE'S A FUNGUS AMONG US** Students will examine the structure of a mushroom.

---

4 Fungi

🔑 **What Are the Characteristics of Fungi?**

🔑 **What Is the Role of Fungi in Nature?**

MY PLANET DIARY

Fungus Farmers

You may have heard of an "ant farm," but have you ever heard of ant farmers? Leafcutter ants act like farmers, growing fungus for food. First, the ants cut pieces of leaves from trees. Then the ants carry the leaves to an underground nest, where the leaves are crushed and chewed to make a mulch. Surprisingly, the ants don't eat the mulched leaves. They place them in a special growing chamber or "garden." Then they move strands of fungus from an existing garden to the new chamber, where it grows on the leaves. The ants help the fungus grow by removing harmful bacteria and mold. Finally, the ants eat the fungus!

FUN FACTS

Write your answer to each question below.

1. How do the ants act like farmers?

   <u>They prepare special places</u>
   <u>for the fungus to grow and</u>
   <u>remove bacteria and mold.</u>

2. How do the leafcutter ants and the fungus benefit from their relationship?

   <u>Sample: The ants make a</u>
   <u>chamber for the fungus</u>
   <u>to grow. The fungus</u>
   <u>provides food for the ants.</u>

> **PLANET DIARY** Go to **Planet Diary** to learn more about fungi.

 Lab zone Do the Inquiry Warm-Up *There's a Fungus Among Us.*

What Are the Characteristics of Fungi?

You accidentally left an orange in your backpack. When you find it is covered in white fuzz! The orange is being digested by a mold which is a type of fungus. You may be familiar with other kinds of fungi, too. For example, the molds that grow on stale bread and the mushrooms that sprout in forests are also fungi.

SUPPORT ALL READERS

Lexile Measure = 960L   Lexile Word Count = 1786

Prior Exposure to Content: May be the first time students have encountered this topic

Academic Vocabulary: *evidence, identify, observe*

Science Vocabulary: *fungus, hyphae, lichen*

Concept Level: Generally appropriate for most students in this grade

Preteach With: My Planet Diary "Fungus Farmers" and Figure 1 activity

Go to **My Reading Web** to access leveled readings that provide a foundation for the content.

MY SCIENCE online.com

Vocabulary
- fungus • hyphae • fruiting body
- budding • lichen

Skills
- ◉ Reading: Identify Supporting Evidence
- △ Inquiry: Observe

Most **fungi** (singular *fungus*) share several important characteristics. ▭ **Fungi are eukaryotes that have cell walls, are heterotrophs that feed by absorbing their food, and use spores to reproduce.** In addition, fungi need moist, warm places in which to grow. They thrive on damp tree barks, moist foods, lawns coated with dew, damp forest floors, and even wet bathroom tiles.

Cell Structure Fungi range in size from tiny unicellular yeasts to large multicellular fungi. The cells of all fungi are surrounded by cell walls. Except for the simplest fungi, such as unicellular yeasts, the cells of most fungi are arranged in structures called **hyphae** (HY fee; singular *hypha*), shown in **Figure 1.** Hyphae are the branching, threadlike tubes that make up the bodies of multicellular fungi. The hyphae of some fungi are continuous threads of cytoplasm that contain many nuclei. Substances move quickly and freely through the hyphae. What a fungus looks like depends on how its hyphae are arranged. In fuzzy-looking molds, the threadlike hyphae are loosely tangled. In other fungi, the hyphae are packed tightly together.

Obtaining Food Although fungi are heterotrophs, they do not take food into their bodies as you do. Instead, fungi absorb food through hyphae that grow into the food source.

First, the fungus grows hyphae into a food source. Then digestive chemicals ooze from the hyphae into the food. The chemicals break down the food into small substances that can be absorbed by the hyphae. Some fungi feed on dead organisms. Other fungi are parasites that break down the chemicals in organisms.

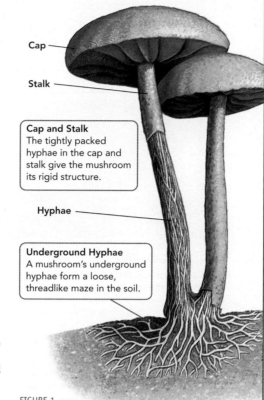

Cap

Stalk

Cap and Stalk
The tightly packed hyphae in the cap and stalk give the mushroom its rigid structure.

Hyphae

Underground Hyphae
A mushroom's underground hyphae form a loose, threadlike maze in the soil.

FIGURE 1 ⋯⋯⋯⋯⋯⋯
Structure of a Mushroom
The largest known organism on Earth is an underground fungus that is larger than a thousand football fields.

✎ **Infer** What function might the underground hyphae in this mushroom perform?

Underground hyphae anchor the fungus and get water and nutrients from soil.

67

Explain
Introduce Vocabulary
To help students understand the terms *fungi* and *hyphae*, have them focus on the plural Latin endings of these two nouns. Write the words on the board along with their singular forms (*fungus, hypha*). Explain that the suffixes *-i* and *-ae* are plural forms from the Latin and Greek languages, respectively.

Teach Key Concepts ▭
Explain to students that fungi are eukaryotes and are heterotrophs that feed by absorbing their food. Fungi use spores to reproduce and the cells of fungi have cell walls. Ask: **What is an example of a unicellular fungus?** *(Yeast)* **What are hyphae?** *(Branching, threadlike tubes that form the bodies of multicellular fungi)* Explain that in most fungi, cytoplasm flows freely through the hyphae. Ask: **How do hyphae help a fungus in its life processes?** *(By allowing essential materials to be broken down, and absorbed into the fungus)*

Lead a Discussion
MUSHROOM HABITAT Ask students to describe what they know about how mushrooms grow. Some students may have seen mushrooms growing in the woods, while others may have seen cultivated mushrooms in stores. Point out that the familiar mushroom shape is only part of the fungus. Direct students' attention to **Figure 1.** Ask: **What part of the fungus do you see in the woods or in a lawn?** *(The cap and the stalk)* **What part of the fungus to you not see?** *(The hyphae that grow underground)* Tell students that the visible part of the fungus is the reproductive structure, which appears for a short time. The underground hyphae may extend for a great distance and do not die when the reproductive structures dry out and die back.

My Planet Diary provides an opportunity for students to explore real-world connections to fungi.

Ⓔ Ⓛ Ⓛ Support

1 Content and Language
Write *fungi* and *hyphae* on the board. Point out that *hyphae* contains the plural noun suffix *-ae*. Explain that the suffix *-i* is another Latin suffix for plural nouns. Write the singular noun forms *fungus* and *hypha* on the board, as well.

2 Frontload the Lesson
Have students share any experiences they have had with fungi such as

discovering mold on bread or other foods, soil, or hard surfaces such as bathroom tiles. Tell students they will learn how certain fungi cause disease, whereas others are used to fight disease.

3 Comprehensible Input
Invite groups to use various materials to make models of a variety of fungi. Help students locate types of fabric, pipe-cleaners, twine, and similar items.

Explain

Lead a Discussion

HOW FUNGI REPRODUCE Have students examine **Figure 2** and **Figure 3**. Ask: **What type of asexual reproduction occurs in yeasts?** *(Budding)* **Under what conditions do most fungi reproduce asexually?** *(Adequate food and moisture)* **What type of reproduction produces fungi that differ genetically from the parents?** *(Sexual reproduction)* **What are fruiting bodies?** *(The reproductive structures of a fungus that contains or produces spores)* **How are fungal spores similar to plant seeds?** *(They have protective coverings and are transported easily by air or water.)*

Teach With Visuals

Tell students to look at **Figure 4**. Ask: **What are the three major groups of fungi?** *(Club, sac, zygote)* **To which group does the fungus in Figure 3 belong?** *(Club)* **Are the club shapes visible to the naked eye?** *(No, instead they are visible under a microscope, as shown in the inset photo.)* Help students understand that these club-shaped structures are present within the chanterelle. The chanterelle is a type of mushroom. Point out the parallel lines visible on the chanterelle. These ridges are called gills and contain the club-shaped reproductive structures. Ask: **Why do you think the ridges are called gills?** *(They look somewhat like the gills of a fish.)* Make sure students understand that the mushroom gills look like the gills of a fish, but have a very different function.

Reproduction in Fungi The way that fungi reproduce guarantees their survival and spread. Most fungi reproduce both asexually and sexually. Fungi usually reproduce by making spores. The lightweight spores are surrounded by a protective covering and can be carried easily through air or water to new sites. Fungi produce millions of spores, more than can ever survive. Only a few spores will fall where conditions are right for them to grow.

Fungi produce spores in reproductive structures called **fruiting bodies.** The appearance of a fruiting body varies from one type of fungus to another. In some fungi, such as mushrooms and puffballs, the visible part of the fungus is the fruiting body. In other fungi, such as bread molds, the fruiting bodies are tiny, stalklike hyphae that grow upward from the other hyphae. A knoblike spore case at the tip of each stalk contains the spores.

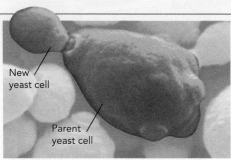

New yeast cell

Parent yeast cell

Asexual Reproduction

When there is adequate moisture and food, fungi make spores asexually. Cells at the tips of the hyphae divide to form spores. The spores grow into fungi that are genetically identical to the parent.

Unicellular yeast cells undergo a form of asexual reproduction called **budding,** shown in **Figure 2.** In budding, no spores are produced. Instead, a small yeast cell grows from the body of a parent cell in a way somewhat similar to how a bud forms on a tree branch. The new cell then breaks away and lives on its own.

FIGURE 2 ···

Yeast Reproduction

The smaller structure in the photo above is a new yeast cell budding from its parent.

✏ **Interpret Photos** How is this new yeast cell similar to its parent?

It is genetically identical.
_____

Hyphae

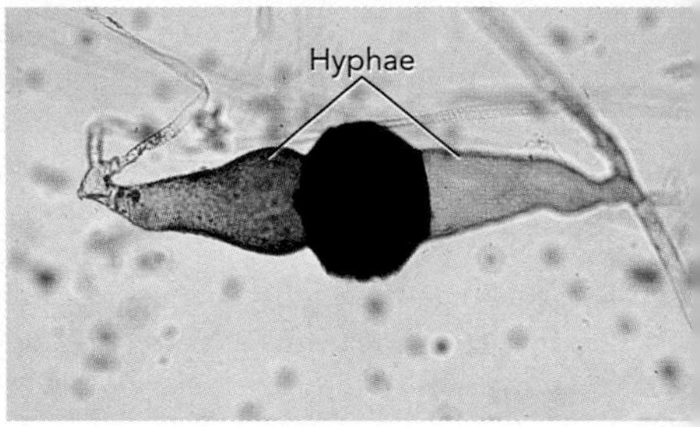

Sexual Reproduction

Most fungi can also reproduce sexually, especially when growing conditions become unfavorable. In sexual reproduction, the hyphae of two fungi grow together and genetic material is exchanged. Eventually, a new reproductive structure grows from the joined hyphae and produces spores. The spores develop into fungi that differ genetically from either parent.

FIGURE 3 ···

Bread Mold Reproduction

Two hyphae in this bread mold have joined together to undergo sexual reproduction. The round object between the hyphae will eventually produce spores.

Classification of Fungi

Three major groups of fungi are the club, sac, and zygote fungi. These groups are classified by the appearance of their reproductive structures. Additional groups include water species that produce spores with flagella and those that form tight associations with plant roots. **Figure 4** shows an example from one of the major groups of fungi.

FIGURE 4 ···

Club Fungus

The reproductive structures of this chanterelle look like tiny clubs. You can see spherical spores forming at the end of one of the club-shaped reproductive structures.

✎ **Predict** What will happen after these spores are released?

They will be carried through air or water to new sites and will possibly reproduce.

 Do the Quick Lab *Do All Molds Look Alike?*

Assess Your Understanding

a. Define What are hyphae?

Branching, threadlike tubes

b. Review What role do spores play in the reproduction of fungi?

Spores are reproductive cells that develop into new fungi.

c. Sequence Outline the steps by which fungi produce spores during sexual reproduction.

Hyphae of two fungi join and exchange genetic material; a reproductive structure grows from the joined hyphae and produces spores.

ot it? ···

◯ **I get it!** Now I know that the characteristics of fungi are *that they are eukaryotes with cell walls, are heterotrophs, and use spores to reproduce.*

◯ **I need extra help with** *See TE note.*

Go to **my science COACH** online for help with this subject.

69

Differentiated Instruction

L1 **Observe Fungi** Group students to allow those with differing proficiencies to work together. Give students a selection of mushrooms from the grocery store, and a hand lens to use to observe them. Challenge students to identify mushroom structures. Have students gently twist off the cap of one mushroom and break open the stalk

from end to end. Ask: Can you pull threadlike structures from the stalk? *(Students will respond in a variety of ways depending on the type of mushroom.)* Tell students that these structures are hyphae. Make sure students wash their hands immediately after the activity.

Elaborate

Build Inquiry

L2 **OBSERVE MUSHROOM SPORES**

Materials mushroom spores in water, eyedropper, microscope, slide, cover slip

Time 15 minutes

Remind students that spores are used for reproduction. Have students use a dropper to place a drop of water with spores on a microscope slide, and cover it with a cover slip. Students can observe the spores under a microscope, and sketch their observations, including the color and shape of the spores.

Ask: **Why will the fungi that grow from spores produced sexually differ from the parent plants that produced them?** *(They will be genetically different.)*

Lab Resource: Quick Lab

L1 **DO ALL MOLDS LOOK ALIKE?** Students will examine, describe, and sketch two molds.

Evaluate

Assess Your Understanding

After students answer the questions, have them evaluate their understanding by completing the appropriate sentence.

RTI Response to Intervention

1a. If students cannot define *hyphae*, **then** have them reread the material about these structures in the paragraphs under *Cell Structure*.

b, c. If students need help explaining the role of spores in the reproduction of fungi, **then** have them review the section *Reproduction in Fungi,* as well as **Figure 3**.

my science COACH Have students go online for help in understanding the characteristics of fungi.

Explain

Teach Key Concepts

Explain to students that fungi may act as decomposers and recyclers, or provide foods for people. Fungi may help fight or cause disease. Some fungi live in a beneficial relationship with other organisms. Ask: **What characteristic do many fungi share with bacteria?** *(Acting as decomposers)* **How do fungi have a positive effect on soil?** *(Decomposition by fungi breaks down huge numbers of dead plants and animals while replenishing the soil with needed nutrients.)* **In what forms are fungi eaten as food?** *(Yeasts are used for making breads and wine; molds are used for making cheese; mushrooms are edible.)* **How have fungi helped people fight disease?** *(Fungi are necessary for the production of penicillin and other antibiotics that are used to treat bacterial infections.)* **Which types of fungi cause disease?** *(Parasites in plants and food crops; athlete's foot and ringworm in people)*

CAUTION: Tell students that they should never eat mushrooms they find in the wild. While some mushrooms are edible, many of them are extremely poisonous.

Elaborate

Teacher Demo Lab zone

L2 SPREAD SPORES

Materials round balloon, cotton balls, tape, stick or ruler about 30 cm long, modeling clay, pin

Time 25 minutes

Break a cotton ball into five equal pieces, roll each piece into a tiny ball, and insert the cotton balls into a balloon. Repeat these steps until the balloon is almost full. Inflate the balloon and tie a knot in its neck. Tape the knotted end of the balloon to a stick. Stand the stick upright in a mound of modeling clay. Ask students to observe what happens as you pop the balloon with a pin. *(The "spores" should fly out from the balloon and land in many directions, fairly far from the balloon.)*

Ask: **How does this demonstration model a fruiting body?** *(Sample: Just as air scattered the cotton balls, air currents catch and carry spores far and wide.)*

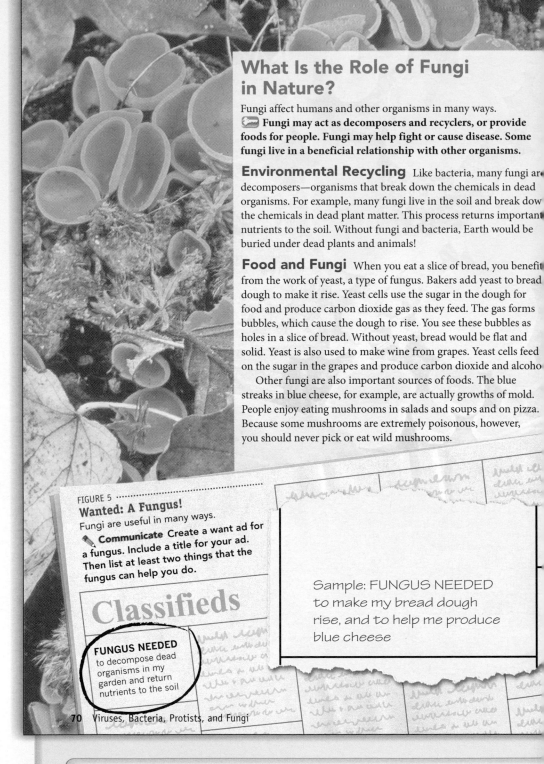

What Is the Role of Fungi in Nature?

Fungi affect humans and other organisms in many ways. Fungi may act as decomposers and recyclers, or provide foods for people. Fungi may help fight or cause disease. Some fungi live in a beneficial relationship with other organisms.

Environmental Recycling Like bacteria, many fungi are decomposers—organisms that break down the chemicals in dead organisms. For example, many fungi live in the soil and break down the chemicals in dead plant matter. This process returns important nutrients to the soil. Without fungi and bacteria, Earth would be buried under dead plants and animals!

Food and Fungi When you eat a slice of bread, you benefit from the work of yeast, a type of fungus. Bakers add yeast to bread dough to make it rise. Yeast cells use the sugar in the dough for food and produce carbon dioxide gas as they feed. The gas forms bubbles, which cause the dough to rise. You see these bubbles as holes in a slice of bread. Without yeast, bread would be flat and solid. Yeast is also used to make wine from grapes. Yeast cells feed on the sugar in the grapes and produce carbon dioxide and alcohol.

Other fungi are also important sources of foods. The blue streaks in blue cheese, for example, are actually growths of mold. People enjoy eating mushrooms in salads and soups and on pizza. Because some mushrooms are extremely poisonous, however, you should never pick or eat wild mushrooms.

FIGURE 5 ·····
Wanted: A Fungus!
Fungi are useful in many ways.
✎ **Communicate** Create a want ad for a fungus. Include a title for your ad. Then list at least two things that the fungus can help you do.

Classifieds

FUNGUS NEEDED to decompose dead organisms in my garden and return nutrients to the soil

Sample: FUNGUS NEEDED to make my bread dough rise, and to help me produce blue cheese

Digital Lesson: Assign the *Apply It* activity online and have students submit their work to you.

my science online.com ▸ Fungi in Nature

Disease-Fighting Fungi In 1928, a Scottish biologist named Alexander Fleming was examining petri dishes in which he was growing bacteria. To his surprise, Fleming noticed <u>a spot of bluish green mold growing in one dish</u>. Curiously, <u>no bacteria were growing near the mold</u>. Fleming hypothesized that the mold, a fungus named *Penicillium*, produced a substance that killed the bacteria near it.

Fleming's work contributed to the development of the first antibiotic, penicillin. It has saved the lives of millions of people with bacterial infections. Since the discovery of penicillin, many other antibiotics have been isolated from both fungi and bacteria.

Disease-Causing Fungi Many fungi are parasites that cause serious diseases in plants. The sac fungus that causes Dutch elm disease is responsible for killing millions of elm trees in North America and Europe. Corn smut and wheat rust are two club fungi that cause diseases in important food crops. Fungal plant diseases also affect other crops, including rice, cotton, and soybeans, resulting in huge crop losses every year.

Some fungi cause diseases in humans. Athlete's foot is an itchy irritation in the damp places between toes. Ringworm shows up as a circular rash on the skin. Because the fungus that causes these diseases produces spores at the site of infection, the diseases spread easily from person to person. Both diseases can be treated with antifungal medications.

✏️ **Identify Supporting Evidence** Underline the evidence in the text that supports the conclusion that *Penicillium* mold kills bacteria.

apply it!

Suppose you are a scientist studying two dishes of the same bacteria. One day, you notice that two dots of mold have started growing in the middle of each dish. The next day you observe what happened.

1 ✍️ **Observe** How were the two dishes of bacteria affected by the mold?

More bacteria on dish A were killed than on dish B.

2 CHALLENGE Are the two dots of mold the same type of fungus? Explain your answer.

No, because the molds did not have the same effect on the bacteria in each dish

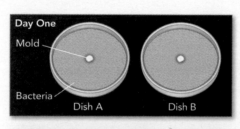
Day One — Mold, Bacteria — Dish A, Dish B

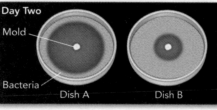
Day Two — Mold, Bacteria — Dish A, Dish B

71

Differentiated Instruction

L3 **Design Experiments** Challenge small groups of students to design experiments that show how yeast reacts with other ingredients to make bread. Suggest that students find simple bread recipes and vary the ingredients for their experiments. Students can make predictions about how different quantities of ingredients will affect the outcome of the baked bread. If possible, bring a bread machine into class so that students can try out their recipes.

Explain

21st Century Learning

INTERPERSONAL SKILLS Tell students that the discovery of the antibiotic nature of the *Penicillium* mold is an example of a scientist recognizing the significance of unexpected results. Direct students' attention to the images in the *Apply It* activity. Fleming saw a similar area, called a zone of inhibition, where the bacteria did not grow. Point out that Fleming was curious to find out what had happened. Invite pairs of students to improvise a conversation Fleming might have had with a lab assistant who wanted to throw the petri dish away. Then ask: **What does Fleming's response tell you about an important characteristic of scientists?** *(They are curious and open to new ideas to research.)*

🔁 **Identify Supporting Evidence** Explain that a conclusion is a statement of what has been learned in an experiment. A conclusion should be supported by evidence, which consists of information whose accuracy can be confirmed by testing or observation.

Lead a Discussion

IDENTIFY A FUNGAL DISEASE Encourage students to share what they know about athlete's foot. Ask: **How does athlete's foot spread?** *(Spores fall from infected feet and are picked up by another person's feet.)* **Where might this be especially likely to occur?** *(In bathrooms, around pools, in gymnasiums, in and around public showers)* **What can you do to avoid getting athlete's foot?** *(Dry between toes; wear shoes in public areas.)* **How would you treat this fungus if you got it?** *(With antifungal medicine)*

Elaborate

Apply It!

L1 Before beginning the activity, review details relating to Alexander Fleming's observations of bacteria and fungi.

◻️ **Observe** Explain to students that when they use one or more of their five senses to gather information about the world, they are observing. Remind them that an observation must be an accurate report of what their senses detect.

Explain

Lead a Discussion

FUNGI AS HELPERS Point out that fungi are involved in two important relationships in nature. If students have previously studied relationships between species, review with them the nature of a mutualistic relationship, a close association in which both species benefit. Ask: **How does a plant benefit from having hyphae grow into its roots?** *(The hyphae give the plant water and nutrients from the soil, which helps the plant grow larger.)* **How does the fungus benefit from its association with the plant?** *(The fungus can feed on food produced by the plant.)* **What is a lichen?** *(A fungus and an alga that live together in a relationship that benefits both organisms)* **How is a lichen like the association of hyphae and plant roots?** *(In both cases, the fungus provides water and nutrients and the partner provides food.)*

Fungus-Plant Root Associations Some fungi help plants grow larger and healthier when their hyphae grow into, or on, the plants' roots. The hyphae spread out underground and absorb water and nutrients from the soil for the plant. With more water and nutrients, the plant grows larger than it would have grown without its fungal partner. The plant is not the only partner that benefits. The fungus gets to feed on the extra food that the plant makes and stores.

Most plants have fungal partners. Many plants are so dependent on the fungi that they cannot survive without them. For example, orchid seeds cannot develop without their fungal partners.

Rico arrives at a dairy factory in Europe. How are bacteria and fungi being used to make dairy products?

Bacteria are used to make yogurt. Bacteria and fungi are used to make cheese.

Before he starts his trip, Rico receives a vaccine. What will this vaccine protect him against?

It will protect him against diseases caused by viruses.

During Rico's first stop in South America, he steps over a rotting tree trunk. What are the roles of bacteria and fungi?

They are decomposing the tree trunk by breaking down complex chemicals.

EXPLORE THE BIG **?**

What in the world?

How are living things other than plants and animals important to Earth?

FIGURE 6 ·······

▶ **REAL-WORLD INQUIRY** Rico is taking a trip around the world. Follow him as he encounters viruses, bacteria, protists, and fungi in the environment.

✎ **Interpret Photos** Answer the question in each box on the lines provided.

Real-World Inquiry allows students to explore the uses of viruses, bacteria, protists, and fungi.

my science online.com | **Fungi in Nature**

Lichens A **lichen** (LY kun) consists of a fungus and either algae or autotrophic bacteria that live together in a relationship that benefits both organisms. You have probably seen some familiar lichens—irregular, flat, crusty patches that grow on tree barks or rocks. The fungus benefits from the food produced by the algae or bacteria. The algae or bacteria, in turn, obtain shelter, water, and minerals from the fungus.

 Do the Quick Lab *Considering Fungi as Decomposers.*

Next, Rico travels to the coast of Africa. He sees people gathering red and brown algae. How might they use the algae?

<u>They may use red algae in</u>
<u>hair products or brown</u>
<u>algae as a thickener in food.</u>

On his way home, Rico sees lichens growing on a rock in Australia. How do the algae and fungus in this lichen help each other?

<u>The fungus gets food from</u>
<u>algae. The algae gets shelter,</u>
<u>food, and water from the</u>
<u>fungus.</u>

🔑 **Assess Your Understanding**

2a. Name What are some foods that are made with fungi?

<u>Bread, wine, and cheese</u>

b. Explain How can fungi be used to treat disease?

<u>Fungi are used to make</u>
<u>antibiotics that treat</u>
<u>disease.</u>

c. ❓ How are living things other than plants and animals important to Earth?

<u>Sample: They produce</u>
<u>medicines, food, and oxygen,</u>
<u>and can recycle important</u>
<u>chemicals.</u>

got it? ∙∙

○ **I get it!** Now I know the roles of fungi in the environment are <u>to recycle,</u>
<u>provide food, cause or fight</u>
<u>disease, or form beneficial</u>
<u>relationships with other</u>
<u>organisms.</u>

○ **I need extra help with** <u>See TE note.</u>

Go to **MY SCIENCE** 🄢 **COACH** online for help with this subject.

73

L1 Fungal Partners Have pairs of students work together to produce drawings that show the concept of fungal partners. Encourage students to study the details about fungal partners in *Fungus-Plant Root Associations.* Students might wish to emphasize the distinctions between fungus and plant by using one color for each. Students' drawings should include detailed labels that help to explain the function of

hyphae and the effect on growth from such a fungus-plant association.

L3 Lichen If possible, provide students with hand lenses and samples of lichens on rocks or tree bark. As students observe the lichens, challenge them to infer why lichens are sensitive to environmental pollution. *(Lichens rapidly absorb substances directly from rainwater, so they are very susceptible to airborne pollutants.)*

Elaborate

Explore the Big Q ❓ UbD

Direct students' attention to images of activities and events in Rico's trip around the world. Have students focus on one photograph at a time as you read its caption, including the question, to students. Point out that three photos deal with the world of nature explicitly, whereas in two of the photographs the viewer must infer the connection to viruses, bacteria, protists, or fungi in the environment. Ask: **What do you think was used to create the vaccine that is injected into Rico's arm?** *(A weakened or dead virus)* **Which of the two types of organisms mentioned is visible on the rotting tree trunk?** *(Fungi)* **Which type of organisms are the red and brown algae that the African person is holding?** *(Red and brown algae are plant-like protists.)* **What types of organisms make up the lichen in the fifth photograph?** *(Lichen is a fungus, and algae is a protist.)*

Lab Resource: Quick Lab

L1 CONSIDERING FUNGI AS DECOMPOSERS
Students will create a compost pile to explore the role of decomposers in creating compost.

Evaluate

Assess Your Understanding

After students answer the questions, have them evaluate their understanding by completing the appropriate sentence.

Answer the Big Q ❓ UbD

To help students focus on the Big Question, lead a class discussion about the importance of living things other than plants and animals.

RTI Response to Intervention

2a. If students cannot name foods made with fungi, **then** have them look again at the two paragraphs under the heading *Food and Fungi.*

b. If students need help explaining how fungi are used to treat disease, **then** remind them of fungi's role in developing antibiotics including penicillin.

c. If students have difficulty explaining the importance of living things other than plants and animals, **then** encourage them to think about how the environment provides food and oxygen for living things, and accepts wastes from living things.

MY SCIENCE 🄢 **COACH** Have students go online for help in understanding the role of fungi in nature.

Lab zone **After the Inquiry Warm-Up**

Fungi

> **Inquiry Warm-Up, *There's a Fungus Among Us***
> In the Inquiry Warm-Up, you investigated the structure of a mushroom. Using what you learned from that activity, answer the questions below.

1. **COMPARE AND CONTRAST** How are the structures of a mushroom similar to the structures of a plant? Explain.

   _____

   _____

2. **COMPARE AND CONTRAST** How are the structures of a mushroom different from the structures of a plant? Explain.

   _____

   _____

3. **OBSERVE** Was the function of the gills easier to understand after viewing them using your hand lens? Explain.

   _____

   _____

4. **OBSERVE** Based on your observations, why were the gills given their name? Explain.

   _____

   _____

Assess Your Understanding

Fungi

What Are the Characteristics of Fungi?

1a. **DEFINE** What are hyphae?

_____

b. **REVIEW** What role do spores play in the reproduction of fungi?

_____

_____

c. **SEQUENCE** Outline the steps by which fungi produce spores during
sexual reproduction.

_____

_____

_____

_____

_____

_____

got it? ....

○ **I get it!** Now I know that the characteristics of fungi are _____

_____

○ **I need extra help with** _____

_____

Fungi

What is the Role of Fungi in Nature?

2a. NAME What are some foods that are made with fungi?

_____

b. EXPLAIN How can fungi be used to treat disease?

_____

_____

_____

c. ANSWER 🔵 How are living things other than plants and animals important to Earth?

_____

_____

_____

_____

got it? ....

○ **I get it!** Now I know the roles of fungi in the environment are _____

_____

_____

_____

○ **I need extra help with** _____

_____

Fungi

What Are the Characteristics of Fungi?

Molds, such as those that grow on fruit and stale bread, are a type of fungus. Most **fungi** share several important characteristics. **Fungi are eukaryotes that have cell walls, are heterotrophs that feed by absorbing their food, and use spores to reproduce.** Fungi need moist, warm places in which to grow. They thrive on damp tree barks, moist foods, lawns coated with dew, damp forest floors, and even wet bathroom tiles. Fungi range in size from tiny unicellular yeasts to large multicellular fungi. Except for the simplest fungi, such as unicellular yeasts, the cells of most fungi are arranged in structures called **hyphae.** Hyphae are the branching, threadlike tubes that make up the bodies of multicellular fungi. Fungi absorb food through hyphae. Most fungi reproduce both sexually and asexually, guaranteeing their survival and spread. Fungi produce spores in reproductive structures called **fruiting bodies.** Unicellular yeast cells undergo a form of asexual reproduction called **budding.** In budding, no spores are produced. The three major groups of fungi are the club, the sac, and the zygote. They are classified by the appearance of their reproductive structures.

What Is the Role of Fungi in Nature?

Fungi affect humans and other organisms in many ways. **Fungi may act as decomposers and recyclers, or provide foods for people. Fungi may help fight or cause disease. Some fungi live in a beneficial relationship with other organisms.** Decomposers are organisms that break down the chemicals in dead organisms. Without fungi and bacteria, Earth would be buried under dead plants and animals. Fungi are important sources of foods such as bread, mushrooms, and blue cheese, and some fungi produce substances that fight bacteria. Yet many other fungi are parasites that cause diseases in plants and crops, including rice, cotton, and soybeans, as well as in humans. Some fungi help plants grow larger and healthier when their hyphae grow into or on the plant's roots. A **lichen** consists of a fungus and either algae or autotrophic bacteria that live together in a relationship that benefits both organisms. The fungus benefits from the food produced by the algae or bacteria. The algae or bacteria, in turn, obtain shelter, water, and minerals from the fungus.

On a separate sheet of paper, explain ways that fungi can be helpful to people and other ways that they can be harmful to people.

Fungi

Understanding Main Ideas
Answer the following questions on a separate sheet of paper.

1. How would you describe the arrangement of cells in most fungi?
2. How do fungi get food?
3. How does reproduction occur in fungi?
4. What roles do fungi play in nature?
5. Describe what would happen if fungi did not exist.

Building Vocabulary
Match each term with its definition by writing the letter of the correct definition in the right column on the line beside the term in the left column.

6. ___ fungi

7. ___ hyphae

8. ___ fruiting body

9. ___ budding

10. ___ lichen

a. reproductive structure that produces spores

b. a form of asexual reproduction in which no spores are produced

c. eukaryotes that have cell walls, feed by absorbing their food, and reproduce sexually or asexually

d. a fungus and either algae or autotrophic bacteria that live together in a relationship that benefits both organisms

e. branching, threadlike tubes that make up the bodies of multicellular fungi

Fungi

> Read the passage and study the table below. Then use the map to answer the questions that follow on a separate sheet of paper.

A Really Big Fungus

In 1982, scientists discovered a specimen of the fungus *Armillaria bulbosa* living beneath about 15,000 square meters of soil in Michigan. They couldn't see the entire fungus directly, so they compared the DNA of fungus samples taken at different locations. Since each individual's DNA is slightly different from that of others of its species, when scientists saw that DNA from fungus samples taken from neighboring locations were identical, they knew they were looking at samples of one very large fungus.

Scientists have taken samples of the fungus *Armillaria bulbosa* at the numbered locations on the map below. Seven DNA types were identified from the samples. Assume that each DNA type identifies an individual fungus.

DNA Type	Location	DNA Type	Location
Type 1	1, 2, 7	Type 5	12, 19, 26, 27
Type 2	8, 14, 15, 22	Type 6	6, 13, 20
Type 3	3, 9, 10, 16, 17, 23, 24, 25	Type 7	21, 28, 29
Type 4	4, 5, 11, 18		

1. Find the locations of each DNA type on the map. Draw lines on the map dividing the DNA types from one another.

2. Assume that each sample location corresponds to an area of 1,600 m². How many square meters do the largest and smallest individual fungi on the map cover?

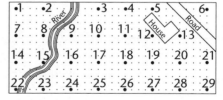

3. Assume that there is 0.75 kg of fungus per square meter of fungus. What are the masses of the largest and smallest fungi on the map?

4. If the hyphae in each square meter of fungus were lined up end to end, they would stretch about 90 m. What is the length in kilometers of the hyphae in the largest fungus on the map?

Lesson Quiz

Fungi

Fill in the blank to complete each statement.

1. _____, such as those that grow on fruit and stale bread, are a type of fungus.

2. Except for the simplest fungi, the cells of most fungi are arranged in structures called _____.

3. The three major groups of fungi are classified by the appearance of their _____ structures.

4. Unicellular yeast cells undergo a form of _____ reproduction called budding.

5. A(n) _____ consists of a fungus and either algae or autotrophic bacteria that live together.

If the statement is true, write *true.* **If the statement is false, change the underlined word or words to make the statement true.**

6. _____ Fungi are <u>prokaryotes</u> that have cell walls, are heterotrophs that feed by absorbing their food, and use spores to reproduce.

7. _____ Fungi need <u>dry, cool</u> places in which to grow.

8. _____ Fungi may act as <u>decomposers</u> and recyclers.

9. _____ Certain fungi can <u>fight or cause</u> disease.

10. _____ Decomposers <u>build up</u> chemicals in dead plant and animal matter.

Fungi

Answer Key

After the Inquiry Warm-Up

1. Mushrooms and plants have stems.

2. Mushrooms have caps and gills, but plants do not. Plants have branches and leaves, but mushrooms do not.

3. Yes, using the hand lens I was able to see some of the spores the mushroom uses to reproduce.

4. The gills on a mushroom resemble the gills of a fish. They are flat and thin like fish gills.

Key Concept Summaries

Fungi help people in their role of decomposers of dead animal and plant materials. Fungi also help people by providing a source of food and by acting as fighters of certain diseases. However, some fungi can cause disease in humans.

Review and Reinforce

1. In most fungi, the cells are arranged in structures called hyphae. These are the threadlike tubes that branch out and give multicellular fungi their bodies.

2. Fungi absorb food through their hyphae.

3. Some fungi undergo asexual reproduction, either through the production of spores or through budding. Other fungi reproduce sexually when the hyphae of two fungi grow together and genetic material is exchanged.

4. Fungi act as decomposers and recyclers of plant and animal material; they are a source of food; they are used to fight diseases; they also can cause diseases.

5. Sample responses might mention that dead organisms would not be decomposed as fast and their nutrients would not recycled as fast. We would not have foods such as mushroom and some cheeses and breads. Some diseases, such as athlete's foot, would not exist, but neither would some antibiotics. Many plants would not survive without the fungi that grow among their roots.

6. c   7. e

8. a   9. b

10. d

Enrich

1. Positions of lines may vary slightly as long as all locations with the same DNA type are in the same area.

2. The area of the largest fungus is 12,800 m², and the area of the smallest fungus is 4,800 m².

3. The mass of the largest fungus is 9.600 kg (0.75 kg/m² × 12,800 m²), and the mass of the smallest is 3,600 kg (0.75 kg/m² × 4,800 m²).

4. $\left(\dfrac{90 \text{ m/m}^2 \times 12,800 \text{ m}^2}{1,000 \text{ m/km}} \right) = 1,152 \text{ km}$

Lesson Quiz

1. Molds   2. hyphae

3. reproductive   4. asexual

5. lichen   6. eukaryotes

7. moist, warm   8. true

9. true   10. break-down

Study Guide

Review the Big Q ? UbD

Have students complete the statement at the top of the page. These Key Concepts support their understanding of the chapter's Big Question. Have students return to the chapter opener pages. What is different about how students view the image of mushrooms now that they have completed the chapter? Thinking about this will help them prepare for the *Apply the Big Q* activity in the Review and Assessment.

Partner Review

Have partners review definitions of vocabulary terms by using the Study Guide to quiz each other. Students could read the Key Concept statements and leave out words for their partner to fill in, or change a statement so that it is false and then ask their partner to correct it.

Class Activity: Concept Map

Have students develop concept maps to show how the information in this chapter is related. Encourage students to brainstorm together to identify Key Concepts, vocabulary, definitions, examples, and important details from each of the four lessons. Suggest that students write pieces of information on self-sticking notes and attach them on poster board, paper, or the board at random. Point out that students can use these notes as they develop a concept map that starts at the top with the chapter's Key Concepts. Ask students to use the following questions to help them organize the information on their sticky notes:

- What are the characteristics of viruses?
- How do viruses interact with the living world?
- What are bacteria?
- How do bacteria get food, get energy, and reproduce?
- What are the characteristics of animal-like protists?
- What are the characteristics of plant-like protists?
- What are the characteristics of fungus-like protists?
- What are the characteristics of fungi?
- What is the role of fungi in nature?

My Science Coach allows students to complete the *Practice Test* online.

The Big Question allows students to complete the *Apply the Big Q* activity about how living things other than plants and animals are important to Earth.

Vocab Flash Cards offer a way to review the chapter vocabulary words.

MY SCIENCE online .com ▸ Viruses, Bacteria, Protists, & Fungi

---

2 Study Guide

 REVIEW THE BIG Q

_Viruses_____ are nonliving. Some protists, such as _algae_____, produce oxygen. Bacteria and fungi both play roles as _Sample: decomposers_.

LESSON 1 Viruses

🔑 Viruses are nonliving, have a protein coat that protects an inner core of genetic material, and cannot reproduce on their own.

🔑 Though viruses can cause disease, they can also be used to treat and prevent illnesses.

Vocabulary
• virus • host • parasite • vaccine

LESSON 2 Bacteria

🔑 Bacteria are prokaryotes. The genetic material in their cells is not contained in a nucleus.

🔑 Bacteria get energy by either making food or eating other organisms, and can reproduce asexually or sexually.

🔑 Bacteria are involved in oxygen and food production, in health maintenance and medicine production, and in environmental cleanup and recycling.

Vocabulary
• bacteria • cytoplasm • ribosome • flagellum • cellular respiration
• binary fission • conjugation • endospore • pasteurization • decomposer

LESSON 3 Protists

🔑 Like animals, animal-like protists are heterotrophs, and most can move to get food.

🔑 Algae are autotrophs, can be unicellular or multicellular, and use pigments to capture the sun's energy.

🔑 Fungus-like protists are heterotrophs, have cell walls, and use spores to reproduce.

Vocabulary
• protist • protozoan • pseudopod • contractile vacuole • cilia • algae • pigment • spore

LESSON 4 Fungi

🔑 Fungi are eukaryotes that have cell walls, are heterotrophs that feed by absorbing their food, and use spores to reproduce.

🔑 Fungi may act as decomposers and recyclers, or provide foods for people. Fungi may help fight or cause disease. Some fungi live in a beneficial relationship with other organisms.

Vocabulary
• fungus • hyphae • fruiting body
• budding • lichen

E L L Support

4 Language Production

Have students play a game "20 Questions" using the vocabulary terms from the chapter. Tell students they can ask you 20 questions in order to identify the vocabulary term you are thinking of. Encourage students to incorporate information from the chapter in their questions.

Beginning

LOW/HIGH Allow students to use words and short phrases as questions.

Intermediate

LOW/HIGH Allow students extra time to formulate their questions.

Advanced

LOW/HIGH Allow students to act as coaches for students with less language proficiency.

Review and Assessment

LESSON 1 Viruses

1. Bacteriophages are viruses that attack and destroy

a. plants.
b. bacteria.
c. humans.
d. other viruses.

2. A _parasite_ is an organism that lives on or in a host and causes it harm.

3. Interpret Diagrams Label the following structures in the diagram below: protein coat, surface proteins, and genetic material.

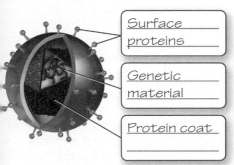

Surface proteins

Genetic material

Protein coat

4. Predict Chickenpox is a disease caused by a virus. The chickenpox vaccine began to be recommended for children in 1995. How do you think the rate of chickenpox infections changed after 1995?

The rate of infection dropped after 1995, because the vaccine prevented infection from the chickenpox virus.

5. [Write About It] Bacteria will grow in agar, a substance containing nutrients. Viruses do not grow in agar. If you needed to grow viruses in the laboratory, what kind of substances would you have to use? Explain your reasoning.

See TE rubric.

LESSON 2 Bacteria

6. Which process is used to kill bacteria in foods such as milk and juice?

a. conjugation
b. pasteurization
c. binary fission
d. decomposition

7. Bacteria reproduce sexually through _conjugation._

8. Classify Look at the photos below. Classify the bacteria according to their shape.

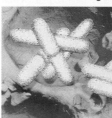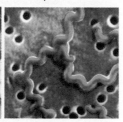

Rodlike and spiral

9. Compare and Contrast Fill in the chart below to describe how bacteria obtain energy.

Type of Bacteria	Methods of Obtaining Energy	
Autotrophic	Use sun's energy to make food	Use chemical energy to make food
Heterotrophic	Consume decaying leaves	Consume other organisms

10. Infer How do bacteria "recycle" Earth's nutrients?

They break down complex chemicals into simpler ones.

Review and Assessment

Assess Understanding

Have students complete the answers to the Review and Assessment questions. Have a class discussion about what students find confusing. Write Key Concepts on the board to reinforce knowledge.

RTI Response to Intervention

1. If students have trouble recalling details about bacteriophages, **then** remind them that bacteriophages are viruses that sometimes look like robots. Point out that their name includes the name of the organisms they attack.

9. If students need help naming methods of getting energy, **then** remind them that the prefixes *hetero-* (other) and *auto-* (self) distinguish bacteria that eat other organisms from those that make their own food.

Alternate Assessment

L1 MAKE A MURAL Have students design and create a four-panel mural that summarizes the chapter content. Each panel should depict the information covered in one lesson. Students should be sure to incorporate all the Key Concepts and vocabulary terms in their murals and to address the Big Question. The class can then use the mural as a way to review chapter material.

CHAPTER 2

| Write About It | Assess student's writing using this rubric. |

SCORING RUBRIC	SCORE 4	SCORE 3	SCORE 2	SCORE 1
Identify substances needed to grow viruses and explain reasoning.	Student correctly identifies substances and clearly explains reasoning.	Student identifies substances and fairly explains reasoning.	Student identifies substances but doesn't clearly explain reasoning.	Student doesn't identify substances nor explains reasoning.

Review and Assessment, Cont.

RTI Response to Intervention

14. If students have trouble predicting the effects of the disappearance of algae, **then** point out that algae are a food source and that they make much of the oxygen in Earth's atmosphere.

18. If students have trouble explaining an advantage and a disadvantage of killing fungi, **then** point out that some fungi work with plants to promote growth, whereas others cause disease in plants.

Apply the Big Q ? UbD

TRANSFER Students should be able to demonstrate understanding of the importance of viruses, bacteria, protists, and fungi by answering this question. See the scoring rubric below.

Connect to the Big Idea ? UbD

BIG IDEA: Living things are alike yet different.

Send students back to the Big Ideas of Science at the beginning of their student edition. Have them read what they wrote about how living things are different yet alike before they started the chapter. Lead a class discussion about how their thoughts have changed. If all chapters have been completed, have students fill in the bottom section for the Big Idea.

L3 WRITING IN SCIENCE Ask students to write a blog entry that explains to readers how living things other than plants and animals are important to Earth.

LESSON 3 Protists

11. Protozoans, such as ciliates and flagellates, are

(a.) animal-like protists. **b.** plant-like protists.
c. fungus-like protists. **d.** bacteria-like protists.

12. Algae may be green, orange, red, yellow, brown, or black depending on the _pigments_ they contain.

13. Make Generalizations Four different groups of protists are classified as "animal-like." What characteristics do these groups share?

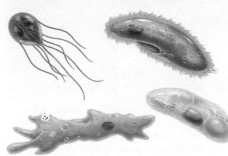

They are all heterotrophs, and most can move.

14. Predict If all algae suddenly disappeared from Earth's waters, how would other living things be affected? Explain your answer.

Organisms that eat the algae would have less food, and there would be less oxygen in the atmosphere.

15. **Write About It** Write a pamphlet describing how homeowners can prevent the growth of slime molds in their basements. Be sure to explain why the suggested action will be effective.

See TE rubric.

LESSON 4 Fungi

16. Which of the following is a characteristic of fungi?

a. They are autotrophic.
b. They lack cell walls.
(c.) They are eukaryotes.
d. They reproduce with seeds.

17. Spores are produced in reproductive structure called _fruiting bodies._

18. Apply Concepts A fungicide is a substance that kills fungi and may be used in crop fields where plants are growing. Describe an advantage and a disadvantage of fungicide use.

It may kill the fungi that cause disease in plants. It could also kill the fungi that have helpful partnerships with plants.

 How are living things other than plants and animals important to Earth?

19. Viruses, bacteria, protists, and fungi are neither plants nor animals. In fact, viruses are not even alive! Still, each plays important roles on Earth. Describe at least three ways in which viruses, bacteria, protists, or fungi are important in your daily life.

Sample: Bacteria and fungi are used to make cheese, which I like to eat. Bacteria and algae produce oxygen so that I am able to breathe. I may not catch the flu because I got a flu vaccine. See TE rubric.

Write About It	Assess student's writing using this rubric.			
SCORING RUBRIC	**SCORE 4**	**SCORE 3**	**SCORE 2**	**SCORE 1**
Describe how to prevent growth of slime molds and explains why action will work.	Student describes how to prevent growth of slime molds and why it will work.	Student describes how to prevent growth of slime mold and somewhat explains why action will work.	Student describes how to prevent growth of slime mold but doesn't explain why it will work.	Student does not describe how to prevent growth of slime molds nor explains why it will work.

? **How are living things other than plants and animals important to Earth?**				
SCORING RUBRIC	**SCORE 4**	**SCORE 3**	**SCORE 2**	**SCORE 1**
Describe three ways, viruses, bacteria, protists, and fungi are important in our daily lives.	Student accurately describes three ways they are important to our daily lives.	Student fairly describes three ways they are important in our daily lives.	Student describes less than three ways they are important in our daily lives.	Student doesn't describe how they are important in our daily lives.

Standardized Test Prep

Multiple Choice

Circle the letter of the best answer.

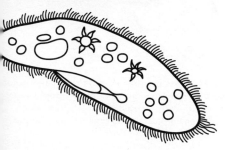

1. Identify the organism shown above and the structure it uses to move.

   Ⓐ paramecium; cilia

   B protozoan; flagella

   C amoeba; pseudopod

   D parasite; contractile vacuole

2. Which of the following statements about fungus reproduction is true?

   A Fungi only reproduce asexually.

   Ⓑ Fungi can reproduce by making spores.

   C Fungi reproduce sexually by budding.

   D Fungi reproduce asexually by joining hyphae and exchanging genetic material.

3. Which part of a virus determines which host cell it can infect?

   A nucleus   B protein coat

   C ribosomes   Ⓓ surface proteins

4. Which statement is correct about plant-like and fungus-like protists?

   A Plant-like protists are all parasitic, while fungus-like protists are not.

   B Plant-like protists are unicellular, while fungus-like protists are multicellular.

   Ⓒ Plant-like protists are usually autotrophs, while fungus-like protists are heterotrophs.

   D Plant-like protists live on land, while fungus-like protists live on land and in water.

5. Yogurt is produced with the help of _____ while bread rises because of _____

   A viruses; fungi.   B fungi; protists.

   Ⓒ bacteria; fungi.   D protists; bacteria.

Constructed Response

Use the diagram below and your knowledge of science to help you answer Question 6. Write your answer on a separate piece of paper.

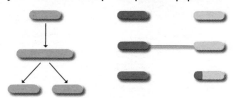

6. Name each process in the drawings of bacteria shown above. Then describe the main differences between these processes.

   See TE note.

Standardized Test Prep

Test-Taking Skills

INTERPRETING DIAGRAMS Explain to students that when they encounter questions like Question 1, which includes a diagram, they should be certain to study all parts of the diagram carefully, including details of the graphic image as well as any labels. Remind students that it is important for them to grasp the nature of the information presented in the diagram before they begin to analyze how the diagram relates to the test question as a whole.

Constructed Response

6. The first drawing shows binary fission, a type of asexual reproduction. The second drawing shows conjugation, a type of sexual reproduction. In binary fission, the offspring are genetically identical to the parent. Conjugation, however, results in bacteria with new combinations of genetic material. Binary fission increases the number of bacteria, but conjugation does not.

Additional Assessment Resources

Chapter Test
ExamView® Computer Test Generator
Performance Assessment
Progress Monitoring Assessments
SuccessTracker™

ⒺⓁⓁ Support

5 Assess Understanding

Have ELLs complete the Alternate Assessment. Provide guidelines on the information it must cover, and a rubric for assessment. Before beginning their murals, have ELLs discuss any questions they have with one another. These discussions will give them additional practice with speaking and listening skills.

Beginning

LOW/HIGH Allow students with extra time to complete their murals.

Intermediate

LOW/HIGH Students can refer to their books or notes when completing their murals.

Advanced

LOW/HIGH Challenge students to incorporate as many vocabulary terms and Key Concepts from the chapter.

Remediate If students have trouble with...

QUESTION	SEE LESSON	STANDARDS
1	3	
2	4	
3	1	
4	3	
5	2, 4	
6	2	

Science Matters

Careers

Have students read *Virus Trackers*. Explain that the word *epidemiology* comes from the Greek language and literally means the study of what is on the people. The first person known to have studied the link between disease and environmental influences was Hippocrates, a doctor in ancient Greece. He created the word *endemic* to describe diseases that were limited to a certain area and *epidemic* to describe diseases that are only present at certain times.

Tell students that many epidemiologists work for the Centers for Disease Control and Prevention, or CDC, in Atlanta, Georgia. It was established in 1946 to help control and eliminate malaria, which at that time was a widespread disease in some areas of the United States. They moved on to control and eliminate tuberculosis as well as many other diseases, and began an immunization program to protect babies. Explain that the CDC is one of the places that has a lab, classified as Biosafety Level 4, where deadly pathogens are studied.

Explain that most epidemiologists become doctors first and then decide to specialize in studying pathogens. Some work in the field, in local public health service offices. These are the people who most frequently encounter pathogens first, since they treat the widest range of patients. Other epidemiologists work in universities, hospitals, or larger organizations like the CDC or the World Health Organization.

Ask: **Why is epidemiology considered dangerous?** *(Epidemiologists come in contact with deadly diseases.)* **Why are epidemiologists' labs protected with airlocks?** *(So that diseases don't get into the air and the disease samples don't get contaminated)*

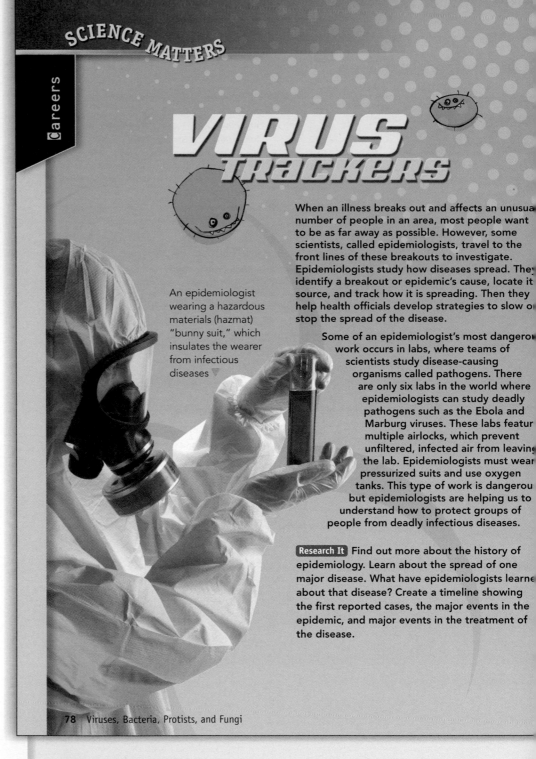

VIRUS TRACKERS

An epidemiologist wearing a hazardous materials (hazmat) "bunny suit," which insulates the wearer from infectious diseases ▼

When an illness breaks out and affects an unusual number of people in an area, most people want to be as far away as possible. However, some scientists, called epidemiologists, travel to the front lines of these breakouts to investigate. Epidemiologists study how diseases spread. They identify a breakout or epidemic's cause, locate its source, and track how it is spreading. Then they help health officials develop strategies to slow or stop the spread of the disease.

Some of an epidemiologist's most dangerous work occurs in labs, where teams of scientists study disease-causing organisms called pathogens. There are only six labs in the world where epidemiologists can study deadly pathogens such as the Ebola and Marburg viruses. These labs feature multiple airlocks, which prevent unfiltered, infected air from leaving the lab. Epidemiologists must wear pressurized suits and use oxygen tanks. This type of work is dangerous but epidemiologists are helping us to understand how to protect groups of people from deadly infectious diseases.

Research It Find out more about the history of epidemiology. Learn about the spread of one major disease. What have epidemiologists learned about that disease? Create a timeline showing the first reported cases, the major events in the epidemic, and major events in the treatment of the disease.

Quick Facts

The Centers for Disease Control and Prevention (CDC) have many more functions than tracking the spread of disease. They are prepared for emergency responses and supply medical treatment in case of disaster. They study environmental health to determine how our environment affects people's health. They raise awareness about healthy living through physical activity, healthy eating, and avoiding risk factors. They also raise awareness about safety, at home and in workplaces. They monitor health conditions around the world and advise people whether it is safe to travel to different countries and what immunizations they might need to travel there that they would not ordinarily need in the United States. Have students research jobs at the CDC and write a paragraph about a job that interests them.

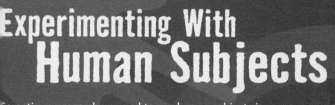

Experimenting With Human Subjects

Sometimes researchers need to use human subjects in order to understand how a new treatment will work on people. How do they weigh whether a decision is appropriate? The research must be unlikely to hurt the subjects. The subjects must also understand the risks and join the study voluntarily.

Debate It Newspapers, buses, and the radio often have advertisements for research studies. These studies may offer volunteers money to try an experimental medicine, such as pain medicine, during recovery from surgery. These advertisements often appeal to college students and unemployed people. With a group of three or four classmates, discuss any ethical issues in advertising for research subjects. With your group, organize a debate about the ethics of these advertisements and studies.

Page 3

January 1, 2009   The Science Daily

MUSHROOMS WORTH THEIR WEIGHT IN GOLD

A mushroom that attracts wild pigs? That's a delicacy? Absolutely! One of these mushrooms even sold for $330,000 at a charity auction.

Truffles live on the roots of certain trees. They feed on the trees, and in turn help the roots of the trees absorb minerals. Animals such as rodents or wild pigs eat the truffles, and their spores are spread around in the animals' feces. Some truffles release an odor that pigs find irresistible. Truffle hunters use pigs to sniff for these tasty underground fungi.

Evaluate It Research efforts to farm truffles using trees that have had truffle spores pumped into them. Were the sources written for young students, scientists, or someone else? Write a paragraph or two explaining your conclusion.

Science and Society

Have students read *Experimenting with Human Subjects.* Tell students that the rules regarding experiments with human subjects are dictated by a document called the Declaration of Helsinki, set forth by the World Medical Association. Included are rules that state research on humans must be for the benefit of society and must be conducted by qualified professionals.

Explain that people often volunteer to take part in experiments because they are hoping to benefit from them. Often, after extensive laboratory trials, new drugs and treatments for diseases are tested on volunteer human subjects. Usually, these people are affected by the disease the trial drug is intended to treat and other treatments have not been effective for the volunteers.

Ask: **What is an example of an acceptable experiment on humans?** *(Sample: testing a drug that could cure a disease)*

Everyday Science

Have students read *Mushrooms Worth Their Weight In Gold.* Explain the process by which the truffle spores are spread is called mycophagy and relates to fungi being eaten and the spores being spread by the waste of the animal that eats it. Tell students that the relationship between the trees and the truffles, where each member of the relationship gets something from the other, is called symbiotic.

Explain that the pigs used to find truffles have a keen sense of smell and an instinct that makes them seek out truffles. Because the pigs are prone to eating too many truffles in the field, truffle hunters sometimes use dogs now, that must be trained to find truffles, but are easier to control.

Ask: **How do trees benefit truffles?** *(Samples: give them a place to live, supply them with food)*

79

Plants

Introduce the Big Q

Have students look at the image and read the Engaging Question and description. Ask students to suggest explanations for the unusual shape of the baobab tree, especially its wide trunk and short, topmost branches. Have volunteers share their explanations. Tell students that baobab trees can store as much as 120,000 liters of water in their swollen trunks. Ask: **Considering where these trees live, why is water storage essential?** *(It prevents the trees from dying during the harsh drought conditions of the dry season.)* Tell students that almost every part of a baobab tree, which is sometimes called the "Tree of Life," is used by native peoples. Leaves and roots are used for medicinal purposes. The bark is used for cloth and rope. The fruit, which is called "monkey bread," is a good source of vitamin C and is eaten, as are the seeds. The trunk and roots can be tapped for water during dry periods. And because mature trees are frequently hollow, they can provide living space for many organisms, including humans. **The baobab tree is indeed unusual. Are there other trees that you might consider unusual or odd looking?** *(Samples: Giant sequoias, giant redwoods, banyans, mangroves, cacti, and the Divi-Divi tree of the Caribbean islands, such as Aruba)*

Untamed Science Video

AMAZING PLANT DEFENSES Before viewing, invite students to suggest ways in which plants defend and protect themselves. Then play the video. Lead a class discussion and make a list of questions that this video raises. You may wish to have students view the video again after they have completed the chapter to see if their questions have been answered.

To access the online resources for this chapter, search on or navigate to *Plants*.

Untamed Science Video explores the ways in which plants protect and defend themselves.

The Big Question allows students to answer the Engaging Question about what makes the trees unusual.

my science online .com | Plants

WHAT'S UNUSUAL ABOUT THESE TREES?

How do you know a plant when you see it?

With its wide trunk and short stubby branches, the baobab tree looks like a sweet potato or an upside-down tree. Seen for miles across the dry African savannah, the baobab can live for over 1,000 years and can grow to over 23 meters high and 27 meters around the trunk. It would take about 18 teenagers with arms spread wide and fingertips touching to encircle a tree that wide!

> UNTAMED SCIENCE Watch the **Untamed Science** video to learn more about plants.

Draw Conclusions Why do you think the baobab tree has such a wide trunk and short branches only at the very top?

<u>The baobab trunk could be thick to retain water and the branches might be short and only at the top so animals cannot reach them.</u>

Professional Development Note | From the Author

Humans are now one of the most significant agents of geologic change on Earth's surface. However, they have a long way to go before their impact equals that of plants. Oxygen in Earth's atmosphere is the result of the evolution of photosynthesizing bacteria—the precursors of modern plants—2.5 billion years ago. For 4 billion years the continents were huge expanses of barren rock devoid of life. Then plants evolved vascular tissue that allowed them to spread across the land, and animal life followed right behind. Even now, plant life controls the rate of land erosion and soil development. So next time you see a plant, acknowledge its contribution and show it a bit of respect.

✐ *Michael Wysession*

CHAPTER 3

Plants

Chapter at a Glance

CHAPTER PACING: 10–16 periods or 5–8 blocks

INTRODUCE THE CHAPTER: Use the Engaging Question and the opening image to get students thinking about plants. Activate prior knowledge and preteach vocabulary using the Getting Started pages.

Lesson 1: What Is a Plant?

Lesson 2: Classifying Plants

Lesson 3: Plant Structures

Lesson 4: Plant Reproduction

Lesson 5: Plant Responses and Growth

Lesson 6: Plants in Everyday Life

ASSESSMENT OPTIONS: Chapter Test, *ExamView®* Computer Test Generator, Performance Assessment, Progress Monitoring Assessments, SuccessTracker™

Preference Navigator, in the online Planning tools, allows you to customize *Interactive Science* to your own teaching style. You can also edit lesson plans by selecting the Lesson Planner option.

Digital Teacher's Edition allows you to access your Teacher's Edition and Resource online.

my science online .com

Differentiated Instruction

L1 **Plants versus Animals** Have students think about a familiar plant or show them a potted plant. Ask students to identify at least two ways in which plants and animals differ. Tell students to record their answers and return to them at the end of the chapter for correction or confirmation.

L1 **Classifying Plants** Tell students that they will be learning about four major types of plants. Have students think about what they already know about plants and identify the types. Tell students to record their answers and return to them at the end of the chapter for correction or confirmation.

L3 **The Baobab Tree** There are several legends that account for the unusual shape of the baobab tree. Have interested students research these legends and share their findings with the class.

81

Getting Started

Check Your Understanding

This activity assesses students' understanding of the classification of plants as autotrophs because they make their own food through the process of photosynthesis. After students have shared their answers, point out that the other classification of organisms based on how they obtain food is heterotrophs, which are living things that eat autotrophs or other heterotrophs to survive.

Preteach Vocabulary Skills

Draw students' attention to the table of Greek word parts and their meanings. Review with students the concept of a word part as having a specific meaning that alone or in combination with another word part forms many of the terms common to science. Tell students that learning the meaning of word parts can help them remember and define new and unfamiliar vocabulary terms. Point out the vocabulary terms *cotyledon* and *zygote*. Tell students that these terms are additional examples of words with Greek origins: *cotyledon* from the Greek meaning "cup-shaped hollow" and *zygote* from the Greek meaning "yoked" or "joined." Have students record these meanings and compare them with the definitions learned later in the chapter.

---

3 Getting Started

Check Your Understanding

1. **Background** Read the paragraph below and then answer the question.

> Rahim and Malika were in the park after school. "Plants are such cool **organisms**," said Rahim. "Can you imagine if humans had green **pigment** in their skin?" "Yeah," said Malika. "If we were **autotrophs**, I'd never have to get up early to pack my lunch!"

An **organism** is a living thing.

A **pigment** is a colored chemical compound that absorbs light.

An **autotroph** is an organism that makes its own food.

- Give an example of an autotrophic organism that has green pigment.

  Sample: a tree _____

> **MY READING WEB** If you had trouble completing the question above, visit **My Reading Web** and type in *Plants*.

Vocabulary Skill

Greek Word Origins Many science words come to English from ancient Greek. Learning the Greek word parts can help you understand some of the vocabulary in this chapter.

Greek Word Part	Meaning	Example Word
chloros	pale green	chloroplast, *n.* green cellular structure in which photosynthesis occurs
petalon	leaf	petal, *n.* colorful, leaflike flower structure

2. **Quick Check** *Chlorophyll* is a pigment found in plants. Which part of the word *chlorophyll* tells you that it is a green pigment?

   Chloro _____

My Reading Web offers leveled readings that provide a foundation for the chapter content.

Vocab Flash Cards offer extra practice with the chapter vocabulary words.

Digital Lesson

- Assign the *Check Your Understanding* activity online and have students submit their work to you.
- Assign the *Vocabulary Skill* activity online and have students submit their work to you.

MY SCIENCE online.com

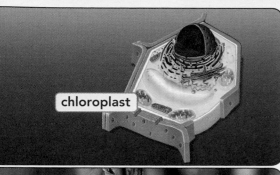

chloroplast

monocot

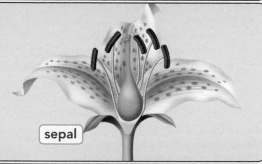

sepal

fruit

Chapter Preview

LESSON 1
- chlorophyll • photosynthesis
- tissue • chloroplast • vacuole
- cuticle • vascular tissue
- 🔄 Compare and Contrast
- △ Predict

LESSON 2
- nonvascular plant • rhizoid
- vascular plant • phloem
- xylem • frond • pollen • seed
- gymnosperm • angiosperm
- cotyledon • monocot
- dicot
- 🔄 Outline
- △ Communicate

LESSON 3
- root cap • cambium • stoma
- transpiration • embryo
- germination • flower
- pollination • sepal • petal
- stamen • pistil • ovary
- 🔄 Relate Cause and Effect
- △ Observe

LESSON 4
- sporophyte • gametophyte
- annual • biennial • perennial
- fertilization • zygote
- cone • ovule • fruit
- 🔄 Summarize
- △ Infer

LESSON 5
- tropism • hormone
- auxin • photoperiodism
- critical night length
- short-day plant • long-day plant
- day-neutral plant • dormancy
- 🔄 Relate Text and Visuals
- △ Draw Conclusions

LESSON 6
- peat
- 🔄 Identify the Main Idea
- △ Pose Questions

83

Preview Vocabulary Terms

Have students create a three-column chart to rate their knowledge of the vocabulary terms before they read the chapter. In the first column of the chart, students should list the terms for the chapter. In the second column, students should identify whether they can define and use the word, whether they have heard or seen the word before, or whether they do not know the word. As the class progresses through the chapter, have students write definitions for each term in the last column of the chart. A list of Academic Vocabulary for each lesson can be found in the Support All Readers box at the start of the lesson.

L1 Have students look at the images on this page as you pronounce the vocabulary word. Have students repeat the word after you. Then read the definition. Use the sample sentence in italics to clarify the meaning of the term.

chloroplast *(KLAWR uh plast)* A plant cell structure in which food is made. *A chloroplast contains the green pigment chlorophyll, which makes it possible for a plant to manufacture its own food.*

monocot *(MAHN oh kaht)* An angiosperm that has only one seed leaf. *Corn is an example of a monocot.*

sepal *(SEE pul)* Leaf-like structure that encloses a flower when it is a bud. *A sepal, often green in color, protects the developing flower and folds back as the flower blooms.*

fruit *(froot)* The ripened ovary and other structures that enclose one or more seeds. *A fruit is the means by which angiosperm seeds are dispersed.*

CHAPTER 3

ⒺⓁⓁ Support

Have students work in small groups to complete their charts cooperatively for the Preview Vocabulary Terms activity. Read aloud and review the vocabulary terms before students begin their charts.

Beginning
LOW Complete the chart using the vocabulary terms in the native language.

HIGH Write a definition for each known vocabulary term in the native language.

Intermediate
LOW/HIGH Discuss the definitions for known vocabulary terms in cooperative groups.

Advanced
LOW/HIGH Write a sentence using each of the vocabulary terms that is already known.

What is a plant?

 How do you know a plant when you see it?

Lesson Pacing: 1–2 periods or $\frac{1}{2}$–1 block

🕐 **SHORT ON TIME?** To do this lesson in approximately half the time, do the Activate Prior Knowledge activity on page 84. A discussion of the Key Concepts on pages 85 and 87 will familiarize students with the lesson content. Have students do the Quick Labs. The rest of the lesson can be completed by students independently.

> **Preference Navigator,** in the online Planning tools, allows you to customize *Interactive Science* to your own teaching style. You can also edit lesson plans by selecting the Lesson Planner option.
>
> **Digital Teacher's Edition** allows you to access your Teacher's Edition and Resource materials online.

my science online.com

Lesson Vocabulary

- chlorophyll
- photosynthesis
- tissue
- chloroplast
- vacuole
- cuticle
- vascular tissue

 ## Content Refresher

Plant Traits and Diversity Plants are defined by a combination of traits. Plants are multicellular eukaryotes, with cell walls that contain cellulose. The great majority of plants are autotrophs—they capture the sun's energy and photosynthesize, thus making their own food. However, some plant species are entirely or partly heterotrophic. For example, dodder is a nonphotosynthetic parasite. Dodder grows on its host plant (such as buckwheat and sage) and completely depends on it for food. Other plants, such as mistletoe, are only partially parasitic, with some photosynthetic parts. Some plants are carnivorous—they attract, trap, digest, and absorb insects to obtain an additional source of nutrients. There is great diversity within the plant kingdom. Carnivorous plants represent only one example.

Land plants in particular have developed successful adaptations that enable them to live in a wide variety of environments. One important adaptation of land plants is the production of lignin, a chemical that stiffens cell walls. Lignin provides strength and support, allowing a plant to grow large and tall. Plants play critical roles in the ecosystems in which they are found. They are primary producers and form the foundation of many food webs. Plants also release oxygen gas, a product of photosynthesis essential for other organisms.

LESSON OBJECTIVES

- Identify the characteristics that all plants share.
- Name all the things that a plant needs to live successfully on land.

Blended Path
Active learning using Student Edition, Inquiry Path, and Digital Path

ENGAGE AND EXPLORE

Teach this lesson using a variety of resources. Begin by reading **My Planet Diary** as a class. Have students discuss a plant project they would like to do at their school. Then have students do the **Inquiry Warm-Up activity.** Students will observe leaves from plants growing in two different environments and infer the growing place of each plant based on leaf thickness. The **After the Inquiry Warm-Up worksheet** sets up a discussion about how leaf thickness, texture, and size may be used to make an inference about a plant's environment. Have volunteers share their answers to question 4, suggesting a question to ask to determine if a leaf is from a plant native to a desert environment.

EXPLAIN AND ELABORATE

Teach Key Concepts by explaining that members of the plant kingdom share certain characteristics: almost all are autotrophs; with the exception of some green algae, all are multicellular; and all have cells surrounded by cell walls. **Lead a Discussion** about photosynthesis, focusing on the raw materials and products. **Support the Big Q** by explaining the structures that are characteristic of plants and their functions.

Teach Key Concepts by explaining the five requirements for plants to live successfully on land. **Lead a Discussion** about the plant adaptations that make plants successful at survival on land. Have students practice the inquiry skill in the **Apply It activity.**

Hand out the **Key Concept Summaries** as a review of each part of the lesson. Students can also use the online **Vocab Flash Cards** to review key terms.

EVALUATE

Have students take the **Lesson Quiz.** For an alternate assessment, see the *ExamView*® Computer Test Generator, Progress Monitoring Assessments, or SuccessTracker™.

ELL Support

1 Content and Language

Have students copy the vocabulary terms into a journal or personal glossary. Then ask them to find the first time the words are used in the chapter. Have them copy the definition of each vocabulary term into their journal or personal glossary.

Lab zone Inquiry Path
Hands-on learning in the Lab zone

ENGAGE AND EXPLORE

To teach this lesson with an emphasis on inquiry, begin with the **Inquiry Warm-Up activity.** Students will observe leaves from plants growing in two different environments and infer the growing place of each plant based on leaf thickness. The **After the Inquiry Warm-Up worksheet** sets up a discussion about how leaf thickness, texture, and size may be used to make an inference about a plant's environment. Have volunteers share their answers to question 4, suggesting a question to ask to determine if a leaf is from a plant native to a desert environment.

EXPLAIN AND ELABORATE

Focus on the **Inquiry Skill** for the lesson. Remind students that when they predict, they make an inference about a future event or situation based on what they already know. What was used to make a prediction about which leaf seemed to have more water in it in the **Inquiry Warm-Up activity?** *(Sample: Water takes up room, so the thicker leaf would have more water in it.)* **Support the Big Q** by explaining the structures that are characteristic of plants and their functions. Have students do the **Quick Lab** to observe algae and plant leaves to determine how they are alike and what evidence supports the idea that plants are descended from green algae.

Before beginning the **Apply It activity,** remind students that when they predict, they make an inference about a future event or situation based on what they already know. Do the **Teacher Demo** to model the work of vascular tissue. Have students do the **Quick Lab** going on a plant hunt around the school describing and drawing as many different species as they can find. Students can use the online **Vocab Flash Cards** to review key terms.

EVALUATE

Have students take the **Lesson Quiz.** For an alternate assessment, see the *ExamView®* Computer Test Generator, Progress Monitoring Assessments, or SuccessTracker™.

Digital Path
Online learning at my science online.com

ENGAGE AND EXPLORE

Teach this lesson using digital resources. Begin by having students learn more and explore real-world connections to plants at **My Planet Diary** online. Have them access the Chapter Resources to find the **Unlock the Big Question activity.** There they can answer the questions and refine their responses as they continue through the lesson. You can re-assign the activity and have students submit their work so you can track their progress.

EXPLAIN AND ELABORATE

Students reading above, at, or below the lexile measure of this lesson can access basic content readings at their level at **My Reading Web.** Encourage students to use the online **Vocab Flash Cards** to preview key terms. Use the **Interactive Art activity** online to show the structure of a plant cell. **Support the Big Q** by explaining the structures that are characteristic of plants and their functions. Have students do the **Quick Lab** to observe algae and plant leaves to determine how they are alike and what evidence supports the idea that plants are descended from green algae.

Assign the **Apply It activity** online and have students submit their work to you. Have students do the **Quick Lab** going on a plant hunt around the school describing and drawing as many different species as they can find. The **Key Concept Summaries** online allow students to read a summary and see an image associated with each part of the lesson. Online remediation is available at **My Science Coach.**

EVALUATE

Have students take the **Lesson Quiz.** For an alternate assessment, see the *ExamView®* Computer Test Generator, Progress Monitoring Assessments, or SuccessTracker™.

2 Frontload the Lesson

Have students survey the visuals in the lesson. Then have them write questions they have about the lesson based on their surveys. After students read the lesson, have them answer the questions they wrote at the start of the lesson.

3 Comprehensible Input

Have students rewrite the Key Concept on page 87, using their own words to explain all the things that a plant needs to live successfully on land.

4 Language Production

Pair or group students with varied language abilities to complete labs collaboratively for language practice. Have each student copy the completed written lab for personal reference.

5 Assess Understanding

Ask students to make notes about Key Concepts from the lesson and use the notes to prepare an oral presentation of the concepts. Encourage students to use the visuals in the lesson to support their presentations.

LESSON 3.1

What Is a Plant?

Establish Learning Objectives

After this lesson, students will be able to:

- Identify the characteristics that all plants share.
- Name all the things that a plant needs to live successfully on land.

Engage

Activate Prior Knowledge

MY PLANET DIARY Read *How Does Your Garden Grow?* with the class. Explain that native plants are those that evolved naturally in a particular area. Emphasize that different areas have different native plants adapted to the conditions there. Ask: **What are some conditions that determine the types of native plants that grow in an area?** *(Temperature, moisture, type of soil, altitude)*

BIG IDEAS OF SCIENCE REFERENCE LIBRARY 📖
Have students look up the following topic: Rain Forest.

Explore

Lab Resource: Inquiry Warm-Up

L1 WHAT DO LEAVES REVEAL ABOUT PLANTS? Students will observe leaves from plants growing in two different environments and infer the growing place of each plant based on leaf thickness, texture, and size.

---

1 What Is a Plant?

- What Characteristics Do All Plants Share?
- What Do Plants Need to Live Successfully on Land?

MY PLANET DIARY

How Does Your Garden Grow?

Students at The Hilldale School in Daly City, California, get to play in the dirt during class. The students planted and maintain a garden filled with native species. Native plants, or plants that have been in an area for a long time, can struggle to survive if new plants are introduced. This creates problems for the insects, animals, and other organisms that rely on the native plants. The students spent three months removing nonnative plants before creating a garden that will help local organisms right outside their school.

PROFILE

Communicate Discuss the question with a group of classmates. Write your answer below.

Describe a plant project you would like to do at your school.

Sample: We could raise tomato plants in the science classroom and have the cafeteria staff use them to prepare a meal.

> **PLANET DIARY** Go to Planet Diary to learn more about plants.

 Do the Inquiry Warm-Up *What Do Leaves Reveal About Plants?*

What Characteristics Do All Plants Share?

Which organisms were the ancestors of today's plants? In search of answers, biologists studied fossils, the traces of ancient life forms preserved in rock and other substances. The oldest plant fossils are about 400 million years old. These fossils show that even at that early date, plants already had many adaptations for life on land.

SUPPORT ALL READERS
Lexile Measure = 940L   **Lexile Word Count = 1115**

Prior Exposure to Content: Many students may have misconceptions on this topic

Academic Vocabulary: *compare, contrast, predict*

Science Vocabulary: *chlorophyll, photosynthesis, chloroplast, vacuole*

Concept Level: Generally appropriate for most students in this grade

Preteach With: My Planet Diary "Your Garden" and Figure 1 activity

Go to **My Reading Web** to access leveled readings that provide a foundation for the content.

my science online.com

Vocabulary
- chlorophyll
- photosynthesis
- tissue
- chloroplast
- vacuole
- cuticle
- vascular tissue

Skills
- Reading: Compare and Contrast
- Inquiry: Predict

Better clues to the origin of plants came from comparing the chemicals in modern plants to those in other organisms. Biologists studied a pigment called chlorophyll. **Chlorophyll** (KLAWR uh fil) is a green pigment found in the chloroplasts of plants, algae, and some bacteria. Land plants and green algae contain the same forms of chlorophyll. Further comparisons of genetic material clearly showed that plants and green algae are very closely related. Today, green algae are classified as plants.

Members of the plant kingdom share several characteristics. **Nearly all plants are autotrophs, organisms that produce their own food. With the exception of some green algae, all plants contain many cells. In addition, all plant cells are surrounded by cell walls.**

Plants Are Autotrophs You can think of a typical plant as a sun-powered, food-making factory. Sunlight provides the energy for this food-making process, called **photosynthesis.** During photosynthesis, a plant uses carbon dioxide gas and water to make food and oxygen.

Compare and Contrast
How do you think the ancient environment of the leaf in the fossil differed from that of the modern leaf in the pictures below?

Sample: The ancient environment would not have been exposed to human-caused pollution. There would be different animals and plants around.

85

ELL Support

1 Content and Language
Write the term *tissue* on the board. Explain that this word has a scientific meaning (a group of similar cells that performs a function) that is different from its everyday meaning (a disposable piece of paper used as a handkerchief).

2 Frontload the Lesson
Invite students to give their ideas and impressions about what plants need to survive. Encourage students to apply their prior knowledge and experiences observing plants in both indoor and outdoor settings, including cultivated as well as wild plants.

3 Comprehensible Input
Have each student create a cluster diagram that identifies the three basic characteristics shared by all plants. Students' diagrams should include a variety of words and phrases relating to each characteristic.

Explain

Introduce Vocabulary
Point out to students the vocabulary terms *photosynthesis, chlorophyll,* and *chloroplast.* On the board, write the word parts for each term: *photo-, synthesis, chloro-, -plast, -phyll.* Remind students of the importance of learning word parts. Have students identify these word parts and define the terms in their own words. Then have them compare their definitions with the accepted ones as they learn them.

Teach Key Concepts
Explain to students that members of the plant kingdom share certain characteristics: almost all are autotrophs; with the exception of some green algae, all are multicellular; and all have cells surrounded by cell walls. Discuss each of these characteristics by first explaining that autotrophs convert energy from sunlight into the chemical energy of the food they make, which plants use to live. Ask: **What is the name of the food-making process in plants?** *(Photosynthesis)* **What are the raw materials and products of photosynthesis?** *(Raw materials are carbon dioxide and water. Products are food and oxygen.)* **In what structures of the plant cell does photosynthesis take place?** *(Chloroplasts)* **What pigment in the chloroplasts is able to capture the energy of sunlight?** *(Chlorophyll)* **Are animals autotrophs? How do you know?** *(No, they eat plants or other animals.)*

Compare and Contrast Tell students that comparing and contrasting involves examining the similarities and differences between things. By comparing and contrasting information, students can determine how concepts, facts, and events are alike and different.

Lead a Discussion
PHOTOSYNTHESIS If students have previously studied cells and cell processes, review the process of photosynthesis, focusing on the raw materials and products. Ask: **What two compounds does a plant use to make food?** *(Carbon dioxide and water)* **What elements will the food contain?** *(Carbon, hydrogen, and oxygen)* **What will the food be?** *(A carbohydrate)*

My Planet Diary provides an opportunity for students to explore real-world connections to plants.

my science online.com | Describing Plants

Explain

Support the Big Q ❓ UbD

PLANT CHARACTERISTICS Review with students the meaning of the term *multicellular,* and point out that with the exception of some green algae, all plants are made up of many cells. Explain to students that similar cells that perform a specific function are organized into tissues. Finally, discuss the structure of a plant cell, noting the differences between plant and animal cells. Ask: **What encloses a plant's cell?** *(Cell wall)* **What is the cell wall made of?** *(Cellulose)* **What is a function of the cell wall?** *(The cell wall is rigid and thus provides support for the plant.)* **What two other structures are characteristic of plant cells? What are their functions?** *(Plant cells contain chloroplasts, the structures in which food is made. They also contain a vacuole, which is a large sac that stores water, wastes, and food.)*

Teach With Visuals

Tell students to look at **Figure 1.** Ask: **Which structures are found only in plant cells?** *(Cell wall, chloroplasts, one large vacuole)* **Which structure makes plant parts stiff?** *(Cell wall)* **In which structure is food made?** *(Chloroplast)*

Elaborate

Lab Resource: Quick Lab

L2 ALGAE AND OTHER PLANTS Students will observe algae and plant leaves to determine how they are alike and what evidence supports the idea that plants are descended from green algae.

Evaluate

Assess Your Understanding

After students answer the questions, have them evaluate their understanding by completing the appropriate sentence.

RTI Response to Intervention

1a. If students need help with the idea that plants are autotrophs, **then** discuss the meaning of the term and the fact that plants contain chlorophyll and carry on photosynthesis.

b. If students cannot remember the function of the cell wall, **then** remind them that it encloses the cell outside the cell membrane.

c. If students have trouble understanding the role of the vacuole as a storage sac for water, **then** review the functions of this cell part.

MY SCIENCE ⓢ COACH Have students go online to understand the characteristics of plants.

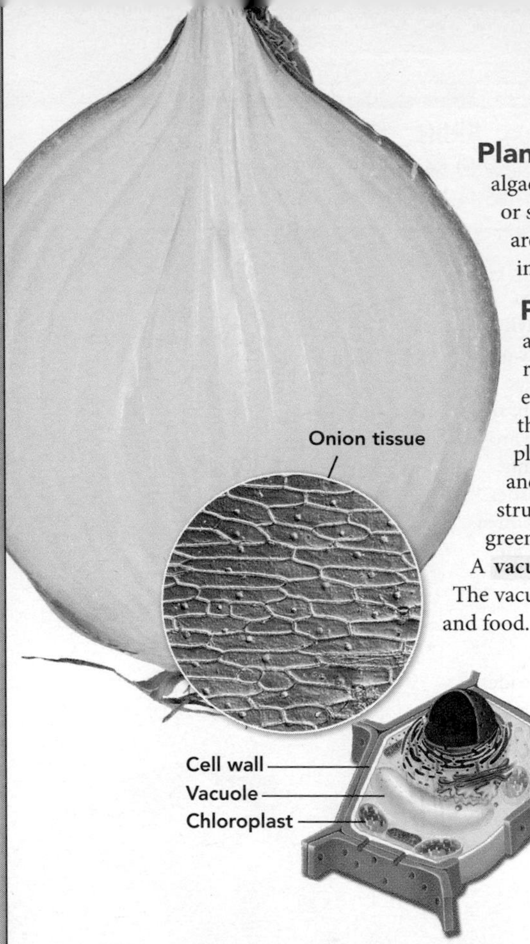

86 Plants

Plants Are Multicellular Except for some green algae, all plants are made of many cells. No matter how large or small a plant is, its cells are organized into **tissues.** Tissues are groups of similar cells that perform a specific function in an organism.

Plant Cells Unlike the cells of animals, a plant's cells are enclosed by a cell wall. See **Figure 1.** The cell wall surrounds the cell membrane and separates the cell from the environment. Plant cell walls contain cellulose, a material that makes the walls rigid. Because their cell walls are rigid, plant cells look like small boxes. Cell walls make apples and carrots crunchy. Plant cells also contain many other structures. **Chloroplasts** (KLAWR uh plasts), which look like green jelly beans, are the structures in which food is made. A **vacuole** is a large storage sac that can expand and shrink. The vacuole stores many substances, including water, wastes, and food. A plant wilts when too much water has left its vacuoles.

Onion tissue

Cell wall
Vacuole
Chloroplast

FIGURE 1 ·············
▶ INTERACTIVE ART **Plant Cells**
Plant cells are different from animal cells. Cell walls make onions crunchy.

✏ **Infer** How does having cell walls affect a plant's ability to grow tall?

Sample: The rigid cell walls provide support for the plant to grow tall.

Lab Do the Quick Lab
zone *Algae and Other Plants.*

🔑 **Assess Your Understanding**

1a. Review Almost all plants (make/do not make) their own food.

b. Explain What is the function of the cell wall in a plant cell?
Sample: The cell wall separates the cell from the environment.

c. Infer What do you think happens to a plant cell if the plant is given too much water?
Sample: The vacuoles will not be able to hold all of the water.

got it? ·············

○ **I get it!** Now I know that nearly all plants *are autotrophs, are multicellular, and have cell walls.*

○ **I need extra help with** *See TE note.*

Go to **MY SCIENCE ⓢ COACH** online for help with this subject.

86 Plants

Interactive Art shows the structure of a plant cell.

MY SCIENCE online.com **Describing Plants**

What Do Plants Need to Live Successfully on Land?

Imagine multicellular algae floating in the ocean. The algae obtain water and other materials directly from the water around them. They are held up toward the sunlight by the water. Now imagine plants living on land. What adaptations would help them meet their needs without water all around them? **For plants to survive on land, they must have ways to obtain water and other nutrients from their surroundings, retain water, support their bodies, transport materials, and reproduce.**

Obtaining Water and Other Nutrients Recall that all organisms need water to survive. Obtaining water is easy for algae because water surrounds them. To live on land, plants need adaptations for obtaining water from the soil. One adaptation is the way the plant produces its roots, as shown in **Figure 2**. Plants must also have ways of obtaining other nutrients from the soil.

Saguaro cactus

Acacia tree

FIGURE 2 ·······

Getting Water in the Desert
The saguaro cactus and the acacia tree both live in deserts with limited water. Saguaro roots spread out horizontally. When it rains, the roots quickly absorb water over a wide area. Acacia trees in the Negev Desert of Israel get their water from deep underground instead of at the surface.

✏️ **Interpret Diagrams** Draw the roots of the acacia tree. Then describe how the growth of the roots differs between the plants.

<u>Sample: The cactus roots grow horizontally, while the acacia roots grow vertically.</u>

87

Explain ——————

Teach Key Concepts 🗝

Explain to students that algae live in water, and as a result, they can obtain water and nutrients directly from the water. Tell students that the evolution of plants from water-dwellers to land-dwellers required that such plants have adaptations that would help them meet their needs without water all around them. Discuss with students the five requirements of plants to live successfully on land. Ask: **What do plants need to survive on land?** *(Plants must have ways to obtain water and other nutrients from their surroundings, retain water, support their bodies, transport materials to all plant parts, and reproduce.)* **Where do plants get water and nutrients?** *(From the soil)* **What plant adaptation helps a plant get water from the soil?** *(Roots)* **Are all roots alike? Explain.** *(No, plant roots differ depending on the environment and the soil conditions.)*

Address Misconceptions

L1 PLANTS OR ANIMALS FIRST? When discussing the history of life on land, students often think of some exotic animal emerging from the sea, breathing air, and starting the long line of land-dwelling organisms to come. Students do not always consider whether plants beat animals to it. Ask: **What did animals need to survive on land?** *(A source of food and oxygen)* **Where did these requirements come from?** *(Plants that were already thriving on land)*

21st Century Learning 🅳🅺

CREATIVITY Have students read *Rain Forest* in the **Big Ideas of Science Reference Library.** Ask students to write a letter to the editor of a local newspaper that educates readers about the ecological importance of rain forests and persuades them to take a stand against the destruction caused by deforestation.

Differentiated Instruction

L1 Plant Cell Structure Have student pairs draw a large illustration of a cell. Then have them make several sticky labels for each cell feature: 1 for nucleus, 2 for cytoplasm, 1 for cell wall, 1 for vacuole, and 3 for chloroplast. Have students take turns placing a sticky note in the appropriate part of the illustration as they describe the cell part. For example, "A plant cell has many chloroplasts."

L1 Plant Adaptations Have students use old magazines or newspapers to find a photograph of a land plant. Have them label the plant with the five adaptations that a plant needs to survive on land.

L3 Botany The scientific study of plants is known as *botany*. Have interested students find out about the various areas of specialization in botany as well as the numerous career opportunities the subject offers.

Explain

Lead a Discussion

PLANT ADAPTATIONS Continue to discuss the plant adaptations that make plants successful at survival on land. Ask: **What plant adaptation reduces water loss?** (Cuticle) **Why does a plant tend to lose water?** (When the amount of water in plant cells is less than the amount of water in the air, water moves out of the cells and into the air.) Discuss with students the need for land plants to support their body and to transport essential materials throughout the body. Ask: **Why must land plants support their body?** (They must position those parts of their body that make food in such a way to get maximum sunlight.) **How do they accomplish this?** (Cell walls and vascular tissue strengthen and support plant bodies.) **What is vascular tissue?** (A system of tubelike structures for transporting water, minerals, and food)

Make Analogies

VASCULAR SYSTEMS Discuss with students the role of the vascular system in plants in transporting materials from one part of the plant body to another. Then remind students of the cardiovascular system in humans. Ask: **What does the term *vascular* refer to?** (A system of vessels that have certain functions in getting material to and from cells) **How are the two systems similar?** (They both transport vital materials to and from all parts of the body.)

Elaborate

CRITICAL THINKING Tell students that some of the earliest land plants to appear on Earth were very tiny plants that lived in moist environments. These plants were sometimes described as being only partly adapted to life on land. Ask: **Why is this description appropriate?** (Because they were small, they did not have to have an extensive vascular system to transport materials throughout the plant or support the plant. Because they grew in moist places, water and nutrients were available and plentiful. Water for reproduction was also available.)

Apply It!

L1 Before beginning the activity, remind students that a graph shows the relationship between two variables—in this case the time of day and the amount of water loss.

△ **Predict** Remind students that when they predict, they make an inference about a future event or situation based on what they already know.

FIGURE 3 ....
Waterproof Leaves
The waxy cuticle of many leaves, like the one below, look shiny under light.

Retaining Water When there is more water in plant cells than in the air, the water leaves the plant and enters the air. The plant could dry out if it cannot hold onto water. One adaptation that helps a plant reduce water loss is a waxy, waterproof layer called the **cuticle.** You can see the cuticle on the leaf in **Figure 3.**

Support A plant on land must support its own body. It's easier for small, low-growing plants to support themselves. In larger plants, the food-making parts must be exposed to as much sunlight as possible. Cell walls and tissue strengthen and support the large bodies of these plants.

Transporting Materials A plant needs to transport water, minerals, food, and other materials from one part of its body to another. In general, water and minerals are taken up by the bottom part of the plant, while food is made in the top part. But all of the plant's cells need water, minerals, and food.

In small plants, materials can simply move from one cell to the next. Larger plants need a more efficient way to transport materials from one part of the plant to another. These plants have tissue for transporting materials called vascular tissue. **Vascular tissue** is a system of tubelike structures inside a plant through which water, minerals, and food move. See vascular tissue in action in **Figure 4.**

apply it!

This graph shows how much water a plant loses during the day. Give the graph a title.

❶ **Interpret Graphs** During what part of the day did the plant lose the most water?

<u>Around 2 P.M.</u>

❷ △ **Predict** How might the line in the graph look from 10 P.M. to 8 A.M.? Why?

<u>Sample: The line would</u>
<u>continue to decrease through</u>
<u>the night until morning and</u>
<u>then increase. There is less</u>
<u>water loss when there is no sun.</u>

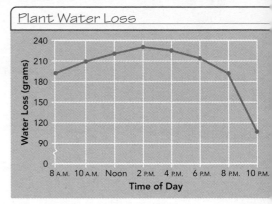

Plant Water Loss

❸ **CHALLENGE** Do you think this graph would be the same for plants all around the world? Why?

<u>Sample: No; plants in different</u>
<u>parts of the world are exposed</u>
<u>to different amounts of sunlight.</u>

Digital Lesson: Assign the *Apply It* activity online and have students submit their work to you.

my science online.com ➤ Plant Survival Needs

Reproduction For algae and some other plants, reproduction can only occur if there is water in the environment. This is because the sperm cells of these plants swim through the water to the egg cells. Land plants need to have adaptations that make reproduction possible in dry environments.

FIGURE 4

Colorful Carnations
These three carnations were left overnight in glasses of water. Blue dye was added to the glass in the middle. The stem of the flower on the right was split in half. Part of the stem was placed in water with blue dye and the other part was placed in water with red dye.

✏️ **Draw Conclusions** Why did the flowers in the glasses with dye change color?

Sample: In both cases,
the dye was trans-
ported through vascular
tissue in the stem into
the flower, changing the
flower's color.

Do the Quick Lab
Local Plant Diversity.

⬜ **Assess Your Understanding**

2a. Define What is a cuticle?
A cuticle is a waxy, waterproof
layer on a leaf that helps the
plant reduce water loss.

b. Apply Concepts Describe the pros and cons of being a tall land plant.
Sample: Tall plants have to
support themselves more than
shorter plants. But, they get
more sunlight if they are taller
than the plants around them.

got it?

○ **I get it!** Now I know that to live on land, plants need to _obtain and retain_
water and nutrients, support
themselves, transport
materials, and reproduce.

○ **I need extra help with** _See TE note._

Go to **MY SCIENCE COACH** online for help with this subject.

89

Differentiated Instruction

L1 Growing Tall To ensure that students understand the importance of vascular tissue as an adaptation of land plants, have them explain why plants can grow to be any height.

L1 Problem/Solution As a summarizing activity, have students make a two-column chart with the headings *Problem* and *Solution*. In the *Problem* column, have them identify the five problems plants had to overcome in

order to successfully live on land. In the *Solution* column, have students identify the plant adaptation that solved each problem.

L3 Plants in Moist Places Have students do the summarizing activity above and add a third column with the heading *Small Plants Growing in Moist Places*. Have students explain how these land plants are adapted to life on land.

Teacher Demo 🧪Lab zone

L1 VASCULAR TISSUE

Materials two celery stalks, medium-sized jar, dark food coloring, water, knife

Time 10 minutes and then observation 24 hours later

Fill the jar one-quarter full with water and color the water with a few drops of food coloring. Place the stalks leaf-side up in the jar of colored water. Have students observe the appearance of the stalks. Leave the stalks undisturbed for 24 hours. Have students again observe the stalks. Remove the stalks from the water. Using the knife, cut off the part of the stalk that was submerged and discard it. Then cut the stalks into cross-sectional pieces and provide students with pieces to observe.

Ask: **What did you observe about the stalk and leaf color?** *(The stalk and leaf started to show streaks the color of the food coloring.)* **What did you observe about the pieces of stalk?** *(There were dots the color of the food coloring in the cross-sectional pieces.)* **What do you think those dots are?** *(The structures that make up the vascular tissue that carried the colored water up the stalk to the leaves)*

Lab Resource: Quick Lab 🧪Lab zone

L2 LOCAL PLANT DIVERSITY Students will go on a plant hunt around the school describing and drawing as many different species as they can find.

Evaluate

Assess Your Understanding

After students answer the questions, have them evaluate their understanding by completing the appropriate sentence.

R T I Response to Intervention

2a. If students have trouble describing a cuticle, **then** remind them that a cuticle is an adaptation of a plant to living on land and aids in water retention.

b. If students need help with identifying the advantages and disadvantages of a tall plant, **then** tell them to think about size in terms of support and of getting the energy required for photosynthesis.

MY SCIENCE COACH Have students go online for help in understanding plant adaptations to life on land

Lab zone **After the Inquiry Warm-Up**

What Is a Plant?

Inquiry Warm-Up, What Do Leaves Reveal About Plants?

In the Inquiry Warm-Up, you investigated how leaf thickness, texture, and size may be used to make an inference about a plant's environment. Using what you learned from that activity, answer the questions below.

1. **COMMUNICATE** Draw the surface of each leaf when viewed through a hand lens.

2. **COMPARE AND CONTRAST** Compare the textures of the two leaves.

   _____

   _____

3. **INFER** Which of the two leaves do you think has more water in it? Explain.

   _____

   _____

4. **POSE QUESTIONS** Based on your observations, what might be a good question for a person to ask to help determine if a leaf is from a plant native to a desert environment?

   _____

Assess Your Understanding

What Is a Plant?

What Characteristics Do All Plants Share?

1a. REVIEW Almost all plants (make/do not make) their own food.

b. EXPLAIN What is the function of the cell wall in a plant cell? _____
_____

c. INFER What do you think happens to a plant cell if the plant is given
too much water? _____
_____

got it? ....

○ **I get it!** Now I know that nearly all plants _____
_____

○ **I need extra help with** _____
_____

What Do Plants Need to Live Successfully on Land?

2a. DEFINE What is a cuticle? _____
_____

b. APPLY CONCEPTS Describe the pros and cons of being
a tall land plant. _____
_____
_____

got it? ....

○ **I get it!** Now I know that to live on land, plants need to _____
_____
_____

○ **I need extra help with** _____
_____

Name _____ Date _____ Class _____

What Is a Plant?

What Characteristics Do All Plants Share?

Scientists gather information about the ancestors of land plants through studying fossils, chemical analysis of the pigment chlorophyll, and analysis of genetic material. **Chlorophyll** is a green pigment found in the chloroplasts of plants, algae, and some bacteria. Because they are very closely related, plants and green algae both belong to the plant kingdom. **Nearly all plants are autotrophs, organisms that produce their own food. With the exception of some green algae, all plants contain many cells. In addition, all plant cells are surrounded by cell walls.**

Sunlight provides the energy for a plant's food-making process, called **photosynthesis.**

During photosynthesis, a plant uses carbon dioxide gas and water to make food and oxygen. Photosynthesis takes place in the cell structure known as the **chloroplast.** Only plant cells have chloroplasts. Another difference between plant and animal cells is that plant cells have a cell wall, which surrounds the cell membrane and separates the cell from the environment. Plants also have one large **vacuole,** or storage sac that can expand and shrink as it fills with water, wastes, and food. With the exception of some green algae, all plants are multicellular, or made up of many cells. These cells are organized into **tissues,** or groups of similar cells that perform a specific function in an organism.

What Do Plants Need to Live Successfully on Land?

For plants to survive on land, they must have ways to obtain water and other nutrients from their surroundings, retain water, support their bodies, transport materials, and reproduce. Plants obtain water and other nutrients from the soil through roots. Plants retain water by having a waxy, waterproof layer called a **cuticle** on their leaves and

stems. Cell walls and vascular tissue strengthen and support the large bodies of plants. **Vascular tissue,** a system of tubelike structures inside a plant, allow water, minerals, and food to move throughout the plant. Land plants also have adaptations that make reproduction possible in dry environments.

On a separate sheet of paper, list the characteristics a pea plant shares with almost all members of the plant kingdom. Then describe some special adaptations that a pea plant has in order to survive on land.

Name _____ Date _____ Class _____

What Is a Plant?

Understanding Main Ideas
Answer the following questions in the spaces provided.

1. What characteristics do all plants share?

   _____

   _____

2. What do plants need to live successfully on land?

   _____

   _____

   _____

Building Vocabulary
Fill in the blank to complete each statement.

3. A group of similar cells that perform a specific function is called a(n)

   _____.

4. The internal transporting system through which water, minerals, and food move inside the plant is called _____.

5. A(n) _____ is a structure inside a plant's cell in which food is made.

6. The process by which plants make food is called _____.

7. A(n) _____ is a waxy, waterproof layer that covers the leaves and stems of most plants.

8. The sac inside a plant cell where water, wastes, and food are stored is called a(n) _____.

9. The green pigment called _____ is necessary to the food-making process in plants.

Enrich

What Is a Plant?

Desert plants have special survival needs. Read the passage and study the diagram below. Then use a separate sheet of paper to answer the questions that follow.

Desert Survival

To obtain water, some desert plants have very deep root systems that can absorb moisture far underground. Others have shallow, horizontal root systems that can quickly absorb a large amount of water when it rains.

The aboveground surfaces of many desert plants are covered with spines. These spines help to shade the plant from the sun and keep it from getting too hot. They also help to reduce water loss from the plant by shielding it from dry winds. Some plants in the desert have thick, fleshy stems that can store water for long periods of time.

Many plants, such as the one shown below, survive dry periods by becoming *dormant,* or inactive. When a plant is dormant, it needs very little water.

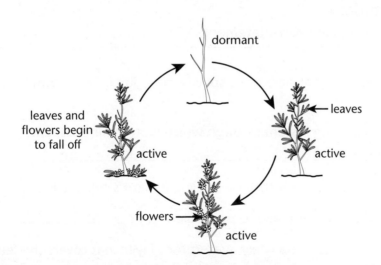

1. What do you think causes the plant in the figure above to come out of dormancy and become active?
2. Why do you think the plant loses its leaves and flowers when it becomes dormant?
3. Do you think the plant shown above is more likely to have deep roots or shallow horizontal roots? Explain.
4. A desert plant called the creosote bush has a double root system: It has both shallow horizontal roots and deep vertical roots. Why would this type of root system be an advantage to a desert plant?
5. Do you think a desert plant is more likely to have a thin or thick cuticle?

Name _____ Date _____ Class _____

What Is a Plant?

Write the letter of the correct answer on the line at the left.

1. ___ Which of the following is thought to be the ancestor of land plants?

   A   bacteria

   B   red algae

   C   ferns

   D   green algae

2. ___ Organisms that produce their own food are called

   A   heterotrophs

   B   autosomes

   C   autotrophs

   D   herbivores

3. ___ The sac inside a plant cell where water, food, and wastes are stored is the

   A   vacuole

   B   chloroplast

   C   chlorophyll

   D   cuticle

4. ___ Two structures found in plant cells but **NOT** in animal cells are

   A   cell wall and cell membrane

   B   chloroplasts and cell membrane

   C   cell wall and chloroplasts

   D   vacuole and nucleus

If the statement is true, write *true*. If the statement is false, change the underlined word or words to make the statement true.

5. _____ The cell wall helps a plant retain water.

6. _____ During photosynthesis, plants produce carbon dioxide.

7. _____ The green pigment found in specialized plant structures is called chlorophyll.

8. _____ The system of tubelike structures inside a plant through which water, minerals, and food move is called root tissue.

9. _____ Nearly all plants are unicellular.

10. _____ The energy for photosynthesis comes from the sun.

What Is a Plant?

Answer Key

After the Inquiry Warm-Up

1. Students' drawings will vary depending on the leaves examined. Students will likely notice and show that veins and cell structure are much more visible in the leaf from a temperate climate.

2. Students' answers will vary depending on the leaves examined. Students will likely notice that the leaf from a desert plant has a smoother, waxier surface. They may also notice that the leaf from a temperate plant is smoother and glossier on one side than on the other.

3. The smaller, thicker leaf seems to have more water in it than the large, thin, flat leaf. Desert plants need to store water.

4. Answers will vary. Sample: Does the plant have small, thick leaves?

Key Concept Summaries

Like nearly all plants, a pea plant is made up of many cells that are surrounded by cell walls, and it produces its own food via photosynthesis. In order to survive on land, a pea plant has roots that enable it to obtain water and other nutrients from the soil. A waxy, waterproof cuticle on its leaves and stems helps it retain that water. Cell walls and tissue strengthen and support a pea plant, enabling it to lift its food-making leaves toward the light of the sun. Water, minerals, and food are transported to all the parts of a pea plant through vascular tissues.

Review and Reinforce

1. Nearly all plants are autotrophs. With the exception of green algae, all are multicellular. All plant cells are surrounded by cell walls.

2. To live successfully on land, plants need ways to obtain water and other nutrients from their surroundings, retain water, support their bodies, transport materials, and reproduce.

3. tissue
4. vascular tissue
5. chloroplast
6. photosynthesis
7. cuticle
8. vacuole
9. chlorophyll

Enrich

1. The plant comes out of dormancy after a rain shower.

2. It loses its leaves and flowers to help conserve water.

3. Because the plant grows leaves and flowers after a rain shower, it probably absorbs a large amount of rainwater. This suggests that the plant has shallow horizontal roots.

4. It could absorb large amounts of water after a rain with its roots near the surface and could get water from deep in the earth during dry periods with its vertical roots.

5. Because desert plants must survive with very little water, they need to reduce water loss as much as possible and they are more likely to have thick cuticles.

Lesson Quiz

1. D
2. C
3. A
4. C
5. cuticle
6. oxygen
7. true
8. vascular
9. multicellular
10. true

Place the outside corner, the corner away from the dotted line, in the corner of your copy machine to copy onto letter-size paper.

Classifying Plants

LESSON

2

How do you know a plant when you see it?

Lesson Pacing: 2–3 periods or 1–1½ blocks

⏱ **SHORT ON TIME?** To do this lesson in approximately half the time, do the Activate Prior Knowledge activity on page 90. A discussion of the Key Concepts on pages 91, 93, and 96 will familiarize students with the lesson content. Have students do the Quick Labs. The rest of the lesson can be completed by students independently.

> **Preference Navigator,** in the online Planning tools, allows you to customize *Interactive Science* to your own teaching style. You can also edit lesson plans by selecting the Lesson Planner option.
>
> **Digital Teacher's Edition** allows you to access your Teacher's Edition and Resource materials online.

my science online.com

Lesson Vocabulary

- nonvascular plant • rhzoid • vascular plant • phloem
- xylem • frond • pollen • seed • gymnosperm
- angiosperm • cotyledon • monocot • dicot

Content Refresher

Vascular Tissue Vascular tissue is responsible for delivering water and nutrients to parts of the plant distant from the roots. This is accomplished by two processes: capillary action and transpiration.

Capillary action involves the attraction of water molecules to the sides of the vascular tubes (adhesion). Transpiration involves the attraction between water molecules, which is strong enough to pull one molecule up to replace one lost through evaporation (cohesion).

The vascular systems of seed plants include xylem and phloem tissues. Phloem, which transports sugar and organic nutrients throughout the plant, is made up of sieve-tube cells. These cells have cytoplasm but no nuclei. Their transverse walls contain channels through which sugars can pass. Lying next to each sieve-tube cell is a companion cell that controls and maintains the life functions of both cells. In angiosperms, xylem has two components—vessel elements and tracheids. Both are hollow and nonliving, but the vessel elements are larger and do not have transverse end walls. As a result, they form a continuous, hollow tube for water and mineral transport. A tracheid is a long, thick wall with pores through which water moves from tracheid to tracheid.

LESSON OBJECTIVES

- Name the major characteristics of nonvascular plants.
- Name the major characteristics of seedless vascular plants.
- Name the major characteristics of seed plants.

Blended Path
Active learning using Student Edition, Inquiry Path, and Digital Path

ENGAGE AND EXPLORE

Teach this lesson using a variety of resources. Begin by reading **My Planet Diary** as a class. Have students discuss using moss instead of grass for lawns. Then have students do the **Inquiry Warm-Up activity.** Students will predict whether peat moss or sand absorbs more water and then test their prediction. The **After the Inquiry Warm-Up worksheet** sets up a discussion about whether peat moss or sand can better absorb water. Have volunteers share their answers to question 4 about what would happen to moss if it were transplanted to a desert area.

EXPLAIN AND ELABORATE

Review the term *vascular* tissue and then **Teach Key Concepts** by explaining the three major characteristics of nonvascular plants: low, growing, have thin cell walls, and do not have roots for absorbing water from the ground. **Lead a Discussion** about two groups of nonvascular plants: liverworts and hornworts.

Teach Key Concepts by explaining that a small group of vascular plants reproduce by producing spores instead of seeds. **Support the Big Q** by using **Figure 3** to talk about the structure of a typical fern. Have students practice the inquiry skill in the **Apply It activity.**

Teach Key Concepts by explaining the characteristics of seed plants. **Lead a Discussion** about the two kinds of seed plants: gymnosperms and angiosperms. **Support the Big Q** by discussing angiosperms and the various types of angiosperms.

Hand out the **Key Concept Summaries** as a review of each part of the lesson. Students can also use the online **Vocab Flash Cards** to review key terms.

EVALUATE

Have students take the **Lesson Quiz.** For an alternate assessment, see the ExamView® Computer Test Generator, Progress Monitoring Assessments, or SuccessTracker™.

ELL Support

1 Content and Language

Have students continue to add terms to a journal or personal glossary. Have students copy the vocabulary terms and then find the first time the words are used in the chapter. Have them copy the definition of each vocabulary term into their journal or personal glossary.

Lab zone Inquiry Path
Hands-on learning in the Lab zone

Digital Path
Online learning at my science online.com

ENGAGE AND EXPLORE

To teach this lesson with an emphasis on inquiry, begin with the **Inquiry Warm-Up activity.** Students will predict whether peat moss or sand absorbs more water and then test their prediction. The **After the Inquiry Warm-Up worksheet** sets up a discussion about whether peat moss or sand can better absorb water. Have volunteers share their answers to question 4 about what would happen to moss if it was transplanted to a desert area.

EXPLAIN AND ELABORATE

Focus on the **Inquiry Skill** for the lesson. Remind students that when communicating with others they should include only pertinent information and write in a clear, concise, and thorough way. Reread the answers written in the **Inquiry Warm-Up activity.** How could the answers be revised to make them clearer, more concise, and more thorough? *(Answers will vary.)* Have students do the **Quick Lab** examining a moss plant to determine how it is adapted to perform its life activities.

Support the Big Q by using **Figure 3** to talk about the structure of a typical fern. Before beginning the **Apply It activity,** review the structure and characteristics of ferns. Do the **Build Inquiry** to demonstrate how quickly water can move upward. Have students do the **Quick Lab** to observe the structure and characteristics of a fern and explain how these features help ferns adapt to life on land.

Do the **Build Inquiry** challenging students to create a map showing the distribution of gymnosperms in your state. **Support the Big Q** by discussing angiosperms and the various types of angiosperms.

Do the **Teacher Demo** comparing and contrasting flowers and fruits. Have students do the **Quick Lab** to examine different seeds and describe their characteristics. Students can use the online **Vocab Flash Cards** to review key terms.

EVALUATE

Have students take the **Lesson Quiz.** For an alternate assessment, see the ExamView® Computer Test Generator, Progress Monitoring Assessments, or SuccessTracker™.

ENGAGE AND EXPLORE

Teach this lesson using digital resources. Begin by having students learn more and explore real-world connections to the classification of plants at **My Planet Diary** online. Have them access the Chapter Resources to find the **Unlock the Big Question activity.** There they can answer the questions and refine their responses as they continue through the lesson. You can re-assign the activity and have students submit their work so you can track their progress.

EXPLAIN AND ELABORATE

Students reading above, at, or below the lexile measure of this lesson can access basic content readings at their level at **My Reading Web.** Encourage students to use the online **Vocab Flash Cards** to preview key terms. Have students do the **Quick Lab** examining a moss plant to determine how it is adapted to perform its life activities.

Support the Big Q by using **Figure 3** to talk about the structure of a typical fern. Assign the **Apply It activity** online and have students submit their work to you. Have students do the **Quick Lab** to observe the structure and characteristics of a fern and explain how these features help ferns adapt to life on land.

Support the Big Q by discussing angiosperms and the various types of angiosperms. Use the **Virtual Lab activity** online to allow students to classify plants. Assign the **Do the Math activity** online and have students submit their work to you. Have students do the **Quick Lab** to examine different seeds and describe their characteristics. Online remediation is available at **My Science Coach.** The **Key Concept Summaries** online allow students to read a summary and see an image associated with each part of the lesson.

EVALUATE

Have students take the **Lesson Quiz.** For an alternate assessment, see the ExamView® Computer Test Generator, Progress Monitoring Assessments, or SuccessTracker™.

2 Frontload the Lesson

Discuss how to interpret the information provided in the chart on page 98. Use several Cloze sentences to give students practice in reading the chart, such as: The leaves on dicots have _____. *(Branched veins)*

3 Comprehensible Input

Have students create a T-chart titled "Nonvascular Plants." Have them write the characteristics of nonvascular plants on one side the chart and their purposes on the other side. Repeat for seedless vascular plants, and then for seed plants.

4 Language Production

Pair or group students with varied language abilities to complete labs collaboratively for language practice. Have each student copy the completed written lab for personal reference.

5 Assess Understanding

Divide the class into small groups. Have each student identify a Key Concept from the lesson to discuss in his or her group. After the discussions, have students talk about the key concepts as a group.

Classifying Plants

Establish Learning Objectives

After this lesson, students will be able to:

🔑 Name the major characteristics of nonvascular plants.

🔑 Name the major characteristics of seedless vascular plants.

🔑 Name the major characteristics of seed plants.

Engage

Activate Prior Knowledge

MY PLANET DIARY Read *The Moss is Greener on the Other Side* with the class. Ask students to describe any mosses with which they are familiar. Ask: **What are some mosses you have seen or know about?** *(Samples: Peat moss, sphagnum moss, moss growing on rocks and/or trees)* **How would you describe the appearance of moss?** *(Green, spongy, soft, moist)*

BIG IDEAS OF SCIENCE REFERENCE LIBRARY 📖
Have students look up the following topic: Ferns.

Explore

Lab Resource: Inquiry Warm-Up 🧪

L1 WILL MOSSES ABSORB WATER? Students will predict whether peat moss or sand absorbs more water and then test their prediction.

LESSON
2 Classifying Plants

🔑 **What Are the Characteristics of Nonvascular Plants?**

🔑 **What Are the Characteristics of Seedless Vascular Plants?**

🔑 **What Are the Characteristics of Seed Plants?**

my pLaneT DiaRY

CAREER

The Moss Is Greener on the Other Side

Tired of mowing the lawn? Never want to pull out another weed? Hire a moss landscaper! Landscapers design beautiful yards, usually planting trees, flowers, bushes, and grasses. These plants need a lot of care. Moss doesn't. Moss grows in the shade where other plants can't.

Landscapers can use moss to cover an entire yard if the conditions are right. Mosses are also better for the environment. People don't have to put toxic chemicals on their moss lawns to kill weeds or keep it green.

Write your answer below.
Do you think people should use moss instead of grass for their lawns? Why?

Sample: Yes; moss is better for the environment, but the conditions must be suitable.

▶ PLANET DIARY Go to **Planet Diary** to learn more about plant classification.

🧪 Do the Inquiry Warm-Up
Will Mosses Absorb Water?

What Are the Characteristics of Nonvascular Plants?

Plants that lack vascular tissue for transporting materials are known as **nonvascular plants.** 🔑 **Nonvascular plants are low-growing, have thin cell walls, and do not have roots for absorbing water from the ground.** Instead, they obtain water and materials directly from their surroundings. The materials then pass from one cell to the next. This means that materials do not travel far or quickly. This slow method helps explain why most nonvascular plants live in damp, shady places. The thin cell walls are why these plants cannot grow more than a few centimeters tall.

SUPPORT ALL READERS

Lexile Measure = 920L   Lexile Word Count = 2031

Prior Exposure to Content: Many students may have misconceptions on this topic

Academic Vocabulary: *communicate, outline*

Science Vocabulary: *rhizoid, phloem, xylem, gymnosperm, angiosperm*

Concept Level: Generally appropriate for most students in this grade

Preteach With: My Planet Diary "The Moss Is Greener" and Figure 5 activity

Go to **My Reading Web** to access leveled readings that provide a foundation for the content.

my science online.com

Vocabulary

- nonvascular plant • rhizoid • vascular plant • phloem
- xylem • frond • pollen • seed • gymnosperm
- angiosperm • cotyledon • monocot • dicot

Skills

🔄 Reading: Outline

△ Inquiry: Communicate

Mosses Have you ever seen mosses growing in the cracks of a sidewalk or in a shady spot? With more than 10,000 species, mosses are by far the most diverse group of nonvascular plants.

If you were to look closely at a moss, you would see a plant that looks something like **Figure 1.** Structures that look like tiny leaves grow off a small, stemlike structure. Thin, rootlike structures called **rhizoids** anchor the moss and absorb water and nutrients. Moss grows a long, slender stalk with a capsule at the end. The capsule contains spores for reproduction.

FIGURE 1 ....

Moss Structure

Diagrams can be easier to read than photographs, but photographs are more realistic.

✏️ **Relate Diagrams and Photos** Label the capsule, stalk, and leaflike structure in the photo. Draw lines from your labels to the structure itself, like in the diagram below.

Capsule

Stalk

Leaflike structure

Stemlike structure

Rhizoid

Capsule

Stalk

Leaflike structure

91

Explain

Introduce Vocabulary

Point out the vocabulary term *pollen*. Tell students that this term is derived from a Latin word that means "fine flour." Have students imagine a surface covered with flour. Tell students that pollen are microscopic structures in a seed plant that can look like a fine dust, or "flour."

Teach Key Concepts 🔑

Review with students the definition of *vascular tissue* and explain that plants that lack vascular tissue are known as *nonvascular plants.* Ask: **What are the three major characteristics of nonvascular plants?** *(They are low-growing, have thin cell walls, and do not have roots for absorbing water from the ground.)* **Why are nonvascular plants short and low to the ground?** *(They have no tissue to provide support or to transport material.)* **Why do nonvascular plants live in damp, shady places?** *(Materials must pass directly from the environment into cells, and then from one cell to the next. This process is slow, so materials do not travel far or quickly.)* Tell students that the three major groups of nonvascular plants are mosses, liverworts, and hornworts. Introduce mosses as the most diverse group of nonvascular plants. Prompt students to think about any mosses they may have seen growing in the cracks of shaded sidewalks or on the north side of tree trunks. Have volunteers describe them as all students look at **Figure 1.** *(Small, soft, green, spongy, moist, fuzzy plants growing together as a coat or carpet)* **What structure acts like roots to hold a moss in place?** *(Rhizoid)* **What is contained in the capsule?** *(Spores)* Emphasize the descriptions of parts of a moss plant as *leaflike, stemlike,* and *rootlike* structures, reminding students that these parts are not true leaves, stems, and roots.

Teach With Visuals

Tell students to look at **Figure 1.** Ask: **What is the function of the rhizoids?** *(They anchor the moss and absorb water and nutrients.)* **What is the function of the stemlike structure, or stalk?** *(It provides some support and holds the capsule.)* **What is the function of the leaflike structures?** *(They carry on photosynthesis.)* **What is the function of the spores?** *(They are reproductive structures.)*

My Planet Diary provides an opportunity for students to explore real-world connections to the classification of plants.

MY SCIENCE online | Nonvascular Plants

ⒺⓁⓁ Support

1 Content and Language

Write the terms *vascular plant* and *nonvascular plant* on the board. Explain that *vascular* comes from the Latin word *vasculum,* meaning "small vessel." Tell students that tissue in a *vascular plant* functions like a vessel, transporting materials throughout the plant. Explain that the prefix *non-* means "not," so a *nonvascular plant* lacks such tissue.

2 Frontload the Lesson

Invite students to brainstorm a list of various plant names and write them on the board. Because students may not know the names of some plants, keep a second list of descriptive words.

3 Comprehensible Input

Have students make a compare/contrast table to organize the similarities and differences among nonvascular plants, seedless vascular plants, and seed plants.

Explain

Lead a Discussion

LIVERWORTS AND HORNWORTS Discuss with students the other two groups of nonvascular plants, liverworts and hornworts. Have students look at the photograph of liverworts to better understand how they got their name. You might want to provide a diagram of the human liver to help students make the association. Ask: **How do liverworts grow?** *(As a thick crust on moist rocks or soil along the sides of a stream)* Use the photograph of hornworts to discuss the shape and growing habits of this group of nonvascular plants. **How did the hornwort get its name?** *(Slender, curved structures that look like horns grow out of the plant.)* **Where do hornworts grow?** *(Unlike mosses and liverworts, hornworts seldom grow on rocks or tree trunks. Rather, they grow in moist soil, often mixed in with grass plants.)*

Outline Tell students that outlining shows the relationship between main ideas and supporting ideas. It is a useful way to organize information.

Elaborate

Lab Resource: Quick Lab

L2 MASSES OF MOSSES Students will examine a moss plant to determine how it is adapted to perform its life activities.

Evaluate

Assess Your Understanding

After students answer the questions, have them evaluate their understanding by completing the appropriate sentence.

RTI Response to Intervention

1a. If students need help identifying the structure that anchors moss and absorbs water and nutrients, **then** have them review the definition of *rhizoids*.

b. If students cannot explain why nonvascular plants are short, **then** remind them of the primary characteristics of nonvascular plants.

c. If students need help comparing and contrasting liverworts and hornworts, **then** have them review the descriptions and images of each plant.

MY SCIENCE COACH Have students go online for help in understanding the three groups of nonvascular plants: mosses, liverworts, and hornworts.

Liverwort ▲

 Outline Fill in the table to the right with what you have learned about liverworts and hornworts.

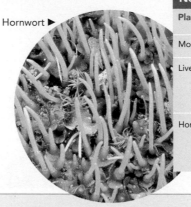

Hornwort ▶

Liverworts and Hornworts Liverworts and hornworts are two other groups of nonvascular plants. There are more than 8,000 species of liverworts. This group of plants is named for the shape of the plant's body, which looks somewhat like a human liver. *Wort* is an old English word for "plant." Liverworts are often found growing as a thick crust on moist rocks or soil along the sides of a stream. There are fewer than 100 species of hornworts. If you look closely at a hornwort, you can see slender, curved structures that look like horns growing out of the plant. Unlike mosses or liverworts, hornworts are seldom found on rocks or tree trunks. Instead, hornworts usually live in moist soil, often mixed in with grass plants.

Nonvascular Plants

Plant	Identifiable Physical Characteristic	Where Found
Mosses	Fuzzy appearance	Shady spots, rocks, tree trunks
Liverworts	Looks like human liver	Moist rocks, soil along streams
Hornworts	Horn-like, curved structures	Moist soil, mixed in with grass

Lab zone Do the Quick Lab *Masses of Mosses.*

🔑 Assess Your Understanding

1a. Review (Vascular tissues/(Rhizoids)) anchor moss and absorb water and nutrients.

b. Explain Why are most nonvascular plants short?
<u>They only have thin cell walls for support.</u>

c. Compare and Contrast How are liverworts and hornworts different?
<u>Sample: They look different; liverworts have more species, and hornworts rarely grow on rocks or trees.</u>

got it?

○ **I get it!** Now I know the characteristics of nonvascular plants are <u>low-growing structures, thin cell walls, and lack of roots.</u>

○ **I need extra help with** <u>See TE note.</u>

Go to **MY SCIENCE COACH** online for help with this subject.

What Are the Characteristics of Seedless Vascular Plants?

If you could have walked through the ancient forests that existed long before the dinosaurs lived, they would have looked very strange to you. You might have recognized the mosses and liverworts that carpeted the moist soil, but you would have seen very tall, odd-looking trees. Among the trees grew huge, tree-sized ferns. Other trees resembled giant sticks with leaves up to one meter long. The odd-looking plants in the ancient forests are the ancestors of the ferns, clubmosses, and horsetails of today. Ferns, club mosses, and horsetails share two characteristics. They have vascular tissue and they do not produce seeds. Instead of seeds, these plants reproduce by releasing spores.

Vascular Tissue Ancient trees were vascular plants. **Vascular plants** are plants with true vascular tissue. Vascular plants can grow tall because their vascular tissue provides an effective way of transporting materials throughout the plant. The vascular tissue also strengthens the plants' bodies. You can see vascular tissue in **Figure 2**. The cells making up the vascular tissue have strong cell walls. Imagine a handful of drinking straws bundled together with rubber bands. The bundle of straws is stronger and more stable than a single straw would be. Arranged similarly, the strong, tubelike structures in vascular plants give the plants strength and stability.

There are two types of vascular tissue. **Phloem** (FLOH um) is the vascular tissue through which food moves. After food is made in the leaves, it enters the phloem and travels to other parts of the plant. Water and minerals, on the other hand, travel in the vascular tissue called **xylem** (ZY lum). The roots absorb water and minerals from the soil. These materials enter the root's xylem and move upward into the stems and leaves.

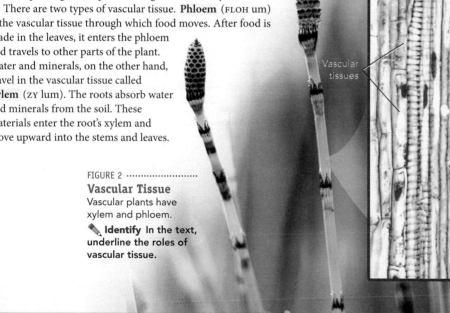

Vascular tissues

FIGURE 2
Vascular Tissue
Vascular plants have xylem and phloem.

✎ **Identify** In the text, underline the roles of vascular tissue.

93

Explain

Teach Key Concepts 🔑

Explain to students that a small group of vascular plants reproduce by producing spores instead of seeds. Ask: **What are the seedless vascular plants?** *(Ferns, club mosses, and horsetails)* Explain to students that the size of the plants indicates an important characteristic of this group of plants. Ask: **What enables these plants to grow taller than mosses?** *(The presence of a vascular system)* **What is vascular tissue?** *(A system of tubelike structures for transporting water, minerals, and food)* **What are the two functions of vascular tissue?** *(Transport materials throughout a plant, and give strength and stability to a plant)* **Why can vascular plants survive in a greater variety of environments than nonvascular plants?** *(Because vascular plants have a system to transport materials to every part of the plant, they can live in dry as well as damp environments.)* Introduce the two types of vascular tissue: xylem and phloem. Discuss the role of each in the transport system. Ask: **What is the function of xylem?** *(To carry water and minerals from the soil to the roots, stems, and leaves of a plant)* **What is the function of phloem?** *(To carry food made in the leaves to other parts of a plant)*

Make Analogies

L1 **XYLEM AND PHLOEM** It might help students remember the function of each of these vascular tissues if you tell them to remember "xylem zips things up and phloem flows them down." Ask: **What materials move up from roots to leaves in a plant?** *(Water and minerals from the soil)* **What material moves down from leaves to roots in a plant?** *(Food)* **What does xylem carry?** *(Xylem carries water and minerals.)* **What does phloem carry?** *(Phloem carries food.)*

Differentiated Instruction

L1 **Strength and Stability** Have students confirm that vascular tissue gives a plant strength and stability by performing the activity described in the text. Working in pairs, have students experiment with 1, 10, and 20 straws bundled together with rubber bands. After bundling the straws, they should hold the base in one hand, apply pressure to the top, and observe what happens.

Explain

Support the Big Q ❓ UbD

FERNS, CLUB MOSSES, AND HORSETAILS Discuss with students the characteristics of ferns. Then point out **Figure 3** as you talk about the structure of a typical fern. Remind students that vascular plants have true roots, stems, and leaves. Ask: **How does a fern's stem differ from most stems you are familiar with?** *(It is underground.)* **How do the roots and leaves of a fern grow?** *(The roots grow downward from the bottom of the stem. The leaves grow upward from the top side of the stem.)* **Which part of the fern is its leaf?** *(The frond)* **What is the waxy coating on the upper surface of a frond called? What is its function?** *(The waxy coating is a cuticle, which helps the plant retain water.)* Tell students that club mosses and horsetails are also vascular plants and have true roots, stems, and leaves. However, neither is as abundant as ferns. Emphasize that club mosses are not true mosses. Ask: **How are club mosses different from true mosses?** *(Club mosses have vascular tissue, true mosses do not.)* **Where do club mosses grow?** *(In damp woodlands and near streams)* **What is unusual about the stems of horsetails?** *(They contain silica, a gritty, abrasive substance.)*

21st Century Learning

CREATIVITY Have students think about the characteristics of ferns. Have them use the information to design several activities to determine what conditions are optimal for growing ferns. Ask: **What conditions might affect the growth of ferns?** *(Moisture, light, soil composition, temperature)* **What does a fern need to grow?** *(Moist soil, shade, humidity, soil with lots of organic matter)* Review students' designs and if practical, have them perform the activities.

Elaborate

Apply It!

L1 Before beginning the activity, review the structure and characteristics of ferns.

△ **Communicate** Tell students that by writing the care instructions for potted ferns, they are sharing information important to customers. Remind students that they should include only pertinent information and write it in a clear, concise, and thorough way.

Ferns There are more than 12,000 species of ferns alive today. They range in size from tiny plants about the size of this letter *M* to tree ferns that grow up to five meters tall. Ferns thrive in shaded areas with moist soil. Some remain green year-round while others turn brown in the fall and regrow in spring.

The Structure of Ferns Like other vascular plants, ferns have stems, roots, and leaves. The stems of most ferns are underground. Leaves grow upward from the top side of the stems, while roots grow downward from the bottom of the stems. Water and nutrients enter the root's vascular tissue and travel through the tissue into the stems and leaves.

Figure 3 shows a fern's structure. Notice that the fern's leaves, or **fronds,** are divided into many smaller parts that look like small leaves. The upper surface of each frond is coated with a cuticle that helps the plant retain water. In many ferns, the developing leaves are coiled at first. Because they resemble the top of a violin, these young leaves are often called fiddleheads. Fiddleheads uncurl as they mature.

FIGURE 3 ·······
Fern Structure
Like other plants, ferns have roots, stems, and leaves.

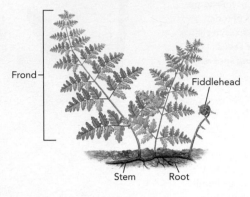

Frond — Fiddlehead — Stem — Root

apply it!

Caring for Your Fern

Sample: Keep your fern out of direct sunlight. A shaded area is best. Soil should be kept moist for best results.

Suppose you ran a flower shop that sold cut flowers and potted plants. You have just received a shipment of potted ferns and several customers are interested in purchasing them. Before they are ready to be sold, you need to make sure your customers can take care of the ferns so they won't regret their purchase.

❶ Communicate On the tag at left, write the care instructions that will be given to your customers who buy potted ferns. Include the conditions that the fern needs for light and water.

❷ CHALLENGE Florists recommend not putting plants like ferns in south- or west-facing windows. Why?

Sample: Shade-loving plants will get too much sun exposure if placed in a window facing these directions.

Digital Lesson: Assign the *Apply It* activity online and have students submit their work to you.

my science online.com **Seedless Vascular Plants**

Club Mosses and Horsetails Like ferns, club mosses and horsetails have true stems, roots, and leaves. However, there are relatively few species of club mosses and horsetails alive today.

Do not be confused by the name *club moss*. Unlike true mosses, club mosses have vascular tissue. You may be familiar with the club moss in **Figure 4.** The plant, which looks a little like a small branch of a pine tree, is sometimes called ground pine or princess pine. Club mosses usually grow in moist woodlands and near streams.

There are about 30 species of horsetails on Earth today. The whorled pattern of growth somewhat resembles the appearance of a horse's tail. The stems contain silica, a gritty substance also found in sand. During colonial times, Americans used the plants to scrub their pots and pans. Another common name for horsetails is scouring brushes.

◄ Horsetail

Club moss ▼

FIGURE 4 ·····························
Moss Imposter?
A club moss is pictured at left.

✎ **Describe** Why is a club moss not a true moss?

<u>Sample: It has vascular</u>
<u>tissue.</u>

Lab zone
Do the Quick Lab
Examining a Fern.

⊃ Assess Your Understanding

a. Identify In plants, water moves through (phloem/⊙xylem⊙). Food moves through (⊙phloem⊙/xylem).

b. Infer Why do you think the developing leaves of a fern are coiled?
<u>Sample: to protect the leaves</u>

c. Develop Hypotheses Why do you think there are more ferns than club mosses?
<u>Accept all reasonable answers.</u>
<u>Sample: Ferns can survive in</u>
<u>more environments. Fewer</u>
<u>animals eat ferns.</u>

got it? ·······························

○ I get it! Now I know the characteristics of seedless vascular plants include <u>having vascular</u> <u>tissue and reproducing by releasing spores instead of seeds.</u>

○ I need extra help with <u>See TE note.</u>

Go to **my science ⑤ coach** *online for help with this subject.*

95

Elaborate ————
Build Inquiry **Lab** zone

L1 **HOW QUICKLY CAN WATER MOVE UPWARD?**

Materials dropper, food coloring, goggles, narrow glass tube, plastic petri dish, water

Time 10 minutes

Caution students to handle the glass tube gently. If they roughly push the glass tube onto the bottom of the Petri dish, the tube may shatter. Tell students to fill the Petri dish half full with water and to add a drop of food coloring to the water. Instruct students to stand the tube on end in the water and hold it upright. Have them observe what happens and record their observations.

Ask: **What happened to the water in the dish?** *(It moved quickly up the glass tube.)* **What do you think would happen to the speed at which the water moves if the tube were wider?** *(The water would not move as quickly.)* **Why is it an advantage for the transporting cells of plants to be arranged in a narrow, tubelike way?** *(This arrangement helps water move quickly up the plant.)*

Lab Resource: Quick Lab **Lab** zone

L2 **EXAMINING A FERN** Students will observe the structure and characteristics of a fern plant and explain how these features help ferns adapt to life on land.

Evaluate ————
Assess Your Understanding

After students answer the questions, have them evaluate their understanding by completing the appropriate sentence.

R T I Response to Intervention

2a. If students cannot distinguish between phloem and xylem tissue, **then** have them locate each highlighted term and review the definitions.

b. If students need help explaining the coils of a fern, **then** discuss with them the nature of developing leaves and their need for protection.

c. If students have difficulty developing a hypothesis that accounts for the greater number of ferns than club mosses, **then** have them review and contrast the characteristics of each.

my science ⑤ coach Have students go online for help in understanding the seedless vascular plants ferns, club mosses, and horsetails.

Differentiated Instruction

L1 **Seedless Vascular Plants** Have students create a Venn diagram that compares ferns, club mosses, and horsetails.

L1 **A Vascular System** Have students illustrate the function of a vascular system by creating a flowchart that shows the movement of food, water, and nutrients through a vascular plant. Urge students to share their flowcharts with a partner for evaluation.

L3 **Fiddleheads** In the spring in New England, the delicacy known as fiddleheads appear. These young fern fronds can be eaten raw or cooked, and are said to have a unique texture and a taste similar to asparagus or okra. Have students research some tempting fiddlehead recipes. If fiddleheads are available, and with your permission, have students select a recipe to make in the classroom.

Explain

Teach Key Concepts 🔑

Explain to students that most of the plants they are familiar with are classified as plants with seeds. Ask: **What two characteristics do all seed plants share?** (*They have vascular tissue and use pollen and seeds to reproduce.*) **Which characteristic makes these plants different from ferns?** (*Ferns reproduce using spores, not seeds.*) **What are the main parts of the body of a seed plant?** (*Roots, stems, and leaves.*) Remind students that seed plants evolved after mosses and ferns. Ask: **How did the evolution of seeds allow plants to live in places where mosses and ferns could not?** (*Seeds provide protection for the young plant. With seeds, plants can reproduce in drier environments.*) Make sure students understand that seed plants produce pollen, which delivers sperm cells directly near the eggs for fertilization. Ask: **What is pollen?** (*Tiny structures that contain the cells that will later become sperm cells*)

Lead a Discussion

TWO KINDS OF SEED PLANTS Tell students that seed plants are divided into two groups: gymnosperms and angiosperms. Explain that *gymnosperm* comes from the Greek root *gymno*, meaning "naked," and *sperma*, meaning "seed." Ask: **What characteristic of a gymnosperm gives the group its name?** (*Gymnosperms have naked seeds, or seeds that are not enclosed in a protective fruit.*) Tell students that other characteristics of many gymnosperms include needle-like or scalelike leaves, deep-growing roots, and being evergreens. Introduce the four types of gymnosperms shown in **Figure 5,** helping students with pronunciation where needed.

Address Misconceptions

L1 **NAKED SEEDS** Students may misinterpret the description of gymnosperms as having naked seeds to mean there is no protection for developing seeds in these plants. Tell students that many gymnosperms produce seeds in cones. Others, such as yews, develop a soft surrounding material for their seeds. Ask: **What cone-producing gymnosperms are you familiar with?** (*Pines, redwoods, firs, spruces, larches, cedars, junipers*) **Why must a seed be protected?** (*A seed contains a young plant, which must be protected so it can grow and develop.*)

What Are the Characteristics of Seed Plants?

Seed plants outnumber seedless plants by more than ten to one. You eat many seed plants—rice, peas, and squash, for example. You wear clothes made from seed plants, such as cotton and flax. You may live in a home built from seed plants—oak, pine, or maple trees. In addition, seed plants produce much of the oxygen you breathe.

Seed plants share two important characteristics. 🔑 **Seed plants have vascular tissue, and they use pollen and seeds to reproduce.** In addition, the bodies of all seed plants have roots, stems, and leaves. Most seed plants live on land. Recall that land plants face many challenges, including standing upright and supplying all their cells with food and water. Like ferns, seed plants meet these two challenges with vascular tissue.

Pollen and Seeds Unlike seedless plants, seed plants can live in a wide variety of environments. Recall that seedless plants need water in their surroundings for fertilization to occur. Seed plants do not need water for sperm to swim to the eggs. Instead, seed plants produce **pollen,** tiny structures that contain the cells that will later become sperm cells. Pollen deliver sperm cells directly near the eggs. After sperm cells fertilize the eggs, seeds develop. A **seed** is a structure that contains a young plant inside a protective covering. Seeds protect the young plant from drying out.

Gymnosperms The giant sequoia trees belong to the group of seed plants known as gymnosperms. A **gymnosperm** (JIM noh spurm) is a seed plant that produces naked seeds. The seeds of gymnosperms are referred to as "naked" because they are not enclosed by a protective fruit.

Many gymnosperms have needlelike or scalelike leaves and deep-growing root systems. Gymnosperms are the oldest type of seed plant. According to fossil evidence, gymnosperms first appeared on Earth about 360 million years ago. Fossils also indicate that there were many more species of gymnosperms on Earth in the past than there are today. Four types of gymnosperms exist today, as shown in **Figure 5.**

Vocabulary Greek Word Origins The word *gymnosperm* comes from the Greek words *gumnos*, meaning "naked," and *sperma*, meaning "seed." Why are the seeds of gymnosperms considered to be naked?

The seeds are not inside of a fruit.

GYMNOSPERM	DESCRIPTION/FUNCTION
Cycads 	About 175 million years ago, the majority of plants were cycads (SY kadz). Today, cycads grow mainly in tropical and subtropical areas. Cycads look like palm trees with cones that can grow as large as a football!
Conifers 	Conifers (KAHN uh furz), or cone-bearing plants, are the largest and most diverse group of modern gymnosperms. Most conifers are evergreens, meaning they keep their leaves or needles year-round.
Ginkgoes 	Ginkgoes (GING kohz) also grew hundreds of millions of years ago. Today, only one species, *Ginkgo biloba*, exists. It probably survived because the Chinese and Japanese cared for it in their gardens. Today, ginkgo trees are planted along city streets because they can tolerate air pollution.
Gnetophytes 	Gnetophytes (NEE tuh fyts) live in hot deserts and in tropical rain forests. Some are trees, some are shrubs, and others are vines. The *Welwitschia* (shown at left) of West Africa can live for more than 1,000 years!

FIGURE 5 ·······························

Types of Gymnosperms
The chart describes the four main groups of gymnosperms.

✎ **Answer these questions.**

1. **Name** Which group of gymnosperms has the most species?

   Conifers

2. **Apply Concepts** What could have happened to the ecosystem the *Ginkgo biloba* tree lived in if the tree had become extinct?

   Sample: The species that depended on the tree may have struggled or gone extinct as well.

97

Teach With Visuals

Tell students to look at **Figure 5.** Explain that these are the four types of gymnosperms. As students read the descriptions, have them identify an outstanding characteristic of each type. Ask: **What plant do cycads resemble?** *(Palm tree)* **Why do you think conifers are the largest group of gymnosperms?** *(Sample: They have adaptations that allow them to live in a wide variety of places. For example, many conifers can live in dry conditions because their long, thin needles limit water loss.)* **What is an evergreen?** *(A plant that keeps its leaves or needles all year long)* **Which gymnosperms can tolerate air pollution?** *(Ginkgoes)* **Which gymnosperms can be trees, shrubs, or vines?** *(Gnetophytes)* Students may enjoy learning that both cycad trees and ginkgo trees are either male or female. This means that the male tree has cones that produce only pollen, and the female tree has cones that produce only eggs. Ginkgoes planted as street trees are usually male, because seeds produced by female trees are surrounded by a fleshy seed coat that when crushed gives off a strong, unpleasant odor.

21st Century Learning

CRITICAL THINKING Emphasize that there were many more species of gymnosperms on Earth in the past than there are today. Ask: **Why do you think this is so?** *(Sample: They could not adapt well to conditions in their environment. The appearance of flowering plants brought about competition.)* **Which type of gymnosperm has been the most successful at survival?** *(Conifers)*

Elaborate

Build Inquiry Lab zone

L3 INTERPRETING DATA ON GYMNOSPERMS

Materials references on gymnosperms, including reliable Internet sites; state map, map pins

Time 20 minutes

Challenge students to create a map showing the distribution of gymnosperms in your state. Allow students to do the research and then place pins on the map (one color for each type of gymnosperm) as they locate an area where each type grows. If students do research on the Internet, remind them to follow prescribed guidelines for Internet use.

Ask: **Which type of gymnosperm is most common in the state? Why?** *(Answers will depend on location and should include reference to the climate conditions in the state.)*

Differentiated Instruction

L1 Comparing Vascular Plants Have students create a Venn diagram that compares seedless vascular plants and vascular plants with seeds. Tell students to include examples of each.

L1 Describing Seed Plants Have students write a descriptive paragraph about seed plants that uses the following terms: *seed, pollen, vascular system, gymnosperm, vascular tissue,* and *reproduction.*

L3 Record Holders The tallest living thing in the world, the largest living thing in the world, and the oldest living thing in the world are all conifers that can be found in California. Have students research the redwood tree Hyperion, the General Sherman sequoia, and a bristlecone pine that grows in the White Mountains to find out more about these record holders. Have students report their findings to the class.

Explain

Support the Big Q ❓ UbD

ANGIOSPERMS Introduce angiosperms as the other group of seed plants. Ask: **How are angiosperms similar to gymnosperms?** *(They both have vascular systems, produce seeds, and have bodies with roots, stems, and leaves.)* **How are they different?** *(Angiosperms produce flowers and enclose their seeds in fruits.)* Emphasize that angiosperms are the most abundant plants on Earth and can live almost anywhere. Ask: **Why do you think angiosperms are so successful at survival?** *(Sample: Angiosperms produce flowers, which are reproductive organs. The seeds, or developing plants, are protected by fruits. They do not need specific conditions for growth and survival, so they can live anywhere.)* Discuss the classification of angiosperms by reviewing the function of a cotyledon. Ask: **What is a cotyledon?** *(A seed leaf that provides food for the developing plant)* **How can you classify angiosperms by the number of cotyledons?** *(A monocot has one seed leaf; a dicot has two seed leaves.)* **What are some examples of each group?** *(Monocots: corn, wheat, rice, lilies, tulips, orchids, onions; dicots: roses, sunflowers, peanuts, peas, violets, dandelions, apples, oak and maple trees)*

Teach With Visuals

Tell students to look at **Figure 6.** Ask: **Which group of angiosperms has plants with one main root?** *(Dicots)* **Which group has leaves with parallel veins?** *(Monocots)* **What can you infer about a cross-section of a fossilized stem that has holes scattered randomly throughout?** *(It was vascular because it had a stem with vascular tissue. It was probably a seed-bearing monocot because the vascular tissue was scattered throughout the stem.)* To help students understand the difference in flowers between the two groups, reinforce the concept of multiples. A multiple of a number is the product of that number and any other whole number. Ask: **What are some multiples of 3? Of 4? Of 5?** *(3: 6, 9, 12; 4: 8, 12, 16; 5: 10, 15)* **Is a flower with 6 petals a monocot or a dicot? Explain.** *(A monocot because 6 is a multiple of 3 and monocots have floral parts in multiples of 3)*

Dicot

Monocot

FIGURE 6 ···

> **VIRTUAL LAB** **Monocots and Dicots**
Use the table below to find your answers.

✏ **Interpret Photos** Label the rafflesia (top) and the other flowers on this page as *monocots* or *dicots.*

Angiosperms You probably associate the word *flower* with a sweet-smelling plant growing in a garden. You certainly wouldn't think of something that smells like rotting meat. That's exactly what the corpse flower, or rafflesia, smells like. This flower, which grows in Asia, produces a meat smell, which attracts flies that spread the flower's pollen. You won't be seeing rafflesia in your local florist shop any time soon! Rafflesia belongs to the group of seed plants known as angiosperms (AN jee uh spurmz). **Angiosperms,** or flowering plants, share two important characteristics. First, they produce flowers. Second, in contrast to gymnosperms, which produce uncovered seeds, angiosperms produce seeds that are enclosed in fruits.

Angiosperms live almost everywhere on Earth. They grow in frozen areas in the Arctic, tropical jungles, and barren deserts. A few angiosperms, such as mangrove trees, live at the ocean's edge.

Types of Angiosperms Angiosperms are divided into two major groups: monocots and dicots. "Cot" is short for cotyledon (kaht uh LEED un). The **cotyledon,** or seed leaf, provides food for the embryo. *Mono-* means "one" and *di-* means "two." **Monocots** are angiosperms that have only one seed leaf. Grasses, including corn, wheat, and rice, and plants such as lilies and tulips, are monocots. **Dicots,** on the other hand, produce seeds with two seed leaves. Dicots include plants such as roses and violets, as well as dandelions. Both oak and maple trees are dicots, as are food plants such as beans and apples. **Figure 6** shows the characteristics of monocots and dicots.

Dicot

Characteristics of Monocots and Dicots					
	Seeds	**Leaves**	**Flowers**	**Stems**	**Roots**
Monocots	Single cotyledon	Parallel veins	Floral parts often in multiples of 3	Vascular tissue bundles scattered throughout stem	Many roots spread out
Dicots	Two cotyledons	Branched veins	Floral parts often in multiples of 4 or 5	Vascular tissue bundles arranged in a ring	One main root

98 Plants

Virtual Lab allows students to classify plants.

Digital Lesson: Assign the *Do the Math* activity online and have students submit their work to you.

my science online.com ▸ **Seed Plants**

do the math!

se the graph of known plant species to answer the questions.

Interpret Graphs Which plant group has the ~~fe~~west species?

Gymnosperms

Calculate Figure out the percentage that each of ~~th~~e following plant groups represents. Round your ~~an~~swer to the nearest tenth.

Green algae _2.3%_

Ferns and relatives _4.0%_

Angiosperms _87.2%_

CHALLENGE Why do you think angiosperms are the largest group?

Sample: Angiosperms live almost everywhere on Earth. Other plant species need specific conditions, like moist soil or direct sunlight, to survive. But angiosperms can take advantage of a variety of conditions.

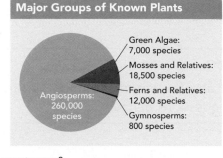

Major Groups of Known Plants

Green Algae: 7,000 species

Mosses and Relatives: 18,500 species

Ferns and Relatives: 12,000 species

Angiosperms: 260,000 species

Gymnosperms: 800 species

 Do the Quick Lab Common Characteristics.

Assess Your Understanding

a. Define What are pollen?

Pollen are tiny structures that contain the cells that will later become sperm.

b. Draw Conclusions Why do you think angiosperms enclose their seeds in fruits?

Sample: The seeds are better protected in a fruit and are more likely to survive.

~~go~~t it?

⬤ I get it! Now I know the characteristics of seed plants include _having vascular tissue and producing seeds and pollen._

⬤ I need extra help with _See TE note._

Go to **my science COACH** online for help with this subject.

99

Differentiated Instruction

L1 Comparing Seed Plants Have students create a Venn diagram that compares gymnosperms and angiosperms. Tell students to include examples of each.

L1 Describing Seed Plants Have students return to the descriptive paragraph they wrote in the previous section about seed plants. Have them add the following terms to the paragraph: *angiosperms, cotyledon,*

monocot, dicot, flower multiples. Have students exchange paragraphs with a partner for evaluation.

L3 Fascinating Angiosperms Carnivorous plants obtain some nutrients by trapping and digesting small animals. Have students research and report on these unusual plants, including the pitcher plant, sundew, butterwort, bladderwort, and Venus' flytrap.

Elaborate

Do the Math!

L1 Tell students that a circle graph is used to display data as parts of a whole. The whole is the circle—the known species of plants—and the sectors are the categories—each major group. To calculate the percentage of each group, they need to divide the number in that group (the part) by the total number of plants (the whole) and multiply by 100.

See the *Math Skill and Problem-Solving Activities* for support.

Teacher Demo

L1 FLOWERS AND FRUITS

Materials pictures of various types of flowering plants, three different fruits cut in half (apple, cherry, peach, avocado, tomato, pepper, banana)

Time 20 minutes

Show students pictures of flowering plants. Ask if they recognize any of the plants. Arrange the fruit on a desk and have students observe them.

Ask: **In what ways are all the plants in the pictures alike?** (*They all have flowers, roots, stems, and leaves.*) **In what ways are they different?** (*Sample: They have different kinds of flowers and leaves, they are different colors, they are different shapes and sizes, and they grow in different places.*) **In what ways are all the fruits alike?** (*They all contain seeds and have a fleshy edible part.*) **In what ways are they different?** (*They vary in color, shape, size, and number of seeds.*)

Lab Resource: Quick Lab

L1 COMMON CHARACTERISTICS Students will examine seeds and describe their characteristics.

Evaluate

Assess Your Understanding

After students answer the questions, have them evaluate their understanding by completing the appropriate sentence.

R T I Response to Intervention

3a. If students cannot define pollen, **then** have them locate the highlighted term and reread the definition.

b. If students need help identifying the function of fruits, **then** remind them that fruits contain seeds, which can develop into new plants.

my science COACH Have students go online for help in understanding some of the characteristics of seed plants.

Lab zone **After the Inquiry Warm-Up**

Classifying Plants

Inquiry Warm-Up, *Will Mosses Absorb Water?*
In the Inquiry Warm-Up, you investigated which better absorbs water: peat moss or sand. Using what you learned from that activity, answer the questions below.

1. **DRAW CONCLUSIONS** In the lab, you learned that mosses do not have vessels to transport water and nutrients throughout the plant. How do you think this affects the shape and size of moss plants?

   _____

   _____

2. **INFER** Based on your observations, do you think moss has a cuticle? What do you think its cell walls are like? Explain.

   _____

   _____

3. **USE PRIOR KNOWLEDGE** In what types of land environments is moss usually found?

   _____

4. **PREDICT** What do you think would happen to moss that was transplanted to a desert area? Explain.

   _____

   _____

Assess Your Understanding

Classifying Plants

What Are the Characteristics of Nonvascular Plants?

1a. REVIEW (Vascular tissues/Rhizoids) anchor moss and absorb water and nutrients.

b. EXPLAIN Why are most nonvascular plants short? _____
_____

c. COMPARE AND CONTRAST How are liverworts and hornworts

different? _____
_____

gotit? ···

○ **I get it!** Now I know the characteristics of nonvascular plants are _____
_____

○ **I need extra help with** _____
_____

What Are the Characteristics of Seedless Vascular Plants?

2a. IDENTIFY In plants, water moves through (phloem/xylem). Food moves through (phloem/xylem).

b. INFER Why do you think the developing leaves of a fern are

coiled? _____

_____

c. DEVELOP HYPOTHESES Why do you think there are more ferns than club

mosses? _____

_____

gotit? ···

○ **I get it!** Now I know the characteristics of seedless vascular plants include _____
_____

○ **I need extra help with** _____
_____

Assess Your Understanding

Classifying Plants

> ## What Are the Characteristics of Seed Plants?

3a. **DEFINE** What are pollen? _____

_____

_____

b. **DRAW CONCLUSIONS** Why do you think angiosperms enclose their

seeds in fruits? _____

_____

_____

got it? ···

○ **I get it!** Now I know the characteristics of seed plants include _____

_____

○ **I need extra help with** _____

_____

Key Concept Summaries

Classifying Plants

What Are the Characteristics of Nonvascular Plants?

Plants that lack vascular tissue for transporting materials are called **nonvascular plants. Nonvascular plants are low-growing, have thin cell walls, and do not have roots for absorbing water from the ground.** Instead, they obtain water and materials directly from their surroundings.

The three groups of nonvascular plants are mosses, liverworts, and hornworts. Mosses are the most diverse group. A moss has thin rootlike structures called **rhizoids** that anchor it to the ground and absorb water and nutrients. Atop a stemlike stalk covered with leaflike structures is a capsule that contains spores for reproduction. Mosses grow in shady spots and on rocks and trees. Liverworts grow as a thick crust on moist rocks or soil along streams. Hornworts usually live in moist soil, often with grass plants.

What Are the Characteristics of Seedless Vascular Plants?

Vascular plants are plants with true vascular tissue, which provides an effective transport system inside the plant and gives the plant strength. The two types of vascular tissue are xylem and phloem. **Xylem** carries water and minerals; **phloem** carries food. **Ferns, club mosses, and horsetails share two characteristics. They have true vascular tissue and they do not produce seeds. Instead of seeds, these plants reproduce by releasing spores.** All vascular plants have true roots, stems, and leaves. A fern's leaves are called **fronds.** The upper surface of a frond is covered with a cuticle that prevents water loss. Ferns thrive in shaded areas with moist soil. Club mosses grow in moist woods and near streams.

What Are the Characteristics of Seed Plants?

Seed plants have vascular tissue, and they use pollen and seeds to reproduce. All seed plants have true roots, stems, and leaves. **Pollen** are tiny structures that contain what will become sperm cells. A **seed** contains a young plant inside a protective covering. A **gymnosperm** is a seed plant that produces "naked" seeds, or seeds that are not enclosed by a protective fruit. The four groups of gymnosperms are the cycads, conifers, ginkgoes, and gnetophytes. An **angiosperm** is a flowering plant that produces seeds that are enclosed in fruits. A **cotyledon,** or seed leaf, provides food for the developing plant. **Monocots** have one cotyledon; **dicots** have two.

On a separate sheet of paper, explain the two key factors that separate nonvascular plants from seedless vascular plants from seed plants.

Review and Reinforce

Classifying Plants

Understanding Main Ideas
Answer the following questions on a separate sheet of paper.

1. In what ways do nonvascular plants, seedless vascular plants, and seed plants differ?
2. How does the absence of vascular tissue in nonvascular plants affect their structure and appearance?
3. Name the two types of vascular tissue and describe their functions.
4. What three structures do the bodies of all vascular plants have?
5. How are gymnosperms and angiosperms different?
6. What are the four types of gymnosperms?
7. Describe the different traits of monocots and dicots.

Building Vocabulary
Match each term with its definition by writing the letter of the correct definition in the right column on the line beside the term in the left column.

8. ___ cotyledon

9. ___ rhizoid

10. ___ frond

11. ___ pollen

a. a thin, rodlike structure that anchors a moss plant and absorbs water and nutrients

b. a seed leaf

c. the leaf of a fern

d. structures that contain cells that will later become sperm cells

Name _____ Date _____ Class _____

Classifying Plants

> Read the passage and study the diagram below. Then use a separate sheet of paper to answer the questions that follow.

Sphagnum Bogs

Bogs are marshy areas often found in cool regions such as Canada, northern Europe, and Russia. The plant life of bogs consists mostly of sphagnum mosses. Sphagnum bogs sometimes form over a small lake or pond. The layers of such a bog are shown below. Eventually the entire lake or pond will be filled with dead moss.

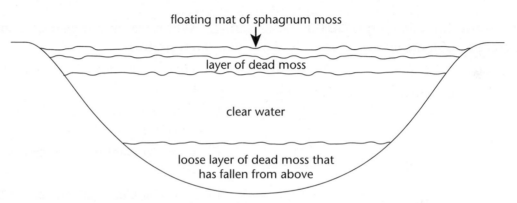

floating mat of sphagnum moss

layer of dead moss

clear water

loose layer of dead moss that has fallen from above

1. A sphagnum bog is said to have a "false" bottom and a "true" bottom. Explain this statement.

2. If you were an archeologist searching for ancient tools, in which layer of the bog would you look?

3. What characteristics of mosses let them form floating mats over small lakes and ponds?

4. Bogs of the type shown above do not form on larger lakes or rivers. Why do you think this is true?

Lesson Quiz

Classifying Plants

Write the letter of the correct answer on the line at the left.

1. ___ Which of the following is **NOT** true of mosses, liverworts, and hornworts?

   A They are nonvascular plants.

   B They have true roots, stems, and leaves.

   C They grow in moist places.

   D They are small and low-growing.

2. ___ Which type of plant has seeds that are encased in a protective fruit?

   A gymnosperms

   B conifers

   C angiosperms

   D horsetails

3. ___ Which of the following is **NOT** a characteristic of a dicot?

   A two cotyledons

   B vascular tissue bundles arranged in a ring

   C floral parts often in multiples of three

   D one main root

4. ___ Which statement best describes a gymnosperm?

   A a nonvascular plant with roots, stems, and leaves

   B a low-growing nonvascular plant lacking true roots

   C a vascular plant that uses spores to reproduce

   D a vascular plant that uses pollen to produce seeds that are not enclosed in protective fruits

If the statement is true, write *true*. If the statement is false, change the underlined word or words to make the statement true.

5. _____ Seedless vascular plants use <u>spores</u> to reproduce.

6. _____ The young leaves of some <u>hornworts</u> are known as fiddleheads.

7. _____ The vascular tissue that conducts water and nutrients in a plant is <u>phloem</u>.

8. _____ All flowering plants are <u>gymnosperms</u>.

9. _____ The rootlike structures that anchor a moss plant and absorb water and nutrients are called <u>rhizomes</u>.

10. _____ <u>Angiosperm</u> species outnumber all other land plant species by about seven to one.

Classifying Plants

Answer Key

After the Inquiry Warm-Up

1. Answers will vary. Sample: Mosses must be small and short so that all parts of the plant can have direct access to water collecting on the ground or other surfaces.

2. Because it is very absorbent moss probably has no cuticle and very thin cell walls. Both will make it much easier to absorb water.

3. Mosses are usually found in damp and shady environments.

4. In a desert, moss would quickly die because there would be little water for it to absorb.

Key Concept Summaries

The two factors that separate nonvascular plants from seedless vascular plants from seed plants are whether they have vascular tissue and whether they uses spores or seeds and pollen to reproduce. Nonvascular plants do not have vascular tissue and reproduce using spores. Seedless vascular plants also reproduce using spores instead of seeds, but they have true vascular tissue, which provides both support and an effective transport system. Seed plants have vascular tissue and use seeds and pollen to reproduce.

Review and Reinforce

1. Nonvascular plants lack vascular tissue and use spores to reproduce. Seedless vascular plants have vascular tissue and use spores to reproduce. Seed plants have vascular tissue and use pollen and seeds to reproduce.

2. Because they have no vascular tissue to support them or transport water and nutrients, nonvascular plants are low-growing, have thin cell walls, and lack roots.

3. The two types of vascular tissue are phloem, through which food moves, and xylem, through which water and minerals move.

4. roots, stems, and leaves

5. Gymnosperms produce "naked" seeds, or seeds not encased in a protective fruit. Angiosperms are flowering plants that produce seeds encased in a protective fruit.

6. cycads, conifers, ginkgoes, and gnetophytes

7. Monocots have a single cotyledon, parallel veins, flower parts that are often in multiples of three, vascular tissue scattered throughout their stems, and many roots spread out. Dicots have two cotyledons, branched veins, flower parts that are often in multiples of four or five, vascular tissue bundles arranged in a ring, and one main root.

8. b   9. a   10. c   11. d

Enrich

1. The false bottom is at the bottom of the layer of clear water. The layer of dead moss below it is not firm. If something dense is dropped into the bog, it will fall through the false bottom to the true bottom of the bog.

2. in the dead layer of moss at the bottom of the bog

3. Their small size and low density compared to water lets them form floating mats on the surface of the water.

4. The water needs to be still. Larger lakes have waves, and rivers have currents, that would break apart the floating mats of moss.

Lesson Quiz

1. B   2. C
3. C   4. D
5. true   6. ferns
7. xylem   8. angiosperms
9. rhizoids   10. true

Plant Structures

 How do you know a plant when you see it?

Lesson Pacing: 2–3 periods or 1–1$\frac{1}{2}$ blocks

SHORT ON TIME? To do this lesson in approximately half the time, do the Activate Prior Knowledge activity on page 100. A discussion of the Key Concepts on pages 100, 102, 104, 106, and 108 will familiarize students with the lesson content. Have students do the Quick Labs. The rest of the lesson can be completed by students independently.

Preference Navigator, in the online Planning tools, allows you to customize *Interactive Science* to your own teaching style. You can also edit lesson plans by selecting the Lesson Planner option.

Digital Teacher's Edition allows you to access your Teacher's Edition and Resource materials online.

my science online.com

Lesson Vocabulary

- root cap
- cambium
- stoma
- transpiration
- embryo
- germination
- flower
- pollination
- sepal
- petal
- stamen
- pistil
- ovary

Content Refresher
Professional Development Note

Structures of Angiosperms Angiosperms, the flowering plants, make up more then 88 percent of all living plant species and can be found almost anywhere on Earth. In addition to being classified according to the number of cotyledons present in the plant embryo, angiosperms can also be classified according to the characteristics of their stems. Woody plants have stems that contain wood and are therefore hard and rigid. Their cells have thick cell walls that support the plant body. Woody plants include trees, shrubs, and woody vines. In contrast, herbaceous plants do not produce wood as they grow. Their stems are soft and smooth. However, some herbaceous plants, such as corn, have stems that are rather hard. Angiosperms have unique characteristics that unify the group—flowers and fruits. Flowers enclose the ovary in which seeds develop. Fruits are the mature ovaries, consisting of a thick wall of tissue that surrounds the seeds. Flowers and fruits play an important role in the reproductive success of angiosperms. The various colors, sizes, shapes, and scents of flowers attract pollinators and help ensure that fertilization occurs. Not all flowers have pleasant scents, however. *Rafflesia arnoldii* emits a smell similar to rotting meat, which probably explains why it attracts its pollinators, carrion-eating flies. Fruits protect the seeds and help the seeds disperse.

LESSON OBJECTIVES

 Describe the functions of roots, stems, and leaves.

Explain how seeds become new plants.

Describe the structures of a flower.

Blended Path
Active learning using Student Edition, Inquiry Path, and Digital Path

ENGAGE AND EXPLORE

Teach this lesson using a variety of resources. Begin by reading **My Planet Diary** as a class. Have students discuss why the ariod plant has such big leaves. Then have students do the **Inquiry Warm-Up activity.** Students will observe common food items and identify them as roots, stems, or leaves. The **After the Inquiry Warm-Up worksheet** sets up a discussion about roots, stems, and leaves. Have volunteers share their answers to question 4, explaining which part of the plant is least likely to have a lot of sugars and starches.

EXPLAIN AND ELABORATE

Teach Key Concepts by explaining that seed plants are vascular plants and they have true roots. Continue to **Teach Key Concepts** by explaining the two main functions of a plant's stem: to carry substances between the plant's roots and leaves and to provide support for the plant. Have students practice the inquiry skill in the **Apply It activity.** Continue to **Teach Key Concepts** that the main function of leaves is to capture the sun's energy and carry out photosynthesis. **Lead a Discussion** about the stomata and guard cells.

Teach Key Concepts by explaining that the cycle of seed to plant involves seed production, dispersal, and germination. **Lead a Discussion** about seed dispersal and germination.

Teach Key Concepts by explaining that the flower is the reproductive structure in angiosperms.

Hand out the **Key Concept Summaries** as a review of each part of the lesson. Students can also use the online **Vocab Flash Cards** to review key terms.

EVALUATE

Have students take the **Lesson Quiz.** For an alternate assessment, see the *ExamView*® Computer Test Generator, Progress Monitoring Assessments, or SuccessTracker™.

ELL Support

1 Content and Language
Have students continue to add terms to a journal or personal glossary. Have students copy the vocabulary terms and then find the first time the words are used in the chapter. Have them copy the definition of each vocabulary term into their journal or personal glossary.

DIFFERENTIATED INSTRUCTION KEY
L1 Struggling Students or Special Needs
L2 On-Level Students **L3** Advanced Students

LESSON PLANNER 3.3

 **Inquiry Path** Hands-on learning in the Lab zone

ENGAGE AND EXPLORE

To teach this lesson with an emphasis on inquiry, begin with the **Inquiry Warm-Up activity.** Students will observe common food items and identify them as roots, stems, or leaves. The **After the Inquiry Warm-Up worksheet** sets up a discussion about roots, stems, and leaves. Have volunteers share their answers to question 4, explaining which part of the plant is least likely to have a lot of sugars and starches.

EXPLAIN AND ELABORATE

Focus on the **Inquiry Skill** for the lesson. Remind students that when they observe, they use one or more of their five senses to gather information about the world. Which sense was used to make observations in the **Inquiry Warm-Up activity?** *(Sight)* Before beginning the **Apply It activity,** review the idea of annual rings. Also, discuss the fact that any damage to the bark of a tree affects the phloem in that area. Such damage could prevent the cells in that area from getting food and growing. Do the **Teacher Demo,** allowing students to examine tree rings. Have students do the **Lab Investigation** to examine stomata in a land plant and in a floating water plant.

Build Inquiry to model seed dispersal. Have students do the **Quick Lab** to observe and describe the external and internal structure of two different seeds.

Build Inquiry to give students the opportunity to observe the structure of a flower. Have students do the **Quick Lab** to make models of flowers with different arrangements of reproductive structures to present to the class and compare and contrast. Students can use the online **Vocab Flash Cards** to review key terms.

EVALUATE

Have students take the **Lesson Quiz.** For an alternate assessment, see the *ExamView®* Computer Test Generator, Progress Monitoring Assessments, or SuccessTracker™.

Digital Path Online learning at my science online.com

ENGAGE AND EXPLORE

Teach this lesson using digital resources. Begin by having students learn more and explore real-world connections to plant structures at **My Planet Diary** online. Have them access the Chapter Resources to find the **Unlock the Big Question activity.** There they can answer the questions and refine their responses as they continue through the lesson. You can re-assign the activity and have students submit their work so you can track their progress.

EXPLAIN AND ELABORATE

Students reading above, at, or below the lexile measure of this lesson can access basic content readings at their level at **My Reading Web.** Encourage students to use the online **Vocab Flash Cards** to preview key terms. Assign the **Apply It activity** online and have students submit their work to you.

Use the **Interactive Art activity** online to allow students to match seeds to the methods used to disperse them. Have students do the **Quick Lab** to observe and describe the external and internal structure of two different seeds.

Use the **Interactive Art activity** to show students the structure of a flower. Have students do the **Quick Lab** to make models of flowers with different arrangements of reproductive structures to present to the class and compare and contrast. The **Key Concept Summaries** online allow students to read a summary and see an image associated with each part of the lesson. Online remediation is available at **My Science Coach.**

EVALUATE

Have students take the **Lesson Quiz.** For an alternate assessment, see the *ExamView®* Computer Test Generator, Progress Monitoring Assessments, or SuccessTracker™.

2 Frontload the Lesson

Have students survey the visuals in the lesson. Then have them write questions they have about the lesson based on their surveys. After students read the lesson, have them answer the questions they wrote at the start of the lesson.

3 Comprehensible Input

Have students rewrite the first section question as three questions. Then ask them to answer each question.

4 Language Production

Pair or group students with varied language abilities to complete labs collaboratively for language practice. Have each student copy the completed written lab for personal reference.

5 Assess Understanding

Make true or false statements using lesson content and have students indicate if they agree or disagree with a thumbs up or thumbs down gesture to check whole-class comprehension.

Lexile Measure = 880L

Plant Structures

Establish Learning Objectives

After this lesson, students will be able to:

 Describe the functions of roots, stems, and leaves.

 Explain how seeds become new plants.

 Describe the structures of a flower.

Engage

Activate Prior Knowledge

MY PLANET DIARY Read *Plant Giants* with the class. Explain that the aroid leaf is almost 3 meters long, which is the height of a basketball hoop off the ground. Tell students that the smallest flower and fruit belong to duckweed plants (genus *Wolffia*) which are about 0.6 mm long, 0.3 mm wide, and 120–150 µg in mass, or the mass of two salt grains. Ask: **What are four important parts of an angiosperm?** *(Roots, stems, leaves, and flowers)*

BIG IDEAS OF SCIENCE REFERENCE LIBRARY 🔲
Have students look up the following topics: Bats, Cactus, Redwoods.

Explore

Lab Resource: Inquiry Warm-Up 🔲

L1 **WHICH PLANT PART IS IT?** Students will observe common food items and identify them as roots, stems, or leaves.

LESSON

3 Plant Structures

 What Are the Functions of Roots, Stems, and Leaves?

 How Do Seeds Become New Plants?

 What Are the Structures of a Flower?

my planet Diary

SCIENCE STATS

Plant Giants

- The aroid plant (as shown here) on the island of Borneo in Asia has leaves that can grow three meters long! These are the largest undivided leaves on Earth!
- The rafflesia flower can grow up to one meter wide and weigh seven kilograms.
- The jackfruit can weigh up to 36 kilograms. That's the world's largest fruit that grows on trees!

Write your answer below. Why do you think the aroid plant has such big leaves?

Sample: so the plant can make more food

▷ **PLANET DIARY** Go to **Planet Diary** to learn more about plant structures.

Lab Do the Inquiry Warm-Up
zone *Which Plant Part Is It?*

What Are the Functions of Roots, Stems, and Leaves?

Each part of a plant plays an important role in its structure and function. Roots, stems, and leaves are just three structures we will look into further.

Roots Have you ever tried to pull a dandelion out of the soil? It's not easy, is it? That is because most roots are good anchors. Roots have three main functions. **Roots anchor a plant in the ground, absorb water and minerals from the soil, and sometime store food.** The more root area a plant has, the more water and minerals it can absorb.

SUPPORT ALL READERS

Lexile Measure = 880L   Lexile Word Count = 2144

Prior Exposure to Content: Many students may have misconceptions on this topic

Academic Vocabulary: *cause, effect, observe, relate*

Science Vocabulary: *stoma, transpiration, pollination, stamen, pistil*

Concept Level: Generally appropriate for most students in this grade

Preteach With: My Planet Diary "Plant Giants" and Figure 8 activity

Go to **My Reading Web** to access leveled readings that provide a foundation for the content.

my science online.com

Vocabulary
- root cap • cambium • stoma • transpiration
- embryo • germination • flower • pollination
- sepal • petal • stamen • pistil • ovary

Skills
- ⊙ Reading: Relate Cause and Effect
- △ Inquiry: Observe

Types of Roots The two main types of root systems are shown in **Figure 1**. A fibrous root system consists of many similarly sized roots that form a dense, tangled mass. Plants with fibrous roots take a lot of soil with them when you pull them out of the ground. Lawn grass, corn, and onions have fibrous root systems. In contrast, a taproot system has one long, thick main root. Many smaller roots branch off the main root. A plant with a taproot system is hard to pull out of the ground. Carrots, dandelions, and cacti have taproots.

FIGURE 1 ··

Root Systems and Structure
There are two main root systems with many structures.

✏ **Interpret Photos** Label the taproot *T* and the fibrous roots *F*.

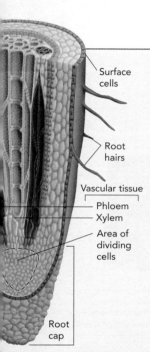

Surface cells

Root hairs

Vascular tissue
- Phloem
- Xylem

Area of dividing cells

Root cap

Root Structure

In **Figure 2,** you can see the structure of a typical root. The tip of the root is rounded and is covered by the root cap. The **root cap** protects the root from injury as the root grows through the soil. Behind the root cap are the cells that divide to form new root cells.

Root hairs grow out of the root's surface. These tiny hairs can enter the spaces between soil particles, where they absorb water and minerals. The root hairs also help to anchor the plant in the soil.

Locate the vascular tissue in the center of the root. The water and nutrients that are absorbed from the soil quickly move into the xylem. From there, these substances are transported upward to the plant's stems and leaves. Phloem transports food manufactured in the leaves to the root. The root tissues then use the food for growth or store it for future use by the plant.

FIGURE 2 ·······································

Root Structure
Roots have many structures.

✏ **Define** What is the function of the root cap?

It protects the root as it grows through
the soil.

101

1 Content and Language
Write the term *transpiration* on the board. Draw students' attention to the Latin suffix *-ation,* which can indicate a state of being, a result, or an action. Encourage students to identify two other vocabulary terms *(germination, pollination)* that share this suffix.

2 Frontload the Lesson
Invite student volunteers to come to the board and draw diagrams of several

flowers. Encourage students to offer their ideas about the names of various structures on these flowers.

3 Comprehensible Input
Invite groups of students to work together to demonstrate the functions of roots, stems, and leaves, using their bodies, movement and gestures, and words. Encourage groups to make presentations of their information to their peers.

Explain
Introduce Vocabulary
Point out to students the three vocabulary terms that contain the suffix *-tion: transpiration, germination,* and *pollination.* Tell students that this suffix is used to form nouns from verbs.

Teach Key Concepts 🔑
Explain to students that unlike nonvascular plants, seed plants are vascular plants and they have true roots. Emphasize that roots have three main functions. Ask: **What do roots do for a plant?** *(Anchor a plant in the ground, absorb water and minerals from the soil, and sometimes store food)* **What types of root systems are there?** *(Some plants have a taproot system, a long, thick main root with many smaller roots branching off. Other plants have a fibrous root system made up of thin fibrous roots that form a tangled mass and take soil with them when they are pulled.)* **What are some examples of each type of root system?** *(Taproot system: carrots, dandelions, cacti; fibrous root system: lawn grass, corn, onions)* **Which root type is likely to be more useful in preventing soil erosion?** *(The fibrous root system holds soil between the root fibers, so it works better than a taproot in preventing erosion.)*

Teach With Visuals
Tell students to look at **Figure 2.** Ask: **Why is the root cap important?** *(Behind the root cap are the cells that divide to form new root cells. They need to be protected. The root cap protects the root as the root grows through the soil.)* **What are the functions of the root hairs?** *(They enter the spaces between soil particles and absorb water and minerals. They also help anchor the plant.)* **What do xylem and phloem do?** *(Xylem transports water and minerals to the stems and leaves. Phloem transports food manufactured in the leaves to the roots.)* **What does the root tissue do with the food?** *(It uses the food for growth or stores it for later use by the plant.)*

My Planet Diary provides an opportunity for students to explore real-world connections to plant structures.

my science online.com | Roots, Stems, and Leaves

Explain

Teach Key Concepts 🔑

Remind students that stems are unique to vascular plants and are an adaptation that allowed vascular plants to survive successfully on land. Explain to students that the stem of a plant has two main functions. Ask: **What are the functions of a stem?** *(The stem carries substances between the plant's roots and leaves. The stem also provides support for the plant and holds up the leaves so they are exposed to the sun. Some stems store food.)* **What are the two types of stems?** *(Woody and herbaceous)* **How can you distinguish between the two types?** *(Woody stems contain wood and are hard and rigid. Herbaceous stems contain no wood and are often green, soft, and flexible.)* **What is the structure of a woody stem?** *(The outermost layer is bark, which includes an outer protective layer called cork and an inner layer of phloem. Interior to the phloem layer is the cambium, the layer that produces new xylem and phloem. Next is the wood, which is made up of sapwood and heartwood. Sapwood is active xylem; heartwood is old, inactive xylem that helps support the tree.)* Tell students that the growth of xylem cells is responsible for a tree's annual rings. Ask: **How would you describe the xylem cells that form in the spring? In the summer?** *(The cells that form in the spring are large and have thin walls because they grow rapidly. They produce a wide, light brown ring. The cells that grow in the summer grow slowly, so they are small and have thick walls. They produce a thin, dark ring.)* **What represents one year's growth?** *(One pair of light and dark rings)*

Address Misconceptions

L1 **GROW UP OR GROW WIDE?** Some students think that trees simply "grow up" the same way that grasses grow. Tell students to look at **Figure 3**. Point out that the heartwood is old xylem and is at the center of the trunk. Ask: **Where would you expect to find new growth?** *(Near the outer portion of the trunk)* **How do trees grow wider?** *(By adding layers to the outside of the stem)*

21st Century Learning

CRITICAL THINKING Reinforce the fact that trees grow by adding layers to the outside of the stem. Tell students that to collect sap from maple trees, farmers cut a "V" shape into the bark of the tree a few feet above ground. Ask: **If a farmer comes back to the same tree in two years, where will the "V" cut be? Explain.** *(At about the same height; as the tree grows wider, its upward growth takes place mainly at the top of the tree.)*

Stems The stem of a plant has two main functions. 🔑 **The stem carries substances between the plant's roots and leaves. The stem also provides support for the plant and holds up the leaves so they are exposed to the sun.** In addition, some stems, such as those of asparagus, store food.

The Structure of a Stem Stems can be either woody or herbaceous (hur BAY shus). Woody stems are hard and rigid, such as in maple trees. Herbaceous stems contain no wood and are often soft. Plants with herbaceous stems include daisies, ivy, and asparagus (pictured left).

Herbaceous and woody stems consist of phloem and xylem tissue as well as many other supporting cells. As you can see in **Figure 3**, a woody stem contains many layers of tissue. The outermost layer is bark. Bark includes an outer protective layer and an inner layer of living phloem, which transports food through the stem. Next is a layer of cells called the **cambium** (KAM bee um), which divides to produce new phloem and xylem. It is xylem that makes up most of what you call "wood." Sapwood is active xylem that transports water and minerals through the stem. The older, darker, heartwood is inactive but provides support.

FIGURE 3 ···

Stem Structure
The woody stem of a tree contains many different structures.

✏️ **Interpret Diagrams** Label the active xylem and phloem on the tree trunk below.

Wood   **Bark**

Xylem
Vascular tissue that transports water; also known as sapwood in trees

Heartwood
Old, inactive xylem that helps support the tree

Cork
Outer bark that protects the cells inside

Phloem
Vascular tissue that transports food

Cambium
Tissue that produces new xylem and phloem

Digital Lesson: Assign the *Apply It* activity online and have students submit their work to you.

my science online.com   ▶ Roots, Stems, and Leaves

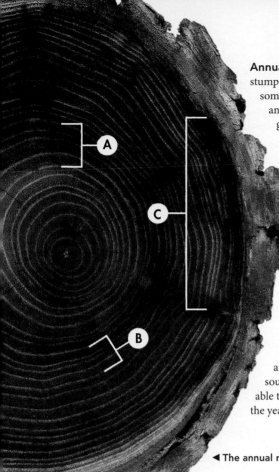

Annual Rings Have you ever looked at a tree stump and seen a pattern of circles that looks something like a target? These circles are called annual rings. They represent a tree's yearly growth. Annual rings are made of xylem. Xylem cells that form in the spring are large and have thin walls because they grow rapidly. They produce a wide, light brown ring. Xylem cells that form in the summer grow slowly and, therefore, are small and have thick walls. They produce a thin, dark ring. One pair of light and dark rings represents one year's growth. You can estimate a tree's age by counting its annual rings.

The width of a tree's annual rings can provide important clues about past weather conditions, such as rainfall. In rainy years, more xylem is produced, so the tree's annual rings are wide. In dry years, rings are narrow. By examining annual rings from some trees in the southwestern United States, scientists were able to infer that severe droughts occurred in the years 840, 1067, 1379, and 1632.

◀ The annual rings in a tree reveal the tree's history.

apply it!

1 Calculate How old was the tree when it was cut down?

About 25 years old

2 Observe The area at Area C is blackened from a fire that affected one side of the tree. Describe how the tree grew after the fire.

Sample: The tree grew more on the side that was not damaged by fire.

3 CHALLENGE Areas A and B both represent four years of growth. What might account for their difference in size?

Sample: Area A was formed when conditions such as rainfall were better for the tree than when Area B formed.

103

Elaborate

Apply It!

L1 Before beginning the activity, review the idea of annual rings. Also discuss the fact that any damage to the bark of a tree affects the phloem in that area. Such damage could prevent the cells in that area from getting food and growing.

▲ **Observe** Tell students that when they observe, they use one or more of their five senses to gather information about the world. In this case, they are gathering information about the growth of the tree by looking at the series of annual rings in Area C.

Teacher Demo

L2 OBSERVING TREE RINGS

Materials cross-sectional slice of a tree trunk (you can obtain by slicing through a log for firewood), hand lens

Time 15 minutes

Show students the slice of tree trunk. Have students arrange themselves in groups of five or six. Pass the slice and the hand lens around the class, allowing each group about two or three minutes to examine the slice. Tell students to find three pairs of dark and light rings of different widths.

Ask: **Which pair represents the year of heaviest rainfall?** *(The ring pair with the greatest width grew in the year of heaviest rainfall.)* **Which pair represents the year of lightest rainfall?** *(The ring pair with the smallest width grew in the year of the lightest rainfall.)* **What are annual rings made of?** *(Xylem)*

21st Century Learning 📖

CRITICAL THINKING Have students read *Redwoods* in the **Big Ideas of Science Reference Library.** Ask students to make up quiz-show questions (along with the answers) based on the information they learned. If time permits, one student can play the role of the host and several students can play contestants.

Differentiated Instruction

L1 Modeling a Tree Stem Have student pairs roll up several sheets of newspaper and place them inside the core of an empty roll of paper toweling or bathroom tissue. Tell students that the core and the paper in it represent the center of a woody stem. Next, have students label five additional sheets of paper *old xylem, active xylem, cambium,* *active phloem,* and *outer bark*. Direct students to wrap these sheets around their model in the correct order. Finally, have partners take turns unwrapping the model, naming and explaining the function of each layer.

L3 Specialized Stems Have students research tubers, bulbs, and rhizomes and find examples of each.

Explain

Teach Key Concepts

Remind students that plants are autotrophs—they make their own food. Discuss the fact that leaves come in all different shapes and sizes, but regardless of shape and size, they all play the same important role in a plant. Ask: **What is the main function of leaves?** *(They capture the sun's energy and carry out photosynthesis.)* **In what structures does photosynthesis take place?** *(Chloroplasts)* **What pigment do chloroplasts contain? What is the function of this pigment?** *(Chloroplasts contain chlorophyll, which traps the sun's energy.)* **Why is the structure of a leaf ideal for carrying out photosynthesis?** *(The cells that contain the most chloroplasts are located near the leaf's upper surface, where they get the most light.)* **Where are the stomata mostly found?** *(On a leaf's underside)* **What do they do?** *(They open to let in carbon dioxide and allow water vapor and oxygen to leave. They close to conserve water.)* **If the temperature is not very hot, when would stomata generally be open and closed?** *(Open during the daytime when sunlight is available and photosynthesis is active; closed at night when open stomata would only lead to water loss)* **What is the process by which water evaporates from a plant's leaves?** *(Transpiration)*

Teach With Visuals

Tell students to look at **Figure 4**. Ask: **Where is the leaf cuticle and what does it do?** *(It covers the leaf's top and bottom surfaces and prevents water loss.)* **What structure contains the xylem and phloem?** *(Vein)* **What are stomata? What do they do?** *(Small pores in the surface layers that that open and close to control when gases enter and leave the leaf)* **What is the benefit of upper leaf cells that are densely packed? Of lower leaf cells that are loosely packed?** *(Densely packed cells can collect more energy for photosynthesis. Loosely packed cells allow carbon dioxide to reach cells and oxygen to escape into the air.)*

Lead a Discussion

STOMATA AND GUARD CELLS Explain to students how stomata, the tiny pores in a leaf's surface layers, open and close. Tell students that each stoma is formed by two slightly curved cells, called guard cells. When the guard cells fill up with water, they arch and curve away from each other, opening the stoma. When the guard cells have less water, they straighten out and come together, closing the stoma. Ask: **In a period of little water, what would the guard cells look like? The stoma?** *(The guard cells would be straight and close together because there is little water in them. The stoma would be closed.)*

104 Plants

Sample: Stomata open and close to let matter in and out of plants. Mouths open and close to let matter in and out of organisms.

Leaves Leaves vary greatly in size and shape. Pine trees have needle-shaped leaves. Birch trees have small rounded leaves with jagged edges. Regardless of their shape, leaves play an important role in a plant. **Leaves capture the sun's energy and carry out the food-making process of photosynthesis.**

The Structure of a Leaf If you were to cut through a leaf and look at the edge under a microscope, you would see the structures in **Figure 4**. The leaf's top and bottom surface layers protect the cells inside. Between the layers of cells are veins that contain xylem and phloem.

The surface layers of the leaf have small openings, or pores, called **stomata** (stoh MAH tuh; *singular* stoma). The stomata open and close to control when gases enter and leave the leaf. When the stomata are open, carbon dioxide enters the leaf, and oxygen and water vapor exit.

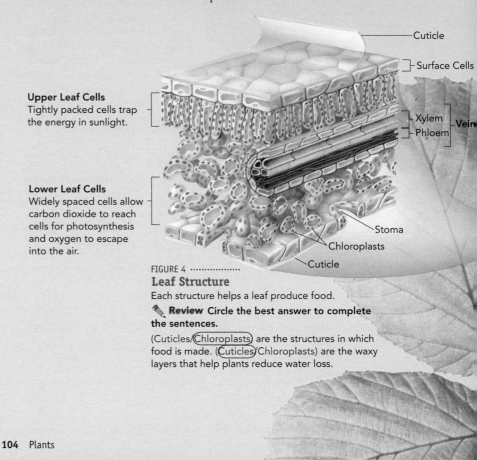

Upper Leaf Cells Tightly packed cells trap the energy in sunlight.

Lower Leaf Cells Widely spaced cells allow carbon dioxide to reach cells for photosynthesis and oxygen to escape into the air.

Cuticle

Surface Cells

Xylem

Phloem

Vein

Stoma

Chloroplasts

Cuticle

FIGURE 4
Leaf Structure
Each structure helps a leaf produce food.

Review Circle the best answer to complete the sentences.

(Cuticles/**Chloroplasts**) are the structures in which food is made. (**Cuticles**/Chloroplasts) are the waxy layers that help plants reduce water loss.

104 Plants

Professional Development Note Teacher to Teacher

Misconception A common misconception that students have about plants is that if all plants died, humans would suffocate from lack of oxygen. In fact, there is enough atmospheric oxygen to breathe for many years. The accumulation of CO_2 would poison humans before they ran out of oxygen, but that could take over 1,000 years. What students do not appreciate is that if all plants died, humans would starve to death long before they suffocated. It has been estimated that if all plants died today, there would be massive starvation within a month, with no food available anywhere within a year.

Joel Palmer, Ed.D.
Mesquite ISD
Mesquite, Texas

The Leaf and Photosynthesis The structure of a leaf is ideal for carrying out photosynthesis. The cells that contain the most chloroplasts are located near the leaf's upper surface, where they get the most light. The chlorophyll in the chloroplasts traps the sun's energy.

Carbon dioxide enters the leaf through open stomata. Water, which is absorbed by the plant's roots, travels up the stem to the leaf through the xylem. During photosynthesis, sugar and oxygen are produced from the carbon dioxide and water. Oxygen passes out of the leaf through the open stomata. The sugar enters the phloem and then travels throughout the plant.

Controlling Water Loss Because such a large area of a leaf is exposed to the air, water can quickly evaporate from a leaf into the air. The process by which water evaporates from a plant's leaves is called **transpiration.** A plant can lose a lot of water through transpiration. A corn plant, for example, can lose almost 4 liters of water on a hot summer day. Without a way to slow down the process of transpiration, a plant would shrivel up and die.

Fortunately, plants have ways to slow down transpiration. One way plants retain water is by closing the stomata. The stomata often close when leaves start to dry out.

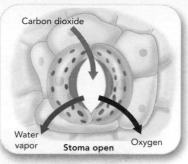

Carbon dioxide

Water vapor — **Stoma open** — Oxygen

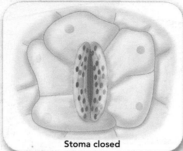

Stoma closed

FIGURE 5 ·······················
Stomata
Stomata can slow water loss.

✏️ **Name** What three substances enter and leave a plant through stomata?

Carbon dioxide, oxygen,
and water vapor

 Lab zone Do the Lab Investigation
Investigating Stomata.

Assess Your Understanding

1a. List What are the functions of a stem?

To carry substances between
roots and leaves, provide
support, and hold up leaves for
sunlight exposure

b. Infer If you forget to water a houseplant for a few days, would its stomata be open or closed? Why?

The stomata would be closed
to prevent water loss.

got it? ···

O **I get it!** Now I know that roots, stems, and leaves perform functions like _anchoring the plant,_
absorbing and transporting nutrients, and making and storing food.

O I need extra help with _See TE note._

Go to **MY SCIENCE COACH** *online for help with this subject.*

105

Differentiated Instruction

L1 The Parts of a Plant Have students create a visual representation of the parts of a plant and their functions. Tell students to make a poster of a generic plant, one that has roots, stem, and leaves. Have students label the parts and then use callouts to describe the functions of each part. Tell students that you will display the posters, so they should be as artistic and accurate as possible.

L3 Specialized Leaves Plants have specialized leaves. Have students research the following plants and describe their leaves: Venus' flytrap, pitcher plant, pea plant, kalanchoe, sundew, cactus, and poinsettia.

21st Century Learning

CRITICAL THINKING Review with students the functions of a leaf and the fact that leaves come in many shapes and sizes. Tell students that the shapes and sizes represent adaptations of the plants to their environments. Ask: **Why do you think plants in shady forests often have large leaves?** *(To capture as much sunlight for photosynthesis as possible)* **Why do you think plants in dry areas have small, thick, wax-coated leaves?** *(To prevent as much water loss as possible)* **Why do you think plants in very rainy areas often have long, pointy leaves?** *(To help shed water and thereby prevent bacteria and fungi that cause disease from growing and damaging the leaves)*

Make Analogies

L1 FOOD FACTORY Explain to students that a plant leaf is often compared to a factory. Ask: **What is true about any type of factory?** *(Sample: It has a process that turns raw materials into products under specific conditions.)* **Using your answer, why is a leaf like a food factory?** *(In a leaf, the raw materials water and carbon dioxide are combined in the presence of light energy in a process called photosynthesis to produce sugar and oxygen.)*

Elaborate ————————

Lab Resource: Lab Investigation

L2 INVESTIGATING STOMATA Students will examine stomata in a land plant and in a floating water plant.

Evaluate ————————

Assess Your Understanding

After students answer the questions, have them evaluate their understanding by completing the appropriate sentence.

R T I Response to Intervention

1a. If students need help identifying the functions of a stem, **then** show them a picture of a plant with an herbaceous stem and have them look at the picture as a volunteer reads aloud the Key Concept about stems.

b. If students have trouble relating the condition of the stomata to environmental conditions, **then** first review the function of stomata and then analyze the environmental condition in terms of water availability.

MY SCIENCE COACH Have students go online for help in understanding the nature of stems and leaves.

Explain

Teach Key Concepts 🔑

Remind students of what a seed is: a structure that contains a young plant inside a protective covering. Tell students that the cycle of seed to plant involves seed production, dispersal, and germination. Explain that all seeds share important similarities. Ask: **What is inside a seed?** *(An embryo and stored food)* **What is the outside covering of a seed called? What is its function?** *(The seed coat keeps the embryo and its food from drying out.)* **Why does the seed contain stored food?** *(The embryo uses the stored food until it can make its own food.)* **What structure surrounds the seeds in many plants?** *(A fruit)*

Teach With Visuals

Tell students to look at **Figure 6.** Ask: **What structures are common to all seeds?** *(Seed coat, embryo, stored food, cotyledon)* **What plant characteristics can be seen in the embryo?** *(The beginnings of roots, stems, leaves)* **Why do you think a seed germinates once it has absorbed water?** *(When a seed absorbs water, the food-storing tissues swell. This cracks open the seed coat.)*

Lead a Discussion

SEED DISPERSAL AND GERMINATION Tell students that seed dispersal, or the scattering of seeds, can happen in various ways. Ask: **What are some ways in which seeds are dispersed?** *(By wind, water, ejection, animals, humans)* Discuss seed germination, or the process by which an embryo begins to grow again and pushes out of the seed. Ask: **What must the seed do in order to germinate?** *(Absorb water)* **How does the seed germinate?** *(After absorbing water, the embryo uses the stored food to start growing. The roots first grow downward and then the stem and leaves grow upward.)* **Why is it an advantage for seeds to be able to remain inactive and not germinate immediately after the embryo forms?** *(This allows for seeds to be dispersed but not germinate until there are ideal growing conditions.)*

🔄 **Relate Cause and Effect** Tell students that science involves many cause-and-effect relationships. A cause makes something happen. An effect is what happens. Relating cause and effect involves looking at two events to see if one caused the other.

How Do Seeds Become New Plants?

Many plants begin their life cycle as a seed. You can follow the cycle from seed to plant in **Figure 6.** All seeds share important similarities. 🔑 **Inside a seed is a partially developed plant. If a seed lands in an area where conditions are favorable, the plant sprouts out of the seed and begins to grow.**

Seed Structure A seed has three main parts—an embryo, stored food, and a seed coat. The young plant that develops from the zygote, or fertilized egg, is called the **embryo.** The embryo already has the beginnings of roots, stems, and leaves. In the seeds of most plants, the embryo stops growing when it is quite small. When the embryo begins to grow again, it uses the food stored in the seed until it can make its own food by photosynthesis. In all seeds, the embryo has one or more seed leaves, or cotyledons. In some seeds, food is stored in the cotyledons. In others, food is stored outside the embryo.

The outer covering of a seed is called the seed coat. The seed coat acts like plastic wrap, protecting the embryo and its food from drying out. This allows a seed to remain inactive for a long time. In many plants, the seeds are surrounded by a structure called a fruit.

FIGURE 6 ·······················
> INTERACTIVE ART Story of a Seed
Read the text on this page and the next page. Then complete the activities about seeds becoming new plants.

✏️ Complete each task.
1. **Review** On the diagram, label the seed's embryo, cotyledons, and seed coat.

Stem and root

Embryo

Cotyledons

Stored food

Seed coat

106 Plants

Interactive Art allows students to match seeds to the methods used to disperse them.

my science online.com ▷ **Seeds to Plants**

Seed Dispersal

After seeds form, they are usually scattered. The scattering of seeds is called seed dispersal. Seeds can be dispersed in many different ways. When animals eat fruit, the seeds inside the fruit pass through the animal's digestive system and are deposited in new areas. Other seeds are enclosed in barblike structures that hook onto fur or clothing. The seeds fall off in a new area. Water also disperses seeds that fall into oceans and rivers. Wind disperses lightweight seeds, such as those of dandelions and maple trees. Some plants eject their seeds. The force scatters the seeds in many directions. A seed that is dispersed far from its parent plant has a better chance of survival. Far away, a seed does not have to compete with its parent for light, water, and nutrients.

Germination

After a seed is dispersed, it may remain inactive for a while before it germinates. **Germination** (jur muh NAY shun) occurs when the embryo begins to grow again and pushes out of the seed. Germination begins when the seed absorbs water. Then the embryo uses stored food to begin to grow. The roots first grow downward. Then its stem and leaves grow upward.

✏️ **Relate Cause and Effect**
Underline a cause of seed dispersal and circle its effect in the text on this page.

2. Explain Give two reasons why this seed can be successfully dispersed by wind.

Sample: It is lightweight and has soft structures to catch the wind.

3. ⟨CHALLENGE⟩ Which young plant, A or B, is more likely to grow into an adult plant? Why?

Plant B; it does not have to compete for resources with as many plants.

Lab zone — Do the Quick Lab *The In-Seed Story.*

🦫 **Assess Your Understanding**

got it?

○ I get it! Now I know that a seed becomes a new plant when it lands in an area with favorable conditions and a new plant sprouts.

○ I need extra help with See TE note.

Go to MY SCIENCE ⓢ COACH online for help with this subject.

107

Differentiated Instruction

L1 Structure of a Seed Have students draw a seed and label the embryo, stored food, and seed coat. Have students describe each part.

L1 All About Seed Plants Have students work in groups of four to write 10 questions about the characteristics of seed plants. Suggest they compose a variety of short-answer, fill-in-the-blank, and matching questions. Remind them to create answer keys as well. Have

groups exchange questions and complete them. Students can check their answers using the answer keys.

L3 Germination Have student pairs design an experiment that illustrates seed germination. Remind students of the necessary conditions for germination. Also remind them that their design should include a control. You may wish to have students perform the experiment for the class.

Elaborate

Build Inquiry 🧪

L2 MODELING SEED DISPERSAL

Materials tissue paper, modeling clay, plastic foam balls, plastic spoons, table tennis balls, hook-and-loop fastener strips, and other arts and crafts materials

Time 25 minutes

Tell students to review the various means of seed dispersal. Explain that the fruit (the structure that encloses the seeds) helps the seeds disperse. Have students work together to build model seeds that can be dispersed by wind, water, or by sticking to clothes or animal fur. Encourage students to predict how far their seeds will travel and then to test their predictions. Students can present their models to the class, identifying how their model seeds are similar to real seeds and how their models could be improved.

Ask: **What characteristics are most important for each method of dispersal?** *(Samples: Animal fur—seed must stick to fur with barbs or similar structures; water—seed must float; wind—seed has structures to catch the wind and seed is lightweight; ejection—seed is small, dense, and compact)* **A coconut produces one of the largest seeds in the plant kingdom. The seed is encased in a tough husk made of strong fibers that have air spaces between them. How do you think coconut seeds are dispersed? Explain.** *(On ocean currents; the fruit can float and the husk prevents the seeds from getting too wet before they reach land.)*

Lab Resource: Quick Lab 🧪

L2 THE IN-SEED STORY Students will observe and describe the external and internal structures of two different seeds.

Evaluate

Assess Your Understanding

Have students evaluate their understanding by completing the appropriate sentence.

R T I Response to Intervention

If students need help describing how seeds become new plants, **then** have them work with a partner to talk through the processes of seed dispersal and seed germination.

MY SCIENCE ⓢ COACH Have students go online for help in understanding how seeds become new plants.

Explain

Teach Key Concepts 🗝

Explain to students that the flower is the reproductive structure in angiosperms. Discuss with students that although flowers come in all sizes, shapes, and colors, they all have the same function—reproduction. Tell students that a typical flower contains four main parts. Ask: **What are the four main parts of a flower?** *(Sepals, petals, stamens, and pistils)* **What are sepals? What function do they perform?** *(Sepals are leaflike structures that protect the developing flower while it is still a bud. Sepals are often green in color.)* **What are petals? What function do they perform?** *(Petals are colorful, leaflike structures that attract pollinators with their color and scent.)* **What is the male part of a flower called? What structures make it up?** *(The stamen consists of filaments and anthers.)* **What is produced in the anther?** *(Pollen)* **What is the female part of a flower called? What structures does it include?** *(The pistil consists of the stigma, style, and ovary.)* **What does the ovary contain?** *(One or more ovules)* Discuss the process of pollination and the role of pollinators. Ask: **What is pollination?** *(The transfer of pollen from male reproductive structures to female reproductive structures)* **What are examples of pollinators?** *(Birds, bats, bees, and flies)*

Teach With Visuals

Tell students to look at **Figure 7.** Ask: **The plants shown here have brightly colored petals or strong scents. Why do you think this is so?** *(Flowers with bright colors or strong scents have a better chance of attracting birds, bats, bees, and flies, which they must do in order to ensure pollination.)* Explain to students that many plants produce flowers without brightly colored petals or strong scents. These plants are usually pollinated by wind. Plants that are pollinated by wind produce much more pollen than plants that are pollinated by animals. Ask: **Why do you think wind-pollinated flowers produce so much pollen?** *(Pollen carried by animals has a better chance of reaching another plant of the same species than does pollen carried by wind.)*

Elaborate

21st Century Learning

CREATIVITY Encourage students to find out about the important role flowers have had in art. Have students compare paintings by artists such as O'Keeffe, Van Gogh, Monet, and Picasso. Ask students to describe how each artist represented the flowers and analyze the differences.

What Are the Structures of a Flower?

Flowers come in all sorts of shapes, sizes, and colors. But, despite their differences, all flowers have the same function—reproduction. A **flower** is the reproductive structure of an angiosperm. 🗝 **A typical flower contains sepals, petals, stamens, and pistils.**

The colors and shapes of most flower structures and the scents produced by most flowers attract insects and other animals. These organisms ensure that pollination occurs. **Pollination** is the transfer of pollen from male reproductive structures to female reproductive structures. Pollinators, such as those shown in **Figure 7,** include birds, bats, and insects such as bees and flies. As you read, keep in mind that some flowers lack one or more of the parts. For example, some flowers have only male reproductive parts, and some flowers do not have petals.

Sepals and Petals When a flower is still a bud, it is enclosed by leaflike structures called **sepals** (SEE pulz). Sepals protect the developing flower and are often green in color. When the sepals fold back, they reveal the flower's colorful, leaflike **petals.** The petals are generally the most colorful parts of a flower. The shapes, sizes, and number of petals vary greatly between flowers.

Stamens Within the petals are the flower's male and female reproductive parts. The **stamens** (STAY munz) are the male reproductive parts. Locate the stamens inside the flower in **Figure 8.** The thin stalk of the stamen is called the filament. Pollen is made in the anther, at the top of the filament.

FIGURE 7 ·······································
Pollinator Matchup

Some pollinators are well adapted to the plants they pollinate. For example, the long tongue of the nectar bat helps the bat reach inside the agave plant, as shown below.

✎ **Apply Concepts** Write the letter of the pollinator on the plant it is adapted to pollinate.

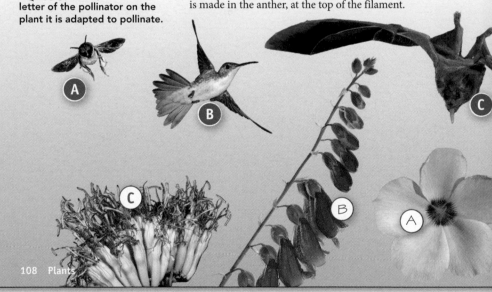

108   Plants

Interactive Art shows the structure of a flower.

my science online.com ▷ | Flower Structures

LESSON 3.3

Pistils The female parts, or **pistils** (PIS tulz), are found in the center of most flowers, as shown in **Figure 8.** Some flowers have two or more pistils; others have only one. The sticky tip of the pistil is called the stigma. A slender tube, called a style, connects the stigma to a hollow structure at the base of the flower. This hollow structure is the **ovary,** which protects the seeds as they develop. An ovary contains one or more ovules.

FIGURE 8 ....
▶ INTERACTIVE ART **Structures of a Typical Flower**
Flowers have many structures.

✎ **Relate Text and Visuals**
Use the word bank to fill in the missing labels.

Sepals
are the small, leaflike parts of a flower. They protect the developing flower.

Petals
are usually the most colorful parts of a flower. Pollinators are attracted by their color and scent.

Stamens
are the male reproductive parts of a flower. Pollen is produced in the anther, at the top of the stalklike filament.

Pistils
are the female reproductive parts of a flower. They consist of a sticky stigma, a slender tube called the style, and a hollow structure called the ovary at the base.

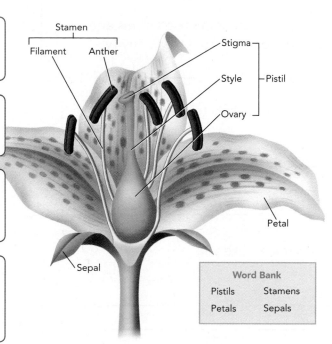

Stamen
Filament   Anther
Stigma
Style — Pistil
Ovary
Petal
Sepal

Word Bank

Pistils	Stamens
Petals	Sepals

Lab zone   Do the Quick Lab Modeling Flowers.

🖐 **Assess Your Understanding**

got it? ....

○ I get it! Now I know that the structures of a flower include sepals, petals, stamens, and pistils.

○ I need extra help with See TE note.

Go to **my science ⑤ COACH** online for help with this subject.

109

Differentiated Instruction

L1 Structure of a Flower Have students make a compare/contrast table listing the male and female parts of a flower.

L1 Flower Parts and Functions Have students summarize what they have learned about flower parts and their

functions by drawing a generic flower with sepals, petals, stamen, and pistil. Have them label each part and describe its functions. Have them exchange their drawings with a classmate for evaluation.

Elaborate ────────────

Build Inquiry **Lab** zone

L1 **OBSERVING THE STRUCTURE OF A FLOWER**

Materials gladiolus flower, paper towel, hand lens, metric ruler, lens paper, safety goggles

Time 25 minutes

Instruct students to wear safety goggles. Provide student pairs with a flower and tell them to observe its parts with the hand lens. Have them draw a diagram of the flower. Have them examine and describe the sepals, petals, stamen, and pistil. Have students observe the structures that make up the stamen and the pistil. Tell students to use the ruler to measure the height of a stamen and a pistil. Have them gently place a small piece of lens paper on the stigma and then remove it.

Ask: **What are the functions of the sepals and petals?** *(The sepals protect the flower bud and the petals attract pollinators with their color or scent.)* **How does the structure of a flower enable it to perform its reproductive function?** *(The stamen produces pollen, which contains sperm cells. The pistil produces eggs in the ovules of the ovary. Reproduction occurs when a sperm fertilizes an egg as a result of pollination.)* **Why might it be an advantage to have a longer stamen? A longer pistil?** *(A longer stamen would ensure that an insect picks up pollen on the anther and transfers to another plant, or that it falls from the anther to the stigma of the same plant. A longer pistil would make it easier for pollinators to land on it.)* **What did you discover about the stigma using the lens paper?** *(It is sticky.)*

Lab Resource: Quick Lab **Lab** zone

L2 **MODELING FLOWERS** Students will make models of flowers with different arrangements of reproductive structures to present to the class and to compare and contrast.

Evaluate ────────────

Assess Your Understanding

Have students evaluate their understanding by completing the appropriate sentence.

R T I Response to Intervention

If students need help identifying the structures of a flower, **then** have them review the highlighted vocabulary terms and **Figure 8.**

my science ⑤ COACH Have students go online for help in understanding the structure of a flower.

Lab zone **After the Inquiry Warm-Up**

Plant Structures

Inquiry Warm-Up, *Which Plant Part Is It?*
In the Inquiry Warm-Up, you investigated vegetables that are common food items and identified them as roots, stems, or leaves. Using what you learned from that activity, answer the questions below.

1. **INFER** If a vegetable is green, which part of a plant is it *most* likely to be from? Explain.

   _____

   _____

   _____

2. **INFER** If a vegetable is green, which part of a plant is it *least* likely to be from? Explain.

   _____

   _____

   _____

3. **INFER** If a vegetable is tough and stringy, which part of a plant is it *least* likely to be from? Explain.

   _____

   _____

   _____

4. **INFER** If a vegetable contains a lot of sugars and starches, which part of the plant is it *least* likely to be from?

   _____

   _____

   _____

Assess Your Understanding

Plant Structures

What Are the Functions of Roots, Stems, and Leaves?

1a. LIST What are the functions of a stem? _____

_____

_____

b. INFER If you forgot to water a houseplant for a few days, would the stomata be open or closed? Why? _____

_____

got**it?** ···

○ **I get it!** Now I know that roots, stems, and leaves perform functions like _____

_____

_____

○ **I need extra help with** _____

_____

How Do Seeds Become New Plants?

got**it?** ···

○ **I get it!** Now I know that a seed become a new plant when _____

_____

○ **I need extra help with** _____

_____

Assess Your Understanding

Plant Structures

What Are the Structures of a Flower?

got it? ··

○ **I get it!** Now I know that the structures of a flower include _____
_____

○ **I need extra help with** _____
_____

Key Concept Summaries

Plant Structures

What Are the Functions of Roots, Stems, and Leaves?

Roots anchor a plant in the ground, absorb water and minerals from the soil, and sometimes store food. The two main types of root systems are fibrous and taproot. A typical root has a rounded tip covered by a protective **root cap.** Root hairs help absorb water. Xylem and phloem are in the center of a root.

The stem carries substances between the plant's roots and leaves. The stem also provides support for the plant and holds up the leaves so they are exposed to the sun. Stems are either herbaceous or woody. In a woody stem, the **cambium** produces new xylem and phloem. Annual rings, which are made of xylem, reveal a tree's history.

Leaves capture the sun's energy and carry out the food-making process of photosynthesis. Stomata, small pores, control the movement of gases in and out of a leaf. The process by which water evaporates from a plant's leaves is called **transpiration.**

How Do Seeds Become New Plants?

Inside a seed is a partially developed plant. If a seed lands in an area where conditions are favorable, the plant sprouts out of the seed and begins to grow. A seed has three main parts: an embryo, stored food, and a seed coat. The **embryo** is the young plant that develops from the zygote, or fertilized egg. It uses the stored food until it can make its own food. The seed coat protects the embryo and stored food from drying out.

Seed dispersal is helped by water, wind, animals, and humans. When **germination** occurs, the embryo begins to grow again and pushes out of the seed. Germination begins when the seed absorbs water.

What Are the Structures of a Flower?

A **flower** is the reproductive structure of an angiosperm. **A typical flower contains sepals, petals, stamens, and pistils.** Leaflike **sepals** enclose and protect a flower bud. **Petals** are usually colored and scented and help the flower attract pollinators. **Stamens,** the male reproductive parts, consist of anthers and filaments. **Pistils** are the female reproductive parts. A stigma, style, and **ovary,** which contains one or more ovules and protects the seeds as they develop, make up a pistil. **Pollination** is the transfer of pollen from male reproductive structures to female reproductive structures.

On a separate sheet of paper, identify the following parts of a plant, as well as their functions: roots, stems, leaves, and flowers.

Review and Reinforce

Plant Structures

Understanding Main Ideas

Answer the following questions on a separate sheet of paper.

1. How is the structure of a root adapted for its functions?
2. How are herbaceous stems and woody stems alike? How are they different?
3. How does the structure of a leaf help in photosynthesis?
4. How does dispersal affect a seed's chances for survival?
5. Describe the structure and function of the male and female reproductive parts of a typical flower.

Building Vocabulary

Match each term with its definition by writing the letter of the correct definition in the right column on the line beside the term in the left column.

6. ___ cambium

7. ___ petal

8. ___ germination

9. ___ embryo

10. ___ transpiration

11. ___ sepal

12. ___ pollination

13. ___ root cap

a. the process by which water evaporates from a plant's leaves

b. the process by which an embryo grows and pushes out of a seed

c. colorful, leaflike structure of a flower

d. the young plant that develops from a fertilized egg

e. the transfer of pollen from male reproductive structures to female reproductive structures

f. the layer of a woody stem that produces new xylem

g. rounded tip that protects a growing root

h. leaflike structure that protects a bud

Plant Structures

Read the passage and study the diagrams below. Then use a separate sheet of paper to answer the questions that follow.

Bubbling Leaves

Carbon dioxide enters leaves through stomata. Oxygen, produced during photosynthesis, passes out of leaves through stomata. April designed an experiment to find out more about these tiny pores on a leaf. She picked a few fresh leaves from the trees near her house. Then, while pinching the stalk of one of the leaves, she dipped the leaf in a glass of hot water. After observing what happened, she did the same thing with the rest of the leaves, one at a time. The diagram below shows what April saw when she dipped two different leaves into the glass of hot water.

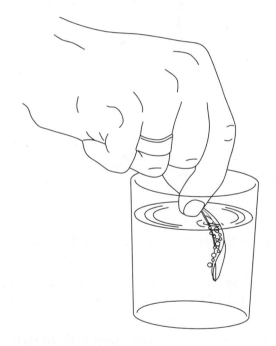

1. What did April observe coming out of the stomata of each leaf?

2. In the figure, bubbles are coming out of both sides of one leaf, while bubbles are coming out of only one side of the other leaf. What does this tell you about the location of the stomata on these two leaves?

3. What do you think would happen if April did not pinch the stalk of the leaf before dipping it into the hot water?

4. In most plants, most of the stomata are located on the lower surface of the leaves. Explain how this adaptation helps control water loss.

5. Would you expect to find the stomata on a lily pad on the top or bottom? Explain your answer.

Lesson Quiz

Plant Structures

Write the letter of the correct answer on the line at the left.

1. ___ Animals are helpful to plants in the process of
   A germination
   B pollination
   C transpiration
   D fertilization

2. ___ Which of the following is **NOT** part of a flower's pistil?
   A stigma
   B ovary
   C style
   D anther

3. ___ Which part of a plant is responsible for absorbing water and minerals and anchoring the plant?
   A roots
   B stems
   C anthers
   D filaments

4. ___ The three parts of a seed are
   A stored food, embryo, cambium
   B embryo, seed coat, ovary
   C cotyledon, seed coat, ovule
   D embryo, stored food, seed coat

Fill in the blank to complete each statement.

5. Seed _____ is the scattering of seeds.

6. A flower bud is protected by leaflike structures called _____.

7. The _____ protects the root as it grows through the soil.

8. A tree has 24 light rings and 24 dark rings. The tree is _____ years old.

9. _____ on the surface of a leaf control the movement of gases into and out of the leaf.

10. The hollow structure at the base of a pistil that protects seeds as they develop is the _____.

Plant Structures

Answer Key

After the Inquiry Warm-Up

1. A green vegetable is most likely a leaf because the green in plants comes from chlorophyll, which plants use to create food from sunlight. Chlorophyll is most often found in the leaves of plants.

2. A green vegetable is least likely to be the root of a plant because there is no reason for chlorophyll to be in a part of the plant that is underground and not exposed to sunlight.

3. A tough stringy vegetable is least likely to be a leaf because the roots and stems of a plant are likely to have the thickest cell walls and the largest parts of the plant's vascular system.

4. A vegetable that contains a lot of sugars and starches is most likely not a leaf because starches and sugars are more likely to be stored in roots and stems.

Key Concept Summaries

Roots anchor a plant in the ground, absorb water and minerals from the soil, and sometimes store food. Vascular tissues in the stem carry substances between the plant's roots and leaves. Xylem carries water and minerals from the roots to the leaves. Phloem carries food made in the leaves down to the roots. The stem also provides support for the plant and holds up the leaves so they are exposed to the sun. Leaves capture the sun's energy and carry out the food-making process of photosynthesis. Flowers are the reproductive structures of an angiosperm.

Review and Reinforce

1. Root hairs growing out of the root's surface anchor the plant and absorb water and minerals. Vascular tissue in the root's center moves water and minerals away from the root and moves food made in the leaves to it.

2. Both woody stems and herbaceous stems carry substances between a plant's roots and leaves, provide support, and hold leaves up to the sun. Woody stems are hard and rigid; herbaceous stems are soft and flexible.

3. Cells that contain the most sunlight-absorbing chloroplasts are tightly packed into the top of a leaf, so they get the most light. Openings in the leaf surface called stomata allow carbon dioxide to enter and oxygen to leave. Widely spaced cells in the bottom of the leaf allow these gases to circulate. A waxy cuticle on top and bottom prevents excessive water loss.

4. The farther a seed is dispersed the better its chance of survival because it will not compete with its parent for light, water, and nutrients.

5. In the male reproductive part, the stamen, a filament holds up an anther, in which pollen is formed. The female reproductive part, the pistil, includes a sticky tip called a stigma that traps pollen, an ovary that protects the seeds as they develop, and a style that connects both parts.

6. f	**7.** c	**8.** b	**9.** d
10. a	**11.** h	**12.** e	**13.** g

Enrich

1. Accept either air bubbles or gas bubbles.

2. One leaf has stomata on one side only, while the other leaf has stomata on both sides.

3. Air inside the leaf might escape.

4. Water would be more readily lost from the upper surface of the leaves, because that is the side more exposed to sun and wind.

5. on the top—the surface that is exposed to air

Lesson Quiz

1. B	**2.** D	**3.** A	**4.** D
5. dispersal	**6.** sepals	**7.** root cap	
8. 24	**9.** Stomata	**10.** ovary	

Plant Reproduction

LESSON

4

How do you know a plant when you see it?

Lesson Pacing: 2–3 periods or 1–1½ blocks

SHORT ON TIME? To do this lesson in approximately half the time, do the Activate Prior Knowledge activity on page 110. A discussion of the Key Concepts on pages 110 and 112 will familiarize students with the lesson content. Have students do the Quick Labs. The rest of the lesson can be completed by students independently.

Preference Navigator, in the online Planning tools, allows you to customize *Interactive Science* to your own teaching style. You can also edit lesson plans by selecting the Lesson Planner option.

Digital Teacher's Edition allows you to access your Teacher's Edition and Resource materials online.

Lesson Vocabulary

- sporophyte
- gametophyte
- annual
- biennial
- perennial
- fertilization
- zygote
- cone
- ovule
- fruit

Content Refresher

Plant Life Cycles All plants have life cycles characterized by a pattern called *alternation of generations:* a diploid sporophyte generation alternates with a haploid gametophyte generation. Thus the plant spends part of its life in a stage that produces spores and the other part in a stage that produces sex cells, or gametes.

Diploid describes a cell that contains a double set of chromosomes, one set from each parent. *Haploid* describes a cell that contains a single set of chromosomes. Haploid gametes are the result of meiosis of diploid cells. Alternation of generations means that a plant reproduces both asexually and sexually during its life cycle. Spores, produced in the sporophyte stage, can begin growing into new plants without fertilization. Gametes (sperm and egg) are produced in the gametophyte generation and produce offspring as a result of fertilization.

Angiosperms can be grouped as annuals, biennials, and perennials, based on their life cycle. Some plants have life cycles that are genetically determined, and these plants will die at a certain point, even when they are grown under favorable conditions. Other plants have life spans that are environmentally determined. When these plants are grown in favorable conditions, they will typically live longer than they would in nature.

LESSON OBJECTIVES

- Identify the stages of a plant's life cycle.
- Describe how plants reproduce.

Blended Path
Active learning using Student Edition, Inquiry Path, and Digital Path

ENGAGE AND EXPLORE

Teach this lesson using a variety of resources. Begin by reading **My Planet Diary** as a class. Have students discuss what can be learned from a 5,000-year-old tree. Then have students do the **Inquiry Warm-Up activity.** Students will model how pollen grains attach to the stigma in flowering plants. The **After the Inquiry Warm-Up worksheet** sets up a discussion about the how in vascular plants a sticky substance made by the ovule helps pollen grains attach to the stigma. Have volunteers share their answers to question 4, explaining whether or not they think a sticky stigma is an adaptation that helps a plant to reproduce.

EXPLAIN AND ELABORATE

Teach Key Concepts by explaining that plants have complex life cycles in which two different stages alternate. One stage represents asexual reproduction and the other sexual reproduction.

Teach Key Concepts by explaining how plants reproduce. Have students practice the inquiry skill in the **Apply It activity. Lead a Discussion** about reproduction in gymnosperms. **Support the Big Q** by discussing the three main steps in sexual reproduction: pollination, fertilization, and seed development and dispersal.

Hand out the **Key Concept Summaries** as a review of each part of the lesson. Students can also use the online **Vocab Flash Cards** to review key terms.

EVALUATE

Have students take the **Lesson Quiz.** For an alternate assessment, see the *ExamView®* Computer Test Generator, Progress Monitoring Assessments, or SuccessTracker™.

ELL Support

1 Content and Language

Explain to students that the terms *cone* and *fruit* have multiple meanings. Have them find the first term in a dictionary, read the definitions, and then use the visuals in the chapter to predict which of the meanings fits the way the term will be used in the chapter. Repeat for the other term. Have them check their predictions as they read.

LESSON PLANNER 3.4

Lab zone Inquiry Path
Hands-on learning in the Lab zone

ENGAGE AND EXPLORE

To teach this lesson with an emphasis on inquiry, begin with the **Inquiry Warm-Up activity.** Students will model how pollen grains attach to the stigma in flowering plants. The **After the Inquiry Warm-Up worksheet** sets up a discussion about how in vascular plants a sticky substance made by the ovule helps pollen grains attach to the stigma. Have volunteers share their answers to question 4, explaining whether or not they think a sticky stigma is an adaptation that helps a plant to reproduce.

EXPLAIN AND ELABORATE

Focus on the **Inquiry Skill** for the lesson. Remind students that inferring involves interpreting an observation. Making an inference combines evidence with experience or prior knowledge to reach a logical conclusion. What was inferred in the **Inquiry Warm-Up activity** to decide which was more likely to catch pollen grains, a plant with a sticky stigma or one with a dry stigma? *(More poppy seeds stuck to a sticky swab than to a dry swab. Therefore, a sticky stigma was more likely to catch more pollen grains.)* Have students do the **Quick Lab** to compare the life cycles of different types of plants.

Before beginning the **Apply It activity,** remind students that grafting is a method of asexual reproduction. Have students think about the advantages and disadvantages of this type of reproduction. **Build Inquiry** by having students gather information to use in designing a garden. **Build Inquiry** to give students the opportunity to examine a mature female pine cone. **Support the Big Q** by discussing the three main steps in sexual reproduction: pollination, fertilization, and seed development and dispersal. Have students do the **Quick Lab** to examine and compare angiosperm flowers and gymnosperm cones. Students can use the online **Vocab Flash Cards** to review key terms.

EVALUATE

Have students take the **Lesson Quiz.** For an alternate assessment, see the *ExamView®* Computer Test Generator, Progress Monitoring Assessments, or SuccessTracker™.

Digital Path
Online learning at my science online.com

ENGAGE AND EXPLORE

Teach this lesson using digital resources. Begin by having students learn more about plant reproduction and explore real-world connections to stages of a plant's life cycle at **My Planet Diary** online. Have them access the Chapter Resources to find the **Unlock the Big Question activity.** There they can answer the questions and refine their responses as they continue through the lesson. You can re-assign the activity and have students submit their work so you can track their progress.

EXPLAIN AND ELABORATE

Students reading above, at, or below the lexile measure of this lesson can access basic content readings at their level at **My Reading Web.** Encourage students to use the online **Vocab Flash Cards** to preview key terms. Have students do the **Quick Lab** to compare the life cycles of different types of plants.

Assign the **Apply It activity** online and have students submit their work to you. **Support the Big Q** by discussing the three main steps in sexual reproduction: pollination, fertilization, and seed development and dispersal. Have students do the **Quick Lab** to examine and compare angiosperm flowers and gymnosperm cones. The **Key Concept Summaries** online allow students to read a summary and see an image associated with each part of the lesson. Online remediation is available at **My Science Coach.**

EVALUATE

Have students take the **Lesson Quiz.** For an alternate assessment, see the *ExamView®* Computer Test Generator, Progress Monitoring Assessments, or SuccessTracker™.

2 Frontload the Lesson
Point out the relationship between the information in the graphic on page 114 and the information in the graphic on page 115. Discuss why the information is shown in two different ways.

3 Comprehensible Input
Have students create a graphic organizer that compares and contrasts annuals, biennials, and perennials. Encourage them to add examples of each to the graphic organizer.

4 Language Production
Pair or group students with varied language abilities to complete labs collaboratively for language practice. Have each student copy the completed written lab for personal reference.

5 Assess Understanding
Ask students to make notes about Key Concepts in the lesson and use the notes to prepare an oral presentation of the concepts. Encourage students to use the visuals in the lesson to support their presentations.

Plant Reproduction

Establish Learning Objectives

After this lesson, students will be able to:

- Identify the stages of a plant's life cycle.
- Describe how plants reproduce.

Engage

Activate Prior Knowledge

MY PLANET DIARY Read *If Trees Could Talk* with the class. Tell students that all living things have a life span, which is the maximum length of time an organism can be expected to live. During its life span, an organism grows, develops, and reproduces—the stages of its life cycle. Tell students that in contrast to the bristlecone pine, the small, flowering plant *Arabidopsis thaliana* has a life span of six to eight weeks. Ask: **Do you think these pines are the oldest living things?** *(Yes)*

BIG IDEAS OF SCIENCE REFERENCE LIBRARY Have students look up the following topic: Flowers.

Explore

Lab Resource: Inquiry Warm-Up

L1 MAKE THE POLLEN STICK Students will model how pollen grains attach to the stigma in flowering plants.

---

4 Plant Reproduction

- What Are the Stages of a Plant Life Cycle?
- How Do Plants Reproduce?

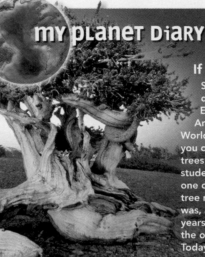

my planet diary

FUN FACT

If Trees Could Talk

Suppose you had been alive during the ancient Egyptian Empire, the Middle Ages, the American Revolution, and both World Wars. Think of the stories you could tell! Bristlecone pine trees can be this old. In 1964, a student got permission to cut down one of these trees. He counted the tree rings to see how old the tree was, and discovered it was 4,900 years old. He had just cut down the oldest living thing in the world! Today, Bristlecone pine forests are protected.

Write your answer below.
What could you learn from a 5,000-year-old tree?

Sample: when droughts occurred, when weather conditions were bad for the tree

> PLANET DIARY Go to **Planet Diary** to learn more about plan[t] reproduction.

Lab Do the Inquiry Warm-Up
Make the Pollen Stick.

What Are the Stages of a Plant's Life Cycle?

Like other living things, plants develop and reproduce through lif[e] stages. **Plants have complex life cycles that include two different stages, the sporophyte stage and the gametophyte stag[e].** In the **sporophyte** (SPOH ruh fyt) stage, the plant produces spore[s] or seeds, tiny cells that can grow into new organisms. The spore o[r] seed develops into the plant's other stage, called the gametophyte. In the **gametophyte** (guh MEE tuh fyt) stage, the plant produces two kinds of sex cells: sperm cells and egg cells. See **Figure 1.**

110 Plants

SUPPORT ALL READERS
Lexile Measure = 910L   Lexile Word Count = 1628

Prior Exposure to Content: Many students may have misconceptions on this topic

Academic Vocabulary: *infer, summarize*

Science Vocabulary: *sporophyte, gametophyte, fertilization, zygote*

Concept Level: Generally appropriate for most students in this grade

Preteach With: My Planet Diary "If Trees Could Talk" and Figure 1 activity

Go to **My Reading Web** to access leveled readings that provide a foundation for the content.

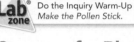

Vocabulary
- sporophyte • gametophyte • annual • biennial
- perennial • fertilization • zygote • cone
- ovule • fruit

Skills
- Reading: Summarize
- Inquiry: Infer

FIGURE 1 ....

Plant Life Cycle
All plants go through two stages in their life cycle.

Interpret Diagrams Label the sporophyte and gametophyte stages.

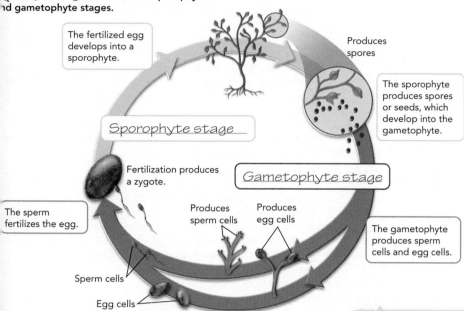

The fertilized egg develops into a sporophyte.

Produces spores

The sporophyte produces spores or seeds, which develop into the gametophyte.

Sporophyte stage

Fertilization produces a zygote.

Gametophyte stage

The sperm fertilizes the egg.

Produces sperm cells

Produces egg cells

The gametophyte produces sperm cells and egg cells.

Sperm cells

Egg cells

Angiosperms are classified based on the length of their life cycles. Flowering plants that complete a life cycle within one growing season are called **annuals.** Annuals include marigolds, petunias, wheat, and cucumbers. Angiosperms that complete their life cycle in two years are called **biennials** (by EN ee ulz). In the first year, biennials germinate and grow roots, very short stems, and leaves. During their second year, biennials lengthen their stems, grow new leaves, and then produce flowers and seeds. Parsley, celery, and foxglove are biennials. Flowering plants that live for more than two years are called **perennials.** Most perennials flower every year.

 Lab zone Do the Quick Lab *Plant Life Cycles.*

📖 Assess Your Understanding

got it? ....

- ○ **I get it!** Now I know that the stages of a plant's life cycle include _the sporophyte stage and the gametophyte stage._

- ○ **I need extra help with** _See TE note._

Go to MY SCIENCE COACH *online for help with this subject.*

111

1 Content and Language
Write *biennial* and *perennial* on the board. Tell students these words share the same root, which comes from the Latin *annus,* meaning "year." Explain that the prefix *bi-* means "two" and the prefix *per-* means "through." So, *biennials* are plants that live for two years, and *perennials* are plants that live for many years.

2 Frontload the Lesson
Invite students to name examples of fruit—apples, pinecones, peas—that come from different types of plants. Then, ask students to think about the relationship between these fruits and the plants' process of reproduction.

3 Comprehensible Input
Have small groups create flowcharts that show the sequence of the two stages in a plant's life cycle.

Explain

Introduce Vocabulary
Help students with the terms *sporophyte* and *gametophyte* by pointing out that *-phyte* comes from a Greek word meaning "plant." These terms identify the stages in a plant life cycle by whether they involve spores or gametes (sperm and eggs).

Teach Key Concepts 🔑
Explain to students that plants have complex life cycles in which two different stages alternate. One stage represents asexual reproduction and the other sexual reproduction. Ask: **Which type of reproduction requires fertilization to produce offspring?** *(Sexual)* **In which stage does this occur?** *(Gametophyte)* Then review the meanings of the terms *annual, biennial,* and *perennial.*

Teach With Visuals
Tell students to look at **Figure 1.** Ask: **Which stage involves sexual reproduction? How can you tell?** *(Gametophyte stage because the plant produces sperm cells and egg cells that join to form a zygote)* **Which stage involves asexual reproduction?** *(Sporophyte)* **What are the reproductive structures in this stage?** *(Spores or seeds)*

Elaborate

Lab Resource: Quick Lab 📋
L1 **PLANT LIFE CYCLES** Students will compare the life cycles of different types of plants.

Evaluate

Assess Your Understanding
Have students evaluate their understanding by completing the appropriate sentence.

RTI Response to Intervention
If students need help identifying stages of a plant's life cycle, **then** have them look at **Figure 1.**

MY SCIENCE COACH Have students go online for help in understanding stages of a plant's life cycle.

My Planet Diary provides an opportunity for students to explore real-world connections to the stages of a plant's life cycle.

MY SCIENCE ONLINE | Plant Life Cycle

Explain

Teach Key Concepts 🔑

Explain to students that plants reproduce in different ways depending on their structures and the environments in which they grow. However, all plants undergo sexual reproduction, which is the union of gametes in a process called fertilization. Ask: **What is the male gamete?** *(Sperm)* **What is the female gamete?** *(Egg)* **What happens during fertilization?** *(A sperm cell unites with an egg cell.)* **What is the fertilized egg called?** *(A zygote)* **How many parents are involved in sexual reproduction?** *(Two)* **What is asexual reproduction?** *(Reproduction that involves only one parent and results in offspring that are identical to the parent and to each other)* **What plant structures can reproduce asexually?** *(Roots, stems, leaves)* **Asexual reproduction has an advantage in that it can happen faster than sexual reproduction. But it also has a disadvantage. What is that?** *(It can reproduce unfavorable traits because there is no new genetic information being passed to offspring.)* Have students recall what they learned about nonvascular plants and seedless vascular plants. Ask: **Why must these plants grow in moist places?** *(The plants release spores into their surroundings. The spores grow into gametophytes, which produce egg cells and sperm cells. There must be water available for the sperm cells to swim to the egg cells so that fertilization can take place.)*

21st Century Learning

CRITICAL THINKING Remind students that a plant's life cycle involves both asexual and sexual reproduction. Have students think about and describe the sequence of stages starting with a zygote Ask: **What does a zygote develop into?** *(A sporophyte)* **What does a sporophyte produce?** *(Spores or seeds)* **What do the spores or seeds develop into?** *(A gametophyte)* **What does the gametophyte produce?** *(Sperm cells and egg cells)* **What happens when sperm meets egg?** *(They unite in fertilization to produce a zygote.)*

How Do Plants Reproduce?

Plants reproduce in different ways depending on their structures and the environment they live in. 🔑 **All plants undergo sexual reproduction that involves fertilization.** **Fertilization** occurs when a sperm cell unites with an egg cell. The fertilized egg is called a **zygote.** For algae and some plants, fertilization can only occur if there is water in the environment. This is because the sperm cells of these plants swim through the water to the egg cells. Other plants, however, have an adaptation that makes it possible for fertilization to occur in dry environments.

Many plants can also undergo asexual reproduction. Recall that asexual reproduction includes only one parent and produces offspring that are identical to the parent. New plants can grow from the roots, leaves, or stems of a parent plant. Asexual reproduction does not involve flowers, pollination, or seeds, so it can happen faster than sexual reproduction. A single plant can quickly spread out in an environment if there are good conditions. However, asexual reproduction can reproduce unfavorable traits since there is no new genetic information being passed to offspring.

Scientists can take advantage of asexual reproduction in plants. A single plant can be used to create identical plants for experiments. Scientists can also copy plants with favorable characteristics. Grafting is one way of copying plants. In grafting, part of a plant's stem is cut and attached to another related plant species, such as a lemon tree and an orange tree. The plant matures and can then produce more than one kind of fruit.

FIGURE 2

Eyes on Potatoes

Did you know that a potato is actually the underground stem of the potato plant? If you have ever left a potato out long enough, you may have noticed it beginning to sprout. A potato can grow new potato plants from buds called eyes, as seen in this photo.

✏ **Apply Concepts** Potato plants also produce flowers and reproduce sexually. How does being able to reproduce asexually benefit the plant?

Sample: The plant can still produce offspring even if something happens to the flowers to stop sexual reproduction.

Digital Lesson: Assign the *Apply It* activity online and have students submit their work to you.

my science online.com ▸ **Plant Reproduction**

apply it!

...citrus farmer was able to graft a ...mon tree branch onto an orange ...ee. Now the same tree produces ...mons and oranges! The farmer plans ...use branches from the same lemon ...ees to create other combined fruit ...ees.

Review The farmer used the lemon ...ee's ability to (sexually/<u>asexually</u>) ...roduce.

⚠ **Infer** Name at least one negative ...ect of using the same lemon tree ...create new trees the farmer should ...ow about.

...ample: The lemons all came from the same parent so they would be ...ulnerable to the same diseases, and the crop could be wiped out.

CHALLENGE Why might the public be opposed to using this ...ethod to create new fruit trees?

...ample: It isn't "natural." People may think the farmer is interfering ...ith nature.

...onvascular and Seedless Vascular ...lants

Mosses, liverworts, hornworts, ferns, club mosses, and ...rsetails need to grow in moist environments. This is because ...e plants release spores into their surroundings, where they grow ...to gametophytes. When the gametophytes produce egg cells and ...erm cells, there must be enough water available for the sperm to ...im toward the eggs.

For example, the familiar fern, with its visible fronds, is the ...orophyte stage of the plant. On the underside of mature fronds, ...ores develop in tiny spore cases. Wind and water can carry ...e spores great distances. If a spore lands in moist, shaded soil, ...develops into a gametophyte. Fern gametophytes are tiny ...nts that grow low to the ground.

Spore cases on the fronds of a fern

113

Elaborate ——————

Apply It!

L1 Before beginning the activity, remind students that grafting is a method of asexual reproduction. Have students think about the advantages and disadvantages of this type of reproduction.

⚠ **Infer** Explain to students that inferring involves interpreting an observation. Making an inference combines evidence with experience or prior knowledge to reach a logical conclusion. In this case, students should already know that asexual reproduction can pass on unfavorable traits because it does not introduce new genetic information.

Build Inquiry 🔬Lab zone

L2 **DESIGN A GARDEN**

Materials garden catalogs, paper, pencil, colored pencils

Time 25 minutes

Have students review the classification of angiosperms based on the length of their life cycle. Give students time to look at catalogs to determine the life cycle for various plants. Have students work in groups to list five or more examples of each category and include a quick sketch of each plant. Students should also note when the plant blooms and whether it can be grown in your area. Have students use the information to design a garden.

Ask: **What are some examples of annuals?** *(Samples: Petunia, zinnia, sweet pea, aster, phlox, marigold, dianthus, impatiens, morning glory)* **What are some examples of biennials?** *(Samples: Foxglove, Sweet William, Canterbury bells, parsley, silverbeet, lunaria)* **What are some examples of perennials?** *(Samples: Bleeding heart, Gerberer daisy, geranium, anthurium, hydrangea, lilac, rose, peony)* Note that some plants are annuals in colder climate zones and perennials in warmer climate zones.

Differentiated Instruction

L1 **Plant Life Cycle** To reinforce the idea of a plant's life cycle consisting of stages characterized by different means of reproduction, have students create their own labeled diagram to represent the process. Tell students to use **Figure 1** as a guide, and to be as artistic and creative as they can. Exhibit students' drawings around the classroom.

L1 **Asexual Versus Sexual Reproduction** Have students develop a compare/contrast table to summarize the two types of reproduction.

L3 **Life Cycles of Mosses and Ferns** Mosses and ferns have life cycles that include a sporophyte generation and a gametophyte generation. Have pairs of students select one of these plants and research its life cycle. Have pairs summarize their findings in a poster.

Explain

Lead a Discussion

REPRODUCTION IN GYMNOSPERMS Tell students that in most gymnosperms, the reproductive structure is the cone. Explain that most gymnosperms produce two types of cones: male cones and female cones. Usually, a single plant produces both types of cones. However, in some types of gymnosperms, individual trees produce either male cones or female cones. Tell students that cones are covered with scales. Refer students to **Figure 3.** Ask: **What process occurs in the male cone?** *(The production of pollen)* **What processes occur in the female cone before fertilization?** *(First, an egg cell forms inside an ovule on a scale on a female cone. Next, pollination takes place on the scales. After pollen falls from a male cone onto a female cone, a sperm cell and an egg cell join in an ovule on the female cone.)* **What process follows fertilization but occurs before seeds mature and disperse?** *(The fertilized egg develops into an embryo.)* **Once the embryo develops, what else must happen for a seed to be ready to disperse?** *(The seed must mature—the seed coat and its stored food develop.)* **Is pollen more or less likely to be dispersed by wind during rainy weather? Explain.** *(Less, because the rain moistens the pollen; the pollen falls to the ground instead of being in the air.)*

21st Century Learning

CRITICAL THINKING Discuss with students the role cones play in the life cycle of most gymnosperms. Have students think about the two types of cones and the ways in which they are alike and different. Ask: **What are the two types of cones?** *(Male and female)* **How are they alike?** *(Both types are the reproductive structures of gymnosperms.)* **How are they different?** *(Male cones produce pollen; female cones have ovules in which eggs are produced. Male cones fall from the tree once they have shed their pollen; female cones stay on the tree as the seed matures.)*

Gymnosperms You can follow the process of gymnosperm reproduction in **Figure 3.**

1 Cone Production
Most gymnosperms have reproductive structures called **cones.** Cones are covered with scales. Most gymnosperms produce two types of cones: male cones and female cones. Usually, a single plant produces both male and female cones. In some types of gymnosperms, however, individual trees produce either male cones or female cones. A few gymnosperms produce no cones.

2 Pollen Production and Ovule Development
(A) Male cones produce pollen grains. Cells in the pollen will mature into sperm cells. (B) The female gametophyte develops in structures called ovules. An **ovule** (OH vyool) is a structure that contains an egg cell. <u>Female cones contain at least one ovule at the base of each scale.</u> The ovule later develops into the seed.

3 Egg Production
<u>Two egg cells form inside each ovule on the female cone.</u>

4 Pollination
The transfer of pollen from a male reproductive structure to a female reproductive structure is called pollination. In gymnosperms, wind often carries the pollen from the male cones to the female cones. The pollen collect in a sticky substance produced by each ovule.

5 Fertilization
Once pollination has occurred, the ovule closes and seals in the pollen. The scales also close, and a sperm cell fertilizes an egg cell inside each ovule. The zygote then develops into the embryo part of the seed.

6 Seed Development
Female cones remain on the tree while the seeds mature. As the seeds develop, the female cone increases in size. It can take up to two years for the seeds of some gymnosperms to mature. Male cones, however, usually fall off the tree after they have shed their pollen.

7 Seed Dispersal
When the seeds are mature, the scales open. The wind shakes the seeds out of the cone and carries them away. Only a few seeds will land in suitable places and grow into new plants.

FIGURE 3

Gymnosperm Reproduction Cycle
The reproduction cycle of a gymnosperm is shown at right.

✎ **Complete each task.**

1. Identify Underline the sentence(s) on this page that use the vocabulary terms *cone* and *ovule*.

2. Describe What is the relationship between cones and ovules?

Sample: Cones contain multiple ovules.

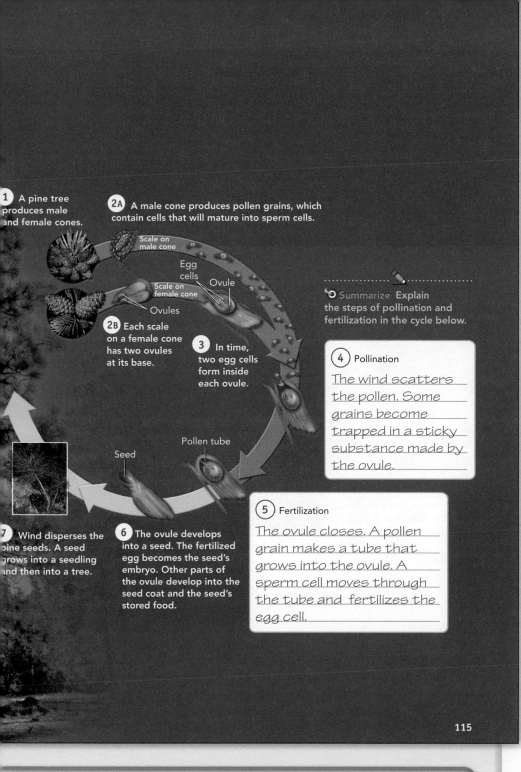

1 A pine tree produces male and female cones.

2A A male cone produces pollen grains, which contain cells that will mature into sperm cells.

Scale on male cone

Egg cells

Ovule

Scale on female cone

Ovules

2B Each scale on a female cone has two ovules at its base.

3 In time, two egg cells form inside each ovule.

Summarize Explain the steps of pollination and fertilization in the cycle below.

4 Pollination

The wind scatters the pollen. Some grains become trapped in a sticky substance made by the ovule.

Pollen tube

Seed

7 Wind disperses the pine seeds. A seed grows into a seedling and then into a tree.

6 The ovule develops into a seed. The fertilized egg becomes the seed's embryo. Other parts of the ovule develop into the seed coat and the seed's stored food.

5 Fertilization

The ovule closes. A pollen grain makes a tube that grows into the ovule. A sperm cell moves through the tube and fertilizes the egg cell.

115

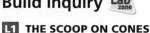

Teach With Visuals

Tell students to look at **Figure 3.** Encourage students to study the photographs of the male and female cones. Ask: **How is the pollen transferred from the male to the female cone?** *(Wind)* **Why are male cones at the tips of branches rather than closer to the trunk?** *(Branch tips allow more efficient pollen distribution.)* **What happens to male cones after they shed their pollen?** *(They fall from the tree.)* **What happens to female cones after fertilization?** *(They stay on the tree as the seed matures.)* **How does the shape of the seed affect its motion in the wind?** *(The shape of the seed allows the wind to carry the seed some distance away from the parent tree.)*

Summarize Tell students that when they summarize, they briefly restate the main ideas of what they have read or heard in their own words. In addition to the main ideas, a summary can contain the most important supporting details. However, a summary must be short and concise.

Elaborate

Build Inquiry

L1 THE SCOOP ON CONES

Materials mature female pine cone, hand lens, sheet of white paper

Time 10 minutes

Check for student allergies before beginning this activity. Make certain that cones have some seeds inside the scales. Provide each student pair with a cone. Have them use a hand lens to look closely at the cone. Then have them gently shake the cone over the sheet of white paper and observe what happens. Tell students to break off one scale from the cone and examine its base. If the scale contains a seed, have students remove it. Then have students use the hand lens to examine that seed or one of the seeds that fell on the white paper. Have students sketch the female cone before returning it to you. Remind students to wash their hands when they have completed the activity.

Ask: **What does the seed form from?** *(The embryo, which develops from the fertilization of an egg by a sperm)* **How does the structure of the cone protect the seeds?** *(The scales protect developing seeds from wind, rain, and very cold temperatures.)* **What do you think might be differences in the appearance of male and female cones?** *(Sample: Size, shape, and structure of the scales)*

Differentiated Instruction

L1 **Gymnosperm Life Cycle** Have students construct a flowchart of the steps in the life cycle of a gymnosperm in their own words. Have students exchange their flowcharts with a classmate for review and evaluation.

L1 **Gymnosperm Reproduction** Have students use the following words in paragraphs to describe gymnosperm reproduction: *ovule, pollen, male, female, male cone, female cone, fertilization, seed, scale.*

L3 **"Fire Pines"** Remind students that once fertilization takes place, the ovule and scales of the female cone close and remain that way until the seeds mature, at which time the scales open and the seeds are dispersed. The cones of the jack pine, however, will remain tightly closed on the forest floor until a certain event causes them to open. Have students find out what this event is and the reason for the nickname.

Explain

Support the Big Q ❓ UbD

REPRODUCTION IN ANGIOSPERMS Remind students that the flower is the reproductive structure in angiosperms. Review the parts of the flower, emphasizing the male and female structures. Then have students identify the three main steps in sexual reproduction: pollination, fertilization, seed development and dispersal. Ask: **What reproductive structures are unique to angiosperms?** *(Flowers and fruits)* **After a plant has produced a mature flower, what is the first step in reproduction?** *(Pollen falls on the stigma.)* **What is this process called?** *(Pollination)* **What happens next?** *(A sperm cell in the pollen joins with an egg cell inside the ovary.)* **What is this process called?** *(Fertilization)* **What is the result of the process?** *(The formation of a zygote)* **What happens to the ovary as the seed develops?** *(The ovary changes into a fruit.)*

Teach With Visuals

Tell students to look at **Figure 4** and follow the reproductive process in flowering plants. Make sure students can identify the ovary and anther in Step 1. Ask: **Why are there Steps 2A and 2B?** *(One step is the male—cells in the anther produce pollen; the other step is the female—cells in each ovule produce egg cells.)* As students review the steps in the visual, have them record what each of these structures produces and its role in the life cycle: anther *(Produce pollen grains)*, ovule *(Develop into a seed)*, pollen grain *(Contain a sperm that will fertilize an ovule)*, ovule's wall *(Become the seed coat)*, and ovary *(Become the fruit)*. Ask: **What is the purpose of the stigma?** *(To trap pollen)* **What happens to the ovule parts that are not the embryo?** *(They develop into a seed coat and stored food.)* **What is the purpose of the fruit?** *(Enclose seeds and aid in seed dispersal)* Students may be curious about the appearance of the trunk and branches of the apple tree in the photograph. Explain to them that those parts have been painted white to repel insects.

Address Misconceptions

FRUITS Students are most likely familiar only with the fruits they eat. They may not realize that every angiosperm that produces a flower also produces a fruit, as the fruit is a ripened ovary. Thus, the term is not synonymous in botany and food preparation. Explain to students that many fruits are treated as vegetables because they are not sweet. Examples include squash, pumpkin, cucumber, tomato, peas, and corn. Ask: **What is the scientific definition of a fruit?** *(A ripened ovary)* **What is a culinary definition of a fruit?** *(Sample: A plant product that has a sweet taste and seeds)*

116 Plants

FIGURE 4 ⋯⋯⋯⋯⋯⋯⋯⋯⋯

Angiosperm Reproduction
Reproduction in angiosperms begins with flowers.

✎ **Relate Text and Visuals**
Look back at the plant life and gymnosperm reproduction cycles in this lesson. What do the yellow and purple colors of the arrows represent?

Yellow represents the sporophyte stage and purple represents the gametophyte stage.

Angiosperms You can follow angiosperm reproduction in **Figure 4**. First, pollen fall on a flower's stigma. In time, the sperm cell and egg cell join together in the flower's ovule. The zygote develops into the embryo part of the seed.

Pollination A flower is pollinated when a grain of pollen falls on the stigma. Some angiosperms are pollinated by the wind, but most rely on other organisms. When an organism enters a flower obtain food, it becomes coated with pollen. Some of the pollen ca drop onto the flower's stigma as the animal leaves. The pollen can also be brushed onto the stigma of the next flower the animal visi

Fertilization If the pollen fall on the stigma of a similar plant, fertilization can occur. A sperm cell joins with an egg cell inside a ovule within the ovary at the base of the flower. The zygote then begins to develop into the seed's embryo. Other parts of the ovule develop into the rest of the seed.

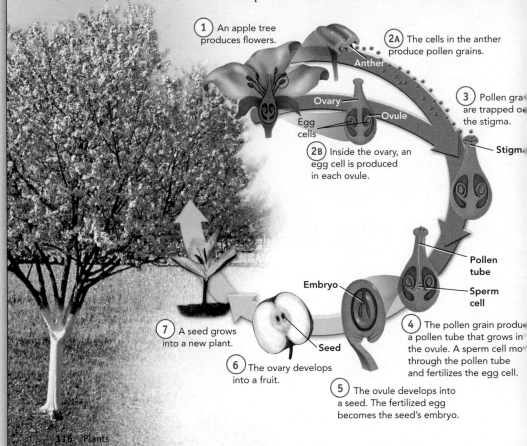

1 An apple tree produces flowers.

2A The cells in the anther produce pollen grains.

Anther

Ovary

Egg cells

Ovule

3 Pollen gra are trapped o the stigma.

Stigm

2B Inside the ovary, an egg cell is produced in each ovule.

Pollen tube

Embryo

Sperm cell

7 A seed grows into a new plant.

Seed

6 The ovary develops into a fruit.

4 The pollen grain produ a pollen tube that grows in the ovule. A sperm cell mo through the pollen tube and fertilizes the egg cell.

5 The ovule develops into a seed. The fertilized egg becomes the seed's embryo.

Fruit Development and Seed Dispersal As the seed develops, the ovary changes into a **fruit**. A fruit is the ripened ovary and other structures that enclose one or more seeds. Fruits include apples, cherries, tomatoes, squash, and many others. Fruits are the means by which angiosperm seeds are dispersed. Animals that eat fruits help to disperse their seeds by depositing them in new areas.

did you
know?

The *Arabidopsis* plant became the first plant to flower and produce seeds in the zero-gravity environment of outer space on a Soviet space station in 1982.

FIGURE 5
Flower to Fruit
Flowers eventually develop into fruit.

Sequence Write the numbers 1 through 4 in the blank circles to show the progression from flower to fruit.

Lab Do the Quick Lab
zone *Where Are the Seeds?*

Assess Your Understanding

Review (Fertilization)/Asexual reproduction) occurs when a sperm cell unites with an egg cell.

Explain Why do plants like liverworts need to live in moist environments?
The sperm cells need water to swim to the egg cells.

c. Relate Cause and Effect Underline the cause and circle the effect in the sentences below.
(Pollination) can occur when pollen on an insect is dropped onto the stigma.
Animals eating fruit is one way (seeds are dispersed.)

got it?

I get it! Now I know that all of the major plant groups reproduce *sexually through fertilization.*

I need extra help with *See TE note.*

Go to **my science COACH** online for help with this subject.

117

Differentiated Instruction

L1 **Angiosperm Reproduction** Help students construct a table listing each reproductive structure, what it produces, and what role the structure plays in the plant's life cycle. Use the headings *Plant Part, Produces,* and *Role*. Entries in the *Plant Part* column should include *anther, ovule, ovary, sperm cells,* and so on.

L1 **Flower and Fruit Roles** Have students describe the roles of an orange blossom and an orange in the reproduction of an orange tree.

L3 **Allergies** Pollen, one of the necessary "ingredients" in plant reproduction, is also the cause of allergies in many people. Tell students that an allergy is a hypersensitive and possibly harmful reaction of the body's immune system to a normally harmless substance. Have students do research on allergies to pollen and look up what the pollen count is for the local area.

CRITICAL THINKING Review with students the role animals play in seed dispersal. Ask: **How do animals that eat fruit help to ensure the germination of seeds?** *(When animals eat fruits, the seeds pass through the animals' digestive system. When the animals travel, they excrete wastes in different places and thereby disperse seeds away from the parent plant. Seeds may then have a better chance of germinating because they will not have to compete with the parent plant for resources.)*

Address Misconceptions

FRUITS DO NOT FEED SEEDS Because students know that fruits like apples, grapes, and oranges are nutritious, they often believe that the fruit contains nutrition to support a germinating seed. Remind students that seeds contain stored fruit in the form of a cotyledon. This, not the surrounding fruit is their source of nourishment.

Elaborate

Lab Resource: Quick Lab **Lab zone**

L2 **WHERE ARE THE SEEDS?** Students will examine and compare angiosperm flowers and gymnosperm cones.

Evaluate

Assess Your Understanding

After students answer the questions, have them evaluate their understanding by completing the appropriate sentence.

RTI Response to Intervention

1a. If students cannot identify fertilization, **then** remind them that the male sex cell, the sperm, fertilizes the female sex cell, the egg.

b. If students need help explaining why water is essential to liverworts for reproduction, **then** remind them that these plants are nonvascular, seedless plants that reproduce sexually and need to get the sperm to the egg.

c. If students have difficulty identifying the cause and effect in pollination and seed dispersal, **then** remind them that the effect is what happens and the cause is the reason it happens.

my science COACH Have students go online for help in understanding how plants reproduce.

Lab zone **fter the Inquiry Warm-Up**

Plant Reproduction

Inquiry Warm-Up, *Make the Pollen Stick*

In the Inquiry Warm-Up, you used a model to investigate how a sticky substance made by the ovule helps pollen grains attach to the stigma of vascular plants. Using what you learned from that activity, answer the questions below.

1. **CALCULATE** Based on the averages you calculated, about how many times more poppy seeds stuck to a sticky swab than stuck to a dry swab?

   _____

2. **GRAPH** Draw a double bar graph to display the results collected in your data table.

3. **DRAW CONCLUSIONS** In a vascular land plant, the stigma usually has to catch pollen grains that are carried by the wind or stuck to an insect. Which do you think is more likely to catch pollen grains, a plant with a sticky stigma or one with a dry stigma?

   _____

   _____

4. **MAKE JUDGMENTS** Do you think having a sticky stigma is an adaptation that helps a plant to reproduce? Explain.

   _____

   _____

Assess Your Understanding

Plant Reproduction

What Are the Stages of a Plant Life Cycle?

got it? ···

○ **I get it!** Now I know that the stages of a plant's life cycle include _____

_____

○ **I need extra help with** _____

_____

How Do Plants Reproduce?

1a. **REVIEW** (Fertilization/Asexual reproduction) occurs when a sperm cell unites with an egg cell.

b. **EXPLAIN** Why do plants like liverworts need to live in moist

environments? _____

_____

c. **RELATE CAUSE AND EFFECT** Underline the cause and circle the effect in the sentences below.

Pollination can occur when pollen on an insect is dropped onto the stigma.

Animals eating fruit is one way seeds are dispersed.

got it? ···

○ **I get it!** Now I know that all of the major plant groups reproduce _____

_____

○ **I need extra help with** _____

_____

Key Concept Summaries

Plant Reproduction

What Are the Stages of a Plant Life Cycle?

Plants have complex life cycles that include two different stages, the sporophyte stage and the gametophyte stage. In the **sporophyte** stage, the plant produces spores or seeds, tiny cells that can grow into new organisms. The spore or seed develops into the plant's other stage, called the gametophyte. In the **gametophyte** stage, the plant produces two kinds of sex cells, sperm cells and egg cells. In the process of fertilization, the egg unites with the sperm to form a zygote, or fertilized egg. The zygote develops into a sporophyte, and the cycle continues.

Angiosperms are classified according to the length of their life cycle. **Annuals** complete a life cycle within one growing season. **Biennials** complete a life cycle in two years and do not flower until the second year of growth. **Perennials** live for more than two years.

How Do Plants Reproduce?

All plants undergo sexual reproduction that involves fertilization. Fertilization is the process in which a sperm cell unites with an egg cell. The fertilized egg is called a **zygote.** Because they release spores, nonvascular plants and seedless vascular plants need a moist environment for fertilization to take place. Seed plants do not.

Gymnosperm reproduction involves structures called **cones.** Most gymnosperms produce both male and female cones. Male cones produce pollen grains that contain cells that will mature into sperm cells. Female cones contain **ovules,** structures that produce egg cells. An ovule later develops into a seed.

Reproduction continues with pollination, fertilization, seed development, and seed dispersal.

In angiosperms, the reproductive structure is the flower. The reproductive processes are the same: development of sperm cells and egg cells, pollination, fertilization, seed development, and seed dispersal. The ovule develops into the seed and the ovary changes into a **fruit.**

Many plants can also undergo asexual reproduction, which involves only one parent and produces offspring that are identical to the parent. New plants can grow from roots, leaves, or stems of a parent plant.

On a separate sheet of paper, describe the two stages of a plant life cycle.

Name _____ Date _____ Class _____

Review and Reinforce

Plant Reproduction

Understanding Main Ideas

Answer the following questions in the spaces provided. Use a separate sheet of paper if you need more room.

1. Describe the two stages of a plant's life cycle.

   _____

   _____

2. Describe how angiosperms are classified according to the length of their life cycle.

   _____

   _____

3. What happens during fertilization?

   _____

4. What are the steps in angiosperm reproduction?

   _____

   _____

   _____

Building Vocabulary

Fill in the blank to complete each statement.

5. A fertilized egg is called a(n) _____.

6. When pollen lands on the stigma of a flower, _____ occurs.

7. A(n) _____ is a ripened ovary.

8. A plant that lives for two years and flowers in the second year is called a(n) _____.

9. The reproductive structure of a gymnosperm is the

   _____.

10. Egg cells develop inside a structure called a(n) _____.

Enrich

Plant Reproduction

Read the passage and study the diagrams below. Then use a separate sheet of paper to answer the questions that follow.

Spore Toss

The tiny spore cases that grow on the undersides of fern fronds are called *sporangia* (singular *sporangium*). Some kinds of ferns can actually throw their spores using their sporangia. The sporangia of these ferns consist of a single layer of thin-walled cells plus an annulus. An *annulus* (plural *annuli*) is a row of thickened cells that encircles the sporangium. In moist conditions, an annulus is curved. When a fern does not have enough water, however, the cells of the annulus begin to dry out. This causes the annulus to pull on the sporangium and the sporangium begins to tear. Once the sporangium is torn completely open, the annulus snaps back to its original curved shape and throws the spores into the air, much like a catapult. Some ferns can toss their spores up to several meters.

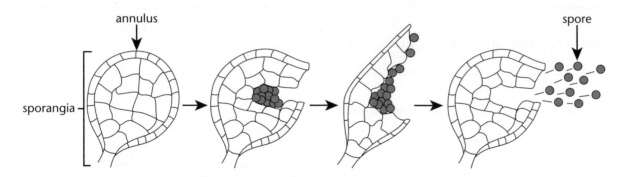

1. Write a caption for each of the illustrations shown above, using what you have learned about how some ferns release their spores.
2. Why is it advantageous to ferns to have their spores carried long distances by wind or water?
3. Some ferns do not throw their spores. Instead, their spores are carried away from their sporangia by the wind. What is one advantage that spore-throwing ferns have over these ferns?
4. What type of weather precedes the release of spores? Explain.

Lesson Quiz

Plant Reproduction

Write the letter of the correct answer on the line at the left.

1. ___ Many angiosperms rely on animals for

A fertilization

B pollination

C photosynthesis

D transpiration

2. ___ Because it lives for many years, a maple tree is a(n)

A perennial

B annual

C biennial

D biannual

3. ___ The product of the union of sperm and egg is a(n)

A embryo

B gametophyte

C fruit

D zygote

4. ___ The ovules of a pine tree are found in its

A fruits

B cones

C ovaries

D seeds

If the statement is true, write _true_. If the statement is false, change the underlined word or words to make the statement true.

5. _____ The <u>gametophyte</u> produces spores or seeds.

6. _____ Most gymnosperms produce both male and female <u>fruit</u>.

7. _____ After a pollen grain lands on the stigma of a flower, a(n) <u>pollen tube</u> grows down into the ovule.

8. _____ The female sex cell is the <u>sperm</u>.

9. _____ Animals that eat fruits help to <u>pollinate</u> their seeds by depositing them in new areas.

10. _____ Grafting is an example of <u>asexual</u> reproduction.

Plant Reproduction

Answer Key

After the Inquiry Warm-Up

1. Answers will vary. Expect students to find that 20–50 times more poppy seeds stuck to a sticky swab.

2. Students should draw a double bar graph showing the results for dry swabs and sticky swabs.

3. A vascular plant with a sticky stigma is more likely to catch pollen grains.

4. Accept all reasonable responses. Sample: Having a sticky stigma is an adaptation that helps a plant to reproduce because it makes it easier for the stigma to catch pollen.

Key Concept Summaries

The life cycle of a plant includes two stages. In the sporophyte stage, the plant produces spores or seeds, tiny cells that can grow into new organisms. The spore or seed develops into the plant's second stage, called the gametophyte. In the gametophyte stage, the plant produces two kinds of sex cells, sperm cells and egg cells. In the process of fertilization, the egg unites with the sperm to form a zygote, or fertilized egg. The zygote develops into a sporophyte and the cycle continues.

Review and Reinforce

1. In the sporophyte stage, the plant produces spores or seeds. The spore or seed develops into the plant's second stage, the gametophyte. In the gametophyte stage, the plant produces sperm cells and egg cells. During fertilization, the egg unites with the sperm to form a zygote. The zygote develops into a sporophyte, and the cycle continues.

2. Annuals complete a life cycle in one growing season. Biennials complete a life cycle in two years. Perennials live for more than two years.

3. A sperm cell unites with an egg cell and a zygote is formed.

4. The plant produces flowers. While the anther on each stamen produces pollen grains, each ovule inside the ovary produces an egg cell. When a pollen grain lands on the stigma pollination occurs. A pollen tube grows down into the ovule and allows a sperm cell to reach the egg. Fertilization takes place, and a zygote is formed. The zygote becomes the seed's embryo, the ovule becomes a seed, and the ovary swells into a fruit. The seed grows into a new plant.

5. zygote
6. pollination
7. fruit
8. biennial
9. cone
10. ovule

Enrich

1. (1) A sporangia under normal conditions (2) Sporangium begins to tear. (3) The sporangium is torn completely open. (4) The annulus snaps back throwing the spores.

2. It gives the spores a chance to grow without competition from their parent fern.

3. Answers may vary. Samples: Spores that are thrown do not have to rely on wind to travel away from their parent plant. Spores that are thrown have a better chance of being caught by the wind.

4. The spores aren't released until the annulus dries out. Therefore, dry weather precedes the release of spores.

Lesson Quiz

1. B
2. A
3. D
4. B
5. sporophyte
6. cones
7. true
8. egg
9. disperse
10. true

Place the outside corner, the corner away from the dotted line, in the corner of your copy machine to copy onto letter-size paper.

Plant Responses and Growth

5

 How do you know a plant when you see it?

Lesson Pacing: 1–2 periods or $\frac{1}{2}$–1 block

🕐 **SHORT ON TIME?** To do this lesson in approximately half the time, do the Activate Prior Knowledge activity on page 118. A discussion of the Key Concepts on pages 119, 121, and 122 will familiarize students with the lesson content. Explore the Big Q by discussing the characteristics that are the most important in identifying a plant. Have students do the Art in Motion activity and the Quick Labs. The rest of the lesson can be completed by students independently.

Preference Navigator, in the online Planning tools, allows you to customize *Interactive Science* to your own teaching style. You can also edit lesson plans by selecting the Lesson Planner option.

Digital Teacher's Edition allows you to access your Teacher's Edition and Resource materials online.

my science online.com

Lesson Vocabulary

- tropism
- hormone
- auxin
- photoperiodism
- critical night length
- short-day plant
- long-day plant
- day-neutral plant
- dormancy

 Content Refresher

Rapid Responses All plants respond to light and gravity: plant shoots move upward toward light and against gravity, while roots move downward away from light and with gravity. The response center for gravity appears to be in the root cap and may be governed by starch molecules. Response to light is governed by a plant hormone called *auxin*.

Some plant responses do not involve growth. If the leaves of *Mimosa pudica,* appropriately called the "sensitive plant," are touched, its leaflets fold together completely within only two or three seconds. The leaflets are held apart due to osmotic pressure at the base of the leaflets, where they join. When a leaf is touched, cells near the center of the leaflets pump out ions and lose water due to osmosis. Pressure from cells on the underside of the leaf, which do not lose water, force the leaflets together.

The carnivorous Venus' flytrap also demonstrates rapid responses. Each plant grows several kidney-shaped leaves with sensitive inner bristles. When a fly triggers sensory cells on the inside of the flytrap's leaf, electrical signals are sent from cell to cell. A combination of changes in osmotic pressure and cell wall expansion causes the leaf to snap shut, trapping the insect inside. Enzymes slowly digest the prey, and specialized glands absorb the nutrients.

LESSON OBJECTIVES

- Identify three stimuli that produce plant responses.
- Describe how plants respond to seasonal changes.

118A Plants

Blended Path

ENGAGE AND EXPLORE

Teach this lesson using a variety of resources. Begin by reading **My Planet Diary** as a class. Have students discuss the challenges to overcome when trying to get plants to succeed in a new area. Then have students do the **Inquiry Warm-Up activity.** Students will determine the responses to touch in various plants and infer an advantage to the plant. The **After the Inquiry Warm-Up worksheet** sets up a discussion about how two different types of plants respond to being touched. Have volunteers share their answers to question 4, comparing how quickly the Venus' flytrap moved in response to the touch of the pencil with how quickly a houseplant on a window sill moves in response to sunlight.

EXPLAIN AND ELABORATE

Teach Key Concepts by explaining that plants move by growing toward or away from a stimulus. **Lead a Discussion** introducing the idea that plants are able to respond to stimuli because they produce hormones.

Teach Key Concepts by explaining how plants respond to seasonal changes. Continue to **Teach Key Concepts** by explain to students that dormancy is another way in which plants respond to seasonal changes. Have students practice the inquiry skill in the **Apply It activity. Explore the Big Q** by discussing the characteristics that are the most important in identifying a plant. **Answer the Big Q** by leading a class discussion about the main characteristics of plants.

Hand out the **Key Concept Summaries** as a review of each part of the lesson. Students can also use the online **Vocab Flash Cards** to review key terms.

EVALUATE

Have students take the **Lesson Quiz.** For an alternate assessment, see the *ExamView*® Computer Test Generator, Progress Monitoring Assessments, or SuccessTracker™.

ELL Support

1 Content and Language

Tell students that the term *dormant* comes from a Latin word that means "to sleep." Discuss the meaning of another word that has the same Latin base, *dormitory.* Review the definition of *dormant* as it is used in the lesson. Discuss how associating the two terms *dormant* and *dormitory* can help them remember the meaning of the term as it is used in the lesson.

Lab zone Inquiry Path
Hands-on learning in the Lab zone

Digital Path
Online learning at my science online.com

ENGAGE AND EXPLORE

To teach this lesson with an emphasis on inquiry, begin with the **Inquiry Warm-Up activity.** Students will determine the responses to touch in various plants and infer an advantage to the plant. The **After the Inquiry Warm-Up worksheet** sets up a discussion about how two different types of plants respond to being touched. Have volunteers share their answers to question 4, comparing how quickly the Venus' flytrap moved in response to the touch of the pencil with how quickly a houseplant on a window sill moves in response to sunlight.

EXPLAIN AND ELABORATE

Focus on the **Inquiry Skill** for the lesson. Remind students that when they draw conclusions, they use what they have learned or observed to summarize or explain related information, or answer related questions. What was used in the **Inquiry Warm-Up activity** to explain how quickly the leaf of the Venus' flytrap closed when touched by a pencil? *(What was observed; the leaf closed very quickly, perhaps in less than a second.)* Use the **Teacher Demo** to model plant response to light. Have students do the **Quick Lab** to explore the effects of gravity on a sprouting seed.

Before beginning the **Apply It activity,** remind students that a graph shows how two variables are related. The graph in the activity shows the relationship between the number germinated seeds and each day of growth for two temperatures at which the seeds are kept. **Explore the Big Q** by discussing the characteristics that are the most important in identifying a plant. Have students do the **Quick Lab** to explore why the leaves of some trees change color when the seasons change. **Answer the Big Q** by leading a class discussion about the main characteristics of plants. Students can use the online **Vocab Flash Cards** to review key terms.

EVALUATE

Have students take the **Lesson Quiz.** For an alternate assessment, see the *ExamView®* Computer Test Generator, Progress Monitoring Assessments, or SuccessTracker™.

ENGAGE AND EXPLORE

Teach this lesson using digital resources. Begin by having students learn more about plant responses and growth and explore real-world connections to plant tropisms at **My Planet Diary** online. Have them access the Chapter Resources to find the **Unlock the Big Question activity.** There they can answer the questions and refine their responses as they continue through the lesson. You can re-assign the activity and have students submit their work so you can track their progress.

EXPLAIN AND ELABORATE

Students reading above, at, or below the lexile measure of this lesson can access basic content readings at their level at **My Reading Web.** Encourage students to use the online **Vocab Flash Cards** to preview key terms.

Assign the **Apply It activity** online and have students submit their work to you. Use the **Art in Motion activity** online to allow students to explore plant tropisms. **Explore the Big Q** by discussing the characteristics that are the most important in identifying a plant. Have students do the **Quick Lab** to explore why the leaves of some trees change color when the seasons change. **Answer the Big Q** by leading a class discussion about the main characteristics of plants. The **Key Concept Summaries** online allow students to read a summary and see an image associated with each part of the lesson. Online remediation is available at **My Science Coach.**

EVALUATE

Have students take the **Lesson Quiz.** For an alternate assessment, see the *ExamView®* Computer Test Generator, Progress Monitoring Assessments, or SuccessTracker™.

---

2 Frontload the Lesson
Have students create a word map by writing the vocabulary terms in the top box. As they read the chapter, they should fill in the bottom boxes with terms, phrases, or images associated with the vocabulary term.

3 Comprehensible Input
Have students use a Venn Diagram to compare long-day plants and short-day plants. Encourage them to find examples in addition to those in the chapter to add to their diagrams.

4 Language Production
Pair or group students with varied language abilities to complete labs collaboratively for language practice. Have each student copy the completed written lab for personal reference.

5 Assess Understanding
Make true or false statements using lesson content and have students indicate if they agree or disagree with a thumbs up or thumbs down gesture to check whole-class comprehension.

Lexile Measure = 860L

Plant Responses and Growth

Establish Learning Objectives

After this lesson, students will be able to:

🔑 Identify three stimuli that produce plant responses.

🔑 Describe how plants respond to seasonal changes.

Engage

Activate Prior Knowledge

MY PLANET DIARY Read *Flower Power* with the class. Initiate a discussion about global climate change. Elicit from students the difference between global warming *(rise in average temperature over surface of Earth)* and global climate change *(changes in regional climate characteristics around the world).* Ask: **How are they related?** *(As temperatures increase, some areas will become drier, others wetter, and severe-weather events will increase.)*

BIG IDEAS OF SCIENCE REFERENCE LIBRARY 📖 Have students look up the following topic: Plant Tricks.

Explore

Lab Resource: Inquiry Warm-Up 🧪

L1 **CAN A PLANT RESPOND TO TOUCH?** Students will determine the response to touch in various plants and infer an advantage to the plant.

LESSON

5 Plant Responses and Growth

🔑 **What Are Three Stimuli That Produce Plant Responses?**

🔑 **How Do Plants Respond to Seasonal Changes?**

MY PLANET DIARY

DISCOVERY

Flower Power

What makes a plant flower? Plants detect the amount of light each day. When there is just enough light, the plant sends a signal to the flower. But what is this signal? For almost 80 years, the answer remained a mystery. In 2008, scientists discovered the protein that was responsible. They linked the protein they thought controlled flowering to a fluorescent, or glowing, protein they obtained from a jellyfish. Then they watched the bright green protein travel with the flowering protein through the stem to make the plant bloom. Why does this experiment matter?

Global climate change is starting to hurt crops. Some places near the equator are becoming too warm to farm. Areas closer to Earth's poles may be needed to grow more crops as they warm. These areas, however, do not get as much sunlight. Scientists could use the flowering protein to encourage plants to flower without direct sunlight.

Communicate Discuss the question with a group of classmates. Then write your answer below.

In addition to getting the plants to flower with no light, what other challenges might scientists have to overcome when trying to get plants to succeed in a new area?

Accept all reasonable answers. Sample: The soil conditions might not be good for the plants. Animals could eat the plants.

▶ **PLANET DIARY** Go to **Planet Diary** to learn more about plant responses and growth.

 Do the Inquiry Warm-Up *Can a Plant Respond to Touch?*

The green you see in these plant cells is from a **fluorescent** protein like the one used in the flowering experiment.

SUPPORT ALL READERS

Lexile Measure = 860L   Lexile Word Count = 1184

Prior Exposure to Content: May be the first time students have encountered this topic

Academic Vocabulary: *conclusions, relate*

Science Vocabulary: *tropism, hormone, photoperiodism, dormancy*

Concept Level: Generally appropriate for most students in this grade

Preteach With: My Planet Diary "Flower Power" and Figure 1 activity

Go to **My Reading Web** to access leveled readings that provide a foundation for the content.

my science online

Vocabulary

- tropism • hormone • auxin • photoperiodism
- critical night length • short-day plant • long-day plant
- day-neutral plant • dormancy

Skills

- ⟳ Reading: Relate Text and Visuals
- △ Inquiry: Draw Conclusions

What Are Three Stimuli That Produce Plant Responses?

You may be one of those people who close their window shades at night because the morning light wakes you up. People respond to many stimuli each day. Did you know plants also respond to some of the same stimuli, including light?

Tropisms Animals usually respond to stimuli by moving. Unlike animals, plants usually respond by growing either toward or away from a stimulus. A plant's growth response toward or away from a stimulus is called a **tropism** (TROH piz um). If a plant grows toward the stimulus, it is said to show a positive tropism. If a plant grows away from a stimulus, it shows a negative tropism. ▭ **Touch, gravity, and light are three important stimuli that trigger growth responses, or tropisms, in plants.**

Touch

Some plants show a response to touch called thigmotropism. The prefix thigmo- comes from a Greek word that means "touch." The stems of many vines, such as morning glories, sweet peas, and grapes, show a positive thigmotropism. As the vines grow, they coil around any object they touch.

FIGURE 1 ·······················

Plant Responses to Stimuli

The stimuli in space are not always the same as those on Earth.

✏ **Develop Hypotheses** How might the roots of a plant grow in space without the influence of gravity?

Sample: The roots would grow
in all directions.

_____

_____

Gravity

Plants can respond to gravity. This response is called gravitropism. Roots show positive gravitropism if they grow downward. Stems, on the other hand, show negative gravitropism. Stems grow upward against gravity.

119

Explain

Introduce Vocabulary

Have students look at the vocabulary term *photoperiodism*. Tell them that *photo* refers to light and *periodism* to a recurring cycle of given length. Thus the term refers to a plant's response to a recurring cycle of light and dark periods of constant length.

Teach Key Concepts 🔑

Explain to students that although plants cannot move from place to place, they can move by growing toward or away from a stimulus. Review with students the meanings of the terms *stimulus* and *response*. Ask: **What is a plant's growth response toward or away from a stimulus called?** *(A tropism)* **In terms of direction of growth, what are the two types of tropisms?** *(A positive tropism is growth toward a stimulus. A negative tropism is growth away from a stimulus.)* **What are three important stimuli to which plants show tropisms?** *(Touch, light, and gravity)* **What is a response to touch called?** *(Thigmotropism)* **How do vines show thigmotropism?** *(They show a positive response by wrapping around objects that they touch.)* **What are two other tropisms plants show?** *(Gravitropism, or response to gravity, and phototropism, or response to light)* **What kind of gravitropism do a plant's roots show?** *(Roots show a positive gravitropism, because they grow downward toward the pull of gravity.)* **Which kind of gravitropism do a plant's stems show?** *(Stems show a negative gravitropism, because they grow upward away from the pull of gravity.)* **How do plants show phototropism?** *(The stems and leaves of a plant grow toward a light source.)*

My Planet Diary provides an opportunity for students to explore real-world connections to plant tropisms.

(E)(L)(L) Support

1 Content and Language

Write the term *photoperiodism* on the board. Explain that *photo* comes from the Greek word for light and that *period* comes from a Greek term meaning "circuit" or "period of time." So, *photoperiodism* relates to how a plant responds to periods of light and dark.

2 Frontload the Lesson

Use **Figure 1** to explain plant responses to different stimuli. Point

to the illustration of one stimulus and ask how a plant might respond to it. Urge students to consider their own knowledge and experience of plants responding to touch, gravity, and light.

3 Comprehensible Input

Discuss the Explore the Big Q image and caption. Review the structure of the compare/contrast table and the terms it includes. Have student pairs complete the Apply Concepts activity.

Explain

Lead a Discussion

PLANT HORMONES Introduce the idea that plants are able to respond to stimuli because they produce hormones. Ask: **What is a hormone?** *(A chemical that affects a plant's growth and development.)* **What hormone controls a plant's response to light? How does it work?** *(Auxin speeds up the rate at which plant cells grow. When light shines on one side of a plant's stem, auxins build up in the cells on the shaded side. Cells on the shaded side grow faster and become longer. The stem bends toward the light.)*

 Relate Text and Visuals Tell students that when they relate text and visuals, they use information they have read to create or illustrate diagrams or graphs.

Elaborate

Teacher Demo

L1 **MODELING PLANT RESPONSE**

Materials coiled spring toy

Time 10 minutes

Have students decide which side of a coiled spring toy will represent the shaded side of a plant. Hold the toy and cause the shaded side to elongate, or "grow." Have students observe how the toy bends.

Ask: **Which way does the toy bend?** *(It bends away from the coils.)* **How does this model a plant's response?** *(A plant bends toward the light.)* **What causes this?** *(Auxin makes the cells on the shaded side grow faster. They become longer.)*

Lab Resource: Quick Lab

L2 **WATCHING ROOTS GROW** Students will explore the effects of gravity on a sprouting seed.

Evaluate

Assess Your Understanding

After students answer the questions, have them evaluate their understanding by completing the appropriate sentence.

RTI **Response to Intervention**

1a. If students cannot define *tropism*, **then** have them reread the definition.

b. If students have trouble identifying the functions of plant hormones, **then** remind them that hormones are chemicals that affect plant growth.

MY SCIENCE COACH Have students go online for help in understanding the nature of tropisms.

Relate Text and Visuals Use what you have read to label the side of the plant with more auxin and the side with less auxin.

Less auxin  More auxin

Light

All plants exhibit a response to light called phototropism. The leaves, stems, and flowers of plants grow toward light. This shows a positive phototropism. A plant receives more energy for photosynthesis by growing toward the light.

Plants are able to respond to stimuli because they produce hormones. A **hormone** produced by a plant is a chemical that affects how the plant grows and develops. One important plant hormone is named **auxin** (AWK sin). Auxin speeds up the rate at which a plant's cells grow and controls a plant's response to light. When light shines on one side of a plant's stem, auxin builds up in the shaded side of the stem. The cells on the shaded side begin to grow faster. The cells on the stem's shaded side are longer than those on its sunny side. The stem bends toward the light.

 Do the Quick Lab
Watching Roots Grow.

Assess Your Understanding

1a. Define What is a tropism?

A tropism is a plant's response toward or away from a stimulus.

b. Predict What do you think would happen if a plant did not create enough of the hormone that controlled flower formation?

Sample: The flowers may not form correctly or may not form at all.

got it?

○ I get it! Now I know that plants respond to touch, gravity, and light.

○ I need extra help with See TE note.

Go to **MY SCIENCE COACH** online for help with this subject.

120 Plants

How Do Plants Respond to Seasonal Changes?

People have long observed that plants respond to the changing seasons. Some plants bloom in early spring, while others don't bloom until summer. The leaves on some trees change color in autumn and then fall off by winter.

Photoperiodism What triggers a plant to flower? The amount of darkness a plant receives determines the time of flowering in many plants. A plant's response to seasonal changes in the length of night and day is called **photoperiodism**.

Plants respond differently to the length of nights. Some plants will only bloom when the nights last a certain length of time. This length, called the **critical night length**, is the number of hours of darkness that determines whether or not a plant will flower. For example, if a plant has a critical night length of 11 hours, it will flower only when nights are longer than 11 hours. You can read more on how different plants respond to night length in **Figure 2**.

Photoperiodism

Plants and Night Length		Examples
Short-day plants flower when the nights are longer than a critical length. They bloom in fall or winter.	Midnight / Noon	Chrysanthemums, poinsettias
Long-day plants flower when nights are shorter than a critical length. They bloom in spring or summer.	Midnight / Noon	Irises, lettuce
Day-neutral plants have a flowering cycle that is not sensitive to periods of light and dark. They can bloom year-round depending on weather.	Midnight / Noon Midnight / Noon	Dandelions, rice, tomatoes

FIGURE 2 · · · · · · · · · · · ·

Photoperiodism

Flowering plants can be grouped as short-day plants, long-day plants, and day-neutral plants.

✎ **Infer** Suppose you are a farmer in a climate that supports plant growth all year-round but night length varies. Based on the categories in the chart, would you plant mostly one type of plant or a mixture of all three? Explain.

Sample: I would plant all three so that there would be plants in bloom all year no matter how long the nights were.

121

Explain

Teach Key Concepts 🔑

Have students think about what happens when the seasons change. Elicit from students the fact that the length of days and nights changes with the change of seasons. Explain to students that the amount of darkness a plant receives determines the time of flowering in many plants. Ask: **Why don't some plants bloom in winter in locations that have seasonal changes?** *(Temperatures are too low and days are too short.)* **What environmental factor triggers plants to flower?** *(The amount of darkness a plant receives)* **What is photoperiodism?** *(A plant's response to hours of light and darkness)* **When does a short-day plant flower?** *(When nights are longer than its critical night length)* **When does a long-day plant?** *(When nights are shorter than its critical night length)* **What is critical night length?** *(The number of hours of darkness that determines whether or not a plant will flower)* **What name is given to plants that bloom no matter what the periods of darkness are?** *(Day-neutral plants)*

Teach With Visuals

Tell students to look at **Figure 2**. Ask: **What do the clock faces represent?** *(The number of hours of darkness and light)* **Which is more important to a plant's flowering, the number of hours of darkness or the number of hours of light?** *(The number of hours of darkness)* **Based on your answer, what would be more appropriate names for the plants?** *(Long-night and short-night)* Point out to students that the terms *short-day plant* and *long-day plant* were used before it was understood that it is the amount of time the plant is in the dark, not the light, that is important to flowering.

21st Century Learning

CRITICAL THINKING Have students think about photoperiodism in plants. Ask: **What is the advantage of different plants flowering at different times of the year?** *(Samples: The plant's pollinators may pollinate only during certain times of the year. Plants have adapted to the climate—for example, a particular plant may not be able to flower during the summer.)* **How might gardeners get plants to bloom out of season?** *(By controlling the temperature and the amount of light the plants receive)*

Differentiated Instruction

L1 Types of Photoperiodism Have students make a compare/contrast table of the types of photoperiodism in plants.

L1 Chrysanthemum Flowers Chrysanthemums are short-day plants. Have students describe the appearance of these plants in the early summer and in the fall. Tell students to explain why the plants appear as they do. If students are unfamiliar with this plant, show them a photograph of one in full bloom.

Encourage students to draw pictures for their explanations.

L3 Flower Induction Invite students to research how greenhouse managers bring flowers, such as poinsettias, to bloom for specific seasons, and how they induce seasonal plants, such as chrysanthemums, to bloom all year. Remind students that some plants are harmful to cats. Poinsettias and lillies are two examples.

LESSON 3.5

Explain

Teach Key Concepts 🔑

Explain to students that dormancy is another way in which plants respond to seasonal changes. Ask: **What is dormancy?** *(A period when an organism's growth or activity stops)* **Why is dormancy beneficial to a plant?** *(It helps plants survive freezing temperatures and the lack of liquid water.)* **What are the changes a tree undergoes as it becomes dormant?** *(The leaves begin to turn color. Sugar and water are transported out of the leaves. The leaves fall off.)* Discuss the changes in leaf color with students. Emphasize that chlorophyll is not changing color; it is breaking down, and the other leaf pigments are now more visible. **Which pigments are visible with the breakdown of chlorophyll?** *(Yellow and orange)* **Which pigment is newly produced?** *(Red)*

Make Analogies

L1 DORMANCY Discuss with students other examples of dormancy. Ask: **To what other event in nature have you heard the term *dormancy or dormant* applied?** *(Sample: volcanoes that have not erupted for a time)* **What do some animals do in winter that is similar to trees becoming dormant?** *(They hibernate.)*

Elaborate

Apply It!

L1 Before beginning the activity, remind students that a graph shows how two variables are related. This graph shows the relationship between the number of germinated seeds and each day of growth for two temperatures at which the seeds are kept. The two sets of data are plotted for each temperature and the relationship between the growing conditions can be seen in a comparison of the slopes of the lines.

△ **Draw Conclusions** Tell students that when they draw conclusions, they use what they have learned or observed to summarize or explain related information, or answer related questions. In this case, they are using the slopes of the two lines to explain how temperature affects seed germination.

Winter Dormancy Some plants prepare differently than others for certain seasons. As winter draws near, many plants prepare to go into a state of **dormancy.** Dormancy is a period when an organism's growth or activity stops. 🔑 **Dormancy helps plants survive freezing temperatures and the lack of liquid water.**

With many trees, the first visible change is that the leaves begin to turn color. Cooler weather and shorter days cause the leaves to stop making chlorophyll. As chlorophyll breaks down, yellow and orange pigments become visible. In addition, the plant begins to produce new red pigments. This causes the brilliant colors of autumn leaves. Over the next few weeks, sugar and water are transported out of the tree's leaves. When the leaves fall to the ground, the tree is ready for winter.

apply it!

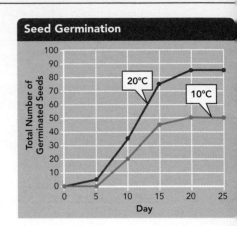

Seed Germination

One hundred radish seeds were planted in two identical trays of soil. One tray was kept at 10°C. The other tray was kept at 20°C. The trays received equal amounts of sun and water. The graph shows how many seeds germinated over time at each temperature.

❶ Read Graphs About how many seeds in the 20°C tray germinated on Day 13?

About 58 seeds
(accept plus/minus 2)

❷ △ Draw Conclusions Based on the graph, what can you conclude about the relationship between the two temperatures and germination?

The number of germinating seeds increased with the higher temperature compared to the lower temperature.

❸ CHALLENGE After the experiment, a fellow scientist concludes that more seeds will *always* germinate at higher temperatures. Is the scientist right? Why?

Sample: No; this experiment does not test temperatures above 20°C. There may be a point at which the temperature is too high for seeds to survive. More experiments with higher temperatures are needed to support that conclusion.

122   Plants

Digital Lesson: Assign the *Apply It* activity online and have students submit their work to you.

Art in Motion allows students to explore plant tropisms.

my science online.com ▶ **Plants and Seasonal Changes**

Roving for Life in Space

How do you know a plant when you see it?

FIGURE 3

ART IN MOTION You are a scientist researching distant planets. You have sent a rover to collect samples from one of the planets and you get some exciting results. The rover has found three living things, and one of them is a plant! But, on the way back to Earth, the rover has a rough landing and the samples get mixed up. You run some tests in your lab to find which sample is the plant. The results are shown below.

Circle the sample that is a plant. Then answer the question below.

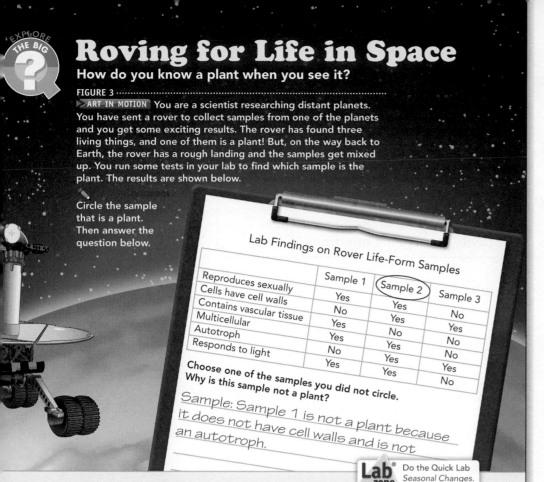

Lab Findings on Rover Life-Form Samples

	Sample 1	Sample 2	Sample 3
Reproduces sexually	Yes	Yes	Yes
Cells have cell walls	No	Yes	No
Contains vascular tissue	Yes	Yes	Yes
Multicellular	Yes	No	No
Autotroph	No	Yes	No
Responds to light	Yes	Yes	Yes

Choose one of the samples you did not circle. Why is this sample not a plant?

Sample: Sample 1 is not a plant because it does not have cell walls and is not an autotroph.

 Lab zone Do the Quick Lab
Seasonal Changes.

Assess Your Understanding

2a. Review (Short-day/(Long-day)) plants flower when nights are shorter than a critical length.

b. Explain Why do the leaves of some trees change color in autumn?

The chlorophyll in the leaves of the trees is breaking down.

c. ANSWER THE BIG How do you know a plant when you see it?

Sample: The organism has the characteristics that all plants share, such as having cell walls and responding to light.

got it?

○ **I get it!** Now I know that plants respond to seasonal changes because _the amount of darkness determines the flowering times of many plants._

○ **I need extra help with** _See TE note._

Go to **MY SCIENCE COACH** online for help with this subject.

123

Differentiated Instruction

L1 Winter Dormancy Have students sketch the steps showing the changes a tree undergoes as winter approaches. Have them label each step and write in their own words what happens.

L1 Plant Response Have students summarize plant response by creating a concept map that includes the following terms: *tropism, stimulus, hormone, auxin, gravitropism, phototropism, thigmotropism.*

L3 Autumn Leaves The colors that leaves exhibit in autumn are often characteristic of a particular type of tree. Have students find out which common trees display the following colors: yellow; purple; light brown or dark brown; bright red and orange; dark red. Then have them use the information to draw or paint a vista of trees in autumn color, labeling each type of tree.

Explore the Big Q ? UbD

Direct students' attention to the scenario in which a rover they have sent to distant planets has collected samples of living things from one of the planets. Only one of the three samples is a plant. Because the samples get mixed up on the journey home, it is now up to the students to identify which is the plant. Remind students that plants have characteristics that distinguish them from other living things. Have students discuss what those characteristics are. Ask: **Does the sample need to have a "yes" in every row of its column? Explain.** *(No, because some plants can be vascular or nonvascular, single-celled or multicellular)* **What characteristics are the most important in identifying a plant?** *(It's an autotroph, with only one exception it is multicellular, its cells are surrounded by cell walls, and it responds to light.)* **Why is Sample 3 not a plant?** *(It does not respond to light and unless it is a green alga, it is not multicellular.)*

Lab Resource: Quick Lab Lab zone

L2 SEASONAL CHANGES Students will explore why the leaves of some trees change color when the seasons change.

Evaluate

Assess Your Understanding

After students answer the questions, have them evaluate their understanding by completing the appropriate sentence.

Answer the Big Q ? UbD

To help students focus on the Big Question, lead a class discussion about the main characteristics of plants.

RTI Response to Intervention

2a. If students need help with photoperiodism, **then** remind them that it is the length of darkness that determines a plant's flowering time. Have them think of the two choices in terms of "night" rather than "day."

b. If students have trouble explaining the color change in leaves in autumn, **then** remind them of the connection between chlorophyll and food-making and the fact that plants are getting ready to be dormant, a state in which growth or activity stops.

MY SCIENCE COACH Have students go online for help in understanding plant responses and growth.

Lab zone **After the Inquiry Warm-Up**

Plant Responses and Growth

Inquiry Warm-Up, *Can A Plant Respond to Touch?*
In the Inquiry Warm-Up, you investigated how two different types of plants respond to being touched. Using what you learned from that activity, answer the questions below.

1. **COMMUNICATE** Draw a two-step diagram to show what happened when you touched the Venus' flytrap.

2. **RELATE CAUSE AND EFFECT** What caused the leaf of the Venus' flytrap to close up?

   _____

   _____

3. **OBSERVE** When touched by the pencil tip, about how quickly did the leaf of the Venus' flytrap close?

   _____

4. **COMPARE AND CONTRAST** Compare how quickly the Venus' flytrap moved in response to the touch of the pencil with how quickly a houseplant on a window sill moves in response to sunlight.

   _____

   _____

   _____

Assess Your Understanding

Plant Responses and Growth

What Are Three Stimuli That Produce Plant Responses?

1a. DEFINE What is a tropism? _____

_____

b. PREDICT What do you think would happen if a plant did not
create enough of the hormone that controlled flower formation? _____

_____

_____

got it? ···

○ **I get it!** Now I know that plants respond to _____

_____

○ **I need extra help with** _____

_____

How Do Plants Respond to Seasonal Changes?

2a. REVIEW (Short-day/Long-day) plants flower when nights
are shorter than a critical length.

b. EXPLAIN Why do the leaves of some trees change
color in autumn? _____

_____

c. ANSWER 🔲 How do you know a plant when you see it? _____

_____

_____

got it? ···

○ **I get it!** Now I know that plants respond to seasonal changes because _____

_____

○ **I need extra help with** _____

_____

Plant Responses and Growth

What Are Three Stimuli That Produce Plant Responses?

Plants respond to stimuli by growing toward or away from the stimulus, a response called a **tropism.** Growth toward a stimulus is a positive tropism; growth away is a negative tropism. **Touch, light, and gravity are three important stimuli to which plants show growth responses, or tropisms.**

A plant's response to touch is called thigmotropism. A vine that curls around an object it touches shows a positive thigmotropism. Gravitropism is plant's response to gravity. As they grow downward, roots show a positive gravitropism. Stems growing up and against gravity show a negative gravitropism. Phototropism is a plant's response to light. Leaves, stems, and flowers that grow toward light show a positive phototropism. Plants respond to stimuli by producing **hormones,** chemicals that affect how a plant grows and develops. **Auxin** is a hormone that speeds up the rate at which a plant's cells grow. As auxin builds up on the shaded side of a stem, cells on that side grow faster and bend the stem toward the light.

How Do Plants Respond to Seasonal Changes?

Plants respond to the changing seasons because the amount of light they receive changes. **The amount of darkness a plant receives determines the time of flowering in many plants.** A plant's response to seasonal changes in the length of night and day is called **photoperiodism.** Some plants will only bloom when the night lasts a certain length of time.

Plants can be grouped according to **critical night length,** or the number of hours of darkness that determines whether or not a plant will flower. **Short-day plants** flower when nights are longer than a critical length. They bloom in fall or winter.

Long-day plants flower when nights are shorter than a critical length. They bloom in spring and summer. **Day-neutral plants** have a flowering cycle that is not sensitive to periods of light and dark. They can bloom year-round, depending on weather.

Some plants prepare for winter by going into a state of **dormancy,** or a period when growth or activity stops. **Dormancy helps plants survive freezing temperatures and the lack of liquid water.** Cooler weather and shorter days may trigger a plant to prepare to become dormant.

On a separate sheet of paper, explain three different types of response a plant may have to light—its direction or the length of time it lasts.

Name _____ Date _____ Class _____

Plant Responses and Growth

Understanding Main Ideas
Answer the following questions on a separate sheet of paper.

1. List three stimuli that produce responses in plants and give the name for each response.
2. What is gravitropism? How can a plant show both a positive and a negative gravitropism?
3. What is photoperiodism? What is its effect in many plants?
4. What happens when a plant enters a state of dormancy?

Building Vocabulary
Match each term with its definition by writing the letter of the correct definition in the right column on the line beside the term in the left column.

5. ___ critical night length

6. ___ auxin

7. ___ short-day plant

8. ___ long-day plant

9. ___ hormone

10. ___ day-neutral plant

11. ___ tropism

a. a hormone that controls a plant's response to light

b. a plant that flowers when the nights are shorter than a critical length

c. a plant's growth response toward or away from a stimulus

d. a chemical that affects the growth and development of a plant

e. a plant whose flowering cycle is not sensitive to periods of light and dark

f. a plant that flowers when the nights are longer than a critical length

g. the number of hours of darkness that determines whether or not a plant will flower

Enrich

Plant Responses and Growth

> Read the passage and study the diagrams below. Then use a separate sheet of paper to answer the questions that follow.

Carnivorous Plants

The Venus' flytrap is an example of the almost 400 species of carnivorous plants. A *carnivorous plant* is a plant that traps and then digests insects and other small animals, obtaining their nitrogen. Most carnivorous plants grow in marshy areas such as swamps and bogs where the soil is low in nitrogen. Because carnivorous plants do not have to rely on nitrogen absorbed from the soil by their roots, they are well suited to their environments.

Carnivorous plants respond to the stimulus of touch to trap their prey. For example, an insect touching a hair on the leaf of a Venus' flytrap triggers a specific response. Water moves from cells on the inside of the flytrap to cells on the outside of the flytrap. This causes the leaf of the flytrap to snap shut, quickly, catching the insect.

Carnivorous plants called sundews use another method to trap their prey. Sundews have small leaves that produce a sweet, sticky liquid at their tips. Insects fly into the stalks and stick to them. This triggers a different response. Other leaves begin to curl inward toward a trapped insect by using cell growth. The cells on one side of the stalks grow faster than the cells on the other side. This causes the leaves to bend. The leaves then produce a chemical that digests the insect, so it can be used to nourish the plant.

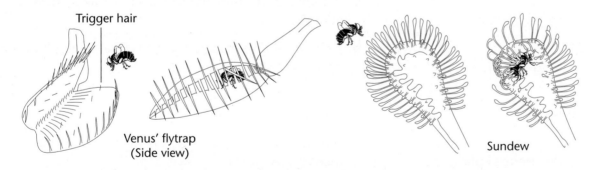

Trigger hair

Venus' flytrap
(Side view)

Sundew

1. How do carnivorous plants get the nitrogen they need?
2. Why is it helpful to a sundew to produce the sweet, sticky liquid?
3. Do you think carnivorous plants also produce food by photosynthesis? Explain your answer.
4. What is one advantage that quick movement gives to a Venus' flytrap?
5. Why doesn't the sundew have to move as quickly as the Venus' flytrap to imprison an insect?

Name _____ Date _____ Class _____

Plant Responses and Growth

Write the letter of the correct answer on the line at the left.

1. ___ A plant stem that grows toward light is an example of a
   A negative thigmotropism
   B negative gravitropism
   C positive phototropism
   D positive gravitropism

2. ___ To which three stimuli do plants respond?
   A water, light, and touch
   B light, gravity, and soil conditions
   C touch, gravity, and chlorophyll
   D touch, gravity, and light

3. ___ When chlorophyll in leaves breaks down,
   A photosynthesis begins
   B red pigments disappear
   C yellow and orange pigments become visible
   D the plant becomes very active

4. ___ Irises and lettuce flower when nights are shorter than a critical length. They can be described as
   A short-day plants
   B long-day plants
   C dormant plants
   D day-neutral plants

If the statement is true, write *true*. If the statement is false, change the underlined word or words to make the statement true.

5. _____ Chemicals produced by a plant that control its growth and development are called <u>hormones</u>.

6. _____ A plant's roots grow away from a rock they hit in the soil. This is an example of a <u>positive</u> thigmotropism.

7. _____ <u>Chlorophyll</u> speeds up that rate at which a plant's cells grow and controls a plant's response to light.

8. _____ The critical night length for a certain plant is 10 hours. This plant will flower only when nights are <u>shorter</u> than 10 hours.

9. _____ A plant adaptation that helps it survive freezing temperatures and lack of liquid water is <u>dormancy</u>.

10. _____ The blooming of poinsettias in winter and irises in spring is an example of <u>phototropism</u>.

Plant Responses and Growth

Answer Key

After the Inquiry Warm-Up

1. In the first part, students should show the open Venus' flytrap. In the second part, students should show the Venus' flytrap closed.

2. The leaf of the Venus' flytrap closed up in response to the touch of the pencil tip.

3. The leaf of the Venus' flytrap closed in less than a second.

4. The leaf of the Venus' flytrap moved much, much more quickly in response to the touch of the pencil than a houseplant on a window sill moves in response to sunlight.

Key Concept Summaries

One plant response to light is phototropism. Leaves, stems, and flowers that grow toward light show a positive phototropism. Another type of plant response to light is photoperiodism, a response to seasonal changes in the length of night and day. Some plants will only bloom when the night lasts a certain length of time. A third type of plant response to light is to enter a state of dormancy, a period when growth or activity stops. Both shorter days and colder weather may trigger dormancy, which can help plants survive freezing temperatures and a lack of liquid water.

Review and Reinforce

1. touch: thigmotropism; gravity: gravitropism; light: phototropism

2. When a plant's roots grow downward, it shows a positive gravitropism. When its stems grow upward against gravity it shows a negative gravitropism.

3. Photoperiodism is a plant's response to seasonal changes in the length of day and night. It determines the time of flowering in many plants.

4. During dormancy a plant's growth or activity stops.

5. g
6. a
7. f
8. b
9. d
10. e
11. c

Enrich

1. by digesting insects and other animals that they trap

2. The sweet sticky liquid acts as bait and trap for insects.

3. Yes the plants still need to make food even though they digest insects to obtain nitrogen.

4. Answers will vary. Sample: Speed allows the Venus' flytrap to trap an insect before the insect can fly away.

5. The sticky liquid traps the insect. Therefore, the plant can move relatively slowly to imprison and digest the insect.

Lesson Quiz

1. C
2. D
3. C
4. B
5. true
6. negative
7. Auxin
8. longer
9. true
10. photoperiodism

Place the outside corner, the corner away from the dotted line, in the corner of your copy machine to copy onto letter-size paper.

Plants in Everyday Life

6 How do you know a plant when you see it?

Blended Path
Active learning using Student Edition, Inquiry Path, and Digital Path

Lesson Pacing: 1–2 periods or $\frac{1}{2}$–1 block

🕐 **SHORT ON TIME?** To do this lesson in approximately half the time, do the Activate Prior Knowledge activity on page 124. A discussion of the Key Concepts on page 125 will familiarize students with the lesson content. Have students do the Quick Lab. The rest of the lesson can be completed by students independently.

Preference Navigator, in the online Planning tools, allows you to customize *Interactive Science* to your own teaching style. You can also edit lesson plans by selecting the Lesson Planner option.

Digital Teacher's Edition allows you to access your Teacher's Edition and Resource materials online.

my science online.com

Lesson Vocabulary
- peat

 Content Refresher

Professional Development Note

Products From Gymnosperms and Angiosperms People have long relied on various wood and nonwood products derived from gymnosperms. Conifers, in particular, are economically very important. They provide wood used in the production of lumber, paper, furniture, and musical instruments. Nonwood products include medicines, edible seeds, decorations, and resins.

Natural resin is a thick, yellowish liquid that is exuded from trees. Pine and fir trees are the source of most natural resin. Resin forms when the bark of the tree is injured, such as when it is affected by severe winds, fire, or lightning. Turpentine is one form of resin. Oil of turpentine is used in the production of oil pastels, and artists use it to clean their paintbrushes. It is used extensively in the manufacture of chemical products such as insecticides, camphor, and synthetic resins, and in the production of plastic.

Angiosperms have greater commercial use than gymnosperms, except in forest products. In addition to angiosperms being a source of food, they also provide people with clothing, rubber, furniture, and medications.

LESSON OBJECTIVE

🔑 Explain how plants are important in everyday life.

ENGAGE AND EXPLORE

Teach this lesson using a variety of resources. Begin by reading **My Planet Diary** as a class. Have students identify plants that are important in their everyday lives. Then have students do the **Inquiry Warm-Up activity.** Students will simulate the distribution of food among the world's population, make observations about how they and others feel, and predict the impact of an increase in global population on the world's food supply. The **After the Inquiry Warm-Up worksheet** sets up a discussion about the impact of an increase in global population on the world's food supply. Have volunteers share their answers to question 4 regarding the amount of food received by a poor country compared to the amount of food received by a wealthy country.

EXPLAIN AND ELABORATE

Teach Key Concepts by explaining that plants are the beginning of the food/energy chain that all organism need in order to survive. **Lead a Discussion** about how people use plants. **Support the Big Q** by reviewing the characteristics of angiosperms and then discussing why we use plants. Have students practice the inquiry skill in the **Apply It activity.**

Hand out the **Key Concept Summaries** as a review of each part of the lesson. Students can also use the online **Vocab Flash Cards** to review key terms.

EVALUATE

Have students take the **Lesson Quiz.** For an alternate assessment, see the *ExamView*® Computer Test Generator, Progress Monitoring Assessments, or SuccessTracker™.

ⒺⓁⓁ Support

1 Content and Language
Direct students to the photograph on page 126. Clarify how peat is dug, laid out to dry, and then stacked in preparation for transport. Then have students describe in their own words the process of readying peat for use as a fuel.

Lab zone Inquiry Path
Hands-on learning in the Lab zone

Digital Path
Online learning at my science online.com

ENGAGE AND EXPLORE

To teach this lesson with an emphasis on inquiry, begin with the **Inquiry Warm-Up activity.** Students will simulate the distribution of food among the world's population, make observations about how they and others feel, and predict the impact of an increase in global population on the world's food supply. The **After the Inquiry Warm-Up worksheet** sets up a discussion about the impact of an increase in global population on the world's food supply. Have volunteers share their answers to question 4 regarding the amount of food received by a poor country compared to the amount of food received by a wealthy country.

EXPLAIN AND ELABORATE

Focus on the **Inquiry Skill** for the lesson. Remind students that when making a decision, it is helpful to gather as much information or evidence as possible. One effective way to gather information is to ask questions. What questions were asked and answered in order to complete the **Inquiry Warm-Up activity?** *(Answers will vary.)* **Support the Big Q** by reviewing the characteristics of angiosperms and then discussing why we use plants. Before beginning the **Apply It activity,** explain that for centuries people have found ways to use plants. Plant-derived chemicals are natural; lab-made chemicals are synthetic. Make sure students understand that there are advantages and disadvantages to using each. Do the **Build Inquiry** to demonstrate the water retention properties of peat moss. Have students do the **Quick Lab** identifying products in the classroom that are made with plants. Students can use the online **Vocab Flash Cards** to review key terms.

EVALUATE

Have students take the **Lesson Quiz.** For an alternate assessment, see the *ExamView®* Computer Test Generator, Progress Monitoring Assessments, or SuccessTracker™.

ENGAGE AND EXPLORE

Teach this lesson using digital resources. Begin by having students learn more about plants in everyday life and explore real-world connections to the roles plants play in life at **My Planet Diary** online. Have them access the Chapter Resources to find the **Unlock the Big Question activity.** There they can answer the questions and refine their responses as they continue through the lesson. You can re-assign the activity and have students submit their work so you can track their progress.

EXPLAIN AND ELABORATE

Students reading above, at, or below the lexile measure of this lesson can access basic content readings at their level at **My Reading Web.** Encourage students to use the online **Vocab Flash Cards** to preview key terms. **Support the Big Q** by reviewing the characteristics of angiosperms and then discussing why we use plants. Assign the **Apply It activity** online and have students submit their work to you. Have students do the **Quick Lab** identifying products in the classroom that are made with plants. The **Key Concept Summaries** online allow students to read a summary and see an image associated with each part of the lesson. Online remediation is available at **My Science Coach.**

EVALUATE

Have students take the **Lesson Quiz.** For an alternate assessment, see the *ExamView®* Computer Test Generator, Progress Monitoring Assessments, or SuccessTracker™.

2 Frontload the Lesson

Have students survey the visuals in the lesson. Then have them write questions they have about the lesson based on their surveys. After students read the lesson, have them answer the questions they wrote at the start of the lesson.

3 Comprehensible Input

Challenge students to make a list of the roles plants play on Earth. Then have them add an example of a plant in each of the roles.

4 Language Production

Pair or group students with varied language abilities to complete labs collaboratively for language practice. Have each student copy the completed written lab for personal reference.

5 Assess Understanding

Have students keep a content area log for this lesson using a two-column format with the headings "What I Understand" and "What I Don't Understand." Follow up so that students can move items from the "Don't Understand" to the "Understand" column.

Lexile Measure = 860L

Plants in Everyday Life

Establish Learning Objective

After this lesson, students will be able to:

🔑 Explain how plants are important in everyday life.

Engage

Activate Prior Knowledge

MY PLANET DIARY Read *George's Blog* with the class. Have students think about the different types of plants they have learned about in the chapter. Make a list on the board. Next to each type, ask volunteers to suggest a product they think is made directly or indirectly from that plant. Then ask students to think of other ways in which plants are essential to life. List these. Ask: **What are some non-product benefits of plants?** (*Samples: oxygen, shade, habitat, soil protection, decoration*)

BIG IDEAS OF SCIENCE REFERENCE LIBRARY 📖
Have students look up the following topics: Farming, Frankenfoods.

Explore

Lab Resource: Inquiry Warm-Up

L1 FEEDING THE WORLD Students will simulate the distribution of food among the world's population, make observations about how they feel, and predict the impact of an increase in global population.

Plants in Everyday Life

🔑 **How Are Plants Important to Everyday Life?**

MY PLANET DIARY

BLOG

Posted by: George

Location: Tacoma, Washington

I never really thought much about how important trees are until my dad and I planted a plum tree in our yard. I've watched it grow over the last couple of years. The first year we didn't get any plums. The next year, we had tons of plums and they were good! This made me think more about all that we get from plants —food to eat, wood to build houses, and cotton to make clothes!

Communicate Discuss the question with a group of classmates. Then write your answer below.

Describe a plant that is important to your everyday life.

<u>Accept all reasonable answers. Sample</u>
<u>My grandfather gives my family fresh</u>
<u>tomatoes from his tomato plants in</u>
<u>the summer.</u>

▶ **PLANET DIARY** Go to **Planet Diary** to learn more about plants in everyday life.

Lab zone Do the Inquiry Warm-Up *Feeding the World.*

124 Plants

SUPPORT ALL READERS

Lexile Measure = 860L   Lexile Word Count = 699

Prior Exposure to Content: May be the first time students have encountered this topic

Academic Vocabulary: *identify, main idea, question*

Science Vocabulary: *peat*

Concept Level: Generally appropriate for most students in this grade

Preteach With: My Planet Diary "George's Blog" and Figure 1 activity

Go to **My Reading Web** to access leveled readings that provide a foundation for the content.

my science online.com

Vocabulary
- peat

Skills
- Reading: Identify the Main Idea
- Inquiry: Pose Questions

How Are Plants Important to Everyday Life?

What did you have for breakfast today? Cereal? Toast? Orange juice? Chances are you have already eaten something today that came from plants. Besides providing food, plants play many roles on Earth. **In addition to food, plants provide habitats. Plants can clean the water and protect the soil in an environment. Plants are also the base of many products important to human life, such as medicines, paper, and clothing.**

The Role of Plants in an Ecosystem Plants play many roles in an ecosystem. You can see some of these roles in Figure 1. Recall that an ecosystem contains living things and the nonliving surroundings. People are included in ecosystems too!

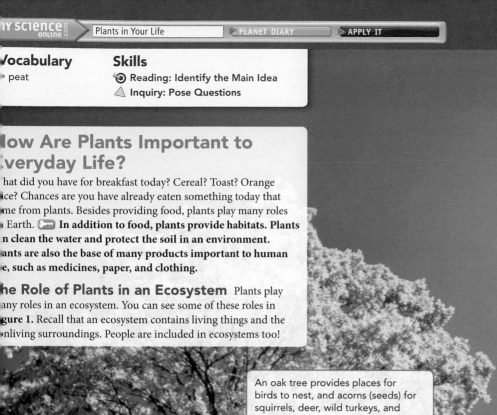

People benefit from the tree as well. It can provide shade in summer and beautiful scenery during autumn. Oak wood is a valuable resource often used to make furniture.

An oak tree provides places for birds to nest, and acorns (seeds) for squirrels, deer, wild turkeys, and other species to eat. Insects eat the leaves, bark, wood, and fungi living in the tree.

The oak's roots hold onto the soil and prevent it from being washed or blown away. The roots also quickly absorb rainwater. Without the roots, the water could flow over the land. The moving water could pick up substances that cause pollution and deposit them into rivers or drinking water supplies.

FIGURE 1 ···
The Roles of an Oak Tree
The roles of plants are often overlooked.

✎ **Identify** List at least two other roles the oak tree serves for living or nonliving things.

Sample: place for kids to climb, shelter from rain

125

---

1 Content and Language
Write the term *peat* on the board. Explain that the word comes from the Latin word *peta*, meaning "turf." Tell students that *peat* is blackish-brown material formed by layers of moss.

2 Frontload the Lesson
Encourage students to discuss plants they may eat as food, as well as the relationship between plants and clothing, paper, and other products. If necessary, remind students to consider the vital role of plants in various habitats on our planet.

3 Comprehensible Input
Encourage students to create cluster diagrams that show a variety of ways that people use plants. Remind students to consider foods, as well as clothing, medicines, and other products.

Explain ————————————————
Introduce Vocabulary
Point out the vocabulary term *peat* and ask students if they are familiar with it. If some students are, find out what they already know about the word. Emphasize the correct spelling of the word and distinguish it from its homophone, the proper name *Pete*.

Teach Key Concepts 🔑
Explain to students that plants are essential to life on Earth. Have students think about one of the characteristics of plants: they make their own food. Ask: **What is the term for organisms that make their own food?** *(Autotrophs)* **How do organisms that cannot make their own food survive?** *(By eating autotrophs or organisms that eat autotrophs)* **How would you describe this important role plants play?** *(Plants are the beginning of the food/energy chain that all organisms need in order to survive.)* Discuss some of the other ways in which plants are important to everyday life by reviewing the list of plant type and product you generated after reading *My Planet Diary*. Finally, make sure students understand the role of plants in ecosystems. **How would you summarize the contributions plants make to your life?** *(Sample: Plants provide food, clothing, medicines, building materials, paper, rubber, fuel. They provide habitats for other living things and protect the soil. Plants provide shade, recreation, hobbies, and scenery.)*

Teach With Visuals
Tell students to look at **Figure 1.** Ask: **What important gas do plants supply to the air?** *(Oxygen)* **How might animals find plants useful in providing protection from predators?** *(Through protective coloration, some animals can hide from predators by blending in with the plants in their surroundings.)* **Why might biologists and ecologists worry about the destruction of plants?** *(All of the benefits plants provide will be decreased and possibly lost if there is large-scale destruction and perhaps extinction of some plants.)*

My Planet Diary provides an opportunity for students to explore real-world connections to the roles plants play in life.

MY SCIENCE online.com | Plants in Your Life

Explain

Lead a Discussion

USING PLANTS Start the discussion by reminding students that green algae are considered plants. Tell students that agar agar (sometimes called just agar), which is made from it, is used as a culture medium to grow bacteria for study. It is also added to ice creams, puddings, and candy to thicken them and keep them from separating. Then discuss the use of moss in agriculture and gardening. Ask: **What kind of moss is used in gardening?** (*Sphagnum moss, which is also called peat moss*) **Where does this type of moss grow?** (*In a type of wetland called a bog*) Tell students that dried sphagnum moss is extremely absorbent and can absorb up to 20 percent of its weight in water. Ask: **How does this absorbency make sphagnum moss useful in agriculture?** (*It is added to soils to increase water absorption.*) **What useful products come from conifers?** (*Paper, lumber, rayon fiber, cellophane, and turpentine*) **How do people use angiosperms?** (*Food, clothing, rubber, furniture, medications*)

Identify the Main Idea Tell students that when they identify the main idea, they determine the most important, idea in a paragraph or section. The other information in the paragraph or section supports or further explains the main idea.

Support the Big Q ❓ UbD

WHY WE USE PLANTS Review the characteristics of angiosperms. Ask: **Why do people grow flowering plants?** (*Flowers have bright petals and a sweet aroma.*) **What makes lettuce, celery, and other foods used in a green salad pleasant to eat?** (*Sample: They are crisp and crunchy.*) **What characteristic of plants gives the food this texture?** (*The cells have cell walls.*) **Why do people eat carrots and beets?** (*They are nutritious because they contain stored food for the plant.*)

Elaborate

Apply It!

L1 Before beginning the activity, explain that for centuries people have found ways to use plants. Plant-derived chemicals are natural; lab-made chemicals are synthetic. Make sure students understand that there are advantages and disadvantages to using each.

△ **Pose Questions** Explain to students that when making a decision, it is helpful to gather as much information or evidence as possible. One effective way is to pose questions. If students are being asked to choose between cleaners, they should ask themselves what characteristics of a cleaner are important.

126 Plants

Identify the Main Idea In the text under the heading How People Use Plants, underline at least three plant groups and circle one product made from each.

apply it!

You are at a grocery store buying cleaning products to clean your bathroom. You can choose a cleaner made from chemicals made in a lab or one made from plant-derived chemicals.

❶ **Pose Questions** What questions should you ask before making your decision?

Sample: Which cleaner works better? Which cleaner releases fewer fumes? Which cleaner is safer to use around pets? Which cleaner is better for the environment?

❷ **CHALLENGE** What could be some disadvantages of the plant-based cleaner?

Sample: It may not work as well or it may be more expensive. It may not kill germs or it may contain some harmful chemicals even if it is plant based.

126 Plants

How People Use Plants People have found ways to directly use almost all plants. Green algae is often used in scientif research and as a thickening agent in some foods. Liverworts, clu mosses, and other plants are used in parts of the world to treat conditions from fevers to itchy skin.

Many people use moss in agriculture and gardening. The moss that gardeners use contains sphagnum (SFAG num) moss. Sphagnum moss grows in a type of wetland called a bog. The still water in a bog is so acidic that decomposers cannot live in the water. When the plants die, they do not decay. Instead, the dead plants accumulate at the bottom of the bog. Over time, the mosse become compressed into layers and form a blackish-brown materi called **peat.** In some parts of Europe and Asia, people use peat as fuel to heat homes and to cook food.

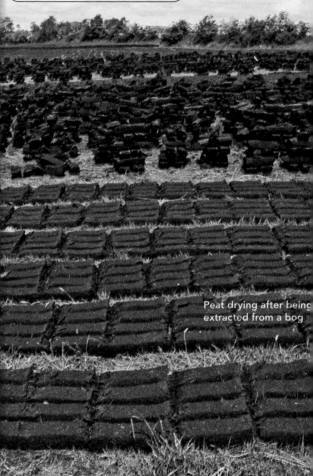

Peat drying after being extracted from a bog

Digital Lesson: Assign the *Apply It* activity online and have students submit their work to you.

my science online.com | **Plants in Your Life**

Gymnosperms provide many useful products. (paper and the lumber) used to build homes come from conifers. The (rayon fibers) in clothes as well the (cellophane wrappers) on some food also come from conifers. (Turpentine and the rosin) used by baseball pitchers, gymnasts, and musicians are made from conifer sap.

Angiosperms are an important source of (food, clothing, and medicine.) People eat a variety of vegetables, fruits, and cereals, all of which are angiosperms. The seeds of cotton plants are covered with cotton fibers. The stems of flax plants provide (linen fibers.) The sap of rubber trees is used to make (rubber for tires and other products.) (Furniture) is often made from the wood maple, cherry, and oak trees. Some important medications come from angiosperms, too. For example, the heart medication (digitalis) comes from the leaves of the foxglove plant.

FIGURE 2 ....

Plants in Your Life
You may not have realized how many things, like clothes and sports equipment, are made of plants!

✏️ **Name** List at least five things in your everyday life that come from plants.

Sample: cereal, cotton clothes, house made of wood, fruits and vegetables, grains, wood furniture, grass on athletic fields, paper

 Do the Quick Lab *Everyday Plants.*

🔲 Assess Your Understanding

1. List Give two uses of moss.
Sample: landscaping, fuel

b. Describe Why is conifer sap important?
The sap is used in products used by athletes and musicians.

c. Make Judgments Should governments spend more money on plant research than they currently do? Why?
Accept all reasonable answers. Sample: Yes; scientists could find important cures for diseases or other products that could help people or animals.

got it? ....

○ **I get it!** Now I know that plants provide many useful things, such as _Sample: food, habitats, clean water, soil protection, and products like paper and medicines._

○ **I need extra help with** _See TE note._

Go to **MY SCIENCE 🅢 COACH** online for help with this subject.

127

Differentiated Instruction

L1 The Importance of Plants Have students summarize the ways in which plants are important to everyday life by creating a T-chart that lists the five categories of plants (green algae, mosses, ferns, gymnosperms, angiosperms) in one column and at least two uses of each type of plant in the other column.

L3 Plant Treasure The ice-bound Norwegian island of Spitsbergen, about 1,300 kilometers from the North Pole, is the site of the Global Seed Vault. Here, in a vault built deep in a mountainside and protected by thick concrete walls and huge steel doors, will reside millions of seeds. Have students research this facility to find out the details of its conception, construction, and use. Have students explain the importance of the treasure stored in this unusual "bank."

Build Inquiry **Lab** zone

L1 HOW MUCH WATER?
Materials small samples of dry sphagnum (peat) moss, beaker of water, large dry beaker, balance or scale

Time 20 minutes

Have students determine the mass of the dry beaker. Then have them add the sample of sphagnum moss to the beaker and determine the mass of both. Tell students to use these values to calculate the mass of their moss sample. Have students pour a large amount of water into the beaker containing the moss and let it remain for 15 minutes. Then have them pour any excess water out of the beaker, making sure the moss remains inside. Have them determine the mass of the beaker and moss now.

Ask: **What happened to the mass of the moss?** *(It increased appreciably.)* **How large was the increase?** *(Answers will depend on the amount of sample used, the time period, and how careful students were to pour off excess water.)* **If you were planting a garden in sandy soil, what would you add to the soil? Why?** *(Adding peat moss would increase the absorbency of sand, which is not a very absorbent soil.)*

Lab Resource: Quick Lab **Lab** zone

L1 EVERYDAY PLANTS Students will identify products in the classroom that are made with plant materials.

Evaluate ─────────
Assess Your Understanding

After students answer the questions, have them evaluate their understanding by completing the appropriate sentence.

R T I Response to Intervention

1a. If students cannot list uses of mosses, **then** remind them of the characteristics of mosses and discuss the formation of peat.

b. If students need help identifying the importance of conifer sap, **then** remind them that rosin is made from it.

c. If students have trouble making a judgment, **then** have them work in pairs to identify the current uses of plants and how plants might be beneficial in the future.

MY SCIENCE 🅢 COACH Have students go online for help in understanding how people use plants.

Lab zone After the Inquiry Warm-Up

Plants in Everyday Life

Inquiry Warm-Up, *Feeding the World*

In the Inquiry Warm-Up, you used a model to investigate how different countries' economic conditions affect food distribution worldwide and predicted the impact of an increase in global population on the world's food supply. Using what you learned from that activity, answer the questions below.

1. **CALCULATE** What fraction of students in the class represented wealthy countries? Poor countries?

    _____

    _____

2. **OBSERVE** About what fraction of the total amount of food distributed went to the students representing wealthy countries? To the students representing poor countries?

    _____

3. **GRAPH** Draw a circle graph that shows about how much of the food distributed in class went to wealthy countries, middle-income countries, and poor countries.

4. **COMPARE AND CONTRAST** How did the amount of food received by each student representing a poor country compare to the amount of food received by each student representing a wealthy country?

    _____

    _____

Name _____ Date _____ Class _____

Plants in Everyday Life

How Are Plants Important to Everyday Life?

1a. **LIST** Give two uses of moss. _____

_____

b. **DESCRIBE** Why is conifer sap important? _____

_____

c. **MAKE JUDGMENTS** Should governments spend more

money on plant research than they currently do? Why? _____

_____

_____

_____

got⎵it? ·

○ **I get it!** Now I know that plants provide many useful things, such as _____

_____

_____

○ **I need extra help with** _____

_____

Key Concept Summary

Plants in Everyday Life

How Are Plants Important to Everyday Life?

Plants play many roles on Earth. **In addition to food, plants provide habitats. Plants can clean the water and protect the soil in an environment. Plants are also the base of many products important to human life, such as medicines, paper, and clothing.**

Plants play many roles in an ecosystem. Plants provide food and shelter for animals and fungi. The roots of plants hold onto soil and prevent it from washing away. They also quickly absorb water, which can help prevent flooding and water pollution. Plants provide people with shade in summer and beautiful scenery in autumn. They also provide us with materials that are used to make many essential products.

People have found ways to directly use almost all plants. Green algae is often used in scientific research and as a thickening agent in some foods. Moss is used in agriculture and gardening. Sphagnum moss grows in a type of wetland called a bog. Over time, dead moss falls to the bottom of the bog and gets

compressed into layers. It forms a blackish-brown material called **peat** that is used in some parts of Europe and Asia as a fuel to heat homes and cook food.

Gymnosperms provide many useful products. Paper and lumber come from conifers, as do rayon fibers in clothes and cellophane. Turpentine and the rosin used by baseball pitchers, gymnasts, and musicians are made from conifer sap.

Angiosperms are an important source of food, clothing, and medicines. People eat a variety of vegetables, fruits, and cereals. The seeds of cotton plants and the stems of flax plants provide fibers that are made into fabric. The sap of rubber trees is used to make rubber for tires. Furniture is often made from the wood of maple, cherry, and oak trees. Some important medicines come from angiosperms, too. For example, the heart medication, digitalis, comes from the leaves of the foxglove plant.

On a separate sheet of paper, describe the various roles a single tree may play in its ecosystem and in the everyday lives of humans.

Name ______________________ Date ____________ Class ____________

Review and Reinforce

Plants in Everyday Life

Understanding Main Ideas

Answer the following questions in the spaces provided.

1. What are the roles plants play in an ecosystem?

2. What are some of the uses of angiosperms? Give specific examples.

3. How is peat formed?

Building Vocabulary

Write a definition for the term on the lines below.

4. peat

Place the outside corner, the corner away from the dotted line, in the corner of your copy machine to copy onto letter-size paper.

Enrich

Plants in Everyday Life

> Read the passage and study the diagram below. Then use a separate sheet of paper to answer the questions that follow.

Hydroponics

Hydroponics is the science of growing plants without soil. A solution of nutrients is used in place of the soil. Plants can be grown by hydroponics either outdoors or indoors. The following figure shows how a plant can be grown without soil.

There are some advantages to using hydroponics to grow plants.

- **FASTER GROWTH**
  Hydroponics works by automatically getting the nutrients and water to the plant's roots. Plants get what they need continuously, so they don't waste a time growing a lot of roots to search for nutrients.

- **NO WEEDS**
  Gardening without soil means that you don't have to worry about weeds.

- **NO PESTS**
  Because most pests live in the soil, you won't have to use any pesticides or other toxic chemicals.

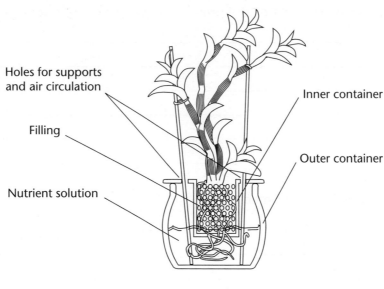

The major disadvantage of hydroponics is that it is costly.

1. What do you think is the purpose of the filling?
2. Will the nutrient solution have to be replaced from time to time? Explain your answer.
3. If plants are grown indoors using hydroponics, what else must be provided for the plants' needs besides the nutrient solution?
4. Do you think hydroponics would be a good method to grow food during long space flights? Explain your answer.
5. Since you don't need weed sprays or pesticides, what do you think makes hydroponics costly?

Lesson Quiz

Plants in Everyday Life

Write the letter of the correct answer on the line at the left.

1. ___ Which of the following products is **NOT** made from angiosperms?

   A   furniture

   B   turpentine

   C   medicine

   D   clothing

2. ___ Plants play a role in the environment by

   A   preventing soil from washing away

   B   providing habitats for animals

   C   providing food for animals

   D   all of the above

3. ___ The moss from which peat is made is

   A   rosin

   B   sphagnum

   C   liverwort

   D   foxglove

4. ___ The rosin that is used by athletes and musicians come from the sap of

   A   conifers

   B   angiosperms

   C   oak trees

   D   acorns

Fill in the blank to complete each statement.

5. Sphagnum moss grows in a type of wetland called a(n) _____.

6. If plant roots did not absorb water, the water could flow over the land picking up substances that might _____ rivers or drinking water supplies.

7. _____ is often used as a thickening agent in foods.

8. Turpentine is made from _____ sap.

9. The stems of flax plants provide fibers that can be spun and woven into the fabric _____.

10. In parts of Europe and Asia, people use _____ as a fuel to heat homes and cook food.

Plants in Everyday Life

Answer Key

After the Inquiry Warm-Up

1. Answers will vary depending on number of students and number of #1 tags and #3 tags distributed.

2. about one third; about one third

3. Students should show that about one third of the food distributed went to each group.

4. Each student representing a poor country received much less food than each student representing a wealthy country.

Key Concept Summary

Sample: A tree may provide food and shelter for animals and fungi. Its roots prevent erosion by holding soil in place. Because a tree absorbs water from the soil, it can help prevent flooding and water pollution. A tree can provide humans with shade in summer and beautiful scenery in autumn. It can also provide us with materials that are used to make products we use everyday, such as wood to build homes and make furniture, fibers to make fabric, and wood pulp to make paper.

Review and Reinforce

1. Plants provide food and shelter to many animals and other organisms. By absorbing rainwater they prevent flooding and pollution. Plant roots also prevent erosion by holding soil in place. Plants provide materials that are used to make many products people use.

2. Angiosperms are a source of food, clothing, building materials, and medicine. They provide all of the fruits, vegetables, and grains that people eat. The seeds of cotton plants provide cotton fibers used to make clothing. The sap of rubber trees is used to make rubber for tires. The wood of maple, cherry, and oak trees is used for furniture. The leaves of the foxglove plant are the source of the heart medication digitalis.

3. Peat is formed when sphagnum moss builds up in bogs. The water in a bog is very acidic, so decomposers cannot live in it. Thus, when the moss plants die, they do not decay but rather accumulate at the bottom of the bog. Over time, the mosses become compressed into layers and form a blackish-brown material called peat.

4. a blackish-brown material formed by the compression of layers of dead sphagnum moss in bogs over time, used as a fuel

Enrich

1. The filling is used to support the roots of the plants.

2. Yes, because the plant will eventually use up all the nutrients in the solution.

3. Plants must also be provided with appropriate amounts of light.

4. Answers may vary. Sample: Yes, because plants will grow faster, saving scarce room on the ship, pesticides will not be needed, and carrying heavy soil can be avoided.

5. Answers may vary. Sample: Special containers and supports must be purchased for the plants. Also plants grown with hydroponics might need more care to keep the water and nutrient level right.

Lesson Quiz

1. B		**2.** D	
3. B		**4.** A	
5. bog		**6.** pollute	
7. Green algae		**8.** conifer	
9. linen		**10.** peat	

Place the outside corner, the corner away from the dotted line, in the corner of your copy machine to copy onto letter-size paper.

CHAPTER 3

Study Guide

Review the Big Q

Have students complete the statement at the top of the page. These Key Concepts support their understanding of the chapter's Big Question. Have students return to the chapter opener pages. What is different about how students view the image of baobab trees now that they have completed the chapter? Thinking about this will help them prepare for the *Apply the Big Q* activity in the Review and Assessment.

Partner Review

Have partners review definitions of vocabulary terms by using the Study Guide to quiz each other. Students could read the Key Concept statements and leave out words for their partner to fill in, or change a statement so that it is false and then ask their partner to correct it.

Class Activity: Concept Map

Divide the class into two groups and instruct each group to organize the information they have learned about plants in a concept map. Provide large sheets of paper to accommodate the maps. Encourage students to make their maps colorful and visual, using drawings, photos, and actual plant parts whenever appropriate. Remind students that a concept map organizes and connects ideas, so the information does not have to be treated in order of appearance in the chapter. Display the completed maps and discuss with the class the accuracy, usefulness, and attractiveness of each. Have students keep the following questions in mind as they develop their concept maps:

- What are the characteristics of nearly all plants?
- What do plants need to survive on land?
- How are plants classified?
- What are the functions of plant roots, stems, leaves, seeds, and flowers?
- What are the stages in a plant's life cycle?
- How do plants respond to conditions in their environment?

My Science Coach allows students to complete the *Practice Test* online.

The Big Question allows students to complete the *Apply the Big Q* activity about the characteristics of plants.

Vocab Flash Cards offer a way to review the chapter vocabulary words.

my science online.com | Plants

CHAPTER 3 Study Guide

Nearly all plants have cells surrounded by <u>cell walls</u>, are <u>autotrophs</u> that photosynthesize, and are made of many cells.

LESSON 1 What Is a Plant?

Nearly all plants are autotrophs and contain many cells surrounded by cell walls.

For plants to survive on land, they must have ways to obtain water and nutrients, retain water, support their bodies, transport materials and reproduce.

Vocabulary
- chlorophyll
- photosynthesis • tissue
- chloroplast • vacuole
- cuticle • vascular tissue

LESSON 2 Classifying Plants

Nonvascular plants are low-growing, have thin cell walls, and do not have roots.

Seedless vascular plants have vascular tissue and produce spores.

Seed plants have vascular tissue and seeds.

Vocabulary
- nonvascular plant • rhizoid • vascular plant
- phloem • xylem • frond • pollen • seed
- gymnosperm • angiosperm
- cotyledon • monocot • dicot

LESSON 3 Plant Structures

A plant's roots, stems, and leaves anchor the plant, absorb water and minerals, capture the sun's energy, and make food.

A seed contains a partially developed plant.

A typical flower contains sepals, petals, stamens, and pistils.

Vocabulary
- root cap • cambium • stoma • transpiration
- embryo • germination • flower • pollination
- sepal • petal • stamen • pistil • ovary

LESSON 4 Plant Reproduction

Plants have complex life cycles that include a sporophyte stage and a gametophyte stage.

All plants undergo sexual reproduction that involves fertilization.

Vocabulary
- sporophyte • gametophyte • annual • biennial
- perennial • fertilization • zygote • cone
- ovule • fruit

LESSON 5 Plant Responses and Growth

Plants show growth responses, or tropisms, toward touch, gravity, and light.

The amount of darkness a plant receives determines the time of flowering in many plants. Dormancy helps plants survive winter.

Vocabulary
- tropism • hormone • auxin • photoperiodism
- critical night length • short-day plant
- long-day plant • day-neutral plant • dormancy

LESSON 6 Plants in Everyday Life

In addition to food, plants provide habitats, clean water, and protect soil. Plants are also the base of many products, including medicine, paper, and clothing.

Vocabulary
- peat

128 Plants

E L L Support

4 Language Production

Divide the class into six groups and do a Gallery Walk to review the material from each lesson. Post six large sheets of paper or poster board with the essential questions from each lesson at the top of each sheet. Position each group at one poster. Have them write down all they have learned that responds to the questions. Then have them rotate to the next poster to add information until all groups have worked with all posters.

Beginning

LOW/HIGH Allow students to answer with drawings, single words, or short phrases.

Intermediate

LOW/HIGH Have students draft sentences to answer the questions.

Advanced

LOW/HIGH Have students assist and/or edit the work of classmates with lower language proficiency.

Review and Assessment

LESSON 1 What Is a Plant?

1. In which cellular structure do plants store water and other substances?

a. cuticle   **(b.)** vacuole

c. cell wall   **d.** chloroplast

2. The pigment <u>chlorophyll</u> is found in chloroplasts.

3. Make Generalizations Complete the table below to describe plant adaptions for life on land.

Structure	Function
Roots	Helps obtain water and nutrients
Cuticle	<u>Helps prevent water loss</u>
Vascular tissue	<u>Helps move water and food, gives support</u>

LESSON 2 Classifying Plants

4. Which of the following are seedless vascular plants?

(a.) ferns   **b.** liverworts

c. gymnosperms   **d.** angiosperms

5. Nonvascular plants have rootlike structures called <u>rhizoids.</u>

6. Compare and Contrast How are gymnosperms and angiosperms alike and different?

<u>Sample: Both gymnosperms and angiosperms have vascular tissue. They use pollen or seeds to reproduce. Gymnosperms produce naked seeds while angiosperms produce flowers, seeds, and fruits.</u>

LESSON 3 Plant Structures

7. A plant absorbs water and minerals through

(a.) roots.   **b.** stems.

c. leaves.   **d.** stomata.

8. Transpiration slows down when <u>stomata</u> are closed.

9. Relate Cause and Effect When a strip of bark is removed all the way around the trunk of a tree, the tree dies. Explain why.

<u>Sample: Cutting the bark cuts off the phloem. The tree would not transport food.</u>

10. Write About It Plant structures do not look the same among all plants. For example, some leaves are short and others long. Explain why you think there is so much variation.

See TE rubric.

LESSON 4 Plant Reproduction

11. A zygote is the direct result of

a. pollination.

(b.) fertilization.

c. biennial growth.

d. the sporophyte stage.

12. <u>Annuals</u> complete their life cycles within one growing season.

13. Sequence Describe the major events in the plant life cycle. Use the terms *zygote, sperm, sporophyte, spores, gametophyte,* and *egg.*

<u>Sample: Sperm fertilizes an egg. The resulting zygote develops into a sporophyte, which creates spores. Spores develop into a gametophyte that creates sperm and eggs.</u>

129

Review and Assessment

Assess Understanding

Have students complete the answers to the Review and Assessment questions. Have a class discussion about what students find confusing. Write Key Concepts on the board to reinforce knowledge.

R T I Response to Intervention

3. If students need help describing plant adaptations for life on land, **then** review the functions water served for water-dwelling plants and have students focus on those.

4. If students have trouble identifying the various categories of plants, **then** review the material by creating a T-chart with the classifications in one column and members in the other.

8. If students need help relating the condition of stomata to the process of transpiration, **then** review the structure and function of stomata and how the process of transpiration takes place.

12. If students have difficulty classifying angiosperms that complete their life cycle in one growing season, **then** ask students what the term *annual* means and how that meaning applies to angiosperm classification.

Alternate Assessment

L1 DESIGN A GAME Have students work in small groups to design a game about plants. Students can design a board game that requires players to answer questions in order to advance. Remind students to create rules, spinners, game pieces, and questions for their games. The questions for the game should include vocabulary terms and Key Concepts from the chapter. Students can exchange games or play their own game against other groups.

Write About It	Assess student's writing using this rubric.			
SCORING RUBRIC	**SCORE 4**	**SCORE 3**	**SCORE 2**	**SCORE 1**
Explain the variation in plant parts among all plants.	Explanation is an accurate presentation of plant adaptations to different environments that result in variations in structures.	Explanation includes idea of plants' adaptations to their environments but provides no details.	Explanation includes idea that plants grow in different places but does not refer to adaptation to environment.	Explanation includes inaccurate information and is incomplete.

Review and Assessment, Cont.

RTI Response to Intervention

16. If students need help predicting when a short-day plant will flower based on its critical night length, **then** remind them that the length is the minimum, or least, amount of darkness required.

Apply the Big Q

TRANSFER Students should be able to demonstrate understanding of the characteristics by which plants can be recognized by answering this question. See the scoring rubric below.

Connect to the Big Idea

BIG IDEA: Living things are alike yet different.

Send students back to the Big Ideas of Science at the beginning of their student edition. Have them read what they wrote about the similarities and differences among living things before they started the chapter. Lead a class discussion about how their thoughts have changed. If all chapters have been completed, have students fill in the bottom section for the Big Idea.

L3 WRITING IN SCIENCE Ask students to write a television interview with a botanist that explains to viewers what makes a plant a plant. The interview should cover how plants are classified, plant structures, plant reproduction, how plants grow and respond to their environments, and the uses of plants in everyday life.

CHAPTER 3 Review and Assessment

LESSON 5 Plant Responses and Growth

14. A plant's response to gravity is an example of a
- **a.** dormancy.
- **b.** hormone.
- **(c.)** tropism.
- **d.** critical night length.

15. The plant hormone __auxin__ affects the rate of cell growth.

16. Predict A particular short-day plant has a critical night length of 15 hours. Fill in the chart below to predict when this plant would flower.

Day Length	Night Length	Will It Flower?
9 h	15 h	Yes
10 h	14 h	No
7.5 h	16.5 h	Yes

17. Develop Hypotheses Suppose climate change alters the environment of an oak tree from one with cold and snowy winters to one with warmer winters. Will the tree still go into a state of dormancy? Explain.

Sample: Even if the climate changes, the tree may not be able to change at the same rate. The oak may still go into dormancy with warmer weather.

LESSON 6 Plants in Everyday Life

18. Which of the following is *not* a way that people use plants?
- **a.** for food
- **b.** for clothing
- **c.** for medicines
- **(d.)** for metal extracts

19. Over time, mosses may compact into _peat._

20. Make Judgments Should the government put as much effort into protecting plants as they do animals? Why or why not?

Sample: Yes; I think the government should protect plants as much as animals. We get so many things from plants that we would face many problems without them.

 How do you know a plant when you see it?

21. Plants are all around us. Describe a plant that you see often and then explain what makes it a plant.

Sample: A big tree grows outside of my school. The tree has many cells that have cell walls. The tree also makes its own food through photosynthesis. It responds to things like the seasons by dropping its leaves.
See TE rubric.

How do you know a plant when you see it?
Assess student's response using this rubric.

SCORING RUBRIC	SCORE 4	SCORE 3	SCORE 2	SCORE 1
Identify the characteristics that make a familiar tree a plant.	Student can identify four characteristics that make a familiar tree a plant.	Student can identify three characteristics that make a familiar tree a plant.	Student can identify two characteristics that make a familiar tree a plant.	Student can identify a familiar tree but cannot identify what makes it a plant.

Standardized Test Prep

Multiple Choice

Circle the letter of the best answer.

1. The diagram below shows the parts of a flower. In which flower part does pollination take place?

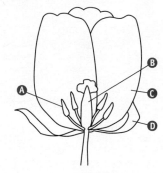

   A   part A
   B   part B
   C   part C
   D   part D

2. You examine plant cells under a microscope and notice many round, green structures within the cells. The structures are most likely

   A   tissues.
   B   vacuoles.
   C   cell walls.
   D   chloroplasts.

3. Most gymnosperms produce _____, while most angiosperms produce _____.

   A   sperm, eggs
   B   pollen, cones
   C   cones, flowers
   D   flowers, fruits

4. What kind of tropism do roots display when they grow downward into the soil?

   A   gravitropism
   B   phototropism
   C   thigmotropism
   D   photoperiodism

5. The vegetables, fruits, and cereals that people eat all come from

   A   peat.
   B   angiosperms.
   C   moss.
   D   nonvascular plants.

Constructed Response

Use the diagrams below to help you answer Question 6. Write your answer on a separate piece of paper.

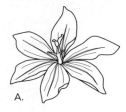   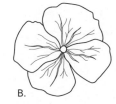

A.   B.

6. Which of the plants above is a monocot? Which is a dicot? Explain your answers.
   See TE note.

Standardized Test Prep

Test-Taking Skills

INTERPRETING A DIAGRAM Tell students that this question involves two steps. The first step is to identify where pollination takes place in a flower. The second step is to find that structure on the diagram and choose its letter as the answer. Pollination is the transfer of pollen from an anther to the stigma of a pistil. Thus Choice **B** is correct. Choice **A** is the anther, where pollen is made. Choice **C** is a petal, which helps attract insects. Choice **D** is a sepal, which protects the flower bud.

Constructed Response

6. Flower A is a monocot and flower B is a dicot. Flower A is a monocot because it has six petals and six is a multiple of three. Flower A also has parallel veins. Flower B is a dicot because it has four petals and branching veins.

Additional Assessment Resources

Chapter Test
ExamView® Computer Test Generator
Performance Assessment
Progress Monitoring Assessments
SuccessTracker™

CHAPTER 3

E L L Support

5 Assess Understanding

Have ELL students complete the Alternate Assessment. Provide guidelines on the information it must cover, and a rubric for assessment. You may have them complete the activity in small groups of varying language proficiencies.

Beginning

LOW/HIGH Allow students to work on designing the game board and pieces.

Intermediate

LOW/HIGH Allow students to write the questions and answers.

Advanced

LOW/HIGH Allow students to write the instructions for playing and scoring the game.

Remediate If students have trouble with...

QUESTION	SEE LESSON	STANDARDS
1	3	
2	1	
3	4	
4	5	
5	6	
6	2	

Science Matters

Everyday Science

Have students read *Grains of Evidence*. Explain that the study of pollen as it relates to forensics is called *forensic palynology*. One interesting idea proposed by forensic palynologists is adding pollen to bullets, making it easier to trace their origin.

Tell students that the essential characteristics of pollen make it very useful in forensics. Its microscopic size and abundance mean that some kind of pollen is found almost everywhere and that it can be found on any object no matter how small. Pollen is very resistant to degradation, meaning the pollen in older pieces of evidence will not have broken down. The structure of each kind of pollen is complex, making it easy to identify which plant the pollen came from.

Tell students that one of the first criminal investigations which used forensic botany was a famous case. In 1932, the son of world-famous aviator Charles Lindbergh was kidnapped from his home. A homemade ladder was found at the crime scene. Dr. Arthur Koehler testified about the wood the ladder was made from, proving it was the same as wood planks in the main suspect's attic. This evidence led to the conviction of Bruno Hauptmann for the kidnapping of Charles Lindbergh, Jr.

As students write about how investigators might use plant evidence, have them list all the plant matter they come in contact with in a day and how that could be helpful.

Ask: **How does pollen on a suspect's clothing help investigators?** *(They can tell whether a suspect was in contact with a plant that was at the crime scene.)* **What might be one drawback of forensic palynology?** *(Sample: Some plants are very common.)*

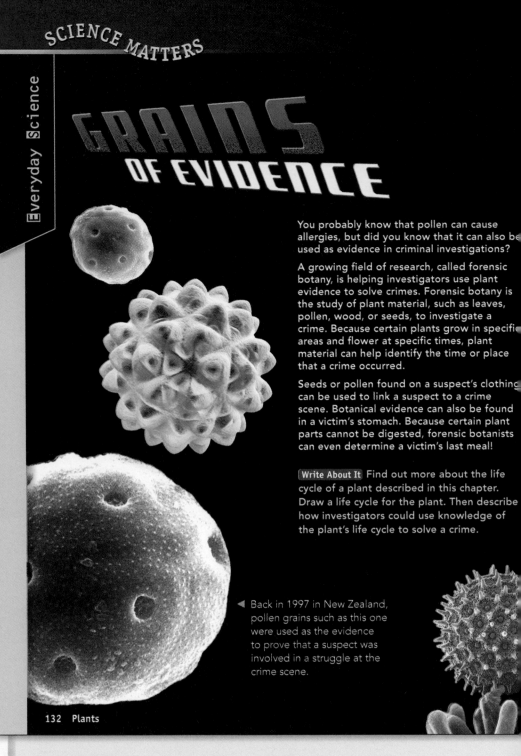

GRAINS OF EVIDENCE

You probably know that pollen can cause allergies, but did you know that it can also be used as evidence in criminal investigations?

A growing field of research, called forensic botany, is helping investigators use plant evidence to solve crimes. Forensic botany is the study of plant material, such as leaves, pollen, wood, or seeds, to investigate a crime. Because certain plants grow in specific areas and flower at specific times, plant material can help identify the time or place that a crime occurred.

Seeds or pollen found on a suspect's clothing can be used to link a suspect to a crime scene. Botanical evidence can also be found in a victim's stomach. Because certain plant parts cannot be digested, forensic botanists can even determine a victim's last meal!

Write About It Find out more about the life cycle of a plant described in this chapter. Draw a life cycle for the plant. Then describe how investigators could use knowledge of the plant's life cycle to solve a crime.

◄ Back in 1997 in New Zealand, pollen grains such as this one were used as the evidence to prove that a suspect was involved in a struggle at the crime scene.

132   Plants

Quick Facts

Forensic botany is a small part of a much larger field called *forensic science*. In general, this term is applied when science can be used to help solve a crime. DNA fingerprinting is one kind of forensic science. Computer or clay reconstruction can help forensic scientists learn the identity of a recently discovered victim of an older crime. Biology and anatomy are useful in determining cause of death during an autopsy. Forensic anthropology is used to determined the identity of skeletal remains. Chemistry is useful in toxicology, where scientists learn what kind of drugs may have been used to commit a crime. In crimes of theft, computer forensics are useful in tracing stolen items. Have students research forensic science and write a paragraph about a job in that field that interests them.

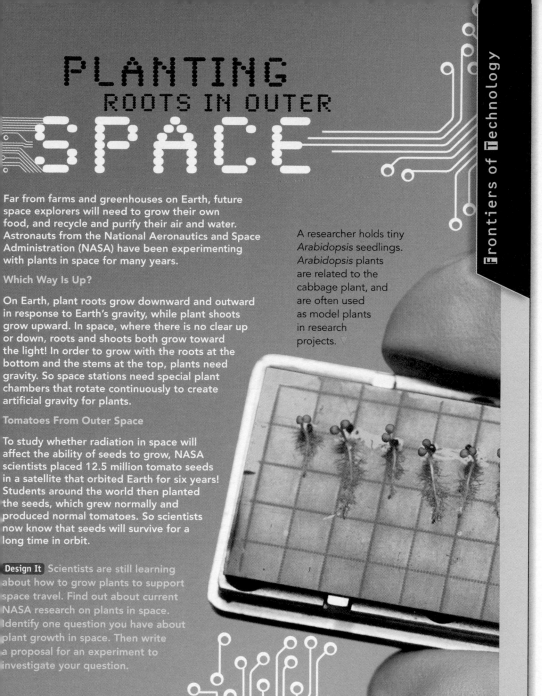

PLANTING
ROOTS IN OUTER
SPACE

Far from farms and greenhouses on Earth, future space explorers will need to grow their own food, and recycle and purify their air and water. Astronauts from the National Aeronautics and Space Administration (NASA) have been experimenting with plants in space for many years.

Which Way Is Up?

On Earth, plant roots grow downward and outward in response to Earth's gravity, while plant shoots grow upward. In space, where there is no clear up or down, roots and shoots both grow toward the light! In order to grow with the roots at the bottom and the stems at the top, plants need gravity. So space stations need special plant chambers that rotate continuously to create artificial gravity for plants.

Tomatoes From Outer Space

To study whether radiation in space will affect the ability of seeds to grow, NASA scientists placed 12.5 million tomato seeds in a satellite that orbited Earth for six years! Students around the world then planted the seeds, which grew normally and produced normal tomatoes. So scientists now know that seeds will survive for a long time in orbit.

Design It Scientists are still learning about how to grow plants to support space travel. Find out about current NASA research on plants in space. Identify one question you have about plant growth in space. Then write a proposal for an experiment to investigate your question.

A researcher holds tiny *Arabidopsis* seedlings. *Arabidopsis* plants are related to the cabbage plant, and are often used as model plants in research projects.

133

Frontiers of Technology

Have students read *Planting Roots in Outer Space*. Explain that one reason these NASA experiments are conducted is so that astronauts can find ways to sustain themselves on extended space voyages. Astronauts bring food with them when they travel into space, but those supplies are limited. Astronauts will be able to stay in space longer and travel farther from Earth if they can grow their own food and do not need to be re-supplied periodically.

Ask students what plants need to grow. Then ask them how they think the plants get those things in space. Tell students that plants are supplied with water that is recycled from other uses aboard a space shuttle or the International Space Station (ISS). Scientists have also built energy-efficient LED lights. For space greenhouses, scientists only supply light in frequencies that plants use to help them grow. No energy is wasted by using these lights. Explain that human waste can be broken down by microbes in bioreactors and then given to the plants to supply valuable nutrients.

Tell students that the best plants to grow in space will be compact, grow well under low light, and have a strong chance of providing a healthy crop with as many edible parts as possible. Scientists are working to identify types of wheat, rice, lettuce, potatoes, and other plants that best meet these criteria.

Ask: **Why do plants need artificial gravity?** *(to get the most growth from the shoots)* **Why would it be helpful to know whether seeds will survive long periods in orbit?** *(Astronauts may need to travel great distances to reach a planet where plants can grow.)*

Introduction To Animals

Introduce the Big Q ? UbD

Have students look at the image and read the Engaging Question and description. Ask the students to infer how the plant and the insect are different. After students have shared their answers, point out that life on Earth displays an amazing amount of variety. Ask: **What do the plant and the insect have in common?** *(They are both green.)* **How are they different?** *(Students might suggest that the insect has legs so it can move. The plant is anchored in one place.)* **Which of these living things makes its own food?** *(Students may know that the plant makes its own food.)*

Untamed Science Video

EATING LIKE AN ANIMAL Before viewing, invite students to discuss what they know about the ways in which some animals have adapted to their environments. Then play the video. Lead a class discussion and make a list of questions that this video raises. You may wish to have students view the video again after they have completed the chapter to see if their questions have been answered.

> **To access the online resources for this chapter, search on or navigate to** *Introduction to Animals.*
>
> **Untamed Science Video** explores animal adaptations.
>
> **The Big Question** allows students to answer the Engaging Question about how the insect and the plant are different.

MY SCIENCE ONLINE.com | Introduction to Animals

HOW ARE THESE TWO LIVING THINGS DIFFERENT?

THE BIG ?

How do you know an animal when you see it?

These living things look alike and are both green. Each needs water and energy to grow. Yet one makes food, and the other has to find food.

Infer What is different about these living things?

One living thing looks like an animal because it has eyes and legs. The other living thing looks like plant leaves.

> **UNTAMED SCIENCE** Watch the **Untamed Science** video to learn more about animals.

Professional Development Note — From the Author

Our planet is home to an amazing array of living things. Animals are just one of the kingdoms in Domain Eukarya. There are nearly 4,600 species of mammals, 6,400 amphibians, 8,250 reptiles, 9,700 birds, 26,000 crustaceans, 20,000 fish, and an estimated four to six million insects living today. However large the number of animal species may be, many are under the threat of extinction owing to poaching of wildlife, overfishing of the oceans, destruction of habitat, and climate change. Once these animals are extinct, they are gone forever. We should think about how we can stop this from happening.

✐ *Don Buckley*

Introduction to Animals

Chapter at a Glance

CHAPTER PACING: 7–12 periods or $3\frac{1}{2}$–6 blocks

INTRODUCE THE CHAPTER: Use the Engaging Question and the opening image to get students thinking about how animals are alike and different. Activate prior knowledge and preteach vocabulary using the Getting Started pages.

Lesson 1: What Is an Animal?

Lesson 2: Animal Body Plans

Lesson 3: Introduction to Invertebrates

Lesson 4: Introduction to Vertebrates

Lesson 5: Vertebrate Diversity

ASSESSMENT OPTIONS: Chapter Test, *ExamView*® Computer Test Generator, Performance Assessment, Progress Monitoring Assessments, SuccessTracker™

Preference Navigator, in the online Planning tools, allows you to customize *Interactive Science* to your own teaching style. You can also edit lesson plans by selecting the Lesson Planner option.

Digital Teacher's Edition allows you to access your Teacher's Edition and Resource online.

my science online.com

Differentiated Instruction

L1 Look for Animals Ask students to keep a record for one full day of any animals they may see. Students can include descriptions or drawings if they do not know the names of the animals. Revisit the list after completing the chapter to add animals or delete items from the list.

L3 Animal Biomes Ask students to choose a biome, such as the rain forest, desert, or tundra. Have them research the animals that live in that biome. Then have students combine their efforts to create a display that shows animals in each biome. Revisit the display throughout the chapter to consider how adaptations help the animals survive in each environment.

Getting Started

Check Your Understanding

This activity assesses students' understanding of what living things need to survive. After students have shared their answers, point out that all living things have certain basic needs. The way they meet those needs might vary, however. For example, an insect might eat a plant leaf and a lion might eat a zebra. Both living things have the basic need for food, but what they eat is very different.

Preteach Vocabulary Skills

Explain to students that learning about prefixes can make it easier to learn new vocabulary words. Point out that a prefix changes the overall meaning of the base word to which it is added. Tell students that the prefix *uni-* means "one," the prefix *di-* means "two," and the prefix *tri-* means "three." Challenge students to think of words with these prefixes, such as *unicycle, bicycle,* and *tricycle.* Discuss how the prefix changes the meaning of the word.

---

4 Getting Started

Check Your Understanding

1. **Background** Read the paragraph below and then answer the question.

Mei's birthday present is a bird. She knows that to **survive,** an **organism** needs food, water, and oxygen. So at home she chooses a stable **environment** in a warm place, away from drafts. Here, she sets up a cage with dishes for food and paper for waste removal. Under Mei's care, her bird will have what it needs to live and grow.

To **survive** is to manage to stay alive, especially in difficult situations.

An **organism** is a living thing.

An **environment** is all the surrounding factors that affect the organism's life.

- What does an organism need to survive?

  An organism needs food, water, oxygen, and a stable environment to survive.

> **MY READING WEB** If you had trouble completing the question above, visit **My Reading Web** and type in *Introduction to Animals.*

Vocabulary Skill

Prefixes A prefix is a word part that is added to the beginning of a word to change its meaning. The table below lists prefixes that will help you learn terms used in this chapter.

Prefix	Meaning of Prefix	Example
endo-	inner	endoskeleton, *n.* internal skeleton
exo-	outer	exoskeleton, *n.* outer skeleton

2. **Quick Check** Complete the following sentence with the correct terms from the table above.

- The _exoskeleton_ of a crab, which is a tough outer shell, differs from the _endoskeleton_ of a cat, which is internal.

My Reading Web offers leveled readings that offer a foundation for the chapter content.

Vocab Flash Cards offer extra practice with the chapter vocabulary words.

Digital Lesson
- Assign the *Check Your Understanding* activity online and have students submit their work to you.
- Assign the *Vocabulary Skill* activity online and have students submit their work to you.

my science online.com

vertebrate

bilateral symmetry

mollusk

endotherm

Chapter Preview

LESSON 1
- homeostasis • adaptation
- vertebrate • invertebrate
- 🔁 Relate Text and Visuals
- △ Classify

LESSON 2
- tissue • organ • radial symmetry
- bilateral symmetry
- 🔁 Relate Cause and Effect
- △ Make Models

LESSON 3
- cnidarian • mollusk
- arthropod • exoskeleton
- echinoderm • endoskeleton
- 🔁 Identify the Main Idea
- △ Classify

LESSON 4
- chordate • notochord
- vertebra • ectotherm
- endotherm
- 🔁 Summarize
- △ Draw Conclusions

LESSON 5
- fish • cartilage • amphibian
- reptile • bird • mammal
- mammary gland
- monotreme • marsupial
- placental mammal • placenta
- 🔁 Compare and Contrast
- △ Interpret Data

> VOCAB FLASH CARDS For extra help with vocabulary, visit **Vocab Flash Cards** and type in *Introduction to Animals.*

137

CHAPTER 4

Preview Vocabulary Terms

Have students create word maps for the vocabulary terms in this chapter. This type of organizer helps students learn vocabulary by associating the terms with related words and images. To fill in a word map, have students write the vocabulary terms in the top box. They should fill in the bottom boxes with terms, phrases, or images that are associated with the vocabulary term. As the class progresses through the chapter, have students continue adding to or refining their word maps. A list of Academic Vocabulary for each lesson can be found in the Support All Readers box at the start of the lesson.

L1 Have students look at the images on this page as you pronounce the vocabulary word. Have students repeat the word after you. Then read the definition. Use the sample sentence in italics to clarify the meaning of the term.

vertebrate *(VUR tuh brit)* An animal that has a backbone. *Mammals are vertebrates because they have backbones.*

bilateral symmetry *(by LAT ur ul   SIM mih tree)* A body plan in which one line can divide it into halves that are mirror images. *A butterfly has bilateral symmetry because its two halves are mirror images of one another.*

mollusk *(MAWL usk)* An invertebrate with a soft, segmented body often protected by a hard shell. *Snails, clams, and squids are examples of mollusks.*

endotherm *(EN doh thurm)* An animal that controls the internal heat it produces and regulates its own temperature. *Polar bears are endotherms that have fur to help keep their temperature constant.*

ⒺⓁⓁ Support

Have students work in small groups to complete their maps cooperatively for the Preview Vocabulary Terms activity. Introduce each term to students by writing it on the board and reading it aloud. You may wish to have students with different language proficiencies work together.

Beginning
LOW/HIGH Complete the map using terms in their native language.

Intermediate
LOW/HIGH Complete the map using single words and short phrases.

Advanced
LOW/HIGH Include an example sentence using each of the vocabulary terms in the word map.

What Is an Animal?

 1

How do you know an animal when you see it?

Lesson Pacing: 1–2 periods or ½–1 block

🕐 **SHORT ON TIME?** To do this lesson in approximately half the time, do the Activate Prior Knowledge activity on page 138. A discussion of the Key Concepts on pages 139 and 140 will familiarize students with the lesson content. Have students do the Quick Labs. The rest of the lesson can be completed by students independently.

> **Preference Navigator,** in the online Planning tools, allows you to customize *Interactive Science* to your own teaching style. You can also edit lesson plans by selecting the Lesson Planner option.
>
> **Digital Teacher's Edition** allows you to access your Teacher's Edition and Resource materials online.
>
> **my science** online.com ▸

Lesson Vocabulary

- homeostasis
- adaptation
- vertebrate
- invertebrate

 Professional Development Note

Content Refresher

Movement A defining characteristic of animals is that they are heterotrophs, organisms that acquire nutrients by consuming other organisms. In order to feed, most animals must move, and to move, animals must overcome two forces—gravity and friction.

The particular adaptations for movement depend on which of the three media—air, land, or water—the animal moves in. Animals encounter less friction in air than in water. However, water provides buoyancy and thereby reduces the effect of gravity. Animals that fly have adaptations, including wings, for overcoming gravity. Aquatic animals tend to be streamlined and shaped like a torpedo, which reduces friction. The amount of energy used is related to an animal's size. Larger animals expend less energy per unit of body mass than do smaller animals. Animals that walk, hop, jump, or run on land require strong muscular and skeletal systems. Not only do land animals need to maintain balance, but they also must overcome gravity to propel themselves. No matter how many feet a land mammal has, it must be steady. When walking, two-footed and four-footed animals tend to only lift one foot off the ground at a time in order to remain stable. However, an animal's momentum keeps it from toppling over, even if multiple feet are lifted from the ground, during running.

LESSON OBJECTIVES

🔑 Identify four functions that enable animals to meet their basic needs.

🔑 Explain how animals are classified.

Blended Path
Active learning using Student Edition, Inquiry Path, and Digital Path

ENGAGE AND EXPLORE

Teach this lesson using a variety of resources. Begin by reading **My Planet Diary** as a class. Have students share ideas about how they think scientists discover new things. Then have students do the **Inquiry Warm-Up activity.** Students will determine if organisms are animals based on their observations. Discuss the characteristics students observed about the organisms. The **After the Inquiry Warm-Up worksheet** sets up a discussion about what one question people could ask to determine if an organism is an animal. Have volunteers share their answers to question 4 about a trait that they thought was characteristic to all animals but is not.

EXPLAIN AND ELABORATE

Teach Key Concepts by explaining that to survive all animals must take in oxygen, reproduce, move, and maintain homeostasis. Identify the animals in the photographs on page 139 and discuss how they are similar and different.

Continue to **Teach Key Concepts** by explaining that animals are classified based on how they are related to other animals. Use **Figure 1** to illustrate how to read a diagram that groups related organisms. Use the **Support the Big Q** to illustrate characteristics scientists must identify when trying to classify organisms as animals. Then have students practice the inquiry skill in the **Apply It activity.** Hand out the **Key Concept Summaries** as a review of each part of the lesson. Students can also use the online **Vocab Flash Cards** to review key terms.

EVALUATE

Have students take the **Lesson Quiz.** For an alternate assessment, see the *ExamView®* Computer Test Generator, Progress Monitoring Assessments, or SuccessTracker™.

ⒺⓁⓁ Support

1 Content and Language

The term *homeostasis* is derived from the Greek *homois* meaning "like" and *stasis* meaning "act of standing."

Inquiry Path — Hands-on learning in the Lab zone

ENGAGE AND EXPLORE

To teach this lesson with an emphasis on inquiry, begin with the **Inquiry Warm-Up activity.** Students will identify organisms as animals. Discuss the characteristics of the organisms. Have students do the **After the Inquiry Warm-Up worksheet.** Talk about one characteristic that most helps to determine if an organism is an animal. Have volunteers share their answers to question 4 about a characteristic that students thought was present in all animals but then discovered is not.

EXPLAIN AND ELABORATE

Focus on the **Inquiry Skill** for the lesson. Point out that when you classify, you observe similar characteristics and group items by these similarities. How were the organisms in the **Inquiry Warm-Up activity** classified? *(As an animal or not)* Have students do the **Quick Lab** to design an animal with a new way of moving and then share their animals.

Use the **Support the Big Q** to determine three specific characteristics that identify an organism as an animal. Review types of vertebrates and invertebrates before beginning the **Apply It activity.** Ask volunteers to identify how they classified the animals. Do the **Quick Lab** to reinforce understanding of how to classify animals based on body structure. Students can use the online **Vocab Flash Cards** to review key terms.

EVALUATE

Have students take the **Lesson Quiz.** For an alternate assessment, see the *ExamView®* Computer Test Generator, Progress Monitoring Assessments, or SuccessTracker™.

Digital Path — Online learning at my science online.com

ENGAGE AND EXPLORE

Teach this lesson using digital resources. Begin by having students explore real-world connections to animals at **My Planet Diary** online. Have them access the Chapter Resources to find the **Unlock the Big Question activity.** There they can answer the questions and refine their responses as they continue through the lesson. You can re-assign the activity and have students submit their work so you can track their progress.

EXPLAIN AND ELABORATE

Students reading above, at, or below the lexile measure of this lesson can access basic content readings at their level at **My Reading Web.** Have students use the online **Vocab Flash Cards** to preview key terms. Do the **Quick Lab** and then ask students to share their results.

Support the Big Q by asking students to list three specific characteristics scientists use to identify an organism as an animal. Have students do the online **Virtual Lab.** Review types of vertebrates and invertebrates before assigning the online **Apply It activity.** Ask volunteers to share which animals are vertebrates and which are invertebrates. Have students submit their work to you. Have students do the **Quick Lab** to classify animals based on body structure. The **Key Concept Summaries** online allow students to read a summary and see an image associated with each part of the lesson. Online remediation is available at **My Science Coach.**

EVALUATE

Have students take the **Lesson Quiz.** For an alternate assessment, see the *ExamView®* Computer Test Generator, Progress Monitoring Assessments, or SuccessTracker™.

2 Frontload the Lesson

Preview the lesson visuals, labels, and captions. Ask students what they know about the terms *invertebrate* and *vertebrate*. Explain the specific meanings these words have in science.

3 Comprehensible Input

Have students make a T-chart of vertebrates and invertebrates.

4 Language Production

Pair or group students with varied language abilities to complete labs collaboratively for language practice. Have each student copy the completed written lab for personal reference.

5 Assess Understanding

Have students create a portfolio of their notes and then do oral presentations of lesson content.

What Is an Animal?

Establish Learning Objectives

After this lesson, students will be able to:

🔑 Identify four functions that enable animals to meet their basic needs.

🔑 Explain how animals are classified.

Engage

Activate Prior Knowledge

MY PLANET DIARY Read *Animal Discoveries* with the class. Students sometimes have the misconception that scientists already know everything there is to know. Point out to students that scientists are always learning and discovering new things. Ask: **How can it be that scientists can still discover new animals?** *(They explore places that have never been explored.)*

BIG IDEAS OF SCIENCE REFERENCE LIBRARY
Have students look up the following topics: Adaptations, Aerogels, Bears, Geckos.

Explore

Lab Resource: Inquiry Warm-Up

L1 **IS IT AN ANIMAL?** Students will observe organisms to determine which ones are animals.

LESSON 1

What Is an Animal?

🔑 **What Are the Functions of Animals?**

🔑 **How Are Animals Classified?**

MY PLANET DiARY

DISCOVERY

Animal Discoveries

What would a mammal never before seen look like? The answer lies in the mountains of Tanzania, Africa. There, scientists discovered a vertebrate, which is a mammal, in 2005. The animal, which has been named *Rhynochocyon udzungwensis,* is a species of giant elephant shrew. It weighs about 700 grams and measures about 30 centimeters in length, which is just a little longer than this book. This newly discovered mammal is larger than other elephant shrews, and it has its own distinctive color.

Other animals have also been discovered in the mountains of Tanzania. Unknown amphibians and reptiles have been discovered there as well. Each discovery reveals more of the diversity of the animals living on Earth.

Read the following question. Then write your answer below.

Do you think it is important to protec areas such as these mountains? Why?

Sample: Yes. The areas need to be protected so the animals can survive and we can study them.

▶ **PLANET DIARY** Go to **Planet Diary** to learn m about animals.

 Do the Inquiry Warm-Up *Is It an Animal?*

What Are the Functions of Animals?

Like plants, animals live almost everywhere on Earth. Animals may have scales, feathers, shells, or fins. They may be brightly colored or completely see-through. Some animals do not have limbs. Others have too many limbs to count. You may wonder if animals have anything in common. Well, they do.

138 Introduction to Animals

SUPPORT ALL READERS
Lexile Measure = 780L   Lexile Word Count = 469

Prior Exposure to Content: May be the first time students have encountered this topic

Academic Vocabulary: *classify, relate, visual*

Science Vocabulary: *homeostasis, adaptation, vertebrate, invertebrate*

Concept Level: Generally appropriate for most students in this grade

Preteach With: My Planet Diary "Animal Discoveries" and Figure 1 activity

Go to **My Reading Web** to access leveled readings that provide a foundation for the content.

MY SCIENCE online.com

Vocabulary
- homeostasis • adaptation
- vertebrate • invertebrate

Skills
- ⊙ Reading: Relate Text and Visuals
- △ Inquiry: Classify

Functions All animals are multicellular organisms that feed on other organisms and perform the same basic functions. 🔑 The main functions of an animal are to obtain food and oxygen, keep internal conditions stable, move in some way, and reproduce. Keeping internal body conditions stable is called **homeostasis** (hoh mee oh stay sis).

Adaptations Structures and behaviors that allow animals to perform their functions are called **adaptations.** Teeth and limbs are adaptations that allow animals to obtain food and move. The pouch of a kangaroo is an adaptation for reproduction.

> ⊙ **Relate Text and Visuals**
> Match each animal to the function(s) it is performing.
>
> Sample:
> Obtaining Food _B, D_
> Animals eat other organisms and raw materials for energy and for growth.
>
> Reproducing _C, D_
> Animals make new individuals like themselves.
>
> Moving _A_
> Animals move to perform other functions as well.

Lab zone Do the Quick Lab *Get Moving.*

Assess Your Understanding

Got it? ....

○ I get it! Now I know that the functions of animals are _to obtain food and oxygen, maintain homeostasis, move in some way, and reproduce._

○ I need extra help with _See TE note._

Go to **my science** 🔵 **COACH** *online for help with this subject.*

139

---

1 Content and Language
Write *homeostasis* on the board. This word combines the Greek words *homeo,* meaning "like," and *stasis,* meaning "to stand or stop." So, *homeostasis* is the process of keeping internal bodily conditions "standing still."

2 Frontload the Lesson
Invite students to share their knowledge and experiences relating to animals. As students offer their ideas, write the animals they mention on the board. Encourage students to be specific about each animal's appearance, behavior, and characteristics.

3 Comprehensible Input
Invite small groups to present an explanation of **Figure 1** to a group of peers. Students should explain how the lines of the graphic represent relationships among invertebrates and vertebrates.

Explain

Introduce Vocabulary
Explain that in some words, the prefix *in-* means "not." Point out that a vertebrate has something—a backbone—that an invertebrate does *not* have.

Teach Key Concepts 🔑
Explain to students that all animals perform the same basic functions. Ask: **How do animals on land take in oxygen?** (They breathe.) **What does it mean for an animal to reproduce?** (It makes more animals like itself.) **Why might it be important for an animal to move?** (It might need to escape predators or find food.) **What is homeostasis?** (It is the maintaining of a stable, or constant, internal environment.)

⊙ **Relate Text and Visuals** The visuals in a textbook are chosen to support the concepts in the text. Referring to visuals as they read can help students better understand the concepts being discussed.

Teach With Visuals
Tell students to look at the pictures. Point out that these photographs all show animals. Ask: **What do the animals have in common?** (They all need food, they all move around, and they all reproduce.) **How are the animals different?** (Students might suggest that they live in different environments, they look different, and they eat different kinds of food.)

Lab Resource: Quick Lab **Lab** zone
L2 GET MOVING Students will design an animal with a new way of moving.

Evaluate

Assess Your Understanding
Have students evaluate their understanding by completing the appropriate sentence.

RTI Response to Intervention
If students have trouble remembering the functions of animals, **then** have them choose a specific animal and consider the things that it does.

my science 🔵 **COACH** Have students go online for help in understanding animal functions.

> **My Planet Diary** provides an opportunity for students to explore real-world connections to animals.

139

Explain

Teach Key Concepts 🔑

Describe examples of classification in everyday life, such as organizing clothes into drawers or books onto shelves. Then explain that scientists classify animals into groups by how they are alike. Ask: **What is a vertebrate?** *(An animal with a backbone)* **What is an invertebrate?** *(An animal without a backbone)* **Why might scientists classify a dog and an eagle in the same group?** *(Both have backbones.)* **Why might scientists classify these two animals in different groups?** *(Sample: Dogs have hair and eagles have feathers.)* **If scientists discover a new animal, how would they go about classifying it?** *(They would look at its characteristics to see if it is similar to a particular group of animals.)*

Teach With Visuals

Tell students to look at **Figure 1.** Ask: **What does each line in the diagram represent?** *(It represents a group of organisms.)* **What does it mean if one line branches off from another?** *(It means that the organisms are more closely related than those described by completely separate lines.)*

Support the Big Q ❓ **UbD**

CLASSIFY ANIMALS Explain that scientists must look for specific characteristics when trying to identify organisms as animals. Have students sketch an animal on a sheet of paper and list three things that make it an animal. Ask: **How is an animal different from a plant?** *(Students may suggest that an animal eats other living things or can move around.)* **How is an animal similar to a plant?** *(Students may suggest that both are living things and both can reproduce.)*

21st Century Learning 🄳🄺

INFORMATION LITERACY Have students read *Geckos* in the **Big Ideas of Science Reference Library.** Ask students to find out more information about how geckos are able to stick to different surfaces. Then have students present their findings in a short presentation. Encourage students to discuss some of the practical applications of gecko adhesion.

How Are Animals Classified?

There are more than 1.6 million species of animals, and more are discovered each year. So far, biologists have classified animals into about 35 major groups. In **Figure 1,** you can see some of the major groups. Notice how the groups are arranged on branches. Animal groups on nearby branches are more closely related than groups on branches farther apart. For example, birds are more closely related to reptiles than they are to mammals.

🔑 **Animals are classified according to how they are related to other animals. These relationships are determined by an animal's body structure, the way the animal develops, and its DNA.** DNA is a chemical in cells that controls an organism's inherited characteristics.

All animals are either vertebrates or invertebrates. **Vertebrates** are animals with a backbone. **Invertebrates** are animals without a backbone.

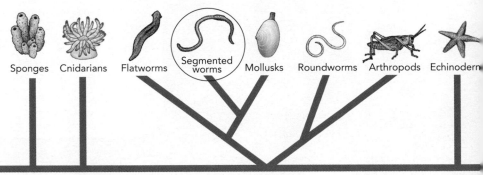

Sponges   Cnidarians   Flatworms   Segmented worms   Mollusks   Roundworms   Arthropods   Echinoderm

Invertebrates

FIGURE 1 ··

> **VIRTUAL LAB** Major Animal Groups

✏ Complete these tasks.

1. **Interpret Diagrams** Are flatworms more closely related to segmented worms or to roundworms? Circle your answer on the diagram.

2. **CHALLENGE** What do you think the bird branch coming off of the reptile branch indicates?

   Sample: They are closely related but birds began to develop differently at some point.

Virtual Lab allows students to classify animals as vertebrates or invertebrates.

Digital Lesson: Assign the *Apply It* activity online and have students submit their work to you.

my science online.com | Animal Classification

apply it!

Use the information in **Figure 1** to help you classify the animals at the right.

❶ **Classify** Write the name of each animal's group in the box provided.

❷ **Identify** Which animals are vertebrates? Which animals are invertebrates?

The cow and bird are vertebrates. The butterfly and scallop are invertebrates.

Mammals

Arthropods

Mollusks

Birds

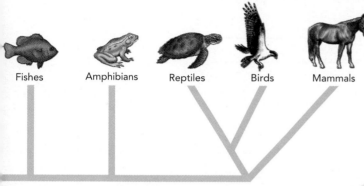

Fishes   Amphibians   Reptiles   Birds   Mammals

Vertebrates

 Lab zone — Do the Quick Lab *Classifying Animals.*

Assess Your Understanding

1a. Define What is a vertebrate?

It is an animal with a backbone.

b. Compare and Contrast How are vertebrates and invertebrates alike? How do they differ?

Both are animals. A vertebrate has a backbone.

got it?

○ I get it! Now I know that animals are classified based on their body structures, the way they develop, and their DNA.

○ I need extra help with See TE note.

Go to my science **COACH** *online for help with this subject.*

141

Elaborate

Apply It!

L1 Review types of vertebrates and invertebrates before beginning the activity.

△ **Classify** Help students understand that to classify means to sort into groups based on similarities. Ask students how items might be classified at home, in a store, or in a library. Point out that there can be more than one way to classify something. An organism can be classified as an animal, as a vertebrate, and as a mammal, for example. Some groupings are more specific than others.

Lab Resource: Quick Lab

L1 **CLASSIFYING ANIMALS** Students will classify animals based on body structure.

Evaluate

Assess Your Understanding

After students answer the questions, have them evaluate their understanding by completing the appropriate sentence.

RTI Response to Intervention

1a. If students cannot describe a vertebrate, **then** have them draw a picture of an animal showing its backbone.

b. If students need help remembering the difference between vertebrates and invertebrates, **then** have them locate the highlighted terms and reread the definitions.

my science **COACH** Have students go online for help in understanding vertebrates and invertebrates.

Differentiated Instruction

L1 **Write a Description** Have students choose an animal they have observed. It might be a classroom pet, a pet at home, or even an animal at the zoo. Tell students to write a paragraph describing how they would classify the animal and why they chose that classification.

L3 **Investigate Heredity** Ask students to research DNA and the role it plays in heredity. Tell students to write a brief summary of what DNA is and why it is important to animals. Have students present their findings to the class.

Name _____ Date _____ Class _____

What Is an Animal?

> **Inquiry Warm-Up, *Is It an Animal?***
> In the Inquiry Warm-Up, you investigated the characteristics of several organisms and then classified each one as an animal or not. Using what you learned from that activity, answer the questions below.

1. **LIST** What are the key characteristics you decided that all animals share?

   _____

   _____

2. **EXPLAIN** Can all the characteristics that you think all animals share be observed immediately and with the naked eye? Explain.

   _____

   _____

   _____

3. **POSE QUESTIONS** Suppose a person is trying to decide if an organism is an animal. What do you think would be a good question to ask to help make a decision?

   _____

   _____

4. **ANALYZE SOURCES OF ERROR** Is there a trait that you originally thought was characteristic of all animals that you later decided was not? Explain why you changed your mind.

   _____

   _____

   _____

What Is an Animal?

What Are the Functions of Animals?

got it? ....

○ **I get it!** Now I know that the functions of animals are _____

_____

_____

○ **I need extra help with** _____

_____

How Are Animals Classified?

1a. DEFINE What is a vertebrate?

_____

_____

b. COMPARE AND CONTRAST How are vertebrates and invertebrates alike?
How do they differ? _____

_____

_____

got it? ....

○ **I get it!** Now I know that animals are classified based on _____

_____

_____

○ **I need extra help with** _____

_____

Name _____ Date _____ Class _____

What Is an Animal?

What Are the Functions of Animals?

The characteristics of animals vary widely, but they do share common traits. All animals are multicellular organisms that feed on other organisms and perform the same basic functions. **The main functions of an animal are to obtain food and oxygen, keep internal conditions stable, move in some way,** **and reproduce.** The process through which animals keep internal conditions stable is called **homeostasis.** Structures or behaviors that allow animals to perform their functions are called **adaptations.** Teeth and limbs, for example, are adaptations that help animals obtain food or move about.

How Are Animals Classified?

There are more than 1.6 million species of animals, and more discovered each year. So far, biologists have classified animals into about 35 major groups. In diagrams, scientists usually arrange these groups on branches. Animal groups on nearby branches are more closely related than groups on branches farther apart.

Animals are classified according to how they are related to other animals. These relationships are **determined by an animal's body structure, the way the animal develops, and its DNA.** DNA is a chemical in cells that controls an organism's inherited characteristics. All animals are either vertebrates or invertebrates. **Vertebrates** are animals with a backbone. **Invertebrates** are animals without a backbone.

On a separate sheet of paper, list the main functions of an animal. Then explain how scientists classify animals into different groups.

Name _____ Date _____ Class _____

What Is an Animal?

Understanding Main Ideas
Answer the following questions in the spaces provided.

1. What are the main functions of an animal?

   _____

   _____

2. Give examples of two animal adaptations and explain how each one helps an animal perform one of its main functions.

   _____

   _____

   _____

3. How do scientists classify animals?

   _____

   _____

   _____

4. When you look at a branched diagram that classifies animals, how can you tell how closely related two groups of animals are?

   _____

   _____

Building Vocabulary
Match each term with its definition by writing the letter of the correct definition in the right column on the line beside the term in the left column.

5. ___ homeostasis

6. ___ vertebrate

7. ___ adaptation

8. ___ invertebrate

a. animal without a backbone

b. keeping internal conditions stable

c. animal with a backbone

d. structure or behavior that helps an animal perform its functions

141D

Enrich

What Is an Animal?

> Related organisms have a common ancestor. The more recently the common answer lived, the more closely related the two organisms are. Read the passage and study the diagram below. Then use a separate sheet of paper to answer the questions that follow.

The Arthropod Tree

A *cladogram* is a tree-shaped diagram with leaves, forks, and branches that shows how closely related to each other different kinds of organisms are. The cladogram shows part of the arthropod evolutionary tree. At the top are the leaves, which are recent arthropods. Each fork in the diagram represents the shared ancestor of all the arthropods above it. Branches connect the ancestors with each other and with recent organisms.

To find the most recent ancestor of any two organisms, just follow the branches down until you reach the first fork that connects them. You can also follow up from a fork to find more and more recent organisms. The two organisms that have the same most recent ancestor are each other's closest relative.

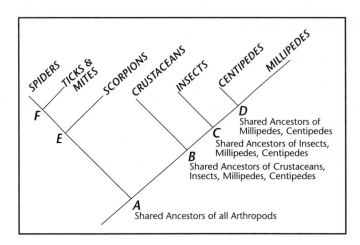

1. Which fork occurred earlier, B or D? How do you know?
2. What does fork B represent?
3. What does fork E represent?
4. Which group are mites and ticks most closely related to? How do you know?

Name _____ Date _____ Class _____

What Is an Animal?

Write the letter of the correct answer on the line at the left.

1. ___ In addition to body structure and development, which of the following is used to classify animals?

   A speed

   B color

   C DNA

   D location

2. ___ Because it has a backbone, how should a hippopotamus be described?

   A vertebrate

   B mollusk

   C echinoderm

   D invertebrate

3. ___ The long neck of a giraffe helps it to find food in tall trees. What term best describes a giraffe's neck?

   A appendage

   B classification

   C homeostasis

   D adaptation

4. ___ Which of the following animals is an invertebrate?

   A goldfish

   B grasshopper

   C turtle

   D horse

If the statement is true, write *true*. If the statement is false, change the underlined word or words to make the statement true.

5. _____ A vertebrate is an animal <u>without</u> a backbone.

6. _____ <u>Adaptations</u> allow animals to perform their functions.

7. _____ Animals perform <u>classification</u> to keep internal body conditions stable.

8. _____ One of the main functions of animals is to get food and <u>oxygen</u>.

9. _____ Animals that are more <u>distantly</u> related are grouped on the same branch of a classification tree.

10. _____ <u>Oxygen</u> is a chemical in cells that controls an organism's inherited characteristics.

What Is an Animal?

Answer Key

After the Inquiry Warm-Up

1. Accept all reasonable answers. Sample: All animals need food, move in some way, and reproduce.

2. Answers will vary. Sample: No, several of the key characteristics of animals involve processes, such as movement, feeding, or reproduction. An animal may not be moving, feeding, or reproducing when it is observed.

3. Answers will vary. Sample: Does the organism move?

4. Answers will vary. Sample: I originally thought all animals had arms or legs. But then I examined the worm, and I know it is an animal but it has no limbs.

Key Concept Summaries

The main functions of an animal are to obtain food and oxygen, keep internal conditions stable, move in some way, and reproduce. Scientists classify animals into groups according to how they are related to other animals. To determine these relationships, scientists consider animals' body structure, the way they develop, and their DNA.

Review and Reinforce

1. The main functions of an animal are to obtain food and oxygen, keep internal conditions stable, move in some way, and reproduce.

2. Answers will vary. Sample: A female kangaroo's pouch is an adaptation that helps in reproduction. A giraffe's long neck is an adaptation that helps it obtain food high in trees.

3. Scientists classify animals according to how they are related to other animals. They determine these relationships by animals' body structure, the way they develop, and their DNA.

4. Animal groups on nearby branches are more closely related than groups on branches that are farther apart.

5. b

6. c

7. d

8. a

Enrich

1. fork B, because it is lower on the tree

2. the most recent common ancestor of crustaceans, insects, centipedes, and millipedes

3. the most recent common ancestor of spiders, ticks, mites, and scorpions (Also accept: the last common ancestor of arachnids)

4. spiders; The most recent common ancestor of mites, ticks, and spiders is at fork F. It is higher on the tree, and therefore more recent than any of their other common ancestors.

Lesson Quiz

1. C
2. A
3. D
4. B
5. with
6. true
7. homeostasis
8. true
9. closely
10. DNA

Place the outside corner, the corner away from the dotted line, in the corner of your copy machine to copy onto letter-size paper.

Animal Body Plans

 How do you know an animal when you see it?

Lesson Pacing: 1–2 periods or $\frac{1}{2}$–1 block

🕐 **SHORT ON TIME?** To do this lesson in approximately half the time, do the Activate Prior Knowledge activity on page 142. A discussion of the Key Concepts on pages 142 and 145 will familiarize students with the lesson content. Use the Explore the Big Q to help students understand how you know an animal when you see it. Do the Quick Labs. The rest of the lesson can be completed by students independently.

Preference Navigator, in the online Planning tools, allows you to customize *Interactive Science* to your own teaching style. You can also edit lesson plans by selecting the Lesson Planner option.

Digital Teacher's Edition allows you to access your Teacher's Edition and Resource materials online.

my science online.com

Lesson Vocabulary

- tissue
- organ
- radial symmetry
- bilateral symmetry

 ## Content Refresher

Types of Symmetry There are three basic kinds of symmetry among living things—spherical, radial, and bilateral. Animals that lack these basic symmetries, such as sponges, are said to be asymmetrical. Spherical symmetry is rare but may be observed in free-floating organisms, such as some protozoans. Amoebas, for example, become spherical at rest.

Some animals exhibit different kinds of symmetry during different stages of their life cycles. For example, echinoderms are radial symmetrical as adults, but the larva are bilaterally symmetrical. Studying symmetry can show relationships between organisms. The presence of bilateral symmetry during the larval stage of echinoderms, for example, is one characteristic that shows the relationship between echinoderms and chordates. There are also two variations of radial symmetry known as tetramerism and pentamerism. Tetramerism is four-fold symmetry and can be seen in many jellyfish. Starfish and sea urchins exhibit five-fold radial symmetry.

LESSON OBJECTIVES

- Describe levels of organization in animal bodies.
- Infer animal body structures based on their symmetry.

Blended Path
Active learning using Student Edition, Inquiry Path, and Digital Path

ENGAGE AND EXPLORE

Teach this lesson using a variety of resources. Begin by reading **My Planet Diary** as a class. Have students share ideas about why scientists study animals. Then have students do the **Inquiry Warm-Up activity.** Students will investigate symmetry and identify animals with each type of body plan symmetry. Discuss the two types of symmetry students discovered while folding paper. The **After the Inquiry Warm-Up worksheet** sets up a discussion about the symmetry of a human compared to the symmetry of a jellyfish and a horse. Have volunteers share their answers to question 4 about what question a person could ask if they wanted to classify organisms according to body plan symmetry.

EXPLAIN AND ELABORATE

Teach Key Concepts by explaining how cells are related to tissues, which are related to organs and an organ system.

Continue to **Teach Key Concepts** by explaining that animals with bilateral symmetry are more complex than animals with radial symmetry. Then have students practice the inquiry skill in the **Apply It activity. Lead a Discussion** about bilateral symmetry in humans and how bilateral symmetry can be advantageous to land animals. Use **Figure 3** to compare and contrast two water animals. **Explore the Big Q** by summarizing the functions, the types of body plan symmetry, and the adaptations animals have. To **Answer the Big Q** lead a class discussion about what makes an animal an animal. Hand out the **Key Concept Summaries** as a review of each part of the lesson. Students can also use the online **Vocab Flash Cards** to review key terms.

EVALUATE

Have students take the **Lesson Quiz.** For an alternate assessment, see the *ExamView®* Computer Test Generator, Progress Monitoring Assessments, or SuccessTracker™.

ⒺⓁⓁ Support

1 Content and Language

Explain to students that the word *radial* comes from the Latin word *radius*. Students should know the word *radius* from mathematics. The *radius* is the distance from the center of a circle to the outside edge. Help them use this knowledge to understand *radial symmetry*.

Lab zone Inquiry Path
Hands-on learning in the Lab zone

Digital Path
Online learning at my science online.com

ENGAGE AND EXPLORE

To teach this lesson with an emphasis on inquiry, begin with the **Inquiry Warm-Up activity.** Students will investigate symmetry and how it relates to animal body plans. Discuss the two types of symmetry students identified while folding paper. Have students do the **After the Inquiry Warm-Up worksheet.** Talk about how the symmetry of humans compares to the symmetry of horses and jellyfish. Have volunteers share their answers to question 4 about one question to ask if a person wanted to classify animals according to body plan symmetry.

EXPLAIN AND ELABORATE

Focus on the **Inquiry Skill** for the lesson. Point out that when you make models, you represent an object or process in order to examine it more carefully. What was modeled in the **Inquiry Warm-Up activity?** *(Body plan symmetry)* Have students do the **Quick Lab** to create models of imaginary animals and then share their results.

The **Teacher Demo** will show students how a mirror image is similar to and different from the original object. Review the two types of symmetry before beginning the **Apply It activity.** Ask volunteers to share the objects with radial symmetry they drew. To **Build Inquiry** have students sort and classify objects based on symmetry. To **Explore the Big Q** have students identify what animals need to survive, how animals adapt, and how their body systems are organized. Do the **Quick Lab** to reinforce understanding of where the five sense organs are located in an animal with bilateral symmetry. Have students **Answer the Big Q** in the student edition and then share how they know an animal when they see it. Students can use the online **Vocab Flash Cards** to review key terms.

EVALUATE

Have students take the **Lesson Quiz.** For an alternate assessment, see the *ExamView®* Computer Test Generator, Progress Monitoring Assessments, or SuccessTracker™.

ENGAGE AND EXPLORE

Teach this lesson using digital resources. Begin by having students explore real-world connections to body plans at **My Planet Diary** online. Have them access the Chapter Resources to find the **Unlock the Big Question activity.** There they can answer the questions and refine their responses as they continue through the lesson. You can re-assign the activity and have students submit their work so you can track their progress.

EXPLAIN AND ELABORATE

Students reading above, at, or below the lexile measure of this lesson can access basic content readings at their level at **My Reading Web.** Have students use the online **Vocab Flash Cards** to preview key terms. Do the **Quick Lab** and then ask students to share their results.

Review bilateral and radial symmetry as well as symmetry before assigning the online **Apply It activity.** Ask volunteers to share the objects they drew that have radial symmetry. Have students submit their work to you. **Explore the Big Q** by determining the functions, adaptations, and body organizations of animals. Have students do the **Quick Lab** to explore the location of the five sense organs in animals with bilateral symmetry. After students **Answer the Big Q** in the student edition, discuss how they know an animal when they see it. The **Key Concept Summaries** online allow students to read a summary and see an image associated with each part of the lesson. Online remediation is available at **My Science Coach.**

EVALUATE

Have students take the **Lesson Quiz.** For an alternate assessment, see the *ExamView®* Computer Test Generator, Progress Monitoring Assessments, or SuccessTracker™.

2 Frontload the Lesson
Preview the lesson visuals, labels, and captions. Ask students what they know about the terms *tissue* and *organ.* Explain the specific meanings these words have in science.

3 Comprehensible Input
Have students study the visuals and their captions on pages 143, 144, and 146 to support the Key Concepts of the lesson.

4 Language Production
Pair or group students with varied language abilities to complete labs collaboratively for language practice. Have each student copy the completed written lab for personal reference.

5 Assess Understanding
Make true or false statements using lesson content and have students indicate if they agree or disagree with a thumbs up or thumbs down gesture to check whole-class comprehension.

LESSON 4.2

Animal Body Plans

Establish Learning Objectives

After this lesson, students will be able to:

 Describe levels of organization in animal bodies.

 Infer animal body structures based on their symmetry.

Engage

Activate Prior Knowledge

MY PLANET DIARY Read *Spiny Sea Animals* with the class. Explain that a sea urchin is a type of invertebrate called an echinoderm. Sand dollars, sea cucumbers, and feather stars are other echinoderms. Ask: **How might spines help sea urchins?** *(They might protect them from predators.)* **How can learning about one animal help scientists learn about other animals?** *(Processes that occur in one type of animal can often occur in other types of animals.)*

BIG IDEAS OF SCIENCE REFERENCE LIBRARY DK
Have students look up the following topics:
Exoskeleton, Patterns in Nature, Symmetry, Whales.

Explore

Lab Resource: Inquiry Warm-Up Lab

L1 **HOW MANY WAYS CAN YOU FOLD IT?**
Students will fold shapes so that the two halves are identical.

---

2 Animal Body Plans

 How Are Animal Bodies Organized?

 How Is Symmetry Related to Body Structure?

MY PLANET DIARY

DISCOVERY

Spiny Sea Animals

What animal do you think of when you hear the word *spiny*? You might think of a porcupine, but sea urchins are spiny, too. These small, colorful creatures live in the ocean. Just by looking at them, you can't tell that studying sea urchins would lead to a major discovery about how animals reproduce.

In 1875, biologist Oskar Hertwig was studying a transparent egg of a sea urchin under a microscope. He saw a sperm, the male sex cell, enter the egg, the female sex cell, and fuse with the nucleus of the egg. He had discovered how sexual reproduction occurs.

> **Answer the question below.**
> How do you think a sea urchin's transparent egg was important to the discovery of how sexual reproduction occurs?
>
> Sample: The transparent egg made it possible to see the sperm enter the egg and fuse with the nucleus.
>
> ▷ **PLANET DIARY** Go to **Planet Diary** to learn more about animal body plans.

Lab zone Do the Inquiry Warm-Up *How Many Ways Can You Fold It?*.

How Are Animal Bodies Organized?

Animals are diverse organisms. But the animals within each phylum have uniquely organized body structures. This organization is called a body plan. **The organization of an animal's cells into higher levels of structure, including tissues, organs, and organ systems, helps to describe an animal's body plan.**

142 Introduction to Animals

SUPPORT ALL READERS
Lexile Measure = 930L   Lexile Word Count = 924

Prior Exposure to Content: May be the first time students have encountered this topic

Academic Vocabulary: *cause, effect, model, relate*

Science Vocabulary: *tissue, organ, radial symmetry, bilateral symmetry*

Concept Level: Generally appropriate for most students in this grade

Preteach With: My Planet Diary "Spiny Sea Animals" and Figure 2 activity

Go to **My Reading Web** to access leveled readings that provide a foundation for the content.

MY SCIENCE ONLINE.com

Vocabulary
• tissue • organ • radial symmetry
• bilateral symmetry

Skills
◉ Reading: Relate Cause and Effect
△ Inquiry: Make Models

Cells and Tissues All animals are made up of many cells. Their cells are usually specialized and organized as tissues. A **tissue** is a group of similar cells that performs a specific function. Muscle tissue, nervous tissue, and connective tissue are all animal tissues. Bone and blood are examples of kinds of connective tissues.

Organs and Organ Systems In most animals, tissues combine to form organs and organ systems. An **organ** is made up of different tissues. For example, the leg bone of a frog shown in **Figure 1** is an organ composed of bone tissue, nervous tissue, and blood. An organ performs more complex functions than the tissues that make it up could perform alone. Groups of organs make up organ systems. These systems perform the animal's broadest functions.

FIGURE 1 ....

A Skeletal System's Organization
Different levels of organization are found in a frog's skeleton.

✎ **Describe** Tell what makes up each level of organization in this frog's skeletal system.

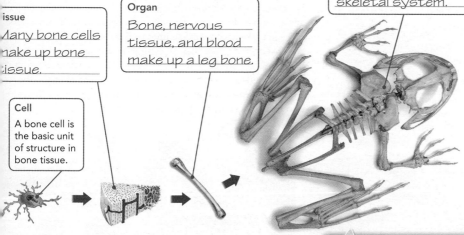

Organ System
All the bones in the body make up the skeletal system.

Organ
Bone, nervous tissue, and blood make up a leg bone.

Tissue
Many bone cells make up bone tissue.

Cell
A bone cell is the basic unit of structure in bone tissue.

Lab zone ® Do the Quick Lab *Organizing Animal Bodies.*

⊜ **Assess Your Understanding**

Got it? ....

○ I get it! Now I know that animal bodies are organized into *cells, tissues, organs, and organ systems.*

○ I need extra help with *See TE note.*

Go to MY SCIENCE COACH online for help with this subject.

143

ELL Support

1 Content and Language
Write the term *bilateral* on the board. Explain that the word *lateral* refers to a side and the prefix *bi-* means "two." Ask students to form a definition of the word based on these words parts.

2 Frontload the Lesson
Invite students to identify exotic animals with dramatically different types of bodies. Invite students to use specific

words and phrases to describe the bodies of several animals on the list.

3 Comprehensible Input
Work with students to classify different objects and shapes in the classroom based on their symmetry. Be sure that students use the correct terms when classifying the items.

Explain ——————

Introduce Vocabulary
Tell students that the prefix *bi-* means "two." Have them think about the meanings of words with this prefix, such as *bicycle* (two wheels). Then explain that *bilateral symmetry* describes a body plan with two identical halves.

Teach Key Concepts
On the board, show students an example of how letters combine to make words, which combine to make sentences. Then, discuss how sentences combine to make paragraphs, which can form chapters of an entire story. Ask: **If letters are the basic units of stories, what are the basic units of organisms?** *(Cells)* **What do related cells combine to form?** *(A tissue)* **What do related tissues work together to form?** *(An organ)* **What is a group of organs that work together?** *(An organ system)*

Explore ——————

Lab Resource: Quick Lab
L1 ORGANIZING ANIMAL BODIES Students will combine tissues, organs, and organ systems to create models of imaginary animals.

Evaluate ——————

Assess Your Understanding
Have students evaluate their understanding by completing the appropriate sentence.

RTI Response to Intervention
If students have difficulty understanding levels of organization, **then** help them review **Figure 1.**

MY SCIENCE COACH Have students go online for help in understanding animal body organization.

My Planet Diary provides an opportunity for students to explore real-world connections to body plans.

MY SCIENCE ONLINE | Animal Body Organization

Explain

Teach Key Concepts

Explain to students that the symmetry of an animal indicates something about its body structure. Animals with bilateral symmetry are more complex than animals with radial symmetry. Ask: **What is a line of symmetry?** *(A line that can divide an object or animal into two halves that are mirror images)* **What is a radius?** *(It is the distance from the edge to the center of a circle.)* **What is radial symmetry?** *(It is a body plan of circular animals in which lines of symmetry can be drawn through the center.)* **Why do animals with radial symmetry not have a front or back end?** *(Their parts are arranged in a circle around a center.)* **What are some characteristics of animals with radial symmetry?** *(They live in water and move slowly.)* **What is bilateral symmetry?** *(It is a body plan in which only one line of symmetry can be drawn.)*

Relate Cause and Effect Explain that a cause is an event, trait, or condition that produces some result, which is the effect. Have students brainstorm examples of cause and effect. Then relate this skill to the effects of an animal being radially symmetrical.

Elaborate

Teacher Demo **Lab** zone

L1 MIRROR IMAGES

Materials paper, scissors, plane mirror

Time 5 minutes

Cut a heart shape out of a sheet of paper. Fold the heart shape in half lengthwise. Cut the heart in half along the line of symmetry. Hold one half of the heart shape next to a plane mirror. Allow students to compare the image they see in the mirror with the other half of the heart shape. Repeat with a variety of different shapes.

Ask: **How is a mirror image similar to the original?** *(It has the same size and shape.)* **How is a mirror image different from the original?** *(It is equal in size, but opposite in direction or arrangement.)*

How Is Symmetry Related to Body Structure?

Have you ever noticed a butterfly perched on a flower? You probably saw its colors and wing patterns. Did you also see that the pattern

A butterfly with bilateral symmetry

on the left side is a mirror image of the pattern on the right side? Many organisms and objects have this balanced display of body parts called symmetry.

Types of Symmetry Animals have different types of symmetry, as you can see in **Figure 2**. Some animals have no symmetry, or are asymmetrical. For example, most sponges are asymmetrical. However, most animals have either radial symmetry or bilateral symmetry.

An animal has **radial symmetry** if many imaginary lines can be drawn through a central point to divide it into two mirror images. For example, from above, the shape of a jellyfish is circular. So any imaginary line drawn through its center divides it into mirror images. These lines are called lines of symmetry.

Most animals have bilateral symmetry. An animal or an object has **bilateral symmetry** if only one line of symmetry can be drawn to divide it into halves that are mirror images. For example, the dashed line you see drawn on the butterfly above divides the animal into halves that are mirror images of each other.

Check students' drawings. Sample symmetry lines shown.

FIGURE 2 ·······························

Types of Symmetry

Identify Write the type of symmetry each animal has. Then draw lines of symmetry on each animal to support your choice.

Radial symmetry   Asymmetrical   Bilateral symmet

Digital Lesson: Assign the *Apply It* activity online and have students submit their work to you.

my science online.com   **Body Symmetry**

Symmetry and Body Structure The structures of animals are related to their symmetry. **The bodies of animals without symmetry are organized simply, with some specialized cells but no tissues. In contrast, animals with radial symmetry have complex body plans with tissues and usually with organ systems. Animals with bilateral symmetry have organ systems.**

Radial Symmetry All animals with radial symmetry live in water. Some creep slowly along the ocean floor. Others stay in one spot as adults. A few can move quickly. Most animals with radial symmetry do not have front or back ends. Also, they do not have heads with specialized sense organs. This kind of symmetry allows them to take in information about their surroundings from all directions. This is an advantage for animals that usually move slowly.

> ⤵ **Relate Cause and Effect**
> In the second paragraph, underline an effect of having radial symmetry.

apply it!

Many objects you see have symmetry, but some do not.

1 Interpret Photos Under each picture, write the type of symmetry shown by the object.

2 Explain Draw lines of symmetry on each object to support your choice.

3 ⚠ Make Models Draw a common object not pictured here that has radial symmetry. Draw lines of symmetry to support your choice.

> Samples: Students may draw a pizza, paper plate, soup can, or other round object, and draw lines of symmetry through the center of the object.
>
> Check students' drawings. Sample symmetry lines shown.

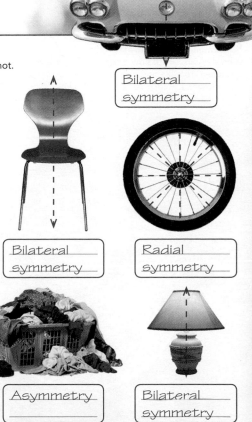

Bilateral symmetry

Bilateral symmetry

Radial symmetry

Asymmetry

Bilateral symmetry

145

Elaborate

21st Century Learning

L3 CREATIVITY Ask students if they have viewed a kaleidoscope. Explain that the image they see has radial symmetry, produced by reflections from two mirrors set at a precise angle. Give students two plane mirrors. Challenge them to make an abstract drawing and then hold the mirrors at right angles to the drawing, changing the angle between the mirrors until they can see a repeating image that has radial symmetry. (A 60-degree angle will work well.)

Apply It!

L1 Review bilateral symmetry, radial symmetry, and asymmetry before beginning the activity. Note that the photo of the lamp has bilateral symmetry, but the actual lamp has radial symmetry. If students could view the lamp from above, they would notice that both the lamp and lampshade have circular shapes. Any imaginary line of symmetry drawn through the center of the lamp and lampshade would divide them into mirror images.

⚠ **Make Models** Remind students that a model does not have to be three-dimensional. A model can also be a drawing. If students have trouble coming up with ideas to draw, use objects in the classroom as examples. As a class, identify lines of symmetry on the objects and then challenge students to come up with their own ideas. They can test their ideas by folding their papers along the lines.

Build Inquiry **Lab** zone

L1 SYMMETRY

Materials simple objects (such as leaves, shells, keys, gloves, scissors)

Time 10 minutes

Distribute objects to the class. Have students work in small groups to sort the objects into two groups—symmetrical and asymmetrical. Then have students take the symmetrical objects and further classify them as having radial symmetry or bilateral symmetry.

Ask: **What characteristics can be used to sort the objects?** (Samples: round or long; irregular or regular)

Differentiated Instruction

L1 Finding Symmetry Ask students to find a picture of an animal with bilateral symmetry and an animal with radial symmetry. Have students use a marker to draw lines of symmetry on the pictures.

L3 Modeling Symmetry Tell students to draw a diagram of an animal with bilateral symmetry, such as a butterfly. Ask them to use the diagram to make a model that shows that two halves of the animal are mirror images.

Explain

Lead a Discussion

SYMMETRY Point out that humans have bilateral symmetry. Ask: **Can you identify a person by looking at either side of his or her face?** *(Yes, because both sides of the face appear almost the same.)* **When does an object have bilateral symmetry?** *(When one line can divide it into halves that are mirror images)* **How does radial symmetry differ from bilateral symmetry?** *(An object with radial symmetry has many lines that go through a central point.)* **What advantage is bilateral symmetry to a land animal?** *(It enables the animal to have sense organs in the front and to be streamlined. The animal can move quickly yet be aware of what is in front of it.)*

Teach With Visuals

Tell students to look at **Figure 3.** Explain that the overlapping circles are known as a Venn diagram. The part where the circles overlap shows characteristics that a sea star and a fish have in common. Ask: **What kind of symmetry does a sea star have?** *(Radial symmetry)* **How many lines of symmetry do these sea stars have?** *(Five)* **What sense organs can you identify on the sea stars?** *(None)* **Where does a sea star live?** *(In water)* **How does it move?** *(It crawls on the ocean floor.)* **What kind of symmetry does a fish have?** *(Bilateral symmetry)* **What sense organs can you identify on the fish?** *(Eyes)* **Where does a fish live?** *(In water)* **How does it move?** *(It swims.)* **Which moves faster, a sea star or a fish?** *(A fish)*

CHALLENGE Why is it an advantage for an animal to have its head be the first part of its body to enter a new area?

Sample: An animal can learn about the area before it enters all the way.

FIGURE 3

A Coral Reef
Many animals with bilateral and radial symmetry live in coral reefs.

Compare and Contrast In the Venn diagram, write how a sea star and a fish are alike and how they are different.

Bilateral Symmetry In general, animals with bilateral symmetry are larger and more complex than animals with radial symmetry. They have complex organ systems that help them function efficiently. Also, most animals with bilateral symmetry have streamlined bodies, which help them move quickly.

Most animals with bilateral symmetry have heads at their front ends. Having a head is important to an animal. Most of an animal's specialized sense organs, such as its eyes, are in its head, as you can see in **Figure 3.** In addition, a concentration of nervous tissue is found in an animal's head. Nervous tissue processes information for the animal and coordinates the animal's responses. In fact, an animal usually moves into a new area with its head first.

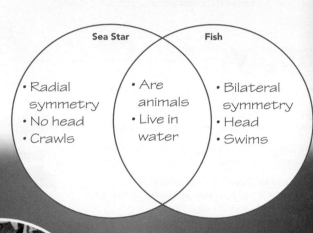

Sea Star | Fish

- Radial symmetry
- No head
- Crawls

- Are animals
- Live in water

- Bilateral symmetry
- Head
- Swims

146 Introduction to Animals

Professional Development Note

Teacher to Teacher

Introduction to Animals To introduce this unit, I pose this question to my students. *Why are all vertebrates and most arthropods bilaterally symmetrical?* To help them visualize this concept we tie a string one meter long tautly between two points. (A thin metal sheet on edge will also work). Students are given a sheet of paper and asked to balance it on the string. After a few unsuccessful tries, they are told that they may fold the paper. Immediately they fold it in half, and the paper will rest stably, hanging from the string. For organisms that fly, swim, walk, run, or crawl, symmetry allows for balanced propulsion and efficient locomotion.

Leslie Pohley
Largo Middle School
Largo, Florida

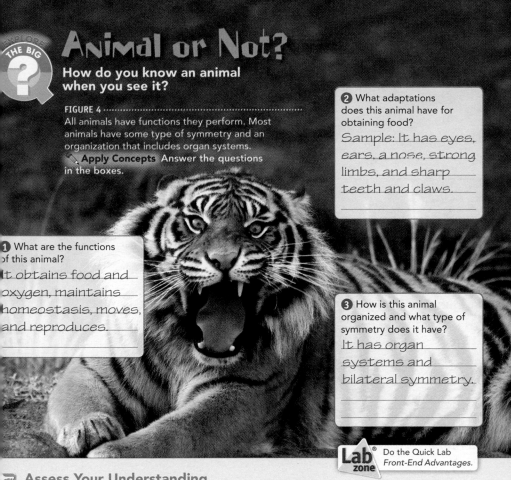

Animal or Not?

How do you know an animal when you see it?

FIGURE 4 ································
All animals have functions they perform. Most animals have some type of symmetry and an organization that includes organ systems.

✏ **Apply Concepts** Answer the questions in the boxes.

1 What are the functions of this animal?

It obtains food and oxygen, maintains homeostasis, moves, and reproduces.

2 What adaptations does this animal have for obtaining food?

Sample: It has eyes, ears, a nose, strong limbs, and sharp teeth and claws.

3 How is this animal organized and what type of symmetry does it have?

It has organ systems and bilateral symmetry.

Lab zone Do the Quick Lab
Front-End Advantages.

Assess Your Understanding

a. Infer Why do you think bilateral symmetry is an advantage for an animal?

Sample: It has a head that includes sense organs.

c. ANSWER THE BIG ? How do you know an animal when you see it?

I know an animal based on its functions, organization, and symmetry.

ot it? ·················

○ **I get it!** Now I know that symmetry relates to body structure because animals without symmetry have only cells, animals with radial symmetry have tissues and often organ systems, and animals with bilateral symmetry have organ systems.

○ **I need extra help with** See TE note.

Go to **MY SCIENCE COACH** *online for help with this subject.*

147

Differentiated Instruction

L1 Describing Animals Ask students to select their favorite animals. Then tell them to create a poster similar to **Figure 4.** They should list the functions, adaptations, organization, and symmetry of the animal.

L3 Comparing Symmetry Ask students to make a poster listing and comparing three animals with radial symmetry and three animals with bilateral symmetry. Students should include drawings or pictures and a brief description of each animal.

Elaborate

Explore the Big Q ? UbD

Direct students' attention to **Figure 4.** Briefly summarize what students have learned about animals so far. Ask: **What do animals need to do to survive?** *(Eat food, breathe oxygen, maintain homeostasis, and reproduce)* **What is an adaptation?** *(A trait or behavior that helps an organism perform its life functions)* **How is an animal body organized?** *(Into cells, tissues, organs, and organ systems)* **What are two common types of symmetry?** *(Radial and bilateral symmetry)*

Lab Resource: Quick Lab

L1 **FRONT-END ADVANTAGES** Students will explore the location of the five sense organs in animals with bilateral symmetry.

Evaluate

Assess Your Understanding

After students answer the questions, have them evaluate their understanding by completing the appropriate sentence.

Answer the Big Q ? UbD

To help students focus on the Big Question, lead a class discussion about what makes an animal an animal.

RTI Response to Intervention

1a. If students have trouble recognizing the importance of bilateral symmetry, **then** show students several photos of animals with bilateral symmetry in which they can identify a head.

  b. If students have difficulty describing animals, **then** review with them the characteristics of animals.

MY SCIENCE COACH Have students go online for help in understanding animal traits.

Name _____ Date _____ Class _____

Animal Body Plans

Inquiry Warm-Up, *How Many Ways Can You Fold It?*
In the Inquiry Warm-Up, you folded paper shapes to investigate two types of symmetry and named animals that have each type of body plan symmetry. Using what you learned from that activity, answer the questions below.

1. **CLASSIFY** Is the human body symmetrical like the triangle or symmetrical like the circle? Explain.

_____
_____
_____

2. **COMPARE AND CONTRAST** Compare the symmetry of a human with the symmetry of a horse.

_____
_____

3. **COMPARE AND CONTRAST** Compare the symmetry of a human with the symmetry of a jellyfish.

_____
_____
_____

4. **POSE QUESTIONS** Suppose a person is trying to classify organisms according to body plan symmetry. What do you think would be a good question to ask to help make a decision?

_____
_____
_____

Name _____ Date _____ Class _____

Animal Body Plans

How Are Animal Bodies Organized?

got it? ···

○ **I get it!** Now I know that animal bodies are organized into _____

_____

○ **I need extra help with** _____

_____

How Is Symmetry Related to Body Structure?

1a. INFER Why do you think bilateral symmetry is an advantage for an

animal? _____

_____

_____

b. ANSWER 🔵 How do you know an animal when you see it? _____

_____

got it? ···

○ **I get it!** Now I know that symmetry relates to body structure because _____

_____

_____

_____

○ **I need extra help with** _____

_____

Key Concept Summaries

Animal Body Plans

How Are Animal Bodies Organized?

The animals within each phylum have uniquely organized body structures. This organization is called a body plan. **The organization of an animal's cells into higher levels of structure, including tissues, organs, and organ systems, helps to describe an animal's body plan.**

A group of similar cells that performs a specific function is a **tissue.** Muscle tissue, nervous tissue, and connective tissue are all animal tissues. Different tissues that work together to perform a task make up an **organ.** An organ performs more complex functions than the tissues that make it up could perform alone. Groups of related organs form an organ system. These systems perform the broadest functions of the animal.

How Is Symmetry Related to Body Structure?

Many organisms have a balance of body parts called symmetry. An animal has **radial symmetry** if many imaginary lines can be drawn through a central point to divide it into two mirror images. For example, as seen from above, a jellyfish is circular. So any imaginary line drawn through its center divides it into mirror images. These lines are called lines of symmetry.

Most animals have bilateral symmetry. An animal has **bilateral symmetry** if only one line of symmetry can be drawn to divide it into halves that are mirror images. Butterflies, crabs, and humans all have bilateral symmetry. If no line can be drawn to divide an animal into halves that are mirror images, the animal is said to be asymmetrical.

Body structure is related to symmetry. **The bodies of animals without symmetry are organized simply, with some specialized cells but no tissues. In contrast, animals with radial symmetry have complex body plans with tissues and usually with organ systems. Animals with bilateral symmetry have organ systems.** All organisms with radial symmetry live in water. Most do not have front and back ends. Also, they do not have heads with specialized sense organs. In general, animals with bilateral symmetry are larger and more complex than animals with radial symmetry. Most animals with bilateral symmetry have heads at their front ends. Most of an animal's specialized sense organs, such as its eyes, are in its head.

On a separate sheet of paper, describe how animal bodies are organized. Then explain how symmetry is related to body structure.

Name _____ Date _____ Class _____

Animal Body Plans

Understanding Main Ideas
Classify the following animals as having no symmetry, bilateral symmetry, or radial symmetry. Write your responses on the lines below the animals.

1.

Sea Urchin

_____

2.

Sponge

_____

3.

Beaver

_____

4.

Frog

_____

5.

Sea Star

_____

6.

Ant

_____

Building Vocabulary
Fill in the blank to complete each statement.

7. If an animal has a head end and a tail, it has _____ symmetry.

8. A(n) _____ is a group of similar cells that performs a specific function.

9. All animals with _____ symmetry live in water.

10. A(n) _____ performs more complex functions than the tissues that make it up could perform alone.

Animal Body Plans

> Follow the procedure below to create models of two animals with different body plans. Then use a separate sheet of paper to answer the questions that follow.

Radial Symmetry and Bilateral Symmetry

Materials

scissors
tape or glue

Procedure

Cut out both models below. Cut along all dotted lines. Tape the two halves of the fish together. Attach the fins to the fish with tape or glue where the letters correspond. Bring the edges of the jellyfish together to overlap and tape them together to form a cone-like figure.

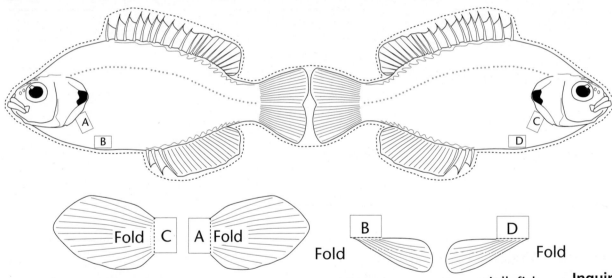

1. What type of symmetry does the fish display? How many lines of symmetry are there?

2. What type of symmetry does the jellyfish display? How many lines of symmetry are there?

3. Which animal do you think is the faster swimmer? Why?

4. This fish has one of some body parts, such as the mouth and tail fin. Other body parts, such as the eyes and small side fins, come in pairs. Make a generalization about where the single body parts occur on a fish's body and where paired body parts occur in relation to the line of symmetry.

Inquiry

Jellyfish

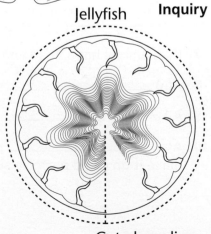

Cut along line

Place the outside corner, the corner away from the dotted line, in the corner of your copy machine to copy onto letter-size paper.

Lesson Quiz

Animal Body Plans

Write the letter of the correct answer on the line at the left.

1. ___ Which structure is found in all animals?

   A organ system

   B head

   C cell

   D bone

2. ___ Which of these is an example of an organ?

   A bone

   B skeleton

   C bone cell

   D bone tissue

3. ___ Because one line can be drawn to divide it into two halves that are mirror images, a butterfly has

   A an organ system

   B radial symmetry

   C no symmetry

   D bilateral symmetry

4. ___ What type of tissue processes information in the head of an animal with bilateral symmetry?

   A muscle tissue

   B nervous tissue

   C bone tissue

   D heart tissue

Fill in the blank to complete each statement.

5. The most basic unit of structure in animal bodies is the _____.

6. A(n) _____ is a group of similar cells that perform a specific function.

7. A jellyfish has _____ symmetry because many lines can be drawn to divide its body into two halves that are mirror images.

8. A group of related tissues work together to form a(n) _____.

9. A sponge is an example of an animal with _____ symmetry.

10. An animal with bilateral symmetry usually has a(n) _____ at its front end.

Animal Body Plans

Answer Key

After the Inquiry Warm-Up

1. The human body is symmetrical like the triangle. The body could be folded into identical halves down the center because the right and left sides of the body have the same structure.

2. Humans and horses have the same type of symmetry. A line can be drawn down the center of each body, and the two sides mirror each other.

3. Humans and jellyfish have different types of symmetry. Only one line can be drawn down the center of a human body so that the two sides mirror each other. An infinite number of lines can be drawn across the top of a jellyfish body so that the two sides mirror each other.

4. Sample: Is there only one line that can be drawn down the center of the organism's body so that the two sides mirror each other, or can an infinite number of lines be drawn so that the two sides mirror each other?

Key Concept Summaries

Animal bodies are organized into higher levels of structure. The basic unit is the cell. A group of similar cells that performs a specific function is a tissue. Different tissues that work together to perform a task make up an organ. Groups of related organs form an organ system. Many organisms have a balance of body parts called symmetry. Asymmetrical animals usually do not have tissues. Animals with radial symmetry have tissues and usually organ systems. Animals with bilateral symmetry are the most complex. They have organ systems and are usually larger.

Review and Reinforce

1. radial symmetry

2. no symmetry

3. bilateral symmetry

4. bilateral symmetry

5. radial symmetry

6. bilateral symmetry

7. bilateral

8. tissue

9. radial

10. organ

Enrich

1. bilateral symmetry; one

2. radial symmetry; many

3. The fish is a faster swimmer. An animal with bilateral symmetry is more streamlined and can move faster.

4. The single body parts occur roughly on the line of symmetry. Paired body parts lie on either side of the line of symmetry.

Lesson Quiz

1. C
2. A
3. D
4. B
5. cell
6. tissue
7. radial
8. organ
9. no
10. head

Place the outside corner, the corner away from the dotted line, in the corner of your copy machine to copy onto letter-size paper.

Introduction to Invertebrates

How do you know an animal when you see it?

Lesson Pacing: 1–2 periods or $\frac{1}{2}$–1 block

🕐 **SHORT ON TIME?** To do this lesson in approximately half the time, do the Activate Prior Knowledge activity on page 148. A discussion of the Key Concept on page 149 will familiarize students with the lesson content. The rest of the lesson can be completed by students independently.

Preference Navigator, in the online Planning tools, allows you to customize *Interactive Science* to your own teaching style. You can also edit lesson plans by selecting the Lesson Planner option.

Digital Teacher's Edition allows you to access your Teacher's Edition and Resource materials online.

myscience.com online

Lesson Vocabulary

- cnidarian
- mollusk
- arthropod
- exoskeleton
- echinoderm
- endoskeleton

Content Refresher

Professional Development Note

Coral Reef Ecology A diverse group of invertebrates can be found in and around coral reefs. In terms of the amount of organic matter available for consumption, coral reefs are the most productive ecosystems on Earth. More productive ecosystems typically support longer food chains and thereby more species diversity.

Another factor that contributes to species diversity in coral reefs is the large number of habitats the reef supports. The coral reef skeleton provides a structure that supports the corals themselves. In addition, the coral reef provides a substrate for sponges, anemones, and other sessile (nonmoving, attached) organisms. These organisms attract dozens of fish species, including predators such as sharks and rays.

Corals contain symbiotic photosynthetic algae from which the coral obtains its nutrients. Corals can survive without the algae, though the rate at which corals lay down reef is diminished. An increase in water temperature can cause the corals to expel their symbiotic algae and die. This fact is behind the well-known concern that coral reefs may be at risk from global warming.

LESSON OBJECTIVE

 Identify the characteristics of invertebrates and describe the major groups of them.

Blended Path
Active learning using Student Edition, Inquiry Path, and Digital Path

ENGAGE AND EXPLORE

Teach this lesson using a variety of resources. Begin by reading **My Planet Diary** as a class. Have students share ideas about how animals defend themselves. Then have students do the **Inquiry Warm-Up activity.** Students will compare natural and synthetic sponges. Discuss the function of pores in a sponge. The **After the Inquiry Warm-Up worksheet** sets up a discussion about what a sponge gets from the water. Have volunteers share their answers to question 4 about why sponges are adapted to take in large amounts of water.

EXPLAIN AND ELABORATE

Teach Key Concepts by explaining the term invertebrates and asking students to identify the main groups of invertebrates. **Lead a Discussion** about the symmetry and body structure of sponges and cnidarians. **Lead a Discussion** about the characteristics of different types of worms. Use **Figure 2** to identify the three major phyla of worms. **Lead a Discussion** about the characteristics of mollusks. Use **Figure 3** to identify the similarities and differences between the three major groups of mollusks. **Lead a Discussion** about arthropods and identify some examples of arthropods. Have students identify what all three arthropods in **Figure 4** have in common. **Lead a Discussion** about echinoderms. **Support the Big Q** by identifying the traits that confirm that the organisms are indeed animals. Hand out the **Key Concept Summaries** as a review of each part of the lesson. Students can also use the online **Vocab Flash Cards** to review key terms.

EVALUATE

Have students take the **Lesson Quiz.** For an alternate assessment, see the *ExamView®* Computer Test Generator, Progress Monitoring Assessments, or SuccessTracker™.

ELL Support

1 Content and Language
The word *arthropod* is made up of the two word parts *artho-* meaning "joint" and *-pod* meaning "foot."

DIFFERENTIATED INSTRUCTION KEY
L1 Struggling Students or Special Needs
L2 On-Level Students **L3** Advanced Students

LESSON PLANNER 4.3

Lab zone Inquiry Path
Hands-on learning in the Lab zone

Digital Path
Online learning at **my science online**.com

ENGAGE AND EXPLORE

To teach this lesson with an emphasis on inquiry, begin with the **Inquiry Warm-Up activity.** Students will compare natural and synthetic sponges. Discuss the function of pores in sponges. Have students do the **After the Inquiry Warm-Up worksheet.** Talk about the function of the pathways in sponges and how they help sponges meet their needs. Have volunteers share their answers to question 4 about why sponges are adapted to take in large amounts of water.

EXPLAIN AND ELABORATE

Focus on the **Inquiry Skill** for the lesson. Point out that when you classify, you group things that are alike in some way. How were the sponges in the **Inquiry Warm-Up activity** classified? (*As natural and synthetic*) **Build Inquiry** by observing the movement of earthworms. Do the **Teacher Demo** to show students how squids and other cephalopods move through water. **Support the Big Q** by discussing the traits of invertebrates that indicate they are animals. Have students do the **Lab Investigation** to test their hypotheses about earthworm preferences for soil and light conditions. Students can use the online **Vocab Flash Cards** to review key terms.

EVALUATE

Have students take the **Lesson Quiz.** For an alternate assessment, see the *ExamView*® Computer Test Generator, Progress Monitoring Assessments, or SuccessTracker™.

ENGAGE AND EXPLORE

Teach this lesson using digital resources. Begin by having students explore real-world connections to invertebrates at **My Planet Diary** online. Have them access the Chapter Resources to find the **Unlock the Big Question activity.** There they can answer the questions and refine their responses as they continue through the lesson. You can re-assign the activity and have students submit their work so you can track their progress.

EXPLAIN AND ELABORATE

Students reading above, at, or below the lexile measure of this lesson can access basic content readings at their level at **My Reading Web.** Have students use the online **Vocab Flash Cards** to preview key terms. Have students do the online **Interactive Art activity** to see the structure of an invertebrate. Assign the **Do the Math activity** online and have students submit their work to you. Do the **Art in Motion** to show students the range of body forms in invertebrates. To **Support the Big Q** identify traits that indicate invertebrates are animals. The **Key Concept Summaries** online allow students to read a summary and see an image associated with each part of the lesson. Online remediation is available at **My Science Coach.**

EVALUATE

Have students take the **Lesson Quiz.** For an alternate assessment, see the *ExamView*® Computer Test Generator, Progress Monitoring Assessments, or SuccessTracker™.

2 Frontload the Lesson
Preview the lesson visuals, labels, and captions. Ask students what they know about the words *exoskeleton* and *endoskeleton*. Explain the specific meanings these words have in science.

3 Comprehensible Input
Have students study the visuals and their captions on pages 149, 150, 151, 152, and 153 to support the Key Concepts of the lesson.

4 Language Production
Pair or group students with varied language abilities to complete labs collaboratively for language practice. Have each student copy the completed written lab for personal reference.

5 Assess Understanding
Have students keep a content area log for this lesson using a two-column format with the headings "What I Understand" and "What I Don't Understand." Follow up so that students can move items from the "Don't Understand" to the "Understand" column.

LESSON 4.3

Introduction to Invertebrates

Establish Learning Objective

After this lesson, students will be able to:

🔑 Identify the characteristics of invertebrates and describe the major groups of them.

Engage

Activate Prior Knowledge

MY PLANET DIARY Read *Ready, Aim, Fire!* with the class. Point out that animals need a way to protect themselves from predators. Ask: **What is a predator?** *(An organism that kills another organism for food or nutrients)* **What are two different ways that animals can protect themselves from predators?** *(They can hide or they can attack.)* **How does the bombardier beetle protect itself from predators?** *(It sprays them with hot chemicals.)*

BIG IDEAS OF SCIENCE REFERENCE LIBRARY 📖
Have students look up the following topics: Jellyfish, Spiders.

Explore

Lab Resource: Inquiry Warm-Up 🔬

L1 **HOW DO NATURAL AND SYNTHETIC SPONGES COMPARE?** Students will observe and compare the properties of natural and synthetic sponges.

LESSON
3
Introduction to Invertebrates

🔑 **What Are Invertebrates?**

my planet diary

Ready, Aim, Fire!

To *bombard* is to "attack with materials that explode." This action is exactly what the bombardier beetle does. This incredible insect sprays predators with an explosion of deadly chemicals from its own body!

Why don't the chemicals kill the beetle? The chemicals needed for the spray are stored in different places in the beetle's body. When the beetle defends itself, the chemicals are combined into a deadly mixture. The mixture is sprayed on a predator at a temperature of 100°C!

FUN FACTS

Communicate Discuss the following question with a partner. Then write your answer below.
What other animals do you know about that have unique forms of self defense? Describe their defenses.

<u>Sample: Some insects look like sticks</u>
<u>so predators do not see them.</u>

▶ **PLANET DIARY** Go to **Planet Diary** to learn more about invertebrates.

 Do the Inquiry Warm-Up *How Do Natural and Synthetic Sponges Compare?*

What Are Invertebrates?

At dusk near the edge of a meadow, a grasshopper leaps through the grass. Nearby, a hungry spider waits in its web. The grasshopper leaps into the web. It's caught! The spider bites the grasshopper to stun it and quickly wraps it in silk. The grasshopper will soon become a tasty meal for the spider.

SUPPORT ALL READERS
Lexile Measure = 840L   **Lexile Word Count = 913**

Prior Exposure to Content: May be the first time students have encountered this topic

Academic Vocabulary: *classify, identify, main idea*

Science Vocabulary: *cnidarian, mollusk, arthropod, echinoderm*

Concept Level: Generally appropriate for most students in this grade

Preteach With: My Planet Diary "Ready, Aim, Fire!" and Figure 3 activity

Go to **My Reading Web** to access leveled readings that provide a foundation for the content.

my science online.com

Vocabulary

- cnidarian • mollusk • arthropod • exoskeleton
- echinoderm • endoskeleton

Skills

- ⊙ Reading: Identify the Main Idea
- △ Inquiry: Classify

Invertebrate Characteristics A grasshopper and a spider are both invertebrates. ⚷ **Animals that do not have backbones are invertebrates. The main invertebrate groups are sponges, cnidarians, flatworms, roundworms, segmented worms, mollusks, arthropods, and echinoderms.** About 96 percent of known animals are invertebrates. They live in every climate.

Sponges Sponges, such as the one shown in **Figure 1**, are asymmetrical invertebrates. They have some specialized cells but no tissues or organs. Unlike most animals you know, adult sponges stay in one place, like plants. But, like other animals, sponges take food into their bodies to get energy.

Cnidarians Jellyfishes and corals are examples of **cnidarians** (ny DEHR ee unz), invertebrates that have stinging cells and take food into a central body cavity. Cnidarians have radial symmetry. Although they lack organs, they do have some tissues.

FIGURE 1 ··································
▶ INTERACTIVE ART **Sponges and Cnidarians**
Both sponges and cnidarians are animals that live in water.

✎ **Interpret Photos** Based on symmetry, label these animals as sponges or cnidarians. Then write how sponges and cnidarians are alike and different.

Both are invertebrates that live in water. Sponges are asymmetrical. Cnidarians have radial symmetry.

Cnidarian

Cnidarian

Sponge

149

Explain

Introduce Vocabulary

Explain that the prefix *exo-* means "out" and the prefix *endo-* means "in." Tell students to use these prefixes to remember that an *exoskeleton* is outside the body and an *endoskeleton* is inside the body.

Teach Key Concepts ⚷

Remind students that animals without backbones are called invertebrates. Ask: **How are invertebrates different from vertebrates?** *(Vertebrates have a backbone.)* **What are the main groups of invertebrates?** *(Sponges, cnidarians, flatworms, roundworms, segmented worms, mollusks, arthropods, echinoderms)* **How does the number of invertebrates compare to the number of vertebrates?** *(Invertebrates make up about 96 percent of all animals.)*

Lead a Discussion

SPONGES AND CNIDARIANS Explain that sponges are considered to be the simplest type of animal in terms of structure. Ask: **What type of symmetry do sponges have?** *(They are asymmetrical.)* **How would you describe their body structure?** *(They have cells, but lack tissues and organs.)* **What type of symmetry do cnidarians have?** *(They have radial symmetry.)* **How would you describe their body structure?** *(They have cells and tissues, but no organs.)* **What are two examples of cnidarians?** *(Jellyfishes and corals)*

My Planet Diary provides an opportunity for students to explore real-world connections to invertebrates.

Interactive Art shows the structure of an invertebrate.

my science online .com ▶ Describing Invertebrates

ⒺⓁⓁ Support

1 Content and Language

Write the terms *exoskeleton* and *endoskeleton* on the board. Explain that the Latin prefix *exo-* means "outside" and that the prefix *endo-* is derived from a Greek word meaning "within."

2 Frontload the Lesson

Have students name an invertebrate they have seen. Encourage students to identify the basic characteristic that is shared by all invertebrates.

3 Comprehensible Input

Have students list the eight groups of invertebrates on horizontal rows of a table. Encourage students to include two or more vertical columns with headings such as *Body Structures, Type of Symmetry,* and *Other Details*. Then, have students work independently or in pairs to fill in their tables.

Explain

Lead a Discussion

WORMS Find out if students have ever seen or touched a worm. Have them describe the characteristics they observed. Ask: **What characteristics do all worms have in common?** *(They are invertebrates with bilateral symmetry. They have tissues, organs, and organ systems.)* **Some worms have an eyespot. What does it do?** *(An eyespot detects light.)* **What does it mean if a worm is segmented?** *(Its body is made up of linked sections.)*

Teach With Visuals

Tell students to look at **Figure 2.** Remind students that a phylum is a level of classification just below kingdom. That means that each group of worms is in the animal kingdom, but they are different enough to be placed into different phyla. Ask: **What are the three phyla of worms?** *(Flatworms, roundworms, and segmented worms)* **In what ways are the worms in the photos different from one another?** *(Students might suggest that the earthworm is round and made up of segments. The round worm is twisted into spirals. The planarian is flat and has an obvious head.)*

△ **Classify** Remind students that when they classify, they put things into groups based on ways in which they are alike.

Explore

Build Inquiry **Lab zone**

L1 INVESTIGATE EARTHWORMS

Materials dark construction paper, earthworm, soil, transparent jar

Time 10 minutes per day for several days

Fill a jar with loose, moist soil and then add the earthworm. Wrap the jar with dark construction paper and keep the jar out of direct sunlight. Have students note the earthworm's location in the soil over several days. They will have to remove the construction paper to observe the worm's location and replace it after each observation. Return the earthworm to natural soil at the end of the activity.

Ask: **How did the earthworm's position change?** *(It tunneled through the soil.)* **In what way do earthworms help soil?** *(They break up soil as they move through it. They also enrich the soil with their waste.)*

Worms If you have ever worked in a garden, you have probably seen some worms. The three major phyla of worms are flatworms, roundworms, and segmented worms, which you can see in **Figure 2.** All worms have bilateral symmetry, with head and tail ends. They also have tissues, organs, and organ systems. Flatworms have flat, soft bodies. Some have eye spots on their heads that detect light. Roundworms look like smooth, thin tubes. They have two body openings: a mouth and an anus. Segmented worms have bodies made up of many linked sections called segments. They are the simplest animals with a brain. Their brains help them detect food and predators.

FIGURE 2 ·················
Worms
The three major phyla of worms are flatworms, roundworms, and segmented worms.

✎ **Classify** In the boxes, write the phylum of each worm. Then write notes that describe each worm.

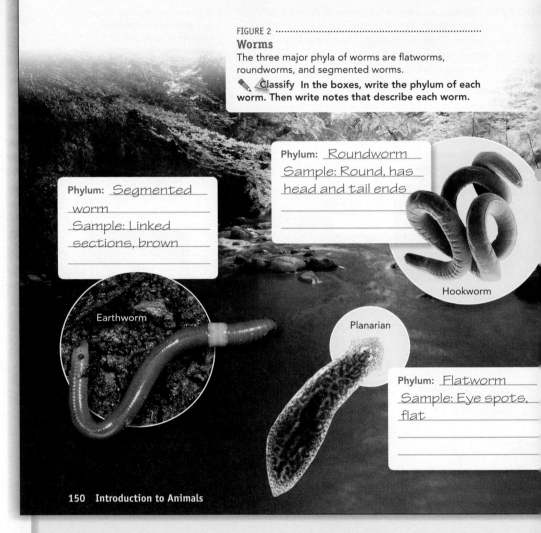

Phylum: _Roundworm_
Sample: Round, has
head and tail ends

Phylum: _Segmented_
worm
Sample: Linked
sections, brown

Hookworm

Earthworm

Planarian

Phylum: _Flatworm_
Sample: Eye spots,
flat

150 **Introduction to Animals**

Mollusks Have you ever picked up seashells on the beach? Those seashells probably belonged to a mollusk. Invertebrates with soft, unsegmented bodies that are often protected by a hard shell are called **mollusks.** All mollusks have a thin layer of tissue called a mantle that covers their internal organs and an organ called a foot. Depending on the type of mollusk, the foot might be used for crawling, digging, or catching prey. **Figure 3** shows some mollusks.

The three major groups of mollusks are gastropods, bivalves, and cephalopods (SEF uh luh pahdz). Gastropods, such as snails, have a single shell or no shell, and a distinct head. Bivalves, such as clams, have two shells and a simple nervous system. Cephalopods may have an external or internal shell or no shell at all. They have good vision and large brains to help them remember what they've learned. A squid is a cephalopod with an internal shell.

✏️ **Identify the Main Idea**
Underline the main idea in the second paragraph. Then circle the supporting details.

FIGURE 3 ·······································

Mollusks
A snail, clam, and squid do not look alike, but they have the same basic structure.

✏️ **Summarize** Fill in each box in the chart for each organism. Then write a title for the chart.

Groups of Mollusks

Characteristics	Gastropod	Bivalve	Cephalopod
	Snail	Clam	Squid
	Foot	Foot	Foot
Number of Shells	1	2	1
Internal or External Shells	External	External	Internal
Uses Foot to ...	Crawl	Dig	Catch prey

151

Differentiated Instruction

L1 Make a Glossary Have students start a personal glossary of vocabulary terms. For each term, students should write the term and its definition. They should also include a simple sketch or drawing to go with the term.

L3 Classify Mollusks Ask students to research mollusks that people eat. Tell students to describe the mollusks and where they might be found.

Explain

Lead a Discussion

MOLLUSKS Explain that mollusks make up a group of invertebrates. Ask: **If you found a new animal in the ocean, what features would you look for to determine whether it is a mollusk?** *(Bilateral symmetry, soft body, mantle, and foot.)* **Why don't you find mollusks in hot dry areas?** *(Their soft bodies would dry out.)* **What are the three major groups of mollusks?** *(Gastropods, bivalves, and cephalopods)*

✏️ **Identify the Main Idea** Tell students that when they identify the main idea, they determine the most important, or biggest, idea in a paragraph or section. The other information in the paragraph or section supports or further explains the main idea.

Teach With Visuals

Tell students to look at **Figure 3.** Point out that all mollusks, no matter how different they look, share common features. Ask: **What do these three mollusks have in common?** *(Each of them has a mantle, a foot, a digestive tract, and a shell.)* **What is a foot?** *(A muscular structure adapted for crawling, digging, or catching prey)*

Elaborate

Teacher Demo 🔬Lab zone

L1 JET PROPULSION

Materials sink, balloon, water

Time 10 minutes

Fill the balloon with water. Pinch the neck to keep water from flowing out. Immerse the balloon in a sink filled with water. Release the balloon.

Ask: **What happen to the balloon? Why?** *(The balloon moved forward because water shot out of the back of the balloon.)* **How is the balloon like a squid or other cephalopod?** *(The balloon models how cephalopods move through water.)*

Explain

Lead a Discussion

ARTHROPODS Tell students that arthropods are another group of invertebrates. Ask: **What is an arthropod?** *(An invertebrate that has an external skeleton, a segmented body, and jointed appendages.)* **What kinds of appendages do arthropods have?** *(Legs, wings, and antennae)* **What are some groups of arthropods?** *(Crustaceans, arachnids, insects, centipedes and millipedes)* Tell students that arthropods are classified according to the number of body sections, legs, and antennae. A crustacean has two or three body sections, five or more pairs of legs, and two pairs of antennae. An arachnid has two body sections, four pairs of legs, and no antennae. Insects have three body sections, three pairs of legs, one pair of antennae, and may have wings. Ask: **What is an example of a crustacean?** *(A crab)* **What is an example of an arachnid?** *(A spider)* **What are some examples of insects?** *(Samples: bees, ants, butterflies, moths, mosquitoes, ladybugs)*

Teach With Visuals

Tell students to look at **Figure 4.** Point out that each animal shown is a type of arthropod. Ask: **What do all three animals have in common?** *(They each have an exoskeleton, segmented bodies, and jointed appendages.)*

Make Analogies

WEARING ARMOR Ask students to imagine what it would feel like to wear a suit of armor. Explain that having an exoskeleton is a lot like wearing armor. Ask: **What is a benefit of an exoskeleton?** *(Sample: It protects the body from damage.)* Tell students that, in addition to protecting the body, an exoskeleton prevents water loss and provides support for the body. Ask: **What would be a disadvantage of wearing a suit of armor all the time?** *(Sample: It would be hard to move. It would be uncomfortable.)* **What might be some disadvantages of having an exoskeleton?** *(Samples: It is stiff and makes movement difficult. It limits growth.)*

Do the Math!

L1 Explain that a circle graph is divided into sections that each represent a part of the whole. The size of each section of the circle graph on this page corresponds to the number of each type of animal. In this graph, the key describes each section by its color.

See the *Math Skill and Problem-Solving Activities* for support.

---

did you know?

Smaller than a paper clip, honeybees are important insects. They collect nectar from flowers to make honey and pollinate some plants. Without the honey bee, an apple tree might not produce the apples you eat.

do the math! Analyzing Data

This circle graph shows a distribution of animal groups.

Distribution of Animal Groups

12% 11% 4%

73%

- Insects
- Noninsect arthropods
- Nonarthropod invertebrates
- Vertebrates

1 Read Graphs What percentage of animals are not insects?

_27%_

2 CHALLENGE What percentage of animals are invertebrates that are not insects?

12% + 11% = 23% are noninsect invertebrates

Arthropods At first you may not think that a crab and a spider have anything in common. But look at the spider and crab in **Figure 4.** Crabs and spiders are **arthropods,** or invertebrates that have hard outer coverings, segmented bodies, and pairs of jointed appendages. Legs, wings, and antennae are appendages. The outer covering is called an **exoskeleton,** or outer skeleton. At times, the exoskeleton is shed and replaced as the animal grows. One arthropod group, crustaceans, includes animals such as crabs. A second group, arachnids, includes animals such as spiders. A third group includes centipedes, millipedes, and insects, such as bees and ants.

Insect

Arachnid

FIGURE 4

Arthropods
Members of the three arthropod groups have different characteristics.

✎ **Observe** Tell how the number of pairs of legs of a spider and a bee differ.

The spider has 4 pairs of legs. The bee has 3 pairs of legs.

Crustacean

Digital Lesson: Assign the *Do the Math* activity online and have students submit their work to you.

Art in Motion shows the range of body forms of invertebrates.

my science online.com   **Describing Invertebrates**

Echinoderms An **echinoderm** is an invertebrate that has an internal skeleton and a system of fluid-filled tubes. An internal skeleton is called an **endoskeleton.** Echinoderms, shown in Figure 5, have radial symmetry. They use their system of tubes to move and obtain food and oxygen. Sea cucumbers, sea stars, sea urchins, and brittle stars are the major echinoderm groups.

Sea cucumber

Sea star

Sea urchins

Brittle stars

FIGURE 5 ....

ART IN MOTION **Echinoderms**
Echinoderms are diverse animals, but all live in salt water.

Compare and Contrast In the chart, write a brief description of the shape and symmetry of each echinoderm.

	Sea Cucumber	Sea Star	Sea Urchin	Brittle Star
Shape	Long, round	Star, short arms	Round, spiny	Star, long arms
Symmetry	Radial	Radial	Radial	Radial

Lab zone Do the Lab Investigation *Earthworm Responses.*

Assess Your Understanding

a. **Identify** How are all cnidarians alike?
   They have stinging cells, a body cavity, and radial symmetry.

b. **Explain** If you saw a worm, how would you identify its phylum?
   I would look at its body shape.

got it?

○ **I get it!** Now I know that invertebrates _are animals that have no backbone._

○ I need extra help with _See TE note._

Go to MY SCIENCE COACH online for help with this subject.

153

Explain

Lead a Discussion

ECHINODERMS Tell students that echinoderms live on the sea floor at different depths throughout the ocean. Explain that echinoderms have endoskeletons. Ask: **What is an endoskeleton?** (*A support system, or skeleton, located on the inside of the body*) **What type of symmetry do echinoderms have?** (*Radial symmetry*)

Support the Big Q ? UbD

RECOGNIZE INVERTEBRATES Have students look at the photographs in this section. Point out that many invertebrates do not look like animals that people are used to seeing. Ask: **What traits would indicate that these organisms are animals?** (*Sample: They move, take in oxygen, eat, and reproduce.*) **What lab skill do scientists use to classify invertebrates as animals?** (*Sample: observing*)

21st Century Learning

CRITICAL THINKING Direct students' attention to **Figure 5.** Ask: **Which of the four echinoderms shown looks least like the others?** (*Students will most likely identify the sea cucumber as being different.*) **If sea cucumbers do not look like other echinoderms, why do you think they are classified in this group?** (*They have endoskeletons and they use a system of tubes to move and get food.*)

Elaborate

Lab Resource: Lab Investigation Lab zone

L2 EARTHWORM RESPONSES Students will test hypotheses regarding earthworm preferences for soil and light conditions.

Evaluate

Assess Your Understanding

After students answer the questions, have them evaluate their understanding by completing the appropriate sentence.

R T I Response to Intervention

1a. If students cannot identify the similarities among all cnidarians, **then** review examples of cnidarians and their traits.

b. If students need help classifying worms, **then** have them look back at the photographs of worms from different phyla.

MY SCIENCE COACH Have students go online for help in understanding invertebrates.

Differentiated Instruction

L1 Summarize Ask students to prepare a poster that summarizes the information they have learned about invertebrates. Tell students to include pictures or drawings along with their descriptions.

L3 Model Suction Explain to students that echinoderms hold on to objects using suction. Tell small groups of students to use a plastic dropper to model the suction of a sea star. Have groups present their models to the class.

Lab zone **After the Inquiry Warm-Up**

Introduction to Invertebrates

Inquiry Warm-Up, *How Do Natural and Synthetic Sponges Compare?*
In the Inquiry Warm-Up, you investigated similarities and differences between a synthetic sponge and a sponge that was once a living animal in the ocean. Using what you learned from that activity, answer the questions below.

1. **USE PRIOR KNOWLEDGE** Your teacher pointed out pores on the surface of the natural sponge. Recall other living things you have studied that have pores. What do you think is the function of the pores in sponge?

   _____

   _____

2. **DEVELOP HYPOTHESES** Your teacher pointed out that the pores on the surface of a natural sponge are the openings of pathways. What do you think is the function of these pathways?

   _____

   _____

3. **USE PRIOR KNOWLEDGE** Recall the things that all animals need. What do you think a sponge gets from the water it takes in?

   _____

   _____

4. **DEVELOP HYPOTHESES** Most sponges are anchored in one location. How do you think this relates to the fact that sponges are adapted to take in large amounts of water?

   _____

   _____

   _____

Assess Your Understanding

Introduction to Invertebrates

What Are Invertebrates?

1a. IDENTIFY How are all cnidarians alike? _____
_____

b. EXPLAIN If you saw a worm, how would you identify its phylum? _____
_____

gotit? ....

○ **I get it!** Now I know that invertebrates _____
_____

○ **I need extra help with** _____
_____

Introduction to Invertebrates

What Are Invertebrates?

Animals that do not have backbones are invertebrates. The main invertebrate groups are sponges, cnidarians, flatworms, roundworms, segmented worms, mollusks, arthropods, and echinoderms. About 96 percent of known animals are invertebrates. They live in every climate.

Sponges are asymmetrical invertebrates. They have some specialized cells, but no tissues or organs. Adult sponges stay in one place.

Jellyfishes and coral are examples of **cnidarians,** invertebrates that have stinging cells and take food into a central body cavity. Cnidarians have radial symmetry. Their bodies have some tissues but no organs.

Worms have bilateral symmetry, a head and tail, as well as tissues, organs, and organ systems. The three major phyla of worms are flatworms, roundworms, and segmented worms. Flatworms have flat, soft bodies. Roundworms look like smooth, thin tubes. Segmented worms have bodies made up of linked sections. They are the simplest animals with a brain.

Mollusks are invertebrates with soft, unsegmented bodies often protect by a hard shell. They have a thin layer of tissue called a mantle that covers their internal organs, as well as an organ called a foot. The three groups of mollusks are gastropods, bivalves, and cephalopods. Gastropods, such as snails, have a single shell or no shell, and a distinct head. Bivalves, such as clams, have two shells and a simple nervous system. Cephalopods, such as squids, may have an internal or external shell or no shell at all.

Arthropods are invertebrates that have hard outer coverings, segmented bodies, and pairs of jointed appendages. Legs, wings, and antennae are possible appendages. The hard outer covering is called an **exoskeleton.** It may be shed as the animal grows. Crustaceans such as crabs, arachnids such as spiders, and centipedes, millipedes, and insects are all arthropods.

Echinoderms are invertebrates with an internal skeleton and a system of fluid-filled tubes. An internal skeleton is called an **endoskeleton.** Echinoderms have radial symmetry. Sea cucumbers, sea stars, sea urchins, and brittle stars are the major echinoderm groups.

On a separate sheet of paper, make a chart that organizes the invertebrates by their symmetry.

Review and Reinforce

Introduction to Invertebrates

Understanding Main Ideas

Match each term with its definition by writing the letter of the correct definition in the right column on the line beside the term in the left column.

1. ___ sponge

2. ___ cnidarian

3. ___ flatworm

4. ___ roundworm

5. ___ segmented worm

6. ___ mollusk

7. ___ arthropod

8. ___ echinoderm

a. a type of worm that may have an eye spot on its head

b. an invertebrate with an exoskeleton, segmented body, and pairs of jointed appendages

c. an invertebrate with an internal skeleton and fluid-filled tubes

d. an animal with a soft, unsegmented body often protected by a hard shell

e. an asymmetrical animal without tissues or organs

f. the simplest animal with a brain

g. a type of worm that looks like a thin tube with a mouth and an anus

h. an invertebrate with stinging cells and a central body cavity

Building Vocabulary

Fill in the blank to complete each statement.

9. Jellyfish are examples of a group of animals called _____.

10. _____ have soft, unsegmented bodies that are often protected by a hard shell.

11. The _____ is the hard, outer covering of an arthropod.

12. Crustaceans and arachnids are two types of _____.

13. Some invertebrates have internal skeletons called _____.

14. A(n) _____ is an invertebrate with a system of fluid-filled tubes used to move and obtain food.

Enrich

Introduction to Invertebrates

> Cnidarians are a type of invertebrate. Read the passage and study the diagram below. Then use a separate sheet of paper to answer the questions that follow.

Cnidarians and Nematocysts

Cnidarians have specialized cells in their tentacles called cnidoblasts. Within the cnidoblasts are tiny stinging capsules called nematocysts. Inside the nematocyst capsule is a coiled thread. This thread injects venom into anything that brushes against the capsule's trigger, called a cniodil. The diagram below will help you understand how this occurs.

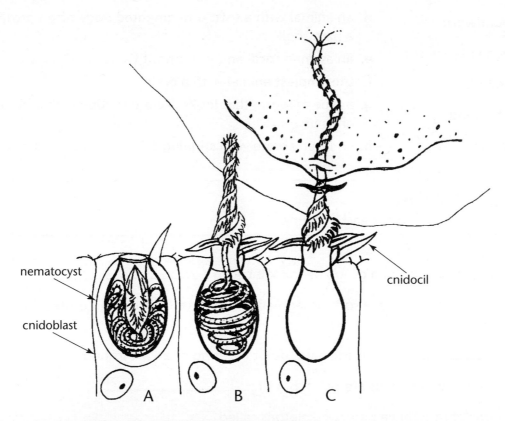

1. Using the information in the text and diagram above, list and describe the steps that occur in A, B, and C when a cnidarian captures food. You will need to include a step D as well. [*Hint:* What does the cnidarian do with the food after it stings it?]

2. People may be stung if they step on a dead jellyfish washed up on the beach. Why do you think this is so?

3. What functions do the stinging cells of a cnidarian serve?

Lesson Quiz

Introduction to Invertebrates

If the statement is true, write *true*. If the statement is false, change the underlined word or words to make the statement true.

1. _____ Echinoderms are different from most other invertebrates because they have an <u>endoskeleton</u>.

2. _____ Depending on a mollusk's type, it may use its <u>mantle</u> to crawl, dig, or catch prey.

3. _____ All worms have <u>bilateral</u> symmetry.

4. _____ <u>Sponges</u> have stinging cells and take food into a central body cavity.

5. _____ The simplest animals with a brain are <u>segmented</u> worms.

6. _____ About <u>50</u> percent of all known animals are invertebrates.

Write the letter of the correct answer on the line at the left.

7. ___ Which of the following is **not** a group of invertebrates?

   A sponges

   B mollusks

   C fishes

   D cnidarians

8. ___ To which group of invertebrates do cephalopods, such as squids, belong?

   A arthropods

   B echinoderms

   C cnidarians

   D mollusks

9. ___ Which of the following are appendages of a bee?

   A wings

   B eyes

   C lungs

   D abdomen

10. ___ Which group of invertebrates uses fluid-filled tubes to move or get food and oxygen?

   A cnidarians

   B echinoderms

   C arthropods

   D worms

Introduction to Invertebrates

Answer Key

After the Inquiry Warm-Up

1. Accept all reasonable answers. Sample: The pores in a sponge allow materials to move in and out of the sponge.

2. Accept all reasonable answers. Sample: The pathways in a sponge allow materials taken it at the pores to circulate within the body of the sponge.

3. Accept all reasonable answers. Sample: A sponge gets its food and oxygen from the water it takes in.

4. Accept all reasonable answers. Sample: Because most sponges are anchored in one location, they cannot move to seek out food. Being adapted to take in large amounts of water helps sponges to get all the food they need while staying in one place.

Key Concept Summary

Most sponges are asymmetrical. Cnidarians and echinoderms have radial symmetry. Worms, mollusks, and arthropods have bilateral symmetry.

Review and Reinforce

1. e		**2.** h	
3. a		**4.** g	
5. f		**6.** d	
7. b		**8.** c	
9. cnidarians		**10.** mollusks	
11. exoskeleton		**12.** arthropods	
13. endoskeletons		**14.** echinoderm	

Enrich

1. **A.** cnidoblast is ready for firing; thread is coiled

   B. cnidocil is touched, and coiled thread begins to shoot out

   C. coiled thread penetrates prey and injects venom; prey is paralyzed or killed

   D. tentacles pull food into mouth, cnidarian digests food

2. Although the jellyfish is dead, the stinging cells are still activated when a person steps on them.

3. obtaining food, defense

Lesson Quiz

1. exoskeleton	**2.** foot
3. true	**4.** cnidarians
5. true	**6.** 96
7. C	**8.** D
9. A	**10.** B

Place the outside corner, the corner away from the dotted line, in the corner of your copy machine to copy onto letter-size paper.

Introduction to Vertebrates

4 How do you know an animal when you see it?

Lesson Pacing: 2–3 periods or 1–1½ blocks

🕐 **SHORT ON TIME?** To do this lesson in approximately half the time, do the Activate Prior Knowledge activity on page 154. A discussion of the Key Concepts on pages 155 and 157 will familiarize students with the lesson content. Have students do the Quick Labs. The rest of the lesson can be completed by students independently.

Preference Navigator, in the online Planning tools, allows you to customize *Interactive Science* to your own teaching style. You can also edit lesson plans by selecting the Lesson Planner option.

Digital Teacher's Edition allows you to access your Teacher's Edition and Resource materials online.

MY SCIENCE ONLINE.com

Lesson Vocabulary

- chordate
- notochord
- vertebra
- ectotherm
- endotherm

 Content Refresher

Professional Development Note

Keeping the Heat Birds and mammals are endotherms. They maintain steady body temperatures regardless of the environmental temperature. This adaptation allows these animals to live in many different habitats and to function throughout the seasons. In contrast, the body temperatures of ectotherms, such as reptiles and amphibians, are greatly affected by the temperature of their surroundings.

Endotherms use a large amount of energy to maintain their body temperatures. The energy allows them to cool themselves in hot environments and to generate heat in cold environments. The metabolic rate—the rate at which an animal generates energy—for a resting endotherm is about six times greater than the metabolic rate of a resting ectotherm that is the same size. Endotherms must therefore eat more food than ectotherms to generate energy. For example, a snake might eat a small mammal only once every several days, yet a shrew—a tiny insect-eating mammal—eats constantly when it is awake.

All vertebrates, whether they are ectotherms or endotherms, need to maintain their body temperatures within a relatively narrow range. One reason is that an animal's enzymes function only within a narrow temperature range.

LESSON OBJECTIVES

🔑 Identify the characters of chordates and vertebrates.

🔑 Compare how vertebrates differ in the way they control body temperature.

Blended Path
Active learning using Student Edition, Inquiry Path, and Digital Path

ENGAGE AND EXPLORE

Teach this lesson using a variety of resources. Begin by reading **My Planet Diary** as a class. Have students share ideas about adaptations other animals have that help them survive in their environments. Then have students do the **Inquiry Warm-Up activity.** Students will investigate how an umbrella is like a skeleton. Discuss how the ribs of an umbrella compare to the exoskeleton of an arthropod. The **After the Inquiry Warm-Up worksheet** sets up a discussion about the characteristics of umbrella ribs and human ribs. Have volunteers share their answers to question 4 about the functions of the human rib cage.

EXPLAIN AND ELABORATE

Teach Key Concepts by explaining the three characteristics that all vertebrates have in common. Use **Figure 1** to illustrate the three characteristics shared by all chordates at some point in their lives. **Lead a Discussion** about backbones. Use the **Support the Big Q** to illustrate how vertebrates use their limbs to move in their environments.

Continue to **Teach Key Concepts** by explaining the differences between *endotherms* and *ectotherms.* Then have students practice the inquiry skill in the **Apply It activity.** Hand out the **Key Concept Summaries** as a review of each part of the lesson. Students can also use the online **Vocab Flash Cards** to review key terms.

EVALUATE

Have students take the **Lesson Quiz.** For an alternate assessment, see the *ExamView®* Computer Test Generator, Progress Monitoring Assessments, or SuccessTracker™.

ELL Support

1 Content and Language

Explain that in the word *ectotherm,* the prefix *ecto-* means "outside." An *ectotherm's* body temperature changes based on the environment outside of its body.

Lab zone Inquiry Path
Hands-on learning in the Lab zone

Digital Path
Online learning at my science online.com

ENGAGE AND EXPLORE

To teach this lesson with an emphasis on inquiry, begin with the **Inquiry Warm-Up activity.** Students will discover how an umbrella is like a skeleton. Discuss how the ribs of an umbrella are like the exoskeleton of an arthropod. Have students do the **After the Inquiry Warm-Up worksheet.** Talk about the key characteristics of the ribs of an umbrella and the ribs in the human body. Have volunteers share their answers to question 4 about functions of the human ribcage.

EXPLAIN AND ELABORATE

Focus on the **Inquiry Skill** for the lesson. Point out that when you draw conclusions, you use knowledge and evidence to make a statement about something. What conclusions can be drawn about the functions of the human ribcages based on the **Inquiry Warm-Up activity?** *(The human ribcages support the body and provide protection for vital organs.)* Use the **Support the Big Q** to illustrate how vertebrates use their limbs to move. Have students do the **Quick Lab** to make inferences about how vertebrates move based on their backbones and then share their results.

Review the characteristics of *ectotherms* and *endotherms* before beginning the **Apply It activity.** Ask volunteers to share the conclusions they drew about the animals. Do the **Quick Lab** to reinforce understanding of what materials are good insulators. Students can use the online **Vocab Flash Cards** to review key terms.

EVALUATE

Have students take the **Lesson Quiz.** For an alternate assessment, see the *ExamView®* Computer Test Generator, Progress Monitoring Assessments, or SuccessTracker™.

ENGAGE AND EXPLORE

Teach this lesson using digital resources. Begin by having students explore real-world connections to living things and their environment at **My Planet Diary** online. Have them access the Chapter Resources to find the **Unlock the Big Question activity.** There they can answer the questions and refine their responses as they continue through the lesson. You can re-assign the activity and have students submit their work so you can track their progress.

EXPLAIN AND ELABORATE

Students reading above, at, or below the lexile measure of this lesson can access basic content readings at their level at **My Reading Web.** Have students use the online **Vocab Flash Cards** to preview key terms. Use the **Support the Big Q** to illustrate how vertebrates move in their environments using their limbs. Do the **Quick Lab** and then ask students to share their results. Have students do the online **Interactive Art activity** to explore an endoskeleton.

Review the characteristics of *endotherms* and *ectotherms* before assigning the online **Apply It activity.** Ask volunteers to share what conclusions they drew about the animals. Have students submit their work to you. Have students do the **Quick Lab** to discover the insulating properties of different materials. The **Key Concept Summaries** online allow students to read a summary and see an image associated with each part of the lesson. Online remediation is available at **My Science Coach.**

EVALUATE

Have students take the **Lesson Quiz.** For an alternate assessment, see the *ExamView®* Computer Test Generator, Progress Monitoring Assessments, or SuccessTracker™.

2 Frontload the Lesson
Preview the lesson visuals, labels, and captions. Ask students what they know about the terms *ectotherm* and *endotherm.* Explain the specific meanings these words have in science.

3 Comprehensible Input
Have students study the visuals and their captions on pages 155 and 156 to support the Key Concepts of the lesson.

4 Language Production
Pair or group students with varied language abilities to complete labs collaboratively for language practice. Have each student copy the completed written lab for personal reference.

5 Assess Understanding
Divide the class into small groups. Have each student identify a Key Concept from the lesson to discuss in his or her group. After the discussions, have students talk about the Key Concepts as a group.

Lexile Measure = 810L

Introduction to Vertebrates

Establish Learning Objectives

After this lesson, students will be able to:

🔑 Identify the characteristics of chordates and vertebrates.

🔑 Compare how vertebrates differ in the way they control body temperature.

Engage

Activate Prior Knowledge

MY PLANET DIARY Read *BRRRR! It's Freezing!* with the class. Remind students that animals have adaptations that help them survive in their environment. Some adaptations are physical traits and others are behaviors. Ask: **What do you do when you get cold?** *(Sample: Put on a sweater, coat, or blanket.)* **What do Emperor penguins do to stay warm?** *(They huddle together.)* **What physical traits do they have to keep warm?** *(They have a layer of fat and stiff feathers.)*

BIG IDEAS OF SCIENCE REFERENCE LIBRARY 📖 Have students look up the following topic: Gila Monster.

Explore

Lab Resource: Inquiry Warm-Up 🔬

L1 HOW IS AN UMBRELLA LIKE A SKELETON? Students will relate the function of the ribs in an umbrella to the bones in the body.

Introduction to Vertebrates

🔑 **What Are the Characteristics of Chordates and Vertebrates?**

🔑 **How Do Vertebrates Control Body Temperature?**

MY PLANET DIARY

BRRRR! It's Freezing!

How can anything survive in Antarctica, the coldest and windiest place on Earth? Emperor penguins have many physical characteristics that help them live there. For example, they have a layer of fat that helps them stay warm. They also have short, stiff feathers that help to insulate and protect them from the freezing air.

However, the penguins' physical characteristics are not enough to stay warm in Antarctica during the winter. Emperor penguins cooperate to keep warm. They huddle together in groups and take turns standing on the outside of the huddle where it is the coldest. This way, every penguin gets a chance to stand in the middle of the huddle where it is the warmest. Now that's teamwork!

FUN FACTS

Read the following questions. Then write your answers below.

1. Why don't emperor penguins freeze to death in Antarctica?

   They have a fat layer, stiff feathers, and huddle together to stay warm.

2. What are other ways you know about that animals use to stay warm?

   Sample: Some animals have fur to stay warm.

▶ **PLANET DIARY** Go to **Planet Diary** to learn more about vertebrates.

🔬 Do the Inquiry Warm-Up *How Is an Umbrella Like a Skeleton?*

154 Introduction to Animals

SUPPORT ALL READERS

Lexile Measure = 810L   Lexile Word Count = 696

Prior Exposure to Content: May be the first time students have encountered this topic

Academic Vocabulary: *conclusion, summarize*

Science Vocabulary: *chordate, notochord, vertebra, ectotherm, endotherm*

Concept Level: Generally appropriate for most students in this grade

Preteach With: My Planet Diary "BRRRR! It's Freezing!" and Figure 2 activity

Go to **My Reading Web** to access leveled readings that provide a foundation for the content.

my science online.com

Vocabulary
• chordate • notochord • vertebra
• ectotherm • endotherm

Skills
↻ Reading: Summarize
△ Inquiry: Draw Conclusions

What Are the Characteristics of Chordates and Vertebrates?

The animals you are probably most familiar with are members of the phylum Chordata. Members of this phylum are called chordates (KAWR dayts). Most chordates, including all fishes, amphibians, reptiles, birds, and mammals, are vertebrates. A few chordates, such as sea squirts and lancelets, do not have backbones.

Chordate Characteristics 🔑 At some point in their lives, all chordates have three characteristics: a notochord, a nerve cord, and pouches in the throat area. Most chordates also have a backbone.

Notochord A notochord is a flexible rod that supports a chordate's back. The name *Chordata* comes from this structure's name.

Nerve Cord All chordates have a nerve cord that runs down their back. Your spinal cord is such a nerve cord. The nerve cord connects the brain to nerves in other parts of the body.

Throat Pouches At some point in their lives, chordates have pouches in their throat area. In fishes and lancelets, like the one shown in **Figure 1**, grooves between these pouches become gill slits. In most other vertebrates, the pouches disappear before birth.

FIGURE 1 ·····································
Chordates
Lancelets show the three characteristics shared by all chordates at some point in their lives.

✎ **Relate Text and Visuals** Circle the labels of the three chordate characteristics. Then explain how a lancelet is different from a fish.

A fish has a backbone, but a lancelet does not have one.
_____
_____

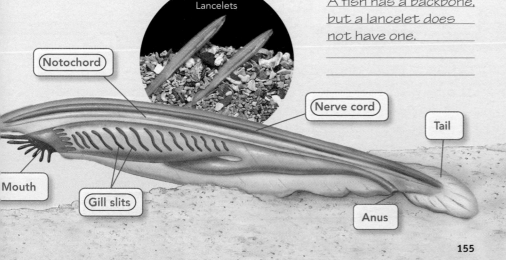

Lancelets

Notochord

Nerve cord

Tail

Mouth

Gill slits

Anus

155

Explain —————————

Introduce Vocabulary

Explain that not all plural words are formed by adding an *s* to the end. Some scientific words come directly from Latin where many singular words end in *a* and the plural forms of these words end in *ae*. A *vertebra* is one small bone in the backbone, but *vertebrae* describes more than one of these bones.

Teach Key Concepts 🔑

Point out that there is great variety among vertebrates, but they all share certain characteristics. Ask: **What three characteristics do all chordates share?** (*At some point in their lives, they have a notochord, a nerve chord, and pouches in the throat area.*) **What does it mean to say "at some point in their lives"?** (*It means that chordates might not have a characteristic as an adult, but they may have had it when they were first developing.*)

Teach With Visuals

Tell students to look at **Figure 1.** Ask a volunteer to read aloud each label on the diagram. Ask: **What is a notochord?** (*A flexible rod that supports a chordates back*) **What is a nerve cord?** (*A structure that runs down the back and connects the brain with nerves throughout the body*) **From what did the gills in this vertebrate form?** (*They formed from throat pouches.*)

21st Century Learning 📖

COMMUNICATION Have students read *Gila Monster* in the **Big Ideas of Science Reference Library** and ask them to use the information from the reading to create a fact sheet about Gila monsters. Fact sheets should include a drawing or illustration of the animal and information about its size, weight, anatomy, habitat, and feeding habits.

My Planet Diary provides an opportunity for students to explore real-world connections to vertebrates.

Explain

Lead a Discussion

BACKBONES Have students feel for their backbones. Ask: **Where is your backbone?** (It runs down the center of the back.) **What is another name for the backbone?** (Spine) **What is the backbone made up of?** (Small bones called vertebrae) **What makes the backbone flexible?** (Each bone is separated by a pad of soft tissue.) **What is the function of the backbone?** (It protects the spinal cord. It also is where the ribs are attached to the rest of the skeleton. It keeps our bodies supported.)

 Summarize Tell students that when they summarize, they briefly restate the main ideas of what they have read or heard.

Support the Big Q ? UbD

MOVEMENT Remind students that movement is a characteristic of animals. Direct students' attention to **Figure 2** and explain that limbs are an important part of a seal's endoskeleton. Ask: **What is the function of the seal's limbs?** (They enable the seal to move.) **How does the seal use its limbs?** (It uses them to push against the water so it can move forward.) **What is another vertebrate that uses limbs to move in its environment?** (Examples will vary, but might include a giraffe that uses its legs to run or a koala that uses its limbs to climb.)

Explore

Lab Resource: Quick Lab Lab zone

L2 **CHARACTERISTICS OF VERTEBRATES** Students will examine vertebrate backbones and make inferences about the way in which each animal moves.

Evaluate

Assess Your Understanding

After students answer the questions, have them evaluate their understanding by completing the appropriate sentence.

RTI Response to Intervention

1a. If students have difficulty defining a notochord, **then** review the description using **Figure 1** as an example.

b. If students do not understand what it means to be flexible, **then** show them examples of flexible objects such as a bendable ruler.

MY SCIENCE COACH Have students go online for help in understanding the characteristics of vertebrates.

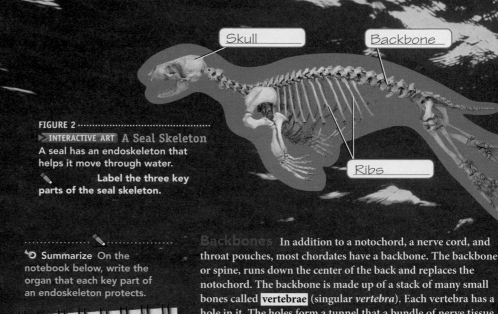

FIGURE 2
▷ INTERACTIVE ART A Seal Skeleton
A seal has an endoskeleton that helps it move through water.

Label the three key parts of the seal skeleton.

Skull   Backbone   Ribs

 Summarize On the notebook below, write the organ that each key part of an endoskeleton protects.

The skull protects the brain. The ribs protect the heart and lungs. The backbone protects the spinal cord.

Backbones In addition to a notochord, a nerve cord, and throat pouches, most chordates have a backbone. The backbone or spine, runs down the center of the back and replaces the notochord. The backbone is made up of a stack of many small bones called **vertebrae** (singular *vertebra*). Each vertebra has a hole in it. The holes form a tunnel that a bundle of nerve tissue, or spinal cord, passes through. A pad of soft tissue separates each vertebra, giving the spine flexibility.

The backbone is a key part of a vertebrate's endoskeleton. It protects the spinal cord. The skull and ribs are other key parts of an endoskeleton. The skull protects the brain. The ribs protect the heart and lungs. An endoskeleton, such as the one you can see in Figure 2, shapes a body and provides muscles with places to attach. It also forms an internal frame that supports the body and allows it to move easily. An endoskeleton grows with the animal. Vertebrates often grow larger than animals without an endoskeleton.

Lab® zone Do the Quick Lab Characteristics of Vertebrates.

🔑 Assess Your Understanding

1a. Define What is a notochord?
It is a flexible rod that supports a chordate's back.

b. Relate Cause and Effect What allows a backbone to be flexible?
The pads of tissue between vertebrae allow it to be flexible.

got it?

○ **I get it!** Now I know that chordates and vertebrates *have a notochord, a nerve cord, and throat pouches. Vertebrates have a backbone, too.*

○ **I need extra help with** *See TE note.*

Go to **MY SCIENCE COACH** online for help with this subject.

Interactive Art allows students to explore an endoskeleton.

MY SCIENCE online.com   **Describing Vertebrates**

How Do Vertebrates Control Body Temperature?

The major groups of vertebrates differ in how they control body temperature. **Some vertebrates do not produce much internal heat. Therefore, their body temperatures change with the environment. Other vertebrates control their internal heat and maintain a constant body temperature.**

Amphibians, reptiles, and most fishes are ectotherms. An animal that produces little internal body heat is called an **ectotherm**. Its body temperature changes with temperature changes in its environment.

Birds and mammals are endotherms. An **endotherm** is an animal that controls the internal heat it produces and regulates its own temperature. An endotherm's body temperature is always fairly constant. Endotherms have adaptations such as sweat glands, fur, and feathers for maintaining body temperature.

Vocabulary Prefixes The prefix *ecto-* means "outside." What do you think the prefix *endo-* means?

It means "inside."

apply it!

Animals control body temperature in different ways.

❶ **Draw Conclusions** Write whether you think each animal is an endotherm or ectotherm.

❷ **CHALLENGE** Would it be more difficult for a penguin to live in a desert or a snake to live in a polar region? Explain.

Sample: It would be more difficult for a snake to live in a polar region because it would not be able to stay warm.

Ectotherm

Endotherm

Endotherm

Ectotherm

Lab zone Do the Quick Lab *Keeping Warm.*

Assess Your Understanding

Got it?

○ I get it! Now I know that vertebrates' body temperature either changes with their environment or is controlled internally.

○ I need extra help with See TE note.

Go to my science COACH *online for help with this subject.*

157

Differentiated Instruction

L1 Describe Vertebrates Ask pairs of students to find or draw a diagram of a vertebrate skeleton. Have students label the parts of the diagram, including skull, ribs, and backbone.

L3 Investigate Endotherms Tell students that endotherms have a variety of strategies for keeping warm or keeping cool. Ask pairs of students to investigate the importance of shivering when cold or sweating when warm. Have them present their findings to the class.

Explain

Teach Key Concepts 🔑

Tell students that vertebrates vary in the way they control body temperature. Ask: **What is an endotherm?** (*An animal that produces internal heat to control its body temperature*) **What types of vertebrates are endotherms?** (*Birds and mammals*) **What is an ectotherm?** (*An animal that does not produce internal heat to control its body temperature*) **What types of vertebrates are ectotherms?** (*Fishes, reptiles, and amphibians*) **How can an ectotherm change its body temperature?** (*It can seek sun to warm itself or shade to cool itself.*)

Apply It!

L1 Review the characteristics of endotherms and ecotherms before beginning the activity.

△ **Draw Conclusions** Explain that a conclusion must be based on observations. Tell students to look carefully at the characteristics of each animal before deciding whether it is an endotherm or an ectotherm.

Elaborate

Lab Resource: Quick Lab

L2 KEEPING WARM Students will investigate the insulating properties of different materials.

Evaluate

Assess Your Understanding

Have students evaluate their understanding by completing the appropriate sentence.

R T I Response to Intervention

If students need help describing how vertebrates control body temperature, **then** review the differences between ectotherms and endotherms.

my science COACH Have students go online for help in understanding vertebrates and body temperature.

Digital Lesson: Assign the *Apply It* activity online and have students submit their work to you.

Interactive Art allows students to make and confirm predictions about where they might find ectotherms and endoderms.

my science online | Ectotherms and Endotherms

157

Lab zone® **After the Inquiry Warm-Up**

Introduction to Vertebrates

Inquiry Warm-Up, *How Is an Umbrella Like a Skeleton?*

In the Inquiry Warm-Up, you investigated the function of skeletons by analyzing the similarities and differences between an umbrella and the human ribcage. Using what you learned from that activity, answer the questions below.

1. **COMPARE AND CONTRAST** How are the ribs of an umbrella similar to the exoskeleton of an arthropod such as a crab? How is it different?

   _____

   _____

   _____

   _____

2. **INFER** Why do you think the parts of the support system of an umbrella are called "ribs"?

   _____

   _____

3. **DESCRIBE** What are the key characteristics of both the ribs of an umbrella and the ribs in the human body?

   _____

   _____

4. **USE PRIOR KNOWLEDGE** What are the functions of the human ribcage?

   _____

   _____

Assess Your Understanding

Introduction to Vertebrates

What Are the Characteristics of Chordates and Vertebrates?

1a. DEFINE What is a notochord? _____

_____

b. RELATE CAUSE AND EFFECT What allows a backbone to be flexible? _____

_____

_____

got it? ··

○ **I get it!** Now I know that chordates and vertebrates _____

_____

_____

○ **I need extra help with** _____

_____

How Do Vertebrates Control Body Temperature?

got it? ··

○ **I get it!** Now I know that vertebrates' body temperature _____

_____

○ **I need extra help with** _____

_____

Key Concept Summaries

Introduction to Vertebrates

What Are the Characteristics of Chordates and Vertebrates?

Members of the phylum Chordata are called **chordates. At some point in their lives, all chordates have three characteristics: a notochord, a nerve chord, and pouches in the throat area. Most chordates also have a backbone.** A **notochord** is a flexible rod that supports a chordate's back. The name *Chordata* comes from this structure's name. All chordates have a nerve cord that runs down their back and connects the brain to nerves in other parts of the body. They also have throat pouches at some point in their lives. In fishes and lancelets, grooves between these pouches become gill slits. In most other vertebrates, the pouches disappear before birth.

In most chordates, the backbone replaces the notochord. The backbone is made up of a stack of many small bones called **vertebrae.** Each vertebra has a hole in it. The holes form a tunnel through which the spinal cord passes. A pad of soft tissue separates each vertebra, giving the spine flexibility.

In addition to the backbone, the skull and ribs are other key parts of a vertebrate's endoskeleton. The skull protects the brain, and the ribs protect the heart and lungs. An endoskeleton shapes the body, provides muscles with paces to attach, and forms an internal frame that supports the body and allows it to move easily. Vertebrates often grow larger than animals without an endoskeleton.

How Do Vertebrates Control Body Temperature?

Vertebrates differ in how they control body temperature. **Some vertebrates do not produce much internal heat. Therefore, their body temperatures change with the environment. Other vertebrates control their internal heat and maintain a constant body temperature.** Amphibians, reptiles, and most fishes are ectotherms.

An **ectotherm** is an animal that produces little internal body heat. Birds and mammals are endotherms. An **endotherm** is an animal that controls the internal heat it produces and regulates its own temperature. Endotherms have adaptations such as sweat glands, fur, and feathers for maintaining body temperature.

On a separate sheet of paper, compare three chordates: a lancelet, a fish, and a human. Explain what characteristics they share as well as the differences between them.

Review and Reinforce

Introduction to Vertebrates

Understanding Main Ideas

Answer the following questions on a separate sheet of paper.

1. What three characteristics do all chordates share?
2. What is a vertebrate?
3. What are three functions of an endoskeleton?

State whether the following animals are ectotherms or endotherms. Write your answer on the line provided.

   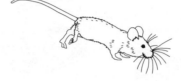   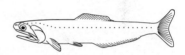

4. _____   5. _____   6. _____

Building Vocabulary

Fill in the blank to complete each statement.

7. The body of a(n) _____ doesn't produce much internal heat.

8. The body of a(n) _____ regulates its temperature.

9. While some chordates keep a(n) _____ all their lives, in others it is replaced by a backbone.

10. The bones that protect the spinal cord are the _____.

Introduction to Vertebrates

The diagrams below show different vertebrates body structures. Read the passage and study the diagrams below. Then use a separate sheet of paper to answer the questions that follow.

Similar but Different

One of the characteristics that separate vertebrates from invertebrates is the presence of a backbone and endoskeleton. All vertebrates have an internal skeleton, but all vertebrate skeletons are not the same.

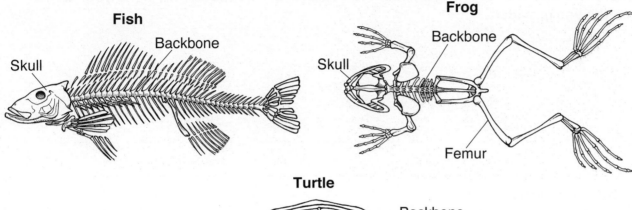

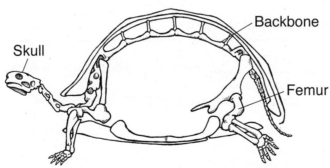

1. Look at the hind legs of the turtle and the frog. Contrast the structures of the bone called the femur in both animals. Which animal's leg bones probably need to support a greater weight? How is this difference reflected in the bones/structures?

2. One function of an endoskeleton is to support the body against the downward pull of gravity. Which animal skeleton pictured above would have to support the least amount of weight? Explain your answer.

3. Do you think the turtle backbone allows as much movement as the backbone of the fish? Why or why not?

4. What bony parts enable frogs and turtles to move on land? Can you see an adaptation for life in the water in the skeleton of the frog?

Name _____ Date _____ Class _____

Introduction to Vertebrates

If the statement is true, write *true*. If the statement is false, change the underlined word or words to make the statement true.

1. _____ The throat pouches connect the brain to nerves in the rest of the body.

2. _____ Pads of soft tissue separate the ribs, giving the spine flexibility.

3. _____ Sweat glands, fur, and feathers are most likely to be found on a(n) endotherm.

4. _____ A flexible rod that supports a chordate's back is called a(n) notochord.

5. _____ Chordates often grow larger than animals without an endoskeleton.

Fill in the blank to complete each statement.

6. Some chordates, such as sea squirts and lancelets, do not have _____.

7. The body temperature of a(n) _____ changes with temperature changes in its environment.

8. In some chordates, such as lancelets, grooves between the throat pouches become _____.

9. A(n) _____ runs down the back of all chordates.

10. The name *Chordata* comes from the term _____.

Introduction to Vertebrates

Answer Key

After the Inquiry Warm-Up

1. The ribs of an umbrella are similar to the exoskeleton of a crab because they are hard, segmented, jointed, and support the soft tissues of the body. The ribs of an umbrella are different from a crab's exoskeleton because they are not on the outside of the umbrella.

2. The parts of the support system of an umbrella are called "ribs" because they resemble and function like the ribs of a skeleton.

3. hardness, strength, linear shape, linked to form a support structure

4. The human ribcage provides support for the body and protects vital organs, including the heart and lungs.

Key Concept Summaries

A lancelet, a fish, and a human are all chordates, so, at some point in their lives, they all have a notochord, nerve chord, and throat pouches. In the lancelet and the fish, the grooves between these pouches become gill slits. In a human, the pouches disappear before birth. Unlike a lancelet, a fish and a human are both vertebrates. They have a backbone that replaces the notochord. A fish is an ectotherm. It produces little body heat, so its temperature changes with the environment. A human, however, is an endotherm. It produces body heat and regulates its own temperature.

Review and Reinforce

1. At some point in their lives, all chordates have a notochord, nerve chord, and pouches in the throat area.

2. A vertebrate is an animal that has a backbone made up of vertebrae.

3. The endoskeleton protects the spinal cord, brain, and organs. It shapes the body and gives muscles a place to attach. It forms a frame that supports the body and allows it to move easily.

4. ectotherm
5. endotherm
6. ectotherm
7. ectotherm
8. endotherm
9. notochord
10. vertebrae

Enrich

1. The turtle's femur looks relatively thicker than the frog's. The turtle femur seems to be an adaptation for supporting the greater weight of the turtle.

2. The endoskeleton of the fish supports the least amount of weight. The downward pull of gravity would be partially offset by the buoyancy of the body of the fish, because it lives in the water and not on land.

3. The turtle backbone does not allow for as much movement as the backbone of the fish. You can see that the fish backbone is divided into smaller and more divisions than the backbone of the turtle, allowing the backbone to bend in more places.

4. Frogs and turtles have four legs. The frog skeleton suggests large webbed feet that would be helpful for swimming.

Lesson Quiz

1. nerve cord
2. vertebrae
3. true
4. true
5. vertebrates
6. backbones
7. ectotherm
8. gill slits
9. nerve cord
10. notochord

Place the outside corner. the corner away from the dotted line, in the corner of your copy machine to copy onto letter-size paper.

Vertebrate Diversity

LESSON

5 **How do you know an animal when you see it?**

Lesson Pacing: 1–2 periods or ½–1 block

🕐 **SHORT ON TIME?** To do this lesson in approximately half the time, do the Activate Prior Knowledge activity on page 158. A discussion of the Key Concept on page 158 will familiarize students with the lesson content. Have students do the Quick Lab. The rest of the lesson can be completed by students independently.

> **Preference Navigator,** in the online Planning tools, allows you to customize *Interactive Science* to your own teaching style. You can also edit lesson plans by selecting the Lesson Planner option.
>
> **Digital Teacher's Edition** allows you to access your Teacher's Edition and Resource materials online.

Lesson Vocabulary

- fish - cartilage - amphibian - reptile - bird - mammal
- mammary gland - monotreme - marsupial - placental mammal
- placenta

Content Refresher
Professional Development Note

Exploring Vertebrate Diversity Remnants of animals are sometimes preserved as fossils. Some fossils are body parts or structures such as bones, claws, teeth, and eggs. Other fossils are trace fossils—footprints, tooth marks, nests, dung, burrows, and so on. There are different forms of fossils: mold fossils preserve impressions, or negative images of an organism; cast fossils occur when a mold fossil is filled in; true-form fossils are the actual animals or parts of animals.

Animals are turned into fossils by several processes. Sometimes they are preserved unaltered, such as an intact insect trapped in amber. Most bone fossils are petrified, which means that original tissues were slowly replaced minerals and harden as rock. Another means of fossilization is carbonization, which leaves only carbon behind.

Many animals that once lived on Earth are now extinct. Studying fossils gives scientists an idea of the kinds of animals that lived in the past. In this way, they can study diversity not only today, but throughout Earth's past.

LESSON OBJECTIVE

🔑 Describe the major groups of vertebrates.

Blended Path
Active learning using Student Edition, Inquiry Path, and Digital Path

ENGAGE AND EXPLORE

Teach this lesson using a variety of resources. Begin by reading **My Planet Diary** as a class. Have students share ideas about different ways humans use their bodies to communicate. Then have students do the **Inquiry Warm-Up activity.** Students will explore vertebrates. Discuss the ways vertebrates can be classified. The **After the Inquiry Warm-Up worksheet** sets up a discussion about how user friendly and all encompassing each group's classification system was. Have volunteers share their answers to question 4 about why it is difficult to set up a classification system.

EXPLAIN AND ELABORATE

Teach Key Concepts by identifying the five groups used to classify vertebrates. **Lead a Discussion** about the similarities and differences between the three groups into which fish are classified. Use **Figure 1** to compare and contrast the characteristics of the fish. **Lead a Discussion** about the unique characteristics of amphibians and reptiles. **Lead a Discussion** about birds. Use **Figure 4** to identify adaptations that help birds to survive in different environments. **Lead a Discussion** about the characteristics of mammals and then ask students to give some examples of mammals. Use the **Support the Big Q** to compare the characteristics of vertebrates. Hand out the **Key Concept Summaries** as a review of each part of the lesson. Students can also use the online **Vocab Flash Cards** to review key terms.

EVALUATE

Have students take the **Lesson Quiz.** For an alternate assessment, see the *ExamView®* Computer Test Generator, Progress Monitoring Assessments, or SuccessTracker™.

ELL Support

1 Content and Language
Tell students that the prefix *amphi-* means "both" and the suffix *-an* means "belonging to." Explain that *amphibians* belong to the group of animals that live on land and in the water.

DIFFERENTIATED INSTRUCTION KEY
L1 Struggling Students or Special Needs
L2 On-Level Students **L3** Advanced Students

LESSON PLANNER 4.5

 **Inquiry Path** Hands-on learning in the Lab zone

ENGAGE AND EXPLORE

To teach this lesson with an emphasis on inquiry, begin with the **Inquiry Warm-Up activity.** Students will explore vertebrates. Discuss the various ways that vertebrates can be classified. Have students do the **After the Inquiry Warm-Up worksheet.** Talk about how inclusive each group's classification system was. Have volunteers share their answers to question 4 about the challenges of creating a classification system.

EXPLAIN AND ELABORATE

Focus on the **Inquiry Skill** for the lesson. Point out that when you interpret data, you draw conclusions based on facts, figures, and other information. What data could be interpreted from the **Inquiry Warm-Up activity?** *(The percentage of animals classified by each group's classification system)* **Build Inquiry** by considering how being green might help some amphibians survive in their environments. To **Build Inquiry** have students investigate why an eggshell must protect a reptile's embryo. **Support the Big Q** by comparing the characteristics of vertebrates photographed in this lesson. Have students do the **Quick Lab** and then ask students to display their planes. Students can use the online **Vocab Flash Cards** to review key terms.

EVALUATE

Have students take the **Lesson Quiz.** For an alternate assessment, see the *ExamView®* Computer Test Generator, Progress Monitoring Assessments, or SuccessTracker™.

Digital Path
Online learning at my science online.com

ENGAGE AND EXPLORE

Teach this lesson using digital resources. Begin by having students explore real-world connections to vertebrate diversity at **My Planet Diary** online. Have them access the Chapter Resources to find the **Unlock the Big Question activity.** There they can answer the questions and refine their responses as they continue through the lesson. You can re-assign the activity and have students submit their work so you can track their progress.

EXPLAIN AND ELABORATE

Students reading above, at, or below the lexile measure of this lesson can access basic content readings at their level at **My Reading Web.** Have students use the online **Vocab Flash Cards** to preview key terms. Assign the **Do the Math activity** online and have students submit their work to you. **Support the Big Q** by reviewing the photographs of animals in this lesson and explaining the characteristics that make each an animal. Do the **Quick Lab** and then ask students to share their planes. The **Key Concept Summaries** online allow students to read a summary and see an image associated with each part of the lesson. Online remediation is available at **My Science Coach.**

EVALUATE

Have students take the **Lesson Quiz.** For an alternate assessment, see the *ExamView®* Computer Test Generator, Progress Monitoring Assessments, or SuccessTracker™.

2 Frontload the Lesson
Preview the lesson visuals, labels, and captions. Ask students what they know about the words *mammal* and *mammary gland.* Explain the specific meanings these words have in science.

3 Comprehensible Input
Have students study the visuals and their captions on pages 159, 160, 161, and 162 to support the Key Concepts of the lesson.

4 Language Production
Pair or group students with varied language abilities to complete labs collaboratively for language practice. Have each student copy the completed written lab for personal reference.

5 Assess Understanding
Have students create a portfolio of their notes and then do oral presentations of lesson content.

LESSON 4.5

Vertebrate Diversity

Establish Learning Objective

After this lesson, students will be able to:

 Describe the major groups of vertebrates.

Engage

Activate Prior Knowledge

MY PLANET DIARY Read *Sending Messages* with the class. Most animals communicate with each other in a variety of ways. Ask: **What do you do when you communicate?** *(Share information with someone else)* **How do you communicate with your friends?** *(Sample: by speaking to them or texting them)* **Are there ways to communicate without speaking or writing?** *(Sample: body language such as eye-rolling or shoulder-shrugging)*

BIG IDEAS OF SCIENCE REFERENCE LIBRARY 📖 Have students look up the following topic: Snakes.

Explore

Lab Resource: Inquiry Warm-Up 🔺Lab zone

L2 EXPLORING VERTEBRATES Students will make a list of vertebrates and organize them in different groups.

LESSON

5 Vertebrate Diversity

  What Are the Major Groups of Vertebrates?

my planet diary

FUN FACTS

Sending Messages

Have you ever felt like stomping your feet to show your frustration? People aren't the only ones who stomp their feet to express themselves. Researchers think that elephants communicate by stomping. For example, they think elephants stomp their feet to greet one another and send warnings.

What if an animal has no feet to stomp? It can sing! Many species of whales communicate with one another through song. They make different sounds to communicate different messages. Who knows what else researchers will discover about animal communication!

Communicate Discuss the following question with a partner. Then write your answers below.

What are three ways you communicate with others without using words?

Sample: I use eye contact, hand gestures, and smiling to communicate.

_____

_____

▶ **PLANET DIARY** Go to **Planet Diary** to learn more about vertebrate diversity.

🔺**Lab zone** Do the Inquiry Warm-Up *Exploring Vertebrates.*

What Are the Major Groups of Vertebrates?

Vertebrates, like all other animals, are diverse. They live in almost all types of environments on Earth and vary in shape, size, and color. **There are five major groups of vertebrates. They are fishes, amphibians, reptiles, birds, and mammals.** Members of each group share certain characteristics.

SUPPORT ALL READERS
Lexile Measure = 830L   Lexile Word Count = 844

Prior Exposure to Content: Many students may have misconceptions on this topic

Academic Vocabulary: *compare, contrast, data, interpret*

Science Vocabulary: *fish, reptile, bird, mammal, marsupial*

Concept Level: Generally appropriate for most students in this grade

Preteach With: My Planet Diary "Sending Messages" and Figure 4 activity

Go to **My Reading Web** to access leveled readings that provide a foundation for the content.

my science online .com

Vocabulary

- fish • cartilage • amphibian • reptile • bird
- mammal • mammary gland • monotreme • marsupial
- placental mammal • placenta

Skills

- Reading: Compare and Contrast
- Inquiry: Interpret Data

Fishes A **fish** is a vertebrate that lives in water and uses fins to move. Most fishes are ectotherms. They have scales and obtain oxygen through gills. They make up the largest group of vertebrates. Based on certain characteristics, fishes are organized into three major groups, which are shown in **Figure 1**.

Jawless fishes have no jaws or scales. They scrape, suck, and stab their food. Their skeletons are made of **cartilage,** a tissue more flexible than bone. Fish with jaws, scales, and skeletons made of cartilage are cartilaginous fishes (kahr tuh LAJ uh nuhs). Bony fishes have jaws, scales, and a pocket on each side of the head that holds the gills. Their skeletons are made of hard bone.

FIGURE 1 ·······················

Types of Fishes

The three groups of fishes are jawless fishes, cartilaginous fishes, and bony fishes.

✎ **Summarize** Write on the notebook the characteristics of each group of fishes.

Jawless fishes have no jaws or scales. Their skeletons are made of cartilage. Cartilaginous fishes have jaws and scales. Their skeletons are made of cartilage. Bony fishes have jaws, scales, and pockets to hold gills. Their skeletons are made of hard bone.

Lamprey

Lamprey's mouth

Jawless fish

Gray reef shark

Cartilaginous fish

Bony fish

Goldfish

Gill pocket

159

Explain

Introduce Vocabulary

Explain that the term *mammary* refers to organs in some female animals that secrete milk. Tell students that the terms *mammary gland* and *mammal* both share the same root.

Teach Key Concepts 🔑

Summarize the five groups of vertebrates. Ask: **What are the groups of vertebrates?** *(Fishes, amphibians, reptiles, birds, and mammals)* **Why would scientists classify vertebrates into smaller groups?** *(Because vertebrates are so diverse, it makes it useful to group them by how they are alike and different.)*

Lead a Discussion

FISHES Point out that fishes make up the largest group of vertebrates. Have students describe examples of fishes they might have seen. Explain that fishes are classified in three groups. Ask: **What are the three groups of fishes?** *(Bony fishes, cartilaginous fishes, and jawless fishes)* **What do fishes in all three groups have in common?** *(They are all vertebrates that live in water and they obtain oxygen through gills.)* **How are they different?** *(Sample: Some are made of bones and others are made of cartilage. Some have jaws and scales and others do not.)*

Teach With Visuals

Tell students to look at **Figure 1.** Help them to compare and contrast the characteristics of each fish. Ask: **How is the lamprey's mouth different from the mouths of the other fishes?** *(It is round.)* **What do you think might be the function of the vertical slits on the side of the shark?** *(Sample: The slits cover the gills and allow gases to pass in and out.)*

My Planet Diary provides an opportunity for students to explore real-world connections to vertebrate diversity.

my science online | Vertebrate Diversity

ⒺⓁⓁ Support

1 Content and Language

Write the terms *mammal* and *mammary gland* on the board. Encourage students to note the similarities between the words *mammal* and *mammary*. Explain that both terms derive from the Latin word *mamma*, meaning "breast."

2 Frontload the Lesson

Invite student volunteers to name types of animals that they—or people they know—have had as pets. Write these terms on the board. Discuss with students the similarities and differences between these animals.

3 Comprehensible Input

Have students work in pairs or groups to present the characteristics of the five major groups of vertebrates—fishes, amphibians, reptiles, birds, and mammals—in an effective graphic form such as a compare/contrast table, cluster diagram, or concept map.

Explain

Lead a Discussion

AMPHIBIANS Describe examples of amphibians that students may have seen—frogs, toads, and salamanders. Ask: **What is a common characteristic of amphibians?** *(Sample: They have slippery skin.)* **What does it mean to say that an amphibian has a "double life?"** *(It spends part of its life in water and part on land.)* **What structure would an amphibian need to live on land?** *(Lungs)* **Why is water always important to amphibians?** *(They lay their eggs in water.)*

Do the Math!

L1 Review the structure of a data table. A table should have a title that describes the data and each column should have a heading to indicate what is listed. In this table, the first column lists the groups of vertebrates. The second column lists the number of species in each group of vertebrates.

Interpret Data Tell students that data are facts, figures, and other information gathered through observations. When students interpret data, they look it over carefully and use what they learn to draw conclusions.

Explore

Build Inquiry

L1 CONSIDER COLOR

Materials yellow and green beads, paper cup, green construction paper, clock or watch with a second hand

Time 10 minutes

Have partners count out 20 yellow and 20 green beads and mix them in a paper cup. Have one partner cover his or her eyes while the other partner scatters the beads onto the construction paper. The first partner should then uncover his or her eyes and pick up as many beads as possible in 15 seconds. The other partner should measure time. At the end of 15 seconds, partners count the number of each color bead picked up. Have students construct a data table and record their observations. Pairs should switch roles and repeat the activity.

Ask: **Which color bead was picked up most often?** *(Students should find that yellow beads were picked up most often.)* **How might you explain your results?** *(The yellow beads were easier to see against the green background.)* **How might having green coloring help some amphibians survive in their environments?** *(Some amphibians live among plants so being a color that blends into the environment makes it harder for predators to see them.)*

Amphibians You may know that some amphibians such as frogs can be noisy neighbors. Frogs, toads, and salamanders are examples of amphibians. An **amphibian** is a vertebrate that is ectothermic and spends its early life in water and its adult life on land. In fact, the word *amphibian* means "double life." Most amphibians spend their adult lives on land. But they return to water to lay eggs and reproduce. Look at the amphibians in **Figure 2**.

FIGURE 2 ....
Amphibian Diversity
Adult salamanders have tails, but almost all adult frogs and toads do not.

✎ **Interpret Photos**
Label each type of amphibian. Explain the evidence in each picture that helped you decide.

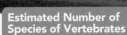

This is a
salamander
because
it has a tail.

This is a frog or a
toad because it
doesn't have a tail.

do the math!

Vertebrate Diversity

The table shows the estimated number of species in each vertebrate group. Use the table to answer the questions.

❶ **Calculate** About how many vertebrate species are there in all?
There are about 61,259 species.

❷ ⚠ **Interpret Data** Which group has the greatest number of species? The least?
Fishes have the greatest. Mammals have the least.

Estimated Number of Species of Vertebrates	
Vertebrate Group	Number of Species
Fishes	30,700
Amphibians	6,347
Reptiles	8,734
Birds	9,990
Mammals	5,488

Digital Lesson: Assign the *Do the Math* activity online and have students submit their work to you.

my science online.com ▶ Vertebrate Diversity

Reptiles The alligator, snake, and chameleon shown in Figure 3 are all reptiles. A **reptile** is an ectothermic vertebrate that has scaly skin and lungs and lays eggs on land. Some reptiles, such as sea turtles, live in water but still breathe air. Most reptiles live on land even though some swim a lot. To live on land, an animal must have adaptations that keep water in its cells. The skin of reptiles is thick and helps keep water inside their bodies. Reptiles also have organs called kidneys that conserve water. Most young reptiles develop inside tough-shelled eggs. The eggshell helps keep water inside the egg.

Chameleon

Sample: A chameleon is a reptile because it lives on land, breathes air, and has scales. Its skin looks thick.

FIGURE 3 ······························

Reptile Diversity

Reptiles are adapted to life on land.

✎ **Complete these tasks.**

1. **Draw Conclusions** In each box, describe how you know that the animal is a reptile.

2. CHALLENGE Explain how a shell keeps water inside an egg.

Sample: The shell prevents the water from evaporating.

Sample: An alligator is a reptile because it breathes air, has scaly, thick skin, and lays its eggs on land.

Alligator

Snake

Sample: A snake is a reptile because it gets oxygen from the air, has scales, and lays eggs on land.

161

Explain

Lead a Discussion

REPTILES Introduce reptiles as the next group of vertebrates. Have students describe examples of reptiles they may have seen. Ask: **What characteristics do all reptiles share?** *(They have scaly skin; they have lungs; they lay eggs on land; they breathe air.)* **How does thick, scaly skin help a reptile survive on land?** *(The skin reduces water loss, which helps keep water in the reptile's body.)* **How are snakes different from other reptiles?** *(Snakes do not have legs.)*

Address Misconceptions

SNAKES ARE NOT SLIMY Many people think that snakes are slimy. Snakes look shiny because their scales are very smooth, not because they are wet or slimy. If your school has a pet snake or lizard, bring it to class for students to observe. If possible, allow students to touch the body while you hold the animal still. Have students look at **Figure 3**. Ask: **How does the skin of the snake look different from the skin of the alligator?** *(The snake's skin looks shiny. The alligator's skin looks dry and dull.)*

Elaborate

Build Inquiry Lab zone

L1 **INVESTIGATE EGGSHELLS**

Materials small pieces of a sponge, resealable plastic bag, water

Time 10 minutes over two class periods

Have students work in small groups. Provide each group with two pieces of sponge and one resealable plastic bag. Explain that the plastic bag models an egg's shell and membranes. Have students wet both sponge pieces thoroughly. Then put one piece in the plastic bag and place the other piece on top of the sealed bag. Tell students to leave their setup overnight. Have students observe both sponges the next day.

Ask: **What is the condition of each sponge?** *(The sponge outside the bag is much drier and more rigid.)* **What would happen to a reptile embryo if it were not protected by an eggshell?** *(It would lose moisture and dry out.)*

Differentiated Instruction

L1 **Amphibians and Reptiles** Have students make a Venn diagram to compare and contrast the characteristics of amphibians and reptiles. They should include details about body characteristics and reproduction.

L3 **Adaptations of Turtles** Turtles live in a variety of environments, including deserts, forests, ponds, and oceans. Have interested students research the adaptations of turtles for different environments.

Explain

Lead a Discussion

BIRDS Have students name or describe some birds they have seen. Ask: **What are some characteristics that you have observed in all these birds?** *(They have feathers, wings, two legs, and bills or beaks.)* **What are some other characteristics of birds that you might not be able to observe easily?** *(They have lightweight bones, a four-chambered heart, and they are endothermic.)*

Teach With Visuals

Tell students to look at **Figure 4.** Ask: **How are long legs helpful to birds that wade in water?** *(They allow birds to go into water that is as deep as their legs are long.)* **How do sharp talons help the owl get food?** *(The talons allow the owl to grasp its prey firmly and hold it while it tears the flesh.)* Point out the way the owl has its tail spread wide. Ask: **Based on the position of the wings, tail, and feet, what do you think this owl was about to do when the photograph was taken?** *(Samples: land on a branch or grab prey)*

Compare and Contrast Explain that comparing and contrasting involves finding similarities and differences between two things. Although all vertebrates share certain characteristics, scientists classify them into more specific groups according to their differences.

Elaborate

21st Century Learning

CRITICAL THINKING Many organisms share some characteristics of birds but are not birds. Ask: **What is an example of an animal that can fly but is not a bird?** *(Bees and bats can fly but are not birds.)* **What is an example of an animal that lays eggs but is not a bird?** *(Sample: a platypus, an alligator, and a snake all lay eggs but are not birds.)* **Why are flight and egg-laying not defining characteristics of birds?** *(Other animals can have these characteristics.)* **Why are feathers defining characteristics of birds?** *(Only birds have feathers.)*

Birds If you have ever watched birds at a feeder, you know how fascinating they are. A **bird** is an endothermic vertebrate that lays eggs and has feathers and a four-chambered heart. Birds are adapted for flight. They have wings and lightweight, nearly hollow bones. Shown in **Figure 4,** birds are the only modern animals with feathers.

FIGURE 4 ⋯⋯⋯⋯⋯⋯⋯⋯⋯⋯⋯⋯⋯⋯⋯⋯
Birds
Different adaptations allow birds to live in different environments.

✎ **Make Generalizations** In each box, underline adaptations the bird has that help it survive. Then explain how you think feathers help birds survive.

Sample: Feathers help birds stay warm and fly.

This ibis wades through water with its tall, thin legs. It uses its long bill to find small prey.

This rainbow bee-eater uses its pointed bill to feed on bees and other insects, which it catches as it flies.

Sharp vision and keen hearing help owls like this tawny owl hunt at night. They use razor-sharp claws to grab prey.

✎
Compare and Contrast In the Venn diagram, list how reptiles and birds are alike and different.

Birds
- Endotherms
- Have feathers
- Live on land

Vertebrates
- Lay eggs
- Get oxygen from air

Reptiles
- Ectotherms
- Have scales
- Most live on land

162 Introduction to Animals

Mammals There are three main groups of mammals. Mammals are endothermic vertebrates that have skin covered with fur or hair, and a four-chambered heart. The young are fed with milk produced by organs, called **mammary glands,** in the mother's body.

The mammal groups differ in how their young develop. **Monotremes** lay eggs. **Marsupials** are born at an early stage of development, and they usually continue to develop in a pouch on the mother's body. A **placental mammal** develops inside its mother's body until its body systems can function independently. Materials are exchanged between the mother and the embryo through an organ called the **placenta.**

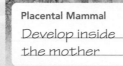
Giraffe

FIGURE 5 ....
Mammals
The main groups of mammals are monotremes, marsupials, and placental mammals.

✎ **Review** In each box, write a note about how the young of the group develops.

Kangaroo

Placental Mammal
Develop inside
the mother

Marsupial
Develop inside
the mother's
body and finish
developing in
mother's pouch

Platypus

Monotreme
Develop in eggs

Lab zone Do the Quick Lab It's Plane to See.

Assess Your Understanding

a. Name Name the three groups of fishes.
The groups are jawless,
cartilaginous, and bony.

b. Relate Cause and Effect Why can mammals live in colder environments than reptiles?
They are endothermic.

ot it? ....

○ I get it! Now I know that the major groups of vertebrates are _fishes, amphibians,_
reptiles, birds, and mammals.

○ I need extra help with _See TE note._

Go to MY SCIENCE COACH *online for help with this subject.*

163

Differentiated Instruction

L1 Relating Terms Ask students to work in pairs to list vocabulary terms from the section. Have them use each term in a sentence. On a separate sheet of paper, have them rewrite the sentences, but insert a blank line in place of the term. Then tell students to switch papers and complete the sentences by filling in the missing terms.

L3 Birds in Language Have students generate a list of expressions that involve birds. For example, "Birds of a feather flock together." Ask students to explain each expression in their own words and tell if they think the expression is based in science.

Explain
Lead a Discussion

MAMMALS Ask students if they know what babies drink when they are born. They might know that babies drink milk. Explain that the reason for this is that humans are examples of mammals. Ask: **What are the characteristics of all mammals?** *(They have hair or fur, they have a four-chambered heart, and the females produce milk for their young.)* **What are some examples of mammals?** *(Samples: Dogs, cats, lions, bears, and horses are all mammals.)* Point out that, like other vertebrates, mammals are divided into smaller groups. Ask: **What are placental mammals?** *(Mammals that develop inside their mother's body)* **What are marsupials?** *(Mammals that are born at an early stage of development and then continue development inside a pouch)* **What are monotremes?** *(Mammals that lay eggs)*

Support the Big Q ? UbD

COMPARE VERTEBRATES Have students review the photographs of animals in this lesson and explain the characteristics that make each one an animal. For example, the platypus shown in **Figure 5** is swimming, and the ability to move is a characteristic of animals. The giraffe and kangaroo are both shown with offspring. Reproduction is a characteristic of animals. You may wish to extend this exercise by having students also identify ways each group of vertebrates differs from the other groups.

Elaborate

Lab Resource: Quick Lab

L3 **IT'S PLANE TO SEE** Students will design a paper airplane with wings shaped like those of a bird.

Evaluate

Assess Your Understanding

After students answer the questions, have them evaluate their understanding by completing the appropriate sentence.

R T I Response to Intervention

1a. If students cannot recall the three types of fishes, **then** have them look back at **Figure 1.**

b. If students need help recognizing the differences between reptiles and mammals, **then** review the characteristics of each.

MY SCIENCE COACH Have students go online for help in understanding mammals.

Lab®zone **After the Inquiry Warm-Up**

Vertebrate Diversity

Inquiry Warm-Up, *Exploring Vertebrates*

In the Inquiry Warm-Up, you investigated different ways to classify vertebrates. Using what you learned from that activity, answer the questions below.

1. **DRAW CONCLUSIONS** Is there only one way that vertebrates can be classified? Explain.

   _____

   _____

2. **MAKE JUDGMENTS** Whose classification system was better, your group's or the other group's? Explain.

   _____

   _____

   _____

   _____

3. **ANALYZE SOURCES OF ERROR** Did either group's list of vertebrates include some animals that could not easily be classified using the other group's system?

   _____

   _____

4. **DRAW CONCLUSIONS** If you answered yes to question 3, what did this show you about classifying?

   _____

   _____

   _____

Name _____ Date _____ Class _____

Vertebrate Diversity

> ## What Are the Major Groups of Vertebrates?

1a. NAME Name the three groups of fishes. _____

_____

b. RELATE CAUSE AND EFFECT Why can mammals live in colder

environments than reptiles? _____

_____

got it? ···

○ **I get it!** Now I know that the major groups of vertebrates are _____

_____

○ **I need extra help with** _____

_____

Name _____ Date _____ Class _____

Vertebrate Diversity

What Are the Major Groups of Vertebrates?

Vertebrates are very diverse. **There are five major groups of vertebrates. They are fishes, amphibians, reptiles, birds, and mammals.**

A **fish** is a vertebrate that lives in water and uses fins to move. Most fish are ectotherms. They have scales and obtain oxygen through gills. They make up the largest group of vertebrates. The three groups of fishes are jawless fishes, cartilaginous fishes, and bony fishes. Jawless fishes have no jaws or scales. Their skeletons are made of **cartilage,** a tissue more flexible than bone. Cartilaginous fishes have skeletons made of cartilage, plus jaws and scales. Bony fishes' skeletons are made of hard bone. They have jaws, scales, and a pocket on each side of the head that holds the gills.

An **amphibian** is an ectothermic vertebrate that spends its early life in water and its adult life on land. All amphibians lay their eggs in water. Frogs, toads, and salamanders are amphibians.

A **reptile** is an ectothermic vertebrate that has scaly skin and lungs and lays eggs on land. Some reptiles, such as sea turtles, live in water but still breathe air.

Most reptiles live on land, so they have adaptations that keep water in their cells. Reptiles have thick skin and organs called kidneys to help conserve water. Alligators, snakes, and chameleons are reptiles.

A **bird** is an endothermic vertebrate that lays eggs and has feathers and a four-chambered heart. Birds are adapted for flight. They have wings and lightweight, nearly hollow bones.

A **mammal** is an endothermic vertebrate with skin covered by hair or fur, and a four-chambered heart. Female mammals produce milk for their young in organs called **mammary glands.** The three main groups of mammals are placental mammals, marsupials, and monotremes. The mammal groups differ in how their young develop. **Monotremes,** such as the platypus, lay eggs. **Marsupials,** such as the kangaroo, are born at an early stage in development and usually continue to develop inside a pouch on the mother's body. A **placental mammal,** such as a giraffe, develops inside its mother's body until it can function on its own. Materials are exchanged between the mother and the embryo through an organ called the **placenta.**

On a separate sheet of paper, compare the major groups of vertebrates: fish, amphibians, reptiles, birds, and mammals. Explain what characteristics they share as well as the differences between them.

Name _____ Date _____ Class _____

Vertebrate Diversity

Understanding Main Ideas
Answer the following questions on a separate sheet of paper.

1. Compare and contrast the three types of fishes.
2. Why are amphibians named with a word that means "double life"?
3. Describe several adaptations that help reptiles to live on land.
4. What are three traits common to all birds?
5. How are monotremes different from other types of mammals?

Building Vocabulary
Match each term with its definition by writing the letter of the correct definition in the right column on the line beside the term in the left column.

6. ___ fish

7. ___ amphibian

8. ___ reptile

9. ___ bird

10. ___ mammal

11. ___ mammary gland

12. ___ placental mammal

13. ___ placenta

14. ___ marsupial

15. ___ cartilage

a. an organ that produces milk

b. an ectothermic vertebrate that has thick skin and kidneys, and lays eggs

c. an ectothermic vertebrate that lives in water and uses fins to move

d. an organ through which materials pass from a mother mammal to her developing embryo

e. an endothermic vertebrate that has a four-chambered heart and feathers, and lays eggs

f. a mammal that develops completely in its mother's body

g. an ectothermic vertebrate that lives its early life in water and adult life on land

h. an endothermic vertebrate that has skin covered by hair or fur, and a four-chambered heart

i. a mammal that completes its development in a pouch on the mother's body

j. a skeletal tissue more flexible than bone

Vertebrate Diversity

Study the drawings below and use the information in the drawings to fill in the table. Some of the information about the birds cannot be determined from the drawings. Then use a separate sheet of paper to answer the question that follows.

What Does That Bird Do?

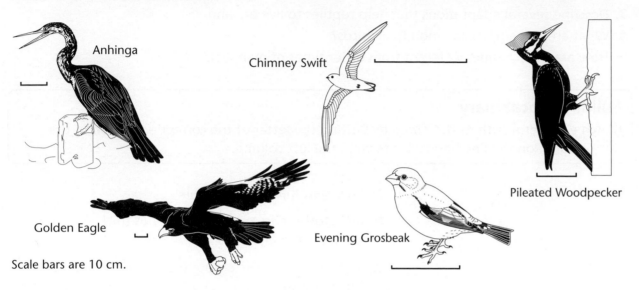

Anhinga

Chimney Swift

Pileated Woodpecker

Golden Eagle

Evening Grosbeak

Scale bars are 10 cm.

Bird	Bird size	Bill size and shape	Foot shape	Wing size and shape
anhinga				
turkey vulture				
chimney swift				
pileated woodpecker				
evening grosbeak				

1. For each bird, use the chart of characteristics and make one inference about the bird. Include the reason for each inference. For example, the evening grosbeak probably flies mainly by flapping because it has small wings.

Name _____ Date _____ Class _____

Vertebrate Diversity

If the statement is true, write *true.* If the statement is false, change the underlined word or words to make the statement true.

1. _____ A(n) <u>marsupial</u> is a mammal that lays eggs.

2. _____ A(n) <u>reptile</u> is an endothermic vertebrate that lays eggs and has a four-chambered heart.

3. _____ The <u>notochord</u> is the organ through which materials pass from a mother mammal to her developing embryo.

4. _____ <u>Bony</u> fishes have pockets on either side of their heads that hold gills.

5. _____ Frogs and toads are types of <u>amphibians</u>.

6. _____ Birds and <u>reptiles</u> are both endothermic vertebrates.

Fill in the blank to complete each statement.

7. A vertebrate that is covered with feathers must be a(n) _____.

8. Mammals have skin covered by fur or _____.

9. _____ fishes have cartilaginous skeletons but no scales.

10. _____ live part of their life in water and part on land.

Vertebrate Diversity

Answer Key

After the Inquiry Warm-Up

1. No, vertebrates can be classified many different ways. Different groups in class came up with different classification systems.

2. Accept all reasonable answers. Look for justifications that focus on how well each classification system covered all vertebrates and/or how easy each system made it to place every vertebrate into a category.

3. Answers will vary.

4. Answers will vary. Sample: This showed me that when you are creating a classification system, you have to be careful to think of all the items that need to be classified.

Key Concept Summary

Almost all fish, amphibians, reptiles, birds, and mammals have backbones. Fishes live in water, have scales, and obtain oxygen through gills. Most are ectotherms. Amphibians are also ectotherms and lay their eggs in water. They spend their early life in water but their adult life on land. Reptiles are also ectothermic, but they lay eggs on land. They have scaly skin and lungs. Most live on land. Birds also lays eggs but are endothermic. They have feathers and a four-chambered heart. Mammals are also endothermic and have a four-chambered heart. Their skin is covered by hair or fur. Female mammals produce milk for their young.

Review and Reinforce

1. Cartilaginous and jawless fishes both have skeletons made of cartilage. While cartilaginous fishes have jaws and scales, jawless fishes do not. Bony fish have hard skeletons, jaws, scales, and a pocket on each side of the head that holds gills.

2. Amphibians spend their early lives in water and their adult lives on land.

3. Reptiles breathe with lungs, have thick skin and kidneys to help them conserve water, and lay tough-shelled eggs that hold water in.

4. All birds lay eggs, and have feathers and four-chambered hearts.

5. Monotremes lay eggs rather than giving birth to live young.

6. c
7. g
8. b
9. e
10. h
11. a
12. f
13. d
14. i
15. j

Enrich

Anhinga: large; long and pointed; webbed; cannot be determined from drawing
Golden eagle: large; large and curved at end; large and heavy; large and wide
Chimney swift: small; cannot be determined from drawing; cannot be determined from drawing; small and narrow
Pileated Woodpecker: medium; long, narrow, and strong; large; medium
Evening grosbeak: small; heavy and powerful; small; medium

1. Answers will vary. Students' inferences should be supported by an observed characteristic.

Lesson Quiz

1. monotreme
2. bird
3. placenta
4. true
5. true
6. mammals
7. bird
8. hair
9. Jawless
10. Amphibians

Place the outside corner, the corner away from the dotted line, in the corner of your copy machine to copy onto letter-size paper.

Study Guide

Review the Big Q **UbD**

Have students complete the statement at the top of the page. These Key Concepts support their understanding of the chapter's Big Question. Have students return to the chapter opener pages. What is different about how students view the image of the insect and the plant now that they have completed the chapter? Thinking about this will help them prepare for the *Apply the Big Q* activity in the Review and Assessment.

Partner Review

Have partners review definitions of vocabulary terms by using the Study Guide to quiz each other. Students could read the Key Concept statements and leave out words for their partner to fill in, or change a statement so that it is false and then ask their partner to correct it.

Class Activity: Concept Map

Have students develop a concept map to show how the information in this chapter is related. Have students brainstorm to identify the Key Concepts, vocabulary, details and examples. They can then write each one on a self-sticking note and attach it at random on chart paper or on the board. Explain that the concept map will begin at the top of the chart with Key Concepts. Ask students to use the following questions to help them organize the information on the notes:

- What are the main functions of an animal?
- How are animals classified?
- How would you describe an animal's body plan?
- What are invertebrates?
- What are vertebrates?
- How are vertebrates classified?

My Science Coach allows students to complete the *Practice Test* online.

The Big Question allows students to complete the *Apply the Big Q* activity about how you can recognize an animal.

Vocab Flash Cards offer a way to review the chapter vocabulary words.

my science online.com ▸ | Introduction to Animals |

---

4 Study Guide

REVIEW THE BIG Q? I would know an animal by its <u>functions</u>, <u>body organization</u>, and <u>symmetry</u>.

LESSON 1 What Is an Animal?

🔑 The main functions of an animal are to obtain food and oxygen, keep internal conditions stable, move in some way, and reproduce.

🔑 Animals are classified according to how they are related to other animals. These relationships are determined by an animal's body structure, the way the animal develops, and its DNA.

Vocabulary
- homeostasis • adaptation
- vertebrate • invertebrate

LESSON 2 Animal Body Plans

🔑 The organization of an animal's cells into higher levels of structure helps to describe an animal's body plan.

🔑 Animals without symmetry have no tissues. Animals with radial symmetry have tissues and usually have organ systems. Animals with bilateral symmetry have organ systems.

Vocabulary
- tissue • organ • radial symmetry
- bilateral symmetry

LESSON 3 Introduction to Invertebrates

🔑 Animals that do not have backbones are invertebrates.

Vocabulary
- cnidarian
- mollusk
- arthropod
- exoskeleton
- echinoderm
- endoskeleton

LESSON 4 Introduction to Vertebrates

🔑 At some point in their lives, all chordates have three characteristics: a notochord, a nerve cord, and pouches in the throat area.

🔑 The body temperatures of some vertebrates change with the environment. Other vertebrates maintain a constant body temperature.

Vocabulary
- chordate • notochord
- vertebra • ectotherm
- endotherm

LESSON 5 Vertebrate Diversity

🔑 There are five major groups of vertebrates. They are fishes, amphibians, reptiles, birds, and mammals.

Vocabulary
- fish • cartilage • amphibian
- reptile • bird
- mammal • mammary gland
- monotreme • marsupial
- placental mammal
- placenta

(E L L) Support

4 Language Production

Divide the students into teams of five. Each member is given a number of 1, 2, 3, 4, or 5. Assign one of the essential questions from the lessons in the chapter to each group member. Groups should work together to answer the questions so that all can agree on the answers. Call out a number and the corresponding member in each group gives their group's answer.

Beginning

LOW/HIGH Allow students to answer with single words or short phrases.

Intermediate

LOW/HIGH Have students work cooperatively to answer the question aloud.

Advanced

LOW/HIGH Have students assist by acting as a coach for each team.

Review and Assessment

LESSON 1 What Is an Animal?

1. The process that the body uses to maintain a stable internal environment is called

a. adaptation.   b. endothermic.
c. homeostasis.   d. sweating.

2. The presence of a ___backbone___ determines whether an animal is a vertebrate or an invertebrate.

3. Identify the Main Idea What are the five main functions of animals?

The functions are to obtain food, obtain oxygen, maintain homeostasis, move in some way, and reproduce.

4. Draw Conclusions Suppose a book titled *Earth's Animals* is about vertebrates. Is its title a good one? Explain your answer.

Sample: No, the title is misleading. The animals on Earth also include invertebrates.

5. Apply Concepts Some insects and birds can fly. Despite this similarity, why are insects and birds classified as different groups?

Sample: They have different body structures and DNA.

6. **Write About It** Choose an animal that you know well and describe a day in its life. Include the functions it carries out and the adaptations it uses to survive in its environment.

See TE rubric.

LESSON 2 Animal Body Plans

7. What is the highest level of organization an animal can have?

a. cells   **b. organ systems**
c. organs   d. tissues

8. An animal with many lines of symmetry has ___radial___ symmetry.

9. Compare and Contrast Describe how the symmetry of a sea star, a sponge, and a fish differ.

A sea star has radial symmetry. A sponge has no symmetry. A fish has bilateral symmetry.

LESSON 3 Introduction to Invertebrates

10. Mollusks with two shells are called

a. cephalopods.   b. sea stars.
c. bivalves.   d. gastropods.

11. An ___echinoderm___ has a system of fluid-filled tubes for obtaining food and oxygen.

12. Make Generalizations Suppose you see an animal. You wonder if it is an arthropod. What characteristics would you look for?

Sample: I would look for an exoskeleton, a segmented body, and pairs of jointed appendages.

13. **Write About It** Explain whether a snail or a sponge has a higher level of organization and how this organization helps the invertebrate.

See TE rubric.

165

Review and Assessment

Assess Understanding

Have students complete the answers to the Review and Assessment questions. Have a class discussion about what students find confusing. Write Key Concepts on the board to reinforce knowledge.

RTI Response to Intervention

3. If students have difficulty understanding the basic functions of animals, **then** work with them to differentiate an animal from an inanimate object such as a boulder.

9. If students confuse the different types of symmetry, **then** have them draw three objects and indicate lines of symmetry when possible.

12. If students forget what an arthropod is, **then** display pictures of several arthropods and describe what they have in common.

Alternate Assessment

L3 PODCAST Have students create a podcast that describes the characteristics by which animals can be recognized. Podcasts should incorporate Key Concepts and relevant vocabulary terms as necessary.

Write About It Assess student's writing using this rubric.

SCORING RUBRIC	SCORE 4	SCORE 3	SCORE 2	SCORE 1
Functions and Adaptations	Student chooses and describes the animal, the functions it performs, and the adaptations it has to perform those functions.	Student describes the animal they have chosen and only one function it performs and one adaptation it has to perform that function.	Student describes the animal they have chosen and either the functions it performs or the adaptations it has.	Student describes the animal they have chosen without specifying its functions or adaptations.

Write About It Assess student's writing using this rubric.

SCORING RUBRIC	SCORE 4	SCORE 3	SCORE 2	SCORE 1
Snails and Sponges	Student explains that snails are more complex than sponges and that they are made up of cells but lack organs and organ systems like the snail.	Student explains that snails are more complex than sponges, but does not correctly name and define organs and organ systems.	Student explains that snails are more complex than sponges, but does not provide an explanation for the reasoning.	Student suggests that sponges are more complex than snails.

165

Review and Assessment, Cont.

R T I Response to Intervention

15. If students have trouble identifying the characteristics of vertebrates, **then** review notochord, nerve cord, and pouches.

23. If students need help with summarizing the main difference between the three mammal groups, **then** have them reread the text for the red heading *Mammals.*

Apply the Big Q ❓ UbD

TRANSFER Students should be able to demonstrate understanding of how they can recognize an animal by answering this question. See the scoring rubric below.

Connect to the Big Idea ❓ UbD

BIG IDEA: Living things are alike yet different

Send students back to the Big Ideas of Science at the beginning of their student edition. Have them read what they wrote before they started the chapter. Lead a class discussion about how their thoughts have changed. If all chapters have been completed, have students fill in the bottom section for the Big Idea.

L3 WRITING IN SCIENCE Ask students to write a radio interview with a biologist that explains to viewers what makes an animal an animal. The interview should explain the characteristics of animals, how different animals are classified, and the diversity of vertebrates.

LESSON 4 Introduction to Vertebrates

14. All vertebrates are
- (a.) chordates.
- **b.** invertebrates.
- **c.** fishes.
- **d.** reptiles.

15. A <u>notochord</u> is replaced by a backbone in many vertebrates.

16. Make Generalizations Why is the endoskeleton important?
   <u>Sample: It protects body parts</u>
   <u>and provides body shape and</u>
   <u>support.</u>

17. Relate Cause and Effect Whales, polar bears, and seals are endotherms. How might their thick layer of fat help them?
   <u>Sample: It helps them trap</u>
   <u>body heat, because they live or</u>
   <u>swim in cold water.</u>

18. Infer Would an ectotherm or an endotherm be more active on a cold night? Explain.
   <u>Sample: Endotherms, because</u>
   <u>they can control their body</u>
   <u>temperatures. Ectotherms'</u>
   <u>body temperatures would drop,</u>
   <u>and they couldn't move quickly.</u>

19. **Write About It** Your friend has both a hamster and a lizard as pets. She wants to buy a heat lamp for each of them to keep them warm. Tell her whether each pet needs a heat lamp to stay warm. Include the two ways animals maintain their body temperatures in your answer.
   See TE rubric.

LESSON 5 Vertebrate Diversity

20. A reptile
- **a.** is an endotherm.
- **b.** lives only in water.
- **c.** has gills.
- (d.) has scaly skin.

21. <u>Birds</u> are the only animals with feathers.

22. Classify Into which group of fishes would you classify a fish with jaws and a skeleton made of cartilage?
   <u>It is a cartilaginous fish.</u>

23. Summarize What is the main difference between the three mammal groups?
   <u>Monotremes, marsupials, and</u>
   <u>placental mammals differ in</u>
   <u>how their young develop.</u>

 How do you know an anima[l] when you see it?

24. Look at the squid below. Describe how you know it is an animal. Include details about its functions and its adaptations to survive.

<u>Sample: A squid is an animal</u>
<u>because it obtains food and</u>
<u>oxygen, moves, maintains</u>
<u>homeostasis, and reproduces.</u>
<u>It has good vision and a foot</u>
<u>to find and catch prey. It has</u>
<u>bilateral symmetry, with a bra[in]</u>
<u>and sense organs in its head.</u>
<u>See TE rubric.</u>

Write About It Assess student's writing using this rubric.

SCORING RUBRIC	SCORE 4	SCORE 3	SCORE 2	SCORE 1
Maintaining Body Temperature	Student explains that only the lizard needs the heat lamp and describes how ectotherms and endotherms maintain body temperature.	Student explains that the lizard needs the heat lamp and partially explains how ectotherms and endotherms maintain body temperature.	Student explains that the lizard needs the heat lamp but does not explain how ectotherms and endotherms maintain body temperature.	Student does not identify an animal or explain how animals maintain body temperature.

❓ **How do you know an animal when you see it?**
Assess student's response using this rubric.

SCORING RUBRIC	SCORE 4	SCORE 3	SCORE 2	SCORE 1
Characteristics of Animals	Student describes the functions of the animal, its adaptations, and its body symmetry.	Student describes either the functions, adaptation, or body structure of the animal.	Student incorrectly describes the functions, adaptations, and structure of the animal.	Student cannot explain why they know the photograph shows an animal.

tandardized Test Prep

ultiple Choice

rcle the letter of the best answer.

A lancelet is shown below. Which of its characteristics belong to a chordate?

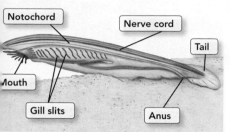

- A the mouth, gill slits, and nerve cord
- Ⓑ the gill slits, notochord, and nerve cord
- C the notochord, nerve cord, and tail
- D the gill slits, notochord, and mouth

Which characteristics do birds and mammals have in common?

- Ⓐ Both are endothermic vertebrates.
- B Both have fur or hair.
- C Both have a three-chambered heart.
- D Both are vertebrates that produce milk.

Which of the following best describes the function of the placenta?

- A delivers oxygen to the body's cells
- B stores food inside the body before swallowing and digesting it
- C directs and coordinates a mammal's complex movements
- Ⓓ passes materials between a mother and her offspring before it is born

4. What kind of evidence is used to determine the relationships between animals?
   - A evidence from the way an animal develops
   - B evidence from an animal's DNA
   - C evidence from an animal's body structure
   - Ⓓ all of the above

5. Which describes an ectothermic animal?
   - A an animal that has a thick coat of fur
   - B an animal that sweats when the environment is too hot
   - Ⓒ an animal that depends on the sun to raise its body temperature
   - D an animal that maintains its body temperature when walking through snow

Constructed Response

Use the photos below and your knowledge of science to help you answer Question 6. Write your answer on a separate sheet of paper.

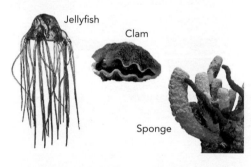

Jellyfish

Clam

Sponge

6. Invertebrates are animals without a backbone. Identify the group each of the invertebrates above belongs to. Then, for each group, name three characteristics that all its members share. *See TE note.*

167

Test-Taking Skills

READING CAREFULLY Remind students that they should be sure to look for details in each question and make sure they know what the question is asking. A chordate can have all of characteristics shown. However, the question asks only for those characteristics that are specific to chordates and not to other kinds of animals.

Constructed Response

6. Jellyfish: cnidarian; clam: mollusk; sponge: sponge. Sample: Cnidarians have radial symmetry, stinging cells, and take food into a central body cavity. Mollusks have a soft, unsegmented body, a mantle, and a foot. Sponges have no symmetry, lack tissues and organs, and stay in one place as adults.

Additional Assessment Resources

Chapter Test
ExamView® Computer Test Generator
Performance Assessment
Progress Monitoring Assessments
SuccessTracker™

Ⓔ Ⓛ Ⓛ Support

5 Assess Understanding

Have ELL students complete the Alternate Assessment. Provide guidelines on the information it must cover, and a rubric for assessment. You may have them complete the activity in groups of varying language proficiencies.

Beginning

LOW/HIGH Allow students extra time to complete their podcasts and the assignment in their native language(s).

Intermediate

LOW/HIGH Allow students to refer to bilingual dictionaries and glossaries as they plan and write their podcasts.

Advanced

LOW/HIGH Guide students through the prewriting step with examples of brainstorming, outlining, and using a graphic organizer to organize information for their podcasts.

Remediate If students have trouble with...

QUESTION	SEE LESSON	STANDARDS
1	4	
2	5	
3	5	
4	1	
5	4	
6	3	

Science Matters

Kids Doing Science

Have students read *Junior Zookeepers*. Tell students that Junior Zookeeper programs are not just a fun way to spend time in the summer, but they can be the foundation to a zookeeper's career. Oftentimes, Junior Zookeepers are invited back for volunteer and internship opportunities at the zoo. Since jobs at zoos are limited, the competition for them can be heavy and having hands-on experience like this can be helpful to people who want to pursue a career in zookeeping.

Explain that Junior Zookeepers learn about many scientific topics in fun, hands-on ways. They can learn about animal anatomy and biology and ecology. They also learn about related jobs in animal care such as veterinarian, exotic animal handler, wildlife protection officer, and wildlife rehabilitator. Tell students that Junior Zookeepers often spend one-on-one time with animals that are friendly with humans.

Explain that some Junior Zookeeper programs keep all the participants together and teach them about different topics each day. Others programs allow students to choose a type of animal they are most interested in and work with the keepers that take care of those animals.

As students design their zoo habitat, have them think about safety concerns for the human visitors as well as environmental concerns for the animals. Encourage them to think of creative ways to engage the visitors.

Ask: **How are Junior Zookeepers helpful to professional zookeepers?** *(They share some of the work of taking care of the animals.)* **What group of animals is the girl in the picture working with?** *(aquatic mammals)*

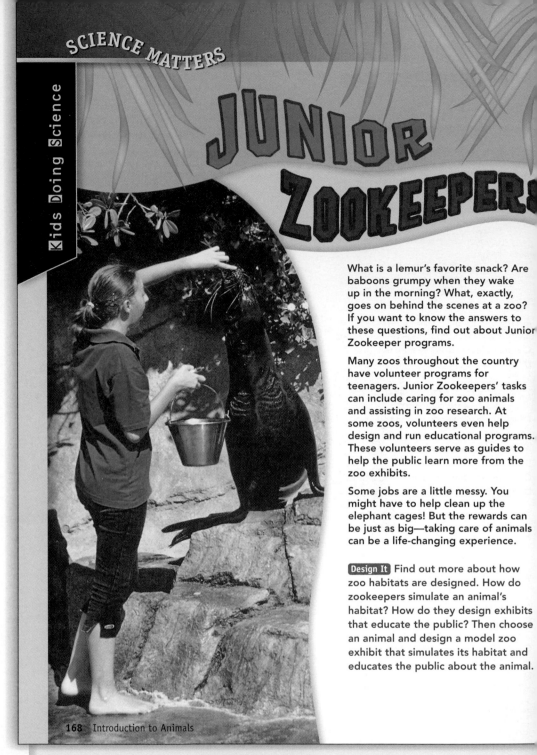

SCIENCE MATTERS

Kids Doing Science

JUNIOR ZOOKEEPERS

What is a lemur's favorite snack? Are baboons grumpy when they wake up in the morning? What, exactly, goes on behind the scenes at a zoo? If you want to know the answers to these questions, find out about Junior Zookeeper programs.

Many zoos throughout the country have volunteer programs for teenagers. Junior Zookeepers' tasks can include caring for zoo animals and assisting in zoo research. At some zoos, volunteers even help design and run educational programs. These volunteers serve as guides to help the public learn more from the zoo exhibits.

Some jobs are a little messy. You might have to help clean up the elephant cages! But the rewards can be just as big—taking care of animals can be a life-changing experience.

Design It Find out more about how zoo habitats are designed. How do zookeepers simulate an animal's habitat? How do they design exhibits that educate the public? Then choose an animal and design a model zoo exhibit that simulates its habitat and educates the public about the animal.

168 Introduction to Animals

Quick Facts

Many creatures that live on the ocean floor have developed features that help them survive there, much like the hagfish's slime. In 2007, divers exploring the Mid-Atlantic Range on the floor of the Atlantic Ocean found specimens of many strange creatures. They discovered a tiny crustacean called a seed shrimp, which is thought to be a new species. The viperfish is a predator that has long sharp translucent teeth. The jewel squid appears delicate but survives under tremendous water pressure at the bottom of the ocean. It is known for having one eye larger than the other, which it uses to look for prey. The glass squid looks like a clear marble with a polka-dot surface. Many deep-sea creatures, such as the amphipod, are transparent to blend in with their surroundings. Have students look for pictures of these strange creatures.

A Slimy Defense

Hot Science

...there were a contest for the most disgusting
...nimal in the sea, the hagfish would probably win.
...his eel-like creature is almost blind, and it feeds
...y burrowing into the flesh of dead animals on
...he ocean floor. If a hagfish is attacked, it releases
...arge amounts of thick slime, which can suffocate
...ny predator foolish enough to attack! This thick
...ooey slime contains threads that are almost as
...trong as spider silk. Studies of hagfish slime
...ay one day help scientists make materials
...hat are stronger than the fabric we now use
...n bulletproof vests!

Write About It Find examples of how biological
...esearch has inspired the development of
...echnology. Then make a poster that
...escribes three examples. Explain how
...e technology affected society.

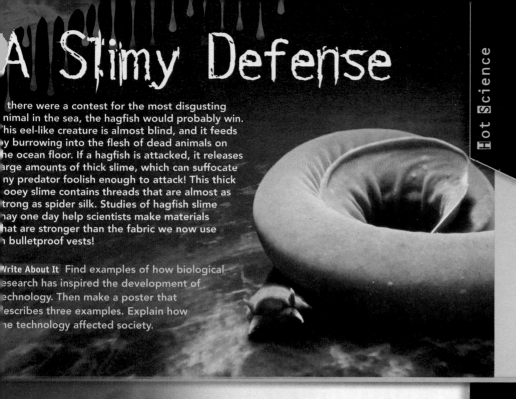

Hot Science

Have students read *A Slimy Defense.* Explain that
hagfish are unique creatures. They have four hearts,
one that is used as a main pump to circulate blood
to three "accessory" hearts that distribute blood
to other parts of the body. They have eyes that can
detect light, but not images. They are also the only
animals that have skulls, which are made of cartilage,
but have no backbone.

Tell students that a hagfish, when held by its tail, will
pull its body into a knot around the object holding it
and slide free. This adaptation also serves to scrape
the slime off their bodies. Scientists think that the
slime is intended to clog the gills of the attacker,
allowing the hagfish to escape.

Ask: **Why do hagfish need a defense like slime?**
*(Sample: They cannot see and would have a difficult
time evading a predator.)*

SUPERCOOLING FROGS

Hot Science

When you think of animals in Alaska, you
probably think of caribou, arctic foxes, polar
bears, and lynx. But what about frogs?
Alaska is also home to a species of frog that
freezes completely during the winter. When
the temperatures warm again, the frog will
thaw and be completely fine!

The wood frog has several adaptations that
allow it to freeze. Much of the water from
the frog's cells moves into its body cavity
before the water freezes. This prevents
the ice from damaging tissues. High levels
of glucose protect the frog's cells from
freezing. Finally, the wood frog may even
ingest bacteria that allow it to control the
rate at which freezing occurs!

Research It Find out about other animals
that have adapted to live in extreme
conditions. Then create an illustrated guide
that shows how three of these animals
survive in extreme environments.

Hot Science

Have students read *Supercooling Frogs.* Point out
that, while the wood frog is native to Alaska and
the most widely distributed frog in that state, it also
inhabits the northern part of the United States and
most regions of Canada. Wood frogs usually live in
forests and breed near water where females lay their
eggs in the spring.

Explain that these frogs do not simply "stop
living" when they freeze, but that they enter a
hibernation period. Often, wood frogs hibernate
underneath a layer of soil, close to breeding pools.
They often migrate north in the winter to hibernate.
The glucose that a wood frog accumulates to
protect its body's cells is used as a cryoprotectant, a
substance that prevents body tissue from freezing.

Ask: **How has the wood frog adapted to its
environment?** *(Its body enables it to survive cold
winter temperatures.)*

169

Getting Around

Introduce the Big Q ⓠ UbD

Have students look at the image and read the Engaging Question and description. Ask students to hypothesize how the bat can alter its course so quickly. Point out the bat's wings in the photo. Have volunteers describe the bones and the skin. Ask: **How does having thin skin on its wings help a bat to fly?** *(It makes them lighter than they would be with thicker skin.)* **In what way do the wings act like a parachute?** *(They can slow the bat's fall as it dives.)* **What does it mean for bones to be flexible?** *(They bend.)*

Untamed Science Video

SCIENCE IN A BAT CAVE Before viewing, invite students to suggest ways in which different animals move. Then play the video. Lead a class discussion and make a list of questions that this video raises. You may wish to have students view the video again after they have completed the chapter to see if their questions have been answered.

> To access the online resources for this chapter, search on or navigate to *Getting Around.*
>
> **Untamed Science Video** explores animal movement.
>
> **The Big Question** allows students to answer the Engaging Question about what makes the bat agile in flight.

my science online.com ▸ Getting Around

WHAT MAKES A BAT AGILE IN FLIGHT?

ⓠ THE BIG How do animals move?

Bats are the only mammals that can truly fly. The wings of a bat are made of a thin skin that stretches from its shoulders to the tips of its long, flexible finger bones. When the bat moves its wings up and down, the skin billows out like a balloon. As a bat flies, its wings are more flexible than your hand waving because the wing bones bend. This little brown bat can reach speeds of 35 km/h as it flies, swoops, or dives after a moth.

Develop Hypotheses How can a bat alter its course so quickly?

Sample: The flexible wings and bendable bones of the bat make it able to change its course quickly.

> ▸ **UNTAMED SCIENCE** Watch the **Untamed Science** video to learn more about how animals move.

Professional Development Note — From the Author

What if humans had an exoskeleton to help them carry more stuff around efficiently and use a bit less effort? Well, we could by attaching a Human Universal Load Carrier (HULC) or a HAL (Hybrid Assistive Limb) Exoskeleton to our bodies. The HULC looks like a backpack and the HAL more like a body suit. Both attach to the body with straps. With either attached, a person is able to carry loads up to about 90 kilograms with minimal effort. When powered with a battery pack, these devices can increase a person's walking and running speeds.

✏ *Don Buckley*

Getting Around

Chapter at a Glance

CHAPTER PACING: 6–9 periods or 3–$4\frac{1}{2}$ blocks

INTRODUCE THE CHAPTER: Use the Engaging Question and the opening image to get students thinking about movement. Activate prior knowledge and preteach vocabulary using the Getting Started pages.

Lesson 1: Skeletons and Muscles

Lesson 2: The Nervous System

Lesson 3: Animal Movement

ASSESSMENT OPTIONS: Chapter Test, *ExamView®* Computer Test Generator, Performance Assessment, Progress Monitoring Assessments, SuccessTracker™

Preference Navigator, in the online Planning tools, allows you to customize *Interactive Science* to your own teaching style. You can also edit lesson plans by selecting the Lesson Planner option.

Digital Teacher's Edition allows you to access your Teacher's Edition and Resource online.

Differentiated Instruction

L1 Think About Movement Ask students to observe one animal over some period of time. It might be a classroom animal, a pet at home, a bird in a tree, or an insect in a garden. Tell students to write down notes to describe how the animal moves. They should also include information about why the animal moves. As students share their results, challenge them to look for some common answers.

L3 Investigate a Planarian Provide students with planarians, flashlights, transparent plastic containers, bottled water, and dark paper. Have students place a planarian in the container and cover it with a few drops of water. Then, have them predict how the planarian will react to light. Students should record their predictions. Tell students to cover half the container with paper and shine the flashlight on the container. Ask students to describe their results.

Getting Started

Check Your Understanding

This activity assesses students' understanding of adaptations that help animals move in specific ways. After students have shared their answers, point out that animals have different adaptations for walking, climbing, flying, and swimming.

Preteach Vocabulary Skills

Review the examples of words that have everyday meanings different from their scientific meanings. Explain to students that many words have more than one meaning. It is important to pay attention to the context in which the word is used so that students can determine the appropriate meaning. After reviewing the table with students, encourage volunteers to identify other words they know that have more than one meaning.

---

5 Getting Started

Check Your Understanding

1. **Background** Read the paragraph below and then answer the question.

Why can you not leap like a frog? Like a frog, you are a **vertebrate.** But frogs have **adaptations** for leaping. A frog's powerful hind legs and sturdy **endoskeleton** allow it to leap and land without injury.

> An animal that has a backbone is a **vertebrate.**
>
> An **adaptation** is a characteristic that enables an animal to live successfully in its environment.
>
> An **endoskeleton** is an internal skeleton.

- What adaptations do frogs have that enable them to leap?

  Sample: Frogs have powerful hind legs and a sturdy endoskeleton that enable them to leap and land without injury.

> **MY READING WEB** If you had trouble completing the question above, visit **My Reading Web** and type in *Getting Around.*

Vocabulary Skill

Identify Multiple Meanings Some words have different meanings in science and in everyday use. The table below lists the multiple meanings for some words in this chapter.

Word	Everyday Meaning	Scientific Meaning
impulse	*n.* a sudden desire, urge, or inclination	*n.* an electrical message that moves from one neuron to another
stimulus	*n.* something that encourages an activity to begin	*n.* a change that an animal detects in its environment

2. **Quick Check** In the table above, circle the meaning of the word *stimulus* as it is used in the following sentence.

- The smell of pancakes was the *stimulus* that made Theo's mouth water.

My Reading Web offers leveled readings that offer a foundation for the chapter content.

Vocab Flash Cards offer extra practice with the chapter vocabulary words.

Digital Lesson

- Assign the *Check Your Understanding* activity online and have students submit their work to you.
- Assign the *Vocabulary Skill* activity online and have students submit their work to you.

my science online.com | **Getting Around**

molting

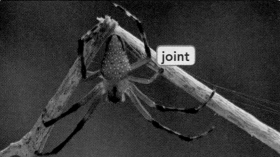
joint

response

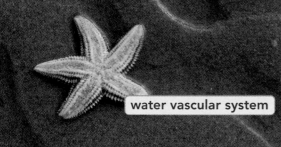
water vascular system

Chapter Preview

LESSON 1
- molting
- cartilage
- joint
- muscle
- ☺ Compare and Contrast
- △ Infer

LESSON 2
- nervous system
- stimulus
- response
- neuron
- impulse
- sensory neuron
- interneuron
- motor neuron
- brain
- ☺ Identify Supporting Evidence
- △ Draw Conclusions

LESSON 3
- water vascular system
- swim bladder
- ☺ Relate Text and Visuals
- △ Calculate

▶ VOCAB FLASH CARDS For extra help with vocabulary, visit **Vocab Flash Cards** and type in **Getting Around.**

173

Preview Vocabulary Terms

Divide the class into small groups. Each group should complete a Frayer Model diagram for the vocabulary terms in the chapter. The diagram should include the definition, characteristics, an example, and a non-example of the term. Have the groups present their diagrams to the class.

L1 Have students look at the images on this page as you pronounce the vocabulary word. Have students repeat the word after you. Then read the definition. Use the sample sentence in italics to clarify the meaning of the term.

molting *(MOHLT ing)* The process through which arthropods shed their outgrown exoskeletons and produce new ones. *A young grasshopper undergoes molting as it grows into an adult.*

joint *(joynt)* A place where two or more bones of the skeleton meet. *Your lower leg bone is attached to your upper leg bone by the knee joint.*

response *(rih SPAHNS)* An animal's reaction to a stimulus. *His response to the hot stove was to pull his hand away.*

water vascular system *(WAWT ur VAS kyuh lur SIS tum)* A system of fluid-filled tubes in an echinoderm's body. *A starfish uses its water vascular system to grip surfaces and move along.*

ⒺⓁⓁ Support

Have students complete the diagrams for the Preview Vocabulary Terms activity. You may wish to have students work in small groups to complete the activity. Write each term and introduce it to students by pointing and saying it aloud.

Beginning
LOW/HIGH Create a drawing or symbol to support the characteristics. Develop a definition using the native language.

Intermediate
LOW/HIGH Brainstorm and write examples and non-examples. Present them to the group.

Advanced
LOW Write the definition and present it.
HIGH Explain to the group how the examples represent the word.

173

Skeletons and Muscles

 How do animals move?

Lesson Pacing: 1–2 periods or $\frac{1}{2}$–1 block

🕐 **SHORT ON TIME?** To do this lesson in approximately half the time, do the Activate Prior Knowledge activity on page 174. A discussion of the Key Concepts on pages 175 and 179 will familiarize students with the lesson content. Have students do the Quick Labs. The rest of the lesson can be completed by students independently.

> **Preference Navigator,** in the online Planning tools, allows you to customize *Interactive Science* to your own teaching style. You can also edit lesson plans by selecting the Lesson Planner option.
>
> **Digital Teacher's Edition** allows you to access your Teacher's Edition and Resource materials online.

Lesson Vocabulary

- molting
- cartilage
- joint
- muscle

Content Refresher
Professional Development Note

Seashells The shells that people find along seashores are the exoskeletons of mollusks. The shell of a mollusk is produced by a layer of tissue called the *mantle*. The shell can become larger over time as the mantle adds material to it. If conditions become harsh, such as a lack of food resources, the mantle can stop producing the material for the shell. When conditions improve, the mantle resumes building the shell. This can leave a growth line along the length of the shell. Sometimes the color and pattern of the shell changes after this type of dormant period.

Some mollusks produce exoskeletons that consist of a single shell, which is usually coiled. These shells are known as *univalves*. Other mollusks produce exoskeletons that consist of two parts joined by a hinge. These are known as *bivalves*. By the time the shells wash up along the beach, the hinge is often broken and only one half remains.

When a parasite or foreign object invades a mollusk, the mollusk surrounds the object in a secretion to isolate it. The process of adding layers of secretions to the object eventually produces a pearl. Most mollusks are capable of producing pearls, but only those produced by some mollusks—such as the pearl oysters—are valuable.

LESSON OBJECTIVES

🔑 Describe the framework for support and protection in animal bodies.

🔑 Explain the role of muscles in animal bodies.

Blended Path
Active learning using Student Edition, Inquiry Path, and Digital Path

ENGAGE AND EXPLORE

Teach this lesson using a variety of resources. Begin by reading **My Planet Diary** as a class. Have students share ideas about how various types of felines capture prey or escape predators. Then have students do the **Inquiry Warm-Up activity.** Students will investigate some of the necessary characteristics of an exoskeleton. Discuss how your movement would be affected if your leg were covered in cardboard. The **After the Inquiry Warm-Up worksheet** sets up a discussion about the differences between an endoskeleton and an exoskeleton. Have volunteers share their answers to question 4 about the parts of the endoskeleton that do protect soft tissues and organs.

EXPLAIN AND ELABORATE

Teach Key Concepts by identifying the three different types of skeletons and the roles of the skeleton. **Lead a Discussion** about the differences between exoskeletons of mollusks and arthropods.

Use **Figure 1** to compare two types of skeletons. **Lead a Discussion** about the characteristics of cnidarians, worms, mollusks, and arthropods. **Lead a Discussion** about the composition of and benefits of endoskeletons. Then have students practice the inquiry skill in the **Apply It activity.**

Continue to **Teach Key Concepts** by explaining that muscles play a role in locomotion and move internal structures as well. Use the **Support the Big Q** to illustrate that muscles occur in pairs so that as one muscle contracts the other muscle relaxes. Hand out the **Key Concept Summaries** as a review of each part of the lesson. Students can also use the online **Vocab Flash Cards** to review key terms.

EVALUATE

Have students take the **Lesson Quiz.** For an alternate assessment, see the *ExamView®* Computer Test Generator, Progress Monitoring Assessments, or SuccessTracker™.

ELL Support

1 Content and Language
Tell students that the word *cartilage* comes from the Latin word *cartilago*, which means "gristle."

Lab zone Inquiry Path
Hands-on learning in the Lab zone

Digital Path
Online learning at my science online.com

ENGAGE AND EXPLORE

To teach this lesson with an emphasis on inquiry, begin with the **Inquiry Warm-Up activity.** Students will investigate some of the characteristics of the exoskeleton. Discuss what happened when your leg was covered with cardboard. Have students do the **After the Inquiry Warm-Up worksheet.** Talk about the functions of an exoskeleton in limbs. Have volunteers share their answers to question 4 about the parts of the endoskeleton that protect soft tissues and organs.

EXPLAIN AND ELABORATE

Focus on the **Inquiry Skill** for the lesson. Point out that when you infer, you interpret observations. In the **Inquiry Warm-Up activity,** what was inferred about the force that moves the bone in the forearm? *(The muscles in the arm move the bone.)* Review the importance of joints before beginning the **Apply It activity.** Ask volunteers to describe how the leg joints enable the lemur to move.

Have students do the **Quick Lab** to compare bone and cartilage and then share their results.

Use the **Support the Big Q** to explain that muscles come in pairs that work together to help animals move their body parts. Do the **Quick Lab** to reinforce understanding of how muscles move. Students can use the online **Vocab Flash Cards** to review key terms.

EVALUATE

Have students take the **Lesson Quiz.** For an alternate assessment, see the *ExamView*® Computer Test Generator, Progress Monitoring Assessments, or SuccessTracker™.

ENGAGE AND EXPLORE

Teach this lesson using digital resources. Begin by having students explore real-world connections to skeletons and muscles at **My Planet Diary** online. Have them access the Chapter Resources to find the **Unlock the Big Question activity.** There they can answer the questions and refine their responses as they continue through the lesson. You can re-assign the activity and have students submit their work so you can track their progress.

EXPLAIN AND ELABORATE

Students reading above, at, or below the lexile measure of this lesson can access basic content readings at their level at **My Reading Web.** Have students use the online **Vocab Flash Cards** to preview key terms. Have students do the online **Interactive Art activity** to classify animals based on their skeletons. Review the importance of joints before assigning the online **Apply It activity.** Ask volunteers to share their inferences about how lemurs move. Have students submit their work to you. Do the **Quick Lab** and then ask students to share their results.

Support the Big Q by having them look at **Figure 3** while discussing how muscles work in pairs to help animals move their body parts. Have students do the **Quick Lab** to explore how muscles move.

The **Key Concept Summaries** online allow students to read a summary and see an image associated with each part of the lesson. Online remediation is available at **My Science Coach.**

EVALUATE

Have students take the **Lesson Quiz.** For an alternate assessment, see the *ExamView*® Computer Test Generator, Progress Monitoring Assessments, or SuccessTracker™.

2 Frontload the Lesson
Preview the lesson visuals, labels, and captions. Ask students what they know about the terms *joint* and *muscle.* Explain the specific meanings these words have in science.

3 Comprehensible Input
Have students study the visuals and their captions on pages 175, 176, 177, 178, and 179 to support the Key Concepts of the lesson.

4 Language Production
Pair or group students with varied language abilities to complete labs collaboratively for language practice. Have each student copy the completed written lab for personal reference.

5 Assess Understanding
Have students keep a content area log for this lesson using a two-column format with the headings "What I Understand" and "What I Don't Understand." Follow up so that students can move items from the "Don't Understand" to the "Understand" column.

LESSON 5.1

Skeletons and Muscles

Establish Learning Objectives

After this lesson, students will be able to:

 Describe the framework for support and protection in animal bodies.

 Explain the role of muscles in animal bodies.

Engage

Activate Prior Knowledge

MY PLANET DIARY Read *Fast Felines* with the class. Make sure that students known that the term *feline* refers to cats. Ask students if they have seen advertisements that use animals to show speed. Ask: **Why are big cats sometimes used to represent high speed?** *(Because they can reach greater speeds than most other animals)* **For what reasons might a cheetah run at top speed?** *(To chase prey or escape a predator)*

BIG IDEAS OF SCIENCE REFERENCE LIBRARY 📖 Have students look up the following topic: Animal Bodies.

Explore

Lab Resource: Inquiry Warm-Up 🔬

L1 **WILL IT BEND AND MOVE?** Students will examine how changes to body structure affect movement.

174 Getting Around

LESSON

1 Skeletons and Muscles

UNLOCK THE BIG ?

🔑 **What Supports and Protects Animal Bodies?**

🔑 **What Is the Role of Muscles?**

MY PLANET DIARY

Fast Felines

Which animal is the fastest sprinter? It is a cheetah. The cheetah's body structure and muscles allow it to reach speeds of up to 112 km/h in only three seconds. Its flexible spine enables the cheetah to extend its limbs to great lengths. This ability allows the cheetah to cover as much ground in one stride as a racehorse. The cheetah also has a high percentage of fast-twitch muscle fibers. These fibers provide power and allow the cheetah to reach its incredible speed faster than a race car can reach the same speed. It's no wonder that the cheetah holds the title of "World's Fastest Land Animal."

Lab zone Do the Inquiry Warm-Up *Will It Bend and Move?*

FUN FACTS

Read the following questions. Then write your answers below.

1. What are two parts of a cheetah's body that help it run fast?
   <u>Sample: It has a flexible spine and a high percentage of fast-twitch muscle fibers.</u>

2. Why do you think a cheetah's speed is an advantage to the animal?
   <u>Sample: Speed can help it get food and avoid enemies.</u>

> **PLANET DIARY** Go to **Planet Diary** to learn more about skeletons and muscles.

174 Getting Around

SUPPORT ALL READERS

Lexile Measure = 830L   Lexile Word Count = 1045

Prior Exposure to Content: Most students have encountered this topic in earlier grades

Academic Vocabulary: *compare, contrast, infer*

Science Vocabulary: *molting, cartilage, joint, muscle*

Concept Level: Generally appropriate for most students in this grade

Preteach With: My Planet Diary "Fast Felines" and Figure 1 activity

Go to **My Reading Web** to access leveled readings that provide a foundation for the content.

MY SCIENCE online.com ▶

Vocabulary
- molting
- joint
- cartilage
- muscle

Skills
- Reading: Compare and Contrast
- Inquiry: Infer

What Supports and Protects Animal Bodies?

Imagine you are watching lions moving slowly through tall grass. They are surrounding a young zebra that has wandered away from its mother. Flies buzz, and beetles chew on grass blades. Buzzards circle in the distance. Nearby, a snake slithers away from one of the lions. Unaware, the zebra continues to graze.

Think about all these different animals. Do they have anything in common? The answer is yes. All of their bodies are supported by skeletons, which have similar functions. **A skeleton is a framework that shapes and supports an animal, protects its internal organs, and allows it to move in its environment.**

Types of Skeletons Most animals have one of three types of skeletons: skeletons without hard parts, exoskeletons, and endoskeletons. An exoskeleton is a hard outer covering, while an endoskeleton is a framework inside the body. Some animals, such as sponges, do not have skeletons. However, most sponges have hard, spikelike structures scattered among their cells. These structures help support and protect them.

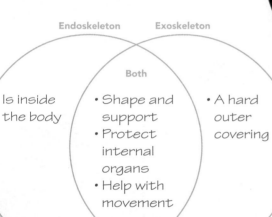

Endoskeleton | **Exoskeleton**

Both

- Is inside the body

- Shape and support
- Protect internal organs
- Help with movement

- A hard outer covering

✏️ **Compare and Contrast**
Complete the Venn diagram to show how endoskeletons and exoskeletons are alike and how they are different.

175

Explain

Introduce Vocabulary
Students who have had pet birds may be familiar with the term *molting*. Explain that molting can refer to any periodic shedding of a body covering, not just to feathers.

Teach Key Concepts 🔑
Display pictures or models of a few animal skeletons. Ask: **What are three roles of a skeleton?** *(It shapes and supports the body, it protects internal organs, and it allows movement.)* **What are the three types of skeletons?** *(Skeletons without hard parts, exoskeletons, and endoskeletons)* **Which type of skeleton do humans have?** *(Endoskeleton)* **Why might different animals have different types of skeletons?** *(Sample: They live in different environments and adapt differently.)*

Compare and Contrast Explain to students that when they compare and contrast, they describe how things are alike and how they are different. Point out that a useful way to compare and contrast is by using a graphic organizer like the one shown. Traits that are alike belong in the overlapping part of the diagram. Traits that are different go in individual parts of the circles.

My Planet Diary provides an opportunity for students to explore real-world connections to skeletons and muscles.

my science online .com | Skeletons

175

Explain

Lead a Discussion

EXOSKELETONS Remind students that a skeleton outside an animal's body is called an *exoskeleton*. Ask: **What are some animals that have exoskeletons?** *(Mollusks and arthropods)* **How are the exoskeletons of mollusks and arthropods different?** *(A mollusk's exoskeleton is its shell. It is made of calcium compounds and it can become larger. An arthropod's exoskeleton is not made of calcium, and it does not grow.)* **What is the advantage of having an exoskeleton?** *(It protects the animal from harm.)* **What are disadvantages of exoskeletons?** *(They can be heavy, which limits motion. The exoskeletons of arthropods cannot grow.)* **How is an arthropod able to grow?** *(By molting, or shedding the exoskeleton.)* Explain that the new exoskeleton forms under the old one, but is soft, so it can expand as the animal grows. Once the exoskeleton hardens, the animal cannot grow any more.

Teach With Visuals

Tell students to look at **Figure 1**. Point out that some skeletons do not have hard parts and some do. Have students use the photos to compare the two types of skeletons. Suggest that students use a graphic organizer to help them make comparisons.

Lead a Discussion

L1 INVERTEBRATE GROUPS To avoid confusion about the different types of animals, review the characteristics and examples of invertebrates: cnidarians, worms, mollusks, and arthropods. Ask students to summarize the characteristics of each invertebrate group. Ask: **What are examples of cnidarians?** *(Jellyfish, coral, hydra)* **What are three types of worms?** *(Roundworms, flatworms, and segmented worms)* **What are examples of mollusks?** *(Clams, scallops, snails, and squid)* **What are examples of arthropods?** *(Crabs, lobsters, and centipedes)*

did you know?

Before this Pacific lobster shed its old exoskeleton, a new one grew right under it. Once the new exoskeleton was ready, the lobster began drinking lots of seawater. As its body swelled with seawater, the old exoskeleton started to split. All the lobster had to do was back out of it, pulling its legs out last. Until its new exoskelton hardens a bit, this lobster will not be able to move.

FIGURE 1 ·····························
> INTERACTIVE ART Two Types of Skeletons
Some animals have skeletons without hard parts, while others have exoskeletons.

✎ **Relate Text and Visuals** In each box, write a description of the type of the animal's skeleton.

Skeletons Without Hard Parts Have you ever seen blobs that look like clear gelatin washed up on beach sand? These blobs are the bodies of jellyfish. They still have some shape because of their skeleton. Jellyfish and other cnidarians, as well as earthworms and some other annelids, have skeletons without hard parts. These skeletons have fluid-filled cavities surrounded by muscle, a tissue used in movement. Like all skeletons, this type of skeleton helps an animal keep its shape and move about.

Exoskeletons Mollusks and arthropods have exoskeletons. Clam and scallop shells are mollusk exoskeletons made of calcium-containing compounds. The exoskeletons of arthropods are made of a different substance. Exoskeletons have some disadvantages. First, exoskeletons have no cells, so they cannot grow the way organisms grow. A mollusk's shell does get larger over time as the animal secretes calcium. But to grow, arthropods must shed their exoskeletons periodically and produce new ones in a process called **molting.** Second, an exoskeleton can be heavy. This weight prevents an animal from growing very large. Look at the skeletons in **Figure 1.**

Cicada

Old skeleton

A cicada has an exoskeleton that does not have calcium and is shed so the cicada can grow.

Earthworm

An earthworm has a skeleton without hard parts. The skeleton is a fluid-filled cavity surrounded by muscle.

Scallo

A scallop has an exoskeleton that is made of calcium-containing compounds.

176 Getting Around

Interactive Art allows students to classify animals based on their skeletons.

my science online.com Skeletons

Endoskeletons Echinoderms and vertebrates have endoskeletons. Like exoskeletons, endoskeletons may contain different materials. For example, a sea star's endoskeleton is made of plates that contain calcium. Sharks and some other fishes have endoskeletons made of **cartilage,** a tissue that is more flexible than bone. The endoskeletons of most other vertebrates are made of mostly bone with some cartilage.

Bone and cartilage contain living cells. As a result, a vertebrate's endoskeleton can grow. In addition, because endoskeletons are relatively light, vertebrates with endoskeletons can grow larger than animals with exoskeletons. Some animals with endoskeletons are shown in **Figure 2.**

FIGURE 2 ·······························

Endoskeletons

Endoskeletons are made of different materials.

✎ **Complete these tasks.**

1. **Relate Text and Visuals** In the table, identify the material that each animal's endoskeleton is made of.

Animal	Material in Endoskeleton
Sea Star	Plates that have calcium
Shark	Cartilage
Bear	Bone and cartilage

2. **Draw Conclusions** Why is having an endoskeleton an advantage to a bird?

A bird needs a light
skeleton to fly.

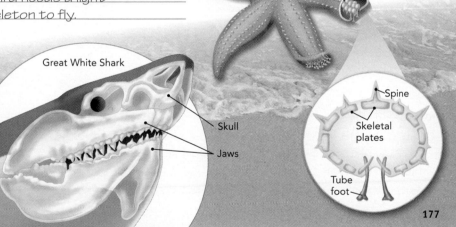

Polar Bear

Foot and leg skeleton

Sea Star

Spines

Spine

Skeletal plates

Tube foot

Great White Shark

Skull

Jaws

177

Explain

Lead a Discussion

ENDOSKELETONS Remind students that an endoskeleton is inside an animal's body. Ask: **What are two materials found in the endoskeletons of some animals?** (Calcium and cartilage) **Why can animals with endoskeletons grow larger than animals with exoskeletons?** (Endoskeletons are lighter than exoskeletons.) **What is another advantage of an endoskeleton?** (It can grow.)

21st Century Learning

INFORMATIONAL LITERACY Direct students' attention to assess the endoskeletons in **Figure 2.** Point out that even though they serve similar roles, not all endoskeletons are the same. Ask: **What do the parts of the sea star's skeleton look like?** (They look like blocks. Some of them have spines sticking up from the block.) Point out that the tube feet of the sea star are not part of the skeleton. Ask: **What do the bones of the polar bear's foot and leg look like?** (The foot has many small bones. The leg has long bones and some small bones.) **Which animal has a more complex skeleton?** (The polar bear)

Differentiated Instruction

L1 Understanding Skeletons Have students use **Figure 1** and **Figure 2** to help them understand the difference between an exoskeleton and an endoskeleton. Have students use the information in these figures to create a two-column table that identifies animals with exoskeletons and animals with endoskeletons. Students can add to their tables as they learn about more animals.

L3 Understanding Cartilage Have students research more information about cartilage. Students can find out what cartilage is made from, the different types of cartilage, and the different types of animals that contain cartilage. Students can also explore the benefits and drawbacks of cartilage in relation to bone. Interested students can present their findings to the class.

177

Explain

Make Analogies

Remind students that a bony skeleton is not made of a single piece of bone. It is made up of separate bones that are attached at joints. Explain that some joints, such as the knee joint of the lemur in the *Apply It* activity, can be compared to a door hinge. Ask: **How is a door attached to a door frame?** *(It is attached at a hinge.)* **What is the purpose of the hinge?** *(It allows the door to swing back and forth.)* **What if the door were nailed into the door frame instead of being attached by hinges?** *(The door would be unable to move.)*

Elaborate

Apply It!

L1 Review the importance of joints before beginning the activity.

△ **Infer** Explain to students that making an inference involves combining evidence with experience or prior knowledge to reach a logical conclusion. In this case, students can observe how the lemur moves and recall what they have learned about joints. Students can combine their observations and knowledge to make an inference about the lemur.

Lab Resource: Quick Lab

L2 COMPARING BONE AND CARTILAGE Students will compare bone and cartilage from a cooked chicken breast.

Evaluate

Assess Your Understanding

After students answer the questions, have them evaluate their understanding by completing the appropriate sentence.

RTI Response to Intervention

1a. If students cannot explain what cartilage is, **then** have them locate the highlighted term and reread the definition.

b. If students need help understanding molting, **then** discuss how students need new clothes as they grow.

MY SCIENCE ⬤ **COACH** Have students go online for help in understanding skeletons.

Joint

Costa Rican Spider

Joints Have you ever tried to run without bending your legs? If you have, then you know it is difficult. Fortunately, most exoskeletons and endoskeletons have joints. A **joint** is a place where two or more parts of a skeleton meet. The way the parts are held together in a joint determines how the joint can move.

Both arthropods and vertebrates have joints. An arthropod's appendages, or jointed attachments, enable the arthropod to move these appendages in different ways. For example, an insect's mouthparts may move from side to side and crush blades of grass. Its legs, however, may move forward and backward, enabling the insect to crawl. Vertebrates also have jointed appendages. As with arthropods, different joints enable vertebrates to move their appendages in different ways.

apply it!

Joints provide flexibility for animals. Look at the picture of the lemur on the right. Then answer the questions.

❶ **Interpret Photos** Circle the joints you see.

❷ △ **Infer** Describe how the leg joints enable the lemur to move.

Sample: The leg joints allow the lemur's legs to bend in at least three places.

Lab Do the Quick Lab *Comparing Bone and Cartilage.*
zone

🔑 **Assess Your Understanding**

1a. Define What is cartilage?

It is tissue that is more flexible than bone.

b. CHALLENGE Why is a lobster more vulnerable to predators when it molts?

The lobster has a soft shell and cannot move until its shell hardens.

got it?

○ **I get it!** Now I know that a skeleton is a framework that shapes and supports an animal, protects its internal organs, and allows it to move.

○ **I need extra help with** See TE note.

Go to **MY SCIENCE** ⬤ **COACH** *online for help with this subject.*

Digital Lesson: Assign the *Apply It* activity online and have students submit their work to you.

MY SCIENCE online.com ▶ **Skeletons**

What Is the Role of Muscles?

🔑 **Muscles help animals move their body parts.** Tissues that contract or relax to create movement are **muscles.** Some muscles are part of an organ. For example, muscles make up most of the walls of some blood vessels. When these <u>muscles contract, or get shorter,</u> they squeeze blood through the vessels.

Other muscles attach to parts of skeletons. Muscles attach to the inside of exoskeletons. In an endoskeleton, muscles attach to the outsides of the bones or cartilage. For both types of skeletons, movement occurs when muscles pull on skeletons.

Muscles attached to skeletons always work in pairs, as shown in **Figure 3.** When one muscle contracts, the other muscle <u>relaxes, or returns to its original length.</u> The contracted muscle pulls on the skeleton and causes it to move in a certain direction. Then, as the contracted muscle relaxes, the relaxed muscle contracts. This action causes the skeleton to move in the opposite direction.

FIGURE 3 ···

Muscle Pairs
✏️ Complete these tasks.

1. **Use Context to Determine Meaning** In the text above, underline key phrases that help you understand the terms *relaxed* and *contracted.*

2. **Interpret Diagrams** Label each muscle as *relaxed* or *contracted* for both types of skeletons.

Endoskeleton

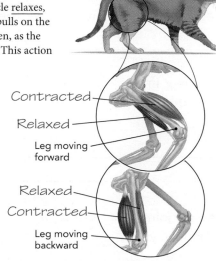

Contracted

Relaxed

Leg moving forward

Relaxed

Contracted

Leg moving backward

Exoskeleton

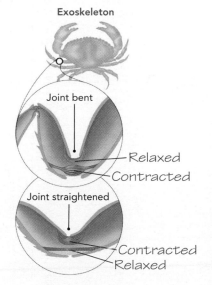

Joint bent

Relaxed
Contracted

Joint straightened

Contracted
Relaxed

 Lab zone | Do the Quick Lab *What Do Muscles Do?*

🔑 **Assess Your Understanding**

got**it?**···

○ I get it! Now I know that muscles help animals <u>move their body parts.</u>

○ I need extra help with <u>See TE note.</u>
Go to **my science ⬤ coach** online for help with this subject.

179

Explain ─────────────

Teach Key Concepts 🔑

Tell students that muscles move the body parts of animals. Students are likely familiar with the role of muscles in locomotion, but they may need to be reminded that muscles move internal structures as well. Ask: **What does a muscle do to cause motion?** *(It contracts.)* **What happens to a muscle when it contracts?** *(It gets shorter.)*

Support the Big Q ❓ UbD

Direct students to look at **Figure 3.** Help them recognize that muscles always occur in pairs. Point out that students can feel a muscle on the front of their arm and the other muscle of the pair at the back of their arm. Ask: **What happens when an animal contracts a muscle?** *(It shortens and pulls on a bone.)* **What does the other muscle in the pair do when the first muscle contracts?** *(It relaxes.)* **Why does the cat's leg require two muscles to move?** *(One muscle is responsible for moving the leg forward, and other muscle is responsible for moving the leg back.)*

Explore ─────────────

Lab Resource: Quick Lab 🔺Lab zone

L1 **WHAT DO MUSCLES DO?** Students will explore how muscles function in movement.

Evaluate ─────────────

Assess Your Understanding

Have students evaluate their understanding by completing the appropriate sentence.

⬛⬛⬛ Response to Intervention

If students have difficulty understanding the role of muscles, **then** have them reread the Key Concept statement.

my science ⬤ coach Have students go online for help in understanding the role of muscles.

LESSON 5.1

Differentiated Instruction

L1 **Modeling Muscles** Have students work in small groups to draw a model of a limb or appendage that might be found in an animal's skeleton. Then, work with students to identify the muscles that would be needed to make the limb or appendage move.

L3 **Muscles and Movement** Have students choose three animals: a mammal, a bird, and a fish. Students should research how each animal moves in its habitat and the muscles each animal has that allows it to move in its particular way. Students should summarize the information they find in a poster that they can display in the classroom.

Lab zone — After the Inquiry Warm-Up

Skeletons and Muscles

Inquiry Warm-Up, *Will It Bend and Move?*
In the Inquiry Warm-Up, you used a model to investigate some of the necessary characteristics of an exoskeleton. Using what you learned from that activity, answer the questions below.

1. **PREDICT** Suppose your partner had enclosed one of your legs in a roll of cardboard. How do you think it would affect your movement? Explain.

   _____

   _____

2. **INFER** Consider how your arm normally bends at the elbow joint. What do you think provides the force that moves the bone in your forearm?

   _____

3. **COMPARE AND CONTRAST** Consider what it was like having the cardboard roll on your arm. Then think about the bones inside your arm. What function does an exoskeleton play in a limb that an endoskeleton does not?

   _____

   _____

4. **USE PRIOR KNOWLEDGE** Consider your answer to question 3. Are there any parts of your endoskeleton that protect soft tissues and organs of your body? Give an example.

   _____

   _____

Skeletons and Muscles

What Supports and Protects Animal Bodies?

1a. DEFINE What is cartilage? _____

_____

b. CHALLENGE   Why is a lobster more vulnerable to predators when it

molts? _____

_____

gotit? ···

○ **I get it!** Now I know that a skeleton is a framework that _____

_____

○ **I need extra help with** _____

_____

What Is the Role of Muscles?

gotit? ···

○ **I get it!** Now I know that muscles help _____

_____

○ **I need extra help with** _____

_____

Name _____ Date _____ Class _____

Skeletons and Muscles

What Supports and Protects Animal Bodies?

A skeleton is a framework that shapes and supports an animal, protects its internal organs, and allows it to move in its environment. Most animals have one of three types of skeletons: skeletons without hard parts, exoskeletons, and endoskeletons. An exoskeleton is a hard outer covering, while an endoskeleton is a framework inside the body.

Jellyfish and other cnidarians, as well as earthworms, have skeletons without hard parts. These skeletons have fluid-filled cavities surrounded by muscle, a tissue used in movement.

Mollusks and arthropods have exoskeletons. Clam and scallop shells are made of calcium-containing compounds. The exoskeletons of arthropods are made of a different substance. Exoskeletons have some disadvantages. First, exoskeletons have no cells, so they cannot grow the way organisms grow.

Growing arthropods must shed their exoskeletons periodically and produce new ones in a process called **molting.** Second, an exoskeleton can be heavy, keeping these animals from growing very large.

Echinoderms and vertebrates have endoskeletons, which may contain different materials. Sharks have endoskeletons made of **cartilage,** a tissue that is more flexible than bone. The endoskeletons of most other vertebrates are made of bone with some cartilage. Because bone and cartilage contain living cells, a vertebrate's endoskeleton can grow. Endoskeletons also are relatively light, so vertebrates with endoskeletons can grow larger than animals with exoskeletons.

A place where two parts of a skeleton meet is called a **joint.** The way the parts are held together determines how the joint can move.

What Is the Role of Muscles?

Muscles help animals move their body parts. Tissues that contract or relax to create movement are **muscles.** Some muscles are part of an organ. Others attach to skeletons. Muscles attach to the inside of exoskeletons. In an endoskeleton, they attach to the outsides of the bones or cartilage. Movement occurs when muscles pull on skeletons. Muscles are found in pairs. When one muscle contracts, or shortens, the other muscle relaxes, or lengthens.

On a separate sheet of paper, tell how muscles and skeletons are related to the movement of an animal.

Name _____ Date _____ Class _____

Skeletons and Muscles

Understanding Main Ideas
Answer the following questions in the spaces provided. Use a separate sheet of paper if you need more room.

1. What are the three types of skeletons found in animals?

   _____

2. Describe the skeleton found in cnidarians and earthworms.

   _____

3. What are two disadvantages of exoskeletons?

   _____

   _____

4. What materials make up the endoskeletons of most vertebrates?

   _____

   _____

5. Why do muscles occur in pairs?

   _____

   _____

Building Vocabulary
Fill in the blank to complete each statement.

6. Tissues that contract or relax to create movement are _____.

7. A shark's endoskeleton is made up of _____, which is a tissue that is more flexible than bone.

8. A(n) _____ is a place where two or more parts of a skeleton meet.

9. During _____, an arthropod sheds its exoskeleton to grow a new one.

Enrich

Skeletons and Muscles

> Read the passage and study the diagrams below. Then complete the table that follows based on your observations of the fossil mollusk shells labeled 1–4.

Describing Mollusk Shells

Three basic factors determine the general shape of most mollusk shells.

1. Almost every mollusk shell is **cone**-shaped. In some mollusks, the shell is nothing but a simple cone. It may be narrow (A) or wide (B).

2. Most mollusk shells are **coiled** (C and D).

3. Often, the coiling is flat (C). In many cases, however, the coil is a three-dimensional spiral (D).

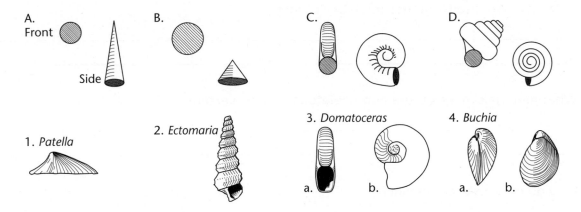

	Narrow or wide cone?	Coiling present?	Three-dimensional spiral present?
Patella			
Ectomaria			
Domatoceras			
Buchia			

Place the outside corner, the corner away from the dotted line, in the corner of your copy machine to copy onto letter-size paper.

Name _____ Date _____ Class _____

Skeletons and Muscles

Write the letter of the correct answer on the line at the left.

1. ___ Which of these animals has a skeleton without hard parts?

    A whale

    B lobster

    C jellyfish

    D goldfish

2. ___ What happens to an arthropod during molting?

    A It sheds its exoskeleton.

    B It grows a new appendage.

    C It replaces cartilage with bone.

    D It contracts its muscles.

3. ___ Which of the follow happens at a joint?

    A Muscle cells grow.

    B A new exoskeleton is formed.

    C Spikelike structures are made in cells.

    D Two parts of a skeleton meet.

4. ___ What factor makes it possible for animals with endoskeletons to grow larger than animals with exoskeletons?

    A Endoskeletons can be removed and replaced.

    B Endoskeletons are lighter than exoskeletons.

    C Endoskeletons are made of fluid-filled tubes.

    D Endoskeletons lack joints that can break down.

If the statement is true, write _true._ If the statement is false, change the underlined word or words to make the statement true.

5. _____ Some <u>muscles</u> are parts of an organ.

6. _____ When a muscle <u>relaxes</u>, it becomes shorter.

7. _____ Cartilage is <u>less</u> flexible than bone.

8. _____ During <u>molting</u> arthropods shed their skeletons in order to grow.

9. _____ <u>Mollusks</u> have spikelike structures among their cells instead of skeletons.

10. _____ A jellyfish skeleton is made up of fluid-filled cavities surrounded by <u>air</u>.

Skeletons and Muscles

Answer Key

After the Inquiry Warm-Up

1. Having a leg enclosed in a roll of cardboard would make it difficult for me to walk because I normally bend my knee when I walk.

2. muscles in the arm

3. An exoskeleton protects the soft tissues and organs inside of it. Often parts of an endoskeleton are inside soft tissues, so they cannot protect them.

4. Yes, my rib cage protects the organs inside my chest.

Key Concept Summaries

Skeletons support and protect animal bodies. Muscles are attached to parts of skeletons. Muscles occur in pairs. When a muscle contracts, it shortens and pulls on part of a skeleton. At the same time, the other muscle relaxes, or lengthens. In this way, the muscles pull on the bones in different ways. This causes them to move, which allows the entire animal to move.

Review and Reinforce

1. skeletons without hard parts, exoskeletons, and endoskeletons

2. Cnidarians and earthworms have skeletons without hard parts. Instead, they have fluid-filled cavities surrounded by muscle.

3. Because they are not made of cells, exoskeletons do not grow. So growing animals need to shed them and grow a new one. Also, exoskeletons are heavy, which limits the size of animals who have them.

4. They are made mostly of bone and cartilage.

5. Muscles can contract or relax. When one muscle in the pair contracts, the other relaxes. By contracting and relaxing, muscles can make skeleton parts move in specific ways.

6. muscles
7. cartilage
8. joint
9. molting

Enrich

Patella: wide cone, coiling absent, three-dimensional spiral absent
Ectomaria: narrow cone, coiling tight, three-dimensional spiral absent
Domatoceras: narrow cone, tight coiling, three-dimensional spiral absent
Buchia: This is a special case, a bivalve, but the same principles apply. The shell has a wide cone, and coiling and a three-dimensional spiral are both absent.

Lesson Quiz

1. C
2. A
3. D
4. B
5. true
6. contracts
7. more
8. true
9. Sponges
10. muscle

Place the outside corner, the corner away from the dotted line, in the corner of your copy machine to copy onto letter-size paper.

The Nervous System

How do animals move?

Lesson Pacing: 2–3 periods or 1–1½ blocks

🕐 **SHORT ON TIME?** To do this lesson in approximately half the time, do the Activate Prior Knowledge activity on page 180. A discussion of the Key Concepts on pages 181 and 183 will familiarize students with the lesson content. Have students do the Quick Labs. The rest of the lesson can be completed by students independently.

Preference Navigator, in the online Planning tools, allows you to customize *Interactive Science* to your own teaching style. You can also edit lesson plans by selecting the Lesson Planner option.

Digital Teacher's Edition allows you to access your Teacher's Edition and Resource materials online.

my science online.com

Lesson Vocabulary

- nervous system
- stimulus
- response
- neuron
- impulse
- sensory neuron
- interneuron
- motor neuron
- brain

Professional Development Note

Content Refresher

Electrical Signals The body systems of animals can send internal messages in different ways. Some messages are sent as chemicals that enter the bloodstream. The nervous system in complex animals depends on the transfer of electrical messages.

Electrical messages involve changes in electrically charged particles. Every cell has a different electrical charge inside the cell membrane than outside. This sets up a membrane potential expressed as voltage. The membrane potential is created by different concentrations of ions inside and outside the cell.

A neuron is said to be at rest when it is not conducting an impulse. When a neuron conducts a stimulus, the movement of ions causes the charge inside and outside the cell membrane to reverse. This change, or impulse, is transferred along a network of nerve cells much like a falling row of dominoes.

Neurons meet at a junction called a *synapse*. There is generally a tiny gap between two neurons. When a nerve impulse reaches a synapse, it triggers the release of neurotransmitters. These molecules make it possible for the impulse to be transferred. Any injuries and chemicals that interfere with the electrical signals and their transmission will affect the responses and movement of the animal.

LESSON OBJECTIVES

🔑 Explain the function of the nervous system.

🔑 Compare how the nervous systems of animals differ.

Blended Path

ENGAGE AND EXPLORE

Teach this lesson using a variety of resources. Begin by reading **My Planet Diary** as a class. Have students share ideas about whom the discovery of nAG could benefit in the future. Then have students do the **Inquiry Warm-Up activity.** Students will model how a signal is transmitted through the nervous system. Discuss the form the message took as it moved from the key to the light bulb. The **After the Inquiry Warm-Up worksheet** sets up a discussion about what would happen if a person's spinal cord was injured. Have volunteers share their answers to question 4 about where in the body stimulus messages and response messages come from.

EXPLAIN AND ELABORATE

Teach Key Concepts by explaining the three roles of the nervous system. Then have students practice the inquiry skill in the **Apply It activity. Lead a Discussion** about neurons and how they transmit information. Before assigning the **Apply It activity,** review the role of the neurons. Have students describe what stimulus the mouse is receiving and what its response is.

Continue to **Teach Key Concepts** by explaining the various arrangements of nervous systems. **Lead a Discussion** about why the cnidarian's entire body responds when it is touched. Use **Figure 1** to compare the nervous systems of the three animals. **Lead a Discussion** about some of the advantages animals have because of their sense organs. Use **Figure 2** to identify a frog's tympanic membrane and discuss its functions. Use the **Support the Big Q** to illustrate the various ways that animals use their sense organs. Hand out the **Key Concept Summaries** as a review of each part of the lesson. Students can also use the online **Vocab Flash Cards** to review key terms.

EVALUATE

Have students take the **Lesson Quiz.** For an alternate assessment, see the *ExamView®* Computer Test Generator, Progress Monitoring Assessments, or SuccessTracker™.

ELL Support

1 Content and Language
The term *interneuron* contains the prefix *inter-* meaning "between." An *interneuron* passes information between neurons.

DIFFERENTIATED INSTRUCTION KEY
L1 Struggling Students or Special Needs
L2 On-Level Students **L3** Advanced Students

LESSON PLANNER 5.2

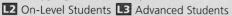 **Inquiry Path** Hands-on learning in the Lab zone

Digital Path Online learning at my science online.com

ENGAGE AND EXPLORE

To teach this lesson with an emphasis on inquiry, begin with the **Inquiry Warm-Up activity.** Students will investigate how a signal is transmitted through the nervous system. Discuss the form the message took as it moved through the model. Have students do the **After the Inquiry Warm-Up worksheet.** Talk about what would happen if a person had a spinal cord injury. Have volunteers share their answers to question 4 about where stimulus messages and response messages come from.

EXPLAIN AND ELABORATE

Focus on the **Inquiry Skill** for the lesson. Point out that when you draw conclusions, you use your observations and evidence to form an opinion or make a decision. Based on the **Inquiry Warm-Up activity,** what conclusion can be drawn about the importance of the fives senses? *(The five senses allow you to gather information about the world around you—they are important to your understanding of the world.)* Use the **Teacher Demo** to show students how their bodies responded to a stimulus. Review the relationship between a stimulus and a response before beginning the **Apply It activity.** Ask volunteers to share the conclusions they drew. Review the role of neurons before assigning the **Apply It activity.** Have students describe what stimulates the response, of the mouse, on page 182. Have students do the **Quick Lab** to design a nervous system and then share their designs.

Use the **Support the Big Q** to illustrate how animals use their senses organs. Do the **Quick Lab** to reinforce understanding of different nervous systems. Students can use the online **Vocab Flash Cards** to review key terms.

EVALUATE

Have students take the **Lesson Quiz.** For an alternate assessment, see the *ExamView®* Computer Test Generator, Progress Monitoring Assessments, or SuccessTracker™.

ENGAGE AND EXPLORE

Teach this lesson using digital resources. Begin by having students explore real-world connections to the nervous system at **My Planet Diary** online. Have them access the Chapter Resources to find the **Unlock the Big Question activity.** There they can answer the questions and refine their responses as they continue through the lesson. You can re-assign the activity and have students submit their work so you can track their progress.

EXPLAIN AND ELABORATE

Students reading above, at, or below the lexile measure of this lesson can access basic content readings at their level at **My Reading Web.** Have students use the online **Vocab Flash Cards** to preview key terms. Review the relationship between a stimulus and a response before assigning the online **Apply It activity.** Ask volunteers to share the conclusions they drew. Have students submit their work to you. Review the role of neurons before beginning the **Apply It activity.** Then have students describe what stimulates the mouse and how it responds. Do the **Quick Lab** and then ask students to share their results.

Have students do the online **Art in Motion activity** to explore how different nervous systems function. **Support the Big Q** by describing how animals use their sense organs to find food, detect danger, and move. Have students do the **Quick Lab** to compare different nervous systems. The **Key Concept Summaries** online allow students to read a summary and see an image associated with each part of the lesson. Online remediation is available at **My Science Coach.**

EVALUATE

Have students take the **Lesson Quiz.** For an alternate assessment, see the *ExamView®* Computer Test Generator, Progress Monitoring Assessments, or SuccessTracker™.

2 Frontload the Lesson
Preview the lesson visuals, labels, and captions. Ask students what they know about the term *impulse.* Explain the specific meaning this word has in science.

3 Comprehensible Input
Have students study the visuals and their captions on pages 182, 183, 184, and 185 to support the Key Concepts of the lesson.

4 Language Production
Pair or group students with varied language abilities to complete labs collaboratively for language practice. Have each student copy the completed written lab for personal reference.

5 Assess Understanding
Divide the class into small groups. Have each student identify a Key Concept from the lesson to discuss in his or her group. After the discussions, have students talk about the Key Concepts as a group.

LESSON 5.2

The Nervous System

Establish Learning Objectives

After this lesson, students will be able to:

🔑 Explain the function of the nervous system.

🔑 Compare how the nervous systems of animals differ.

Engage

Activate Prior Knowledge

MY PLANET DIARY Read *The Nerve of That Newt!* with the class. Explain that some animals can grow new limbs if they lose one. Ask: **Do you know of any animals that can grow a new body part if one is lost?** *(Sample: starfish)* **Why might it be useful for scientists to figure out the process by which animals make new limbs?** *(They might be able to find a way to control the process and use the technology for humans.)*

BIG IDEAS OF SCIENCE REFERENCE LIBRARY 📖
Have students look up the following topic: Dolphins.

Explore

Lab Resource: Inquiry Warm-Up 🧪

L2 SENDING SIGNALS Students will use a telegraph to model how a signal is transmitted through the nervous system.

LESSON

2 The Nervous System

🔑 What Is the Role of the Nervous System?

🔑 How Do Nervous Systems Differ?

MY PLANET DIARY

DISCOVERY

The Nerve of That Newt!

What happens when a newt loses a limb? It grows back! So a newt that loses a limb is not necessarily doomed to having a life on three legs. In 2007, a team of British scientists made an intriguing discovery. They learned that a protein called nAG is needed for a newt to regrow a missing limb. If the nerve that triggers the production of nAG is removed, the newt cannot regrow its limb. However, the scientists developed a way to make the newt's cells artificially produce nAG. When they did this, the newt was able to regrow its limbs, even without the nerve.

Read the following questions. Write your answers below.

1. What role does a nerve play in the newt's ability to regrow a missing limb?

   It triggers the production of nAG, the protein needed to regrow a limb.

2. Why do you think the discovery of nAG is important?

   Sample: It can be used in future research about lost limbs in humans.

▶ PLANET DIARY Go to Planet Diary to learn more about the nervous system of different animals.

🧪 Do the Inquiry Warm-Up *Sending Signals.*

180 Getting Around

SUPPORT ALL READERS

Lexile Measure = 860L   Lexile Word Count = 1020

Prior Exposure to Content: Many students may have misconceptions on this topic

Academic Vocabulary: *conclusions, evidence, identify, supporting*

Science Vocabulary: *stimulus, response, neuron, impulse*

Concept Level: Generally appropriate for most students in this grade

Preteach With: My Planet Diary "The Nerve of That Newt!" and Figure 1 activity

Go to **My Reading Web** to access leveled readings that provide a foundation for the content.

my science online.com

Vocabulary

- nervous system
- stimulus
- response
- neuron
- impulse
- sensory neuron
- interneuron
- motor neuron
- brain

Skills

- Reading: Identify Supporting Evidence
- Inquiry: Draw Conclusions

What Is the Role of the Nervous System?

You are in the yard studying. Your dog, Rugger, is lying beside you. Suddenly, Rugger lifts his head and perks his ears. A few seconds later, a car pulls into the driveway.

Interactions Rugger's actions resulted from interactions of his nervous system. A **nervous system** receives information from the environment and coordinates a response. In this way, it acts like the body's control panel. **A nervous system allows animals to detect signals in their environments, process the signals, and react to them.**

A signal that causes an animal to react in some way is called a **stimulus** (plural *stimuli*). Touch, sound, and the things animals smell, taste, or see are stimuli. After a nervous system detects a stimulus, it processes the information. For animals like Rugger, this process happens in the brain. Processing information results in a response. A **response** is an animal's reaction to a stimulus. Rugger's response to hearing the car was to lift his head and perk his ears. Rugger could have also responded by barking or running.

A chameleon eats insects. When it sees an insect, a chameleon snaps out its long, sticky tongue, which traps the insect on the end.

1 Identify What is the stimulus for this chameleon? What is the response?

The chameleon's stimulus is seeing the fly. The chameleon's response is the extension of its tongue.

2 Draw Conclusions Why is this response important to the chameleon?

It allowed the chameleon to capture its food.

181

E L L Support

1 Content and Language
Write the term *interneuron* on the board. Explain that *neuron* comes from the Greek word for "nerve," and that the Latin prefix *inter-* means "between." An *interneuron* is a nerve cell that passes information between neurons.

2 Frontload the Lesson
Encourage students to identify the sense organs that they use every day. Tell them that in this lesson, they will learn how the brain processes information gathered by these sense organs.

3 Comprehensible Input
Invite groups of students to make simple presentations showing how a nervous system receives, processes, and responds to a stimulus. Urge students to convey the sequence of events with gestures and body movements, as well as concise use of descriptive language.

Explain

Introduce Vocabulary

Explain that students may use the word *nervous* when they are anxious or fearful about something. Point out that how they feel is related to the *nervous system,* which involves the body's response to conditions in the environment.

Teach Key Concepts

Point out that the nervous system has three roles. Ask: **What does it mean to *detect* signals in an environment?** *(Detect means to recognize or become aware of.)* **What does the nervous system do when it processes information?** *(It determines how the signal will affect the body and how the body should respond.)* **What does it mean to *react* to a signal?** *(It means to behave in some way as a result of the signal.)*

Elaborate

Teacher Demo Lab zone

L1 STIMULUS AND RESPONSE

Materials none

Time 5 minutes

Make a sudden loud noise, such as slamming a book onto a desk or dropping it onto the floor. Students will likely flinch or gasp at the sound.

Ask: **What did I just do?** *(Students should describe the sound you made.)* **How did you know I made the noise?** *(We could hear it.)* **What did you do when I made that noise?** *(Students should describe their responses.)* Explain to students that the noise was a stimulus and their reactions were responses to this stimulus.

Apply It!

L1 Review the relationship between a stimulus and a response before beginning the activity.

Draw Conclusions Explain that a conclusion must be based on observations. Have students think about what the chameleon gained by capturing the fly.

My Planet Diary provides an opportunity for students to explore real-world connections to the nervous system.

Digital Lesson: Assign the *Apply It* activity online and have students submit their work to you.

my science online | Describing the Nervous System

Explain

Lead a Discussion

NEURONS Remind students that cells in complex animals are specialized. This means that they have specific roles to perform. Ask: **What are the cells that make up the nervous system?** *(Neurons)* **In what form do neurons transmit information?** *(In the form of electrical impulses)*

◐ Identify Supporting Evidence Explain that supporting evidence consists of details that relate to the main idea of a paragraph.

21st Century Learning

CRITICAL THINKING Ask: **What are the three types of neurons?** *(Sensory neurons, interneurons, and motor neurons)* **Why is it important for an organism to have all three types of neurons?** *(The neurons work together to detect a stimulus, process the information, and provide a response.)* **What might happen if one type of neuron became damaged?** *(The electrical message would not complete its path so a response would not occur.)*

Apply It!

L1 Review the role of neurons before beginning the activity. Tell students to study the diagram. Make sure they follow the path of the arrows, which shows the order in which the events happened.

Lab Resource: Quick Lab

L2 **DESIGN A NERVOUS SYSTEM** Students will design a nervous system.

Evaluate

Assess Your Understanding

After students answer the questions, have them evaluate their understanding by completing the appropriate sentence.

R T I Response to Intervention

1a. If students cannot explain what a stimulus is, **then** discuss several examples of stimuli to which they might respond.

b. If students have trouble relating a stimulus to hunger, **then** ask students to think about things that produce a response when they are hungry.

MY SCIENCE ● COACH Have students go online for help in understanding stimuli and responses.

Types of Cells Animals often respond to a stimulus in fractions of seconds. If they didn't, they might not eat, or they might be eaten. The basic unit of the nervous system, a neuron, enables speedy responses. A **neuron** is a nerve cell with a unique structure for receiving and passing on information. In a nerve cell, information travels as an electrical message called an **impulse**.

Complex animals have three kinds of neurons that work together to take in information, process it, and enable an animal to respond. <u>Sensory neurons are nerve cells that detect stimuli.</u> Organs, such as eyes and ears, contain many sensory neurons. <u>Interneurons are nerve cells that pass information between neurons.</u> <u>Motor neurons are nerve cells that carry response information to muscles and other organs.</u>

◐ Identify Supporting Evidence In the second paragraph, underline three examples of supporting evidence for the statement, "Complex animals have three kinds of neurons."

apply it!

In complex animals, different kinds of neurons work together to transfer information.

❶ Classify Under each picture, write the type of neuron the mouse is using.

❷ Describe Based on these pictures, what stimulus is the mouse receiving? What is its response?

Sample: The mouse sees the cat. It runs away.

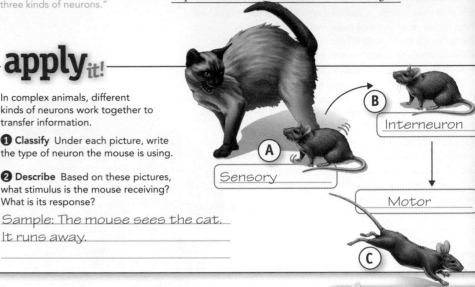

Sensory | Interneuron | Motor

Lab zone Do the Quick Lab *Design a Nervous System.*

🖙 Assess Your Understanding

1a. Review What is a stimulus?

It is a signal that causes an animal to react.

b. Apply Concepts What kind of stimulus would produce a response from a hungry animal?

Sample: Seeing food could produce a response.

got it?

○ I get it! Now I know that a nervous system allows animals to detect, process, and react to signals.

○ I need extra help with See TE note.

Go to **MY SCIENCE ● COACH** online for help with this subject.

Digital Lesson: Assign the *Apply It* activity online and have students submit their work to you.

MY SCIENCE online.com | **Describing the Nervous System**

How Do Nervous Systems Differ?

is hard to imagine an animal without a nervous system. This because most familiar animals have complex nervous systems. ut sponges don't have a nervous system, and many other animals ave very simple ones. **The simplest nervous systems are a etlike arrangement of neurons throughout the body. The most omplex systems have a nerve cord and a brain.**

ypes of Nervous Systems A cnidarian's nervous stem consists of neurons arranged like a net, as you can see in igure 1. This type of nervous system is called a nerve net. Animals ith nerve nets have no specialized neurons. Therefore, a stimulus one neuron sends impulses in all directions.

Many animals have more organized nervous systems an those of cnidarians. For example, a planarian's nervous stem has nerve cords formed from groups of interneurons. rthropods, mollusks, and vertebrates have nervous systems ith brains. A **brain** is an organized grouping of neurons the head of an animal with bilateral symmetry. A brain ceives information, interprets it, and controls an animal's sponse. A complex animal with a brain and nerve cord may ave billions of neurons.

GURE 1 ·····························

ART IN MOTION Nervous Systems ifferent types of nervous systems have fferent functions.

Identify In the table, write the ructures that make up each animal's ervous system.

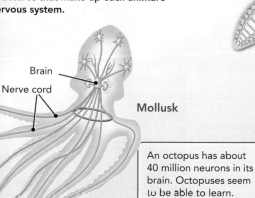

A hydra has a nerve net with no specialized neurons.

Cnidarian

Neurons

Groups of interneurons

Nerve cord

Flatworm

A planarian has two small structures in its head that are formed from groups of interneurons.

Brain
Nerve cord

Mollusk

An octopus has about 40 million neurons in its brain. Octopuses seem to be able to learn.

Nervous System Structures	
Cnidarian	Nerve net
Flatworm	Nerve cord
Mollusk	Nerve cord, brain

183

Differentiated Instruction

L1 Organize Information Have students create a graphic organizer to summarize information about the three types of neurons. They should draw a diagram to represent the role of each type of neuron to include in their organizers. Look at the *Apply It!* activity as a guide.

L3 Draw a Diagram Have students research the shape of a typical neuron. Ask students to make a poster that shows a single nerve cell. Tell students to label the parts of the cell. Challenge them to find out how the shape of the cell relates to its function.

Explain ────────

Teach Key Concepts

Contrast the words *simple* and *complex* for students. Ask volunteers to describe examples of items that are simple and complex in everyday life, such as using a disposable camera and a professional camera. Ask: **How are neurons arranged in the simplest nervous systems?** (In a netlike arrangement) **How are neurons arranged in complex nervous systems?** (In a nerve cord and brain) **What is a brain?** (An organized grouping of neurons in the head of an animal with bilateral symmetry)

Lead a Discussion

A SIMPLE NERVOUS SYSTEM Review with students some examples of cnidarians, such as jellyfish, corals, anemones, and the hydra shown in **Figure 1.** Ask: **How are neurons arranged in the nervous system of a cnidarian?** (In a net) **How are the neurons of a cnidarian different from those of other animals?** (They are not specialized; there are no interneurons.) **What structure found in complex nervous systems is not found in a cnidarian?** (A brain) Point out to students that the lack of interneurons and a brain causes a cnidarian to have no localization of sensation. If you touch a hydra with a probe, the entire body responds, not just the area that was touched.

Teach With Visuals

Tell students to look at **Figure 1** and have them compare the nervous systems of the three animals. Ask: **What structure does the flatworm have that the hydra does not?** (Structures containing interneurons) **To what stimulus does this structure respond?** (Light) **How is the nervous system of the octopus different from the other two?** (It has a brain and nerve cord.)

Make Analogies

A BUSY SYSTEM Describe the signals of the nervous system traveling at high speeds in all directions throughout the body. Ask: **How might the signals of the nervous system be like buses on a busy highway system?** (Just as the buses all travel toward different destinations, so do the impulses of the nervous system.)

Art in Motion allows students to explore how different nervous systems function.

my science online | Types of Nervous Systems

Explain

Lead a Discussion

Explain that a sense organ gathers information from stimuli. Ask: **What are the five senses in humans?** *(Hearing, seeing, tasting, touching, and smelling)* **What organs are responsible for each of these senses?** *(Ears, eyes, mouth/tongue, skin, and nose)* **How is having many sense organs an advantage for an animal to have?** *(Many sense organs enable an animal to gather and process lots of information at the same time.)* **What sense is usually not concentrated only at the head of an animal?** *(Touch)* **Why is it important for this sense to be spread out over the body?** *(Light, sound, and smells reach the body from a distance, so the whole body does not need to sense these stimuli. But any part of the body can be touched, so the body needs to have that sense everywhere.)*

Teach With Visuals

Tell students to look at **Figure 2.** If students have already studied the human body, they may recognize the term *tympanic membrane.* If they do not know this term, point out that the frog's tympanic membrane is visible on the head. In many other animals, including humans, the tympanic membrane is inside the skull, with an air passage or an ear canal leading to it. Direct students' attention to the frog's eyes. Ask students if they have ever seen a frog floating in a pond. Most of the frog is under the water, but the eyes and the front of the head are above the waterline. Ask: **Why is it useful for the frog to have its eyes out of the water?** *(So it can see insects it might catch for food and see predators that might harm it)*

Address Misconceptions

L1 **SENSE ORGANS** Students often have difficulty thinking beyond their own experiences, or in this case, their own bodies. As a result, students may have the misconception that all animals have the same sense organs. Extend your discussion of **Figure 2** by pointing out that the kind and number of sense organs depend on the animal. Ask: **How might an animal's sense organs be related to the environment in which it lives?** *(Sample: An animal that lives in water might have sense organs that detect movements in water.)*

21st Century Learning

CRITICAL THINKING Have students read *Dolphins* in the **Big Ideas of Science Reference Library.** Ask them to write a blog entry about what they learned in the reading.

Sense Organs The more complex an animal's nervous system is, the more specialized its sense organs are. Sense organs such as ears, eyes, and noses detect stimuli in the form of sound, light, odor, and touch. Many, but not all, sense organs are located in the head. For example, a grasshopper has compound eyes and antennae on its head, which detect chemicals and touch. It also has membranes on its body that detect vibrations.

Animals with many sense organs can process many stimuli at the same time. This is because different areas of the brain respond to different stimuli at the same time. For example, when an animal such as your dog is around food, its brain processes messages about the food's color, smell, taste, and temperature all at the same time. Look at Figure 2 to learn about some animals' sense organs.

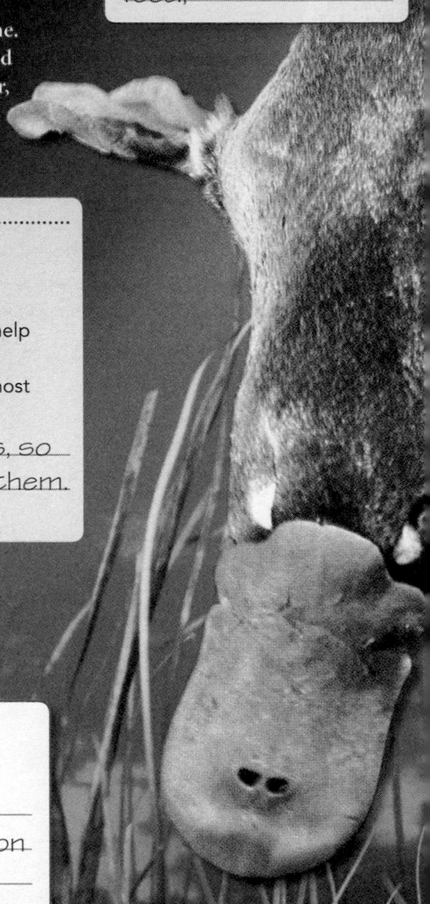

While under water, a platypus uses its bill to detect the movements of other animals.

Sample: It might provide information about where to find food.

FIGURE 2 ....
Sense Organs
✎ **Read about each animal. Then answer the questions below.**

1. **Infer** Write in the boxes how the sense organ might help the animal.

2. **CHALLENGE** Where are the sense organs located on most animals with bilateral symmetry? Why?

Sample: They are on their front ends, so they can detect what is in front of them.

A frog detects vibrations in the air with its tympanic membrane.

Sample: It might provide information about another animal approaching.

184 Getting Around

Professional Development Note **Teacher to Teacher**

Activity The ways in which animals gather stimuli takes a variety of forms. Integrate writing skills into an activity that illustrates the differences in various animal nervous systems, from simple to complex. Have students write descriptions and make illustrations of sense organs of several different animals. Encourage students to include information related to structural differences, what they can sense, and a list of organisms that have a similar structure. Have students share their work with the class. Lead a discussion about the connection between the complexity of the nervous system and the organism's survival needs.

✏ *Rick Towle*
Noblesville Middle School
Noblesville, Indiana

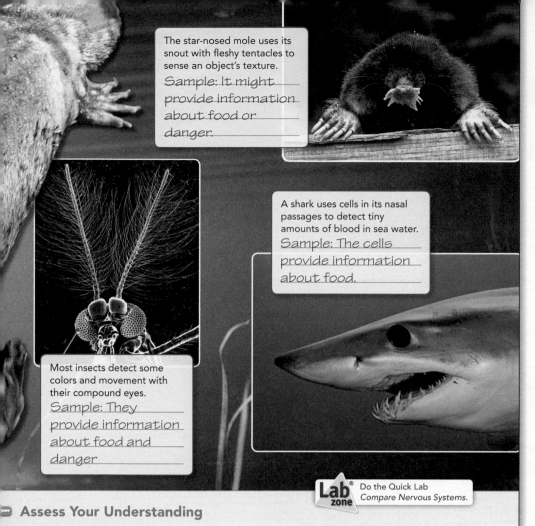

The star-nosed mole uses its snout with fleshy tentacles to sense an object's texture.

Sample: It might provide information about food or danger.

A shark uses cells in its nasal passages to detect tiny amounts of blood in sea water.

Sample: The cells provide information about food.

Most insects detect some colors and movement with their compound eyes.

Sample: They provide information about food and danger

Lab zone® Do the Quick Lab Compare Nervous Systems.

Assess Your Understanding

a. Define What is a brain?

A brain is an organized grouping of neurons in the head of an animal that has bilateral symmetry.

b. Infer Why is having many sense organs an advantage for an animal?

Sample: They provide many types of information about the environment.

got it? ....

○ **I get it!** Now I know that structures in a simple nervous system differ from those in a complex nervous system in that they have a netlike arrangement of neurons instead of a nerve cord and a brain.

○ **I need extra help with** See TE note.

Go to **MY SCIENCE COACH** online for help with this subject.

185

Differentiated Instruction

L3 Snake Senses Snakes have unique sense organs when compared with most other animals. Have students research the sense organs of snakes or another animal not described in the section. Ask them to present their finding to the class. Students should include a photograph or diagram showing the location and structure of the sense organs. Students should also explain how they help the animal to survive in its environment.

L1 Summarize Sense Organs Remind students that the sense organs of animals can be very different. Ask students to make a table. In one column, they should list the animals shown on these two pages. In the other column, they should list the sense organs described.

Support the Big Q ❓ UbD

Point out that an animal uses its sense organs to find food and detect danger. Ask: **How might the use of senses be related to an animal's movement?** (An animal would move toward food or away from danger.) **Why is it an advantage to have most of the sense organs on or near the head?** (If the animal moves forward, the animal can detect danger before it gets too close.)

Elaborate

21st Century Learning

COMMUNICATION Ask students if they have pets at home, or have observed animals outside. Invite volunteers to describe the way animals respond to stimuli. Are different animals more likely to respond to smells, sounds, or sights? Can students tell if a pet is listening to something by the way it holds its head or moves its ears? How does a pet respond to the presences of a stranger?

Lab Resource: Quick Lab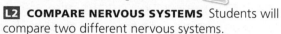

L2 COMPARE NERVOUS SYSTEMS Students will compare two different nervous systems.

Evaluate

Assess Your Understanding

After students answer the questions, have them evaluate their understanding by completing the appropriate sentence.

R T I Response to Intervention

2a. If students cannot specify the role of the brain, **then** have them locate the highlighted term and reread the definition.

b. If students have trouble explaining the advantage of sense organs, **then** have them use humans as an example to consider the usefulness of being able to sense several stimuli at the same time.

MY SCIENCE COACH Have students go online for help in understanding sense organs.

Lab zone **After the Inquiry Warm-Up**

The Nervous System

Inquiry Warm-Up, *Sending Signals*
In the Inquiry Warm-Up, you used a model to investigate how a signal is transmitted through the nervous system. Using what you learned from that activity, answer the questions below.

1. **INFER** What form did the message take as it moved from the telegraph key to the light bulb? What do you think traveled through the wire?

   _____

   _____

2. **PREDICT** Suppose you cut the wire. What would happen to the message being sent from the telegraph key to the light bulb?

   _____

   _____

3. **USE PRIOR KNOWLEDGE** Consider your answer to question 2. Can you think of a similar situation that can occur in the human body? Give an example.

   _____

   _____

4. **USE PRIOR KNOWLEDGE** Consider the various stimulus messages that were sent during the lab, such as "This is hot." Where in your body do stimulus messages come from? Where do you think response messages come from?

   _____

   _____

Name _____ Date _____ Class _____

The Nervous System

What Is the Role of the Nervous System?

1a. REVIEW What is a stimulus? _____

_____

b. APPLY CONCEPTS What kind of stimulus would produce a response

from a hungry animal? _____

_____

got it? ·······································

○ **I get it!** Now I know that a nervous system allows animals to _____

_____

○ **I need extra help with** _____

_____

How Do Nervous Systems Differ?

2a. DEFINE What is a brain? _____

_____

_____

b. INFER Why is having many sense organs an advantage for an

animal? _____

_____

_____

got it? ·······································

○ **I get it!** Now I know that structures in a simple nervous system differ from those in a

complex nervous system in that they have a _____

○ **I need extra help with** _____

_____

Key Concept Summaries

The Nervous System

What Is the Role of the Nervous System?

A **nervous system** receives information from the environment and coordinates a response. **A nervous system allows animals to detect signals in their environments, process the signals, and react to them.**

A signal that causes an animal to react in some way is called a **stimulus.** Touch, sound, and the things animals smell, taste, or see are stimuli. After a nervous system detects a stimulus, it processes the information. This results in a **response,** an animal's reaction to a stimulus.

The basic unit of the nervous system is a **neuron,** which is a nerve cell with a unique structure for receiving and passing on information. In a nerve cell, information travels as an electrical message called an **impulse.** Complex animals have three kinds of neurons. **Sensory neurons** detect stimuli. **Interneurons** pass information between neurons. **Motor neurons** carry response information to muscles and other organs.

How Do Nervous Systems Differ?

The simplest nervous systems are a netlike arrangement of neurons throughout the body. The most complex systems have a nerve cord and a brain. A cnidarian's nervous system is called a nerve net. It consists of neurons arranged like a net. There are no specialized neurons, so a stimulus to one neuron sends impulses in all directions.

Many animals have more organized nervous systems. A planarian's nervous system includes nerve cords and eye spots. Both are formed from groups of interneurons. Arthropods, mollusks, and vertebrates have nervous systems that include a brain. A **brain**

is an organized grouping of neurons in the head of an animal with bilateral symmetry. A brain receives information, interprets it, and controls an animal's response. A complex animal with a brain and nerve cord may have billions of neurons.

The more complex an animal's nervous system is, the more specialized its sense organs are. Sense organs, such as eyes, ears, and noses, are structures that detect stimuli. Many sense organs are located in the head. Animals with many sense organs can process many stimuli at the same time because different areas of the brain respond to different stimuli.

On a separate sheet of paper, explain the role of the nervous system. Then, give an example of an environmental stimulus and describe how, in an animal with a brain, each of the three types of neurons functions to produce a response to that stimulus.

Review and Reinforce

The Nervous System

Understanding Main Ideas

Answer the following questions on a separate sheet of paper.

1. How are a stimulus and a response related?
2. How do the three different types of neurons function?
3. What is a nerve net? How many specialized neurons does a nerve net include?
4. What are the three functions of a brain?
5. How are animals with many sense organs able to process many stimuli at the same time?

Building Vocabulary

Match each term with its definition by writing the letter of the correct definition in the right column on the line beside the term in the left column.

6. ___ stimulus

7. ___ impulse

8. ___ neuron

9. ___ brain

10. ___ response

11. ___ nervous system

a. an animal's reaction to a stimulus

b. a collection of organs that act like the body's control panel

c. an organized grouping of neurons in the head of an animal with bilateral symmetry

d. a signal that causes an animal to react in some way

e. a nerve cell with a unique structure for receiving and passing on information

f. information that travels as an electrical message

The Nervous System

> The cephalopod has a unique nervous system. Read the passage below. Then, use a separate sheet of paper to answer the questions that follow.

The "Smart" Invertebrate

What class of invertebrates can move by jet propulsion, has a member who has been described in poetry by the father of a Justice of the Supreme Court of the United States, and has the most complex nervous system of any of the invertebrates? The answer to these questions is the cephalopod.

Cephalopods move by jet propulsion. They squeeze a stream of water from their mantle cavity and through a tube. And off they go! Oliver Wendell Holmes, a physician and father of Supreme Court Justice Olive Wendell Holmes Jr. describes a member of the class in his poem, "The Chambered Nautilus." And more importantly, the cephalopod has the most complex nervous system of any invertebrate, making it the most intelligent of the invertebrates. Its ratio of brain to body mass is high and falls between that of cold- and warm-blooded vertebrates.

Cephalopods live in oceans because they need salt water; they are social creatures; they often have colored pigments and can bioluminesce. They have bilateral body symmetry, prominent heads, modified feet, and arms or tentacles. There are two classes of cephalopods: one with internal or no shells and the other with shells.

However, their nervous system may be their most interesting characteristic. Cephalopods have advanced vision that allows them to see prey. Their brain allows them to learn and remember strategies to catch prey and solve simple puzzles.

1. Name two characteristics of cephalopods.
2. Why are cephalopods considered the most intelligent invertebrates?
3. How do the advanced nervous systems of cephalopods help them catch their prey?

Lesson Quiz

The Nervous System

Fill in the blank to complete each statement.

1. A(n) _____ is an animal's reaction to a stimulus.

2. The _____ is the part of a complex animal's nervous system that receives information, interprets it, and controls the animal's response.

3. Eyes and ears are examples of _____ organs.

4. The odor of baking bread is an example of a(n) _____.

5. A(n) _____ is an electrical message that travels through the nervous system.

If the statement is true, write *true*. If the statement is false, change the underlined word or words to make the statement true.

6. _____ <u>Sensory</u> neurons carry response information to organs.

7. _____ A(n) <u>brain</u> is a nerve cell with a unique structure for receiving and passing on information.

8. _____ Blinking in bright light is an example of a(n) <u>response</u>.

9. _____ A(n) <u>ear</u> is a sense organ that detects stimuli in the form of sight.

10. _____ An impulse is sent through the body as a(n) <u>electrical</u> signal.

The Nervous System

Answer Key

After the Inquiry Warm-Up

1. The message traveled through the wire as an electrical impulse.

2. The message being sent would not reach the light bulb.

3. Answers will vary. Sample: When a person is injured in an accident, if the spinal cord cut or damaged he or she may become paralyzed.

4. Stimulus messages come from your body, from your five senses. Response messages come from the brain.

Key Concept Summaries

Sample: A nervous system allows animals to detect signals in their environments, process the signals, and react to them. For example, when a bird sees a cat nearby, sensory neurons detect the cat and produce an electrical impulse to send the message, "There's a cat!" Interneurons transfer the electrical impulse to the brain. The brain processes the information and produces an electrical impulse to send the response, "Move away!" Motor neurons carry an electrical impulse to the muscles in the bird's wings, which results in the bird flying away.

Review and Reinforce

1. A stimulus is a signal that causes an animal to react in some way. A response is an animal's reaction to that stimulus.

2. Sensory neurons detect stimuli. Interneurons transfer information between neurons. Motor neurons carry response information.

3. A nerve net is a netlike arrangement of neurons found in the simplest of animals, such as cnidarians. A nerve net has no specialized neurons.

4. A brain receives information, interprets it, and controls an animal's response.

5. Animals with many sense organs can process many stimuli at the same time because different areas of the brain respond to different stimuli.

6. d
7. f
8. e
9. c
10. a
11. b

Enrich

1. Characteristics of cephalopods include bilateral symmetry, prominent heads, modified feet, arms or tentacles, complex nervous systems, and a means of movement.

2. They have the most complex nervous systems including advanced vision and large brains.

3. Their advanced vision allows cephalopods to see prey while their brains allow them to plan strategies to catch prey.

Lesson Quiz

1. response
2. brain
3. sense
4. stimulus
5. impulse
6. Motor
7. neuron
8. true
9. eye
10. true

Place the outside corner, the corner away from the dotted line, in the corner of your copy machine to copy onto letter-size paper.

Animal Movement

Lesson Pacing: 2–3 periods or 1–1½ blocks

🕐 **SHORT ON TIME?** To do this lesson in approximately half the time, do the Activate Prior Knowledge activity on page 186. A discussion of the Key Concepts on pages 187 and 188 will familiarize students with the lesson content. Use the Explore the Big Q to help students understand how animals move. Do the Quick Lab and have students do the Real-World Inquiry online. The rest of the lesson can be completed by students independently.

Preference Navigator, in the online Planning tools, allows you to customize *Interactive Science* to your own teaching style. You can also edit lesson plans by selecting the Lesson Planner option.

Digital Teacher's Edition allows you to access your Teacher's Edition and Resource materials online.

my science online.com

Lesson Vocabulary

- water vascular system
- swim bladder

Content Refresher
Professional Development Note

Natural Selection Animals survive in the environment to which they are best suited. Their level of success in an environment depends on the adaptations they have. According to the theory of natural selection, those organisms best suited to an environment survive and reproduce. As a result, their offspring share similar traits. Those organisms that cannot survive do not pass on their traits to the next generation.

Adaptations can involve both behaviors and physical traits. Some adaptations help an organism find food or mates, escape predators, obtain prey, or build a home. Other adaptations enable an animal to move from one place to another.

Evaluating the usefulness of a physical trait means considering the environment in which the trait is used. Adaptations that help an animal move in water are those that help it move through the water most efficiently. These might include fins, flippers, and streamlined bodies. Adaptations that help an animal move on land are those that help it get to its food and avoid predators. These can vary greatly depending on the type of animal. Some animals have legs for walking. Others have thick skin on which to slither. Adaptations that help an animal move in air are those that make it light in weight and can exert a force on air, such as wings.

LESSON OBJECTIVES

 Explain how muscles, the skeleton, and the nervous system interact to allow animal movement.

 Compare adaptations in organisms that help them move in a specific environment.

Blended Path
Active learning using Student Edition, Inquiry Path, and Digital Path

ENGAGE AND EXPLORE

Teach this lesson using a variety of resources. Begin by reading **My Planet Diary** as a class. Have students share ideas about how their perspective would change if they could fly. Then have students do the **Inquiry Warm-Up activity.** Students will observe the movements of a hydra. Discuss what students observed about the hydra before and after they touched it with a toothpick. The **After the Inquiry Warm-Up worksheet** sets up a discussion about stimuli and responses. Have volunteers share their answers to question 4 about what would happen if a tiny water animal touched a hydra.

EXPLAIN AND ELABORATE

Teach Key Concepts by explaining that an animal moves when its nervous system, muscular system, and skeletal system work together to make movement happen.

Continue to **Teach Key Concepts** by asking students how they move in different environments and which movements are most natural to them. **Lead a Discussion** about the function of water vascular systems in sea stars and other echinoderms. Use **Figure 1** to illustrate body adaptations for life in the water. **Lead a Discussion** about how various land animals move. Use **Figure 2** to describe each type of movement exhibited by the animals in the images. **Lead a Discussion** about how animals move through the air. Use **Figure 3** to compare and contrast the traits that help the animals in the photos to move. **Explore the Big Q** by describing the adaptations the animals in **Figure 4** have that allow them to move. **Answer the Big Q** by leading a discussion about how different animals move. Hand out the **Key Concept Summaries** as a review of each part of the lesson. Students can also use the online **Vocab Flash Cards** to review key terms.

EVALUATE

Have students take the **Lesson Quiz.** For an alternate assessment, see the *ExamView®* Computer Test Generator, Progress Monitoring Assessments, or SuccessTracker™.

ELL Support

1 Content and Language
Streamline is a compound word made up from the words *stream* and *line*. Have students use what they know about these two words to write a definition of *streamline*.

Lab zone Inquiry Path
Hands-on learning in the Lab zone

Digital Path
Online learning at my science online.com

ENGAGE AND EXPLORE

To teach this lesson with an emphasis on inquiry, begin with the **Inquiry Warm-Up activity.** Students will observe the movement of a hydra. Discuss students' diagrams of the hydra before and after touching it with a toothpick. Have students do the **After the Inquiry Warm-Up worksheet.** Talk about the response and stimulus the hydra exhibited. Have volunteers share their answers to question 4 about how a hydra would respond to the touch of a tiny water animal.

EXPLAIN AND ELABORATE

Focus on the **Inquiry Skill** for the lesson. Point out that when you calculate, you use mathematical equations to determine a value. What tool could be used to calculate the length of the hydra's tentacles? *(A metric ruler)* Have students do the **Lab investigation** to observe how a snail responds to temperature.

To **Build Inquiry** have students use water and a dropper to model how a sea star's water vascular system allows it to move. Do the **Teacher Demo** to model how a squid, jellyfish, and octopus move. **Explore the Big Q** by describing the adaptations of the animals in **Figure 4** that allow them to move. The **Real-World Inquiry** allows students to explore how different animal's nervous systems are adapted to their particular environments. Have students do the **Quick Lab** to compare bare fingers underwater to wearing a plastic bag on their hands and then share their results. Discuss how different animals move to help students **Answer the Big Q.** Students can use the online **Vocab Flash Cards** to review key terms.

EVALUATE

Have students take the **Lesson Quiz.** For an alternate assessment, see the *ExamView*® Computer Test Generator, Progress Monitoring Assessments, or SuccessTracker™.

ENGAGE AND EXPLORE

Teach this lesson using digital resources. Begin by having students explore real-world connections to animal movement at **My Planet Diary** online. Have students access the Chapter Resources to find the **Unlock the Big Question activity.** There students can answer the questions and refine their responses as they continue through the lesson. You can re-assign the activity and have students submit their work so you can track their progress.

EXPLAIN AND ELABORATE

Students reading above, at, or below the lexile measure of this lesson can access basic content readings at their level at **My Reading Web.** Have students use the online **Vocab Flash Cards** to preview key terms.

Have students do the online **Interactive Art activity** to show animal adaptations for moving in the water. Do the online **Interactive Art activity** to compare and contrast different types of movement. Assign the **Do the Math activity** online and have students submit their work to you. **Explore the Big Q** by reviewing with students the adaptations that allow the animals in **Figure 4** to move. Have students do **Real-World Inquiry** online to explore how different animals' nervous systems are adapted to their particular environments. Do the **Quick Lab** and then ask students to share their results. Have students **Answer the Big Q** and then ask volunteers to share their responses. The **Key Concept Summaries** online allow students to read a summary and see an image associated with each part of the lesson. Online remediation is available at **My Science Coach.**

EVALUATE

Have students take the **Lesson Quiz.** For an alternate assessment, see the *ExamView*® Computer Test Generator, Progress Monitoring Assessments, or SuccessTracker™.

2 Frontload the Lesson
Preview the lesson visuals, labels, and captions. Ask students what they know about the terms *vascular* and *bladder.* Explain the specific meanings these words have in science.

3 Comprehensible Input
Have students identify three animals from different environments and write a summary of the adaptations that allow these animals to move in their respective environments.

4 Language Production
Pair or group students with varied language abilities to complete labs collaboratively for language practice. Have each student copy the completed written lab for personal reference.

5 Assess Understanding
Make true or false statements using lesson content and have students indicate if they agree or disagree with a thumbs up or thumbs down gesture to check whole-class comprehension.

Lexile Measure = 880L

Animal Movement

Establish Learning Objectives

After this lesson, students will be able to:

🔑 Explain how muscles, the skeleton, and the nervous system interact to allow animal movement.

🔑 Compare adaptations in organisms that help them move in a specific environment.

Engage

Activate Prior Knowledge

MY PLANET DIARY Read *Dylan's Blog* with the class. Have students discuss different forms of transportation. Ask: **What are different vehicles that people can use to travel from one place to another?** *(Bicycle, car, bus, train, airplane, hot-air balloon, boat)* **What are different ways that animals can move from one place to another?** *(Walk, crawl, swim, climb, fly)*

BIG IDEAS OF SCIENCE REFERENCE LIBRARY 📖
Have students look up the following topics: Birds, Exoskeleton, Marsupials, Sea Turtles.

Explore

Lab Resource: Inquiry Warm-Up 🔬

L2 **HYDRA DOING?** Students will observe the movements of a hydra.

Animal Movement

 UNLOCK THE BIG ❓

🔑 **What Causes Animals to Move?**

🔑 **How Do Adaptations for Movement Compare?**

MY PLANET DIARY

Posted by: Dylan
Location: Newton, Massachusetts

Often in the summer when I am walking down the beach, I think of myself running and taking off, soaring into the open sky and looking down at the coastline. Being able to fly is a dream of mine because it seems like a quick way to travel. Also, I want to be the first person in the world that can fly. I want to fly for leisure, not "fight evil with my powers" like superheroes do in the movies. I think many people dream of being able to fly. Who knows, maybe someday that dream will come true.

Communicate Discuss the following questions with a partner. Then write your answers below.

1. In what ways can people fly today?
   Sample: People can fly in airplanes and hot air balloons.

2. Would it affect your life in a positive or negative way if people could fly unassisted? Why?
   Accept all reasonable responses.

▶ PLANET DIARY Go to **Planet Diary** to learn more about animal movement.

🔬 Lab zone   Do the Inquiry Warm-Up *Hydra Doing?*

186 Getting Around

SUPPORT ALL READERS

Lexile Measure = 880L   Lexile Word Count = 1209

Prior Exposure to Content: Many students may have misconceptions on this topic

Academic Vocabulary: *calculate, relate*

Science Vocabulary: *water vascular system, swim bladder*

Concept Level: Generally appropriate for most students in this grade

Preteach With: My Planet Diary "Dylan's Blog" and Figure 2 activity

Go to **My Reading Web** to access leveled readings that provide a foundation for the content.

MY SCIENCE online.com ▶

Vocabulary
- water vascular system
- swim bladder

Skills
- 🔁 Reading: Relate Text and Visuals
- △ Inquiry: Calculate

What Causes Animals to Move?

All animals move about in certain ways during their lives. They may swim, walk, slither, crawl, run, hop, fly, soar, jump, or swing through trees. However, all animal movements have something in common. 🔑 **An animal moves about when its nervous system, muscular system, and skeletal system work together to make movement happen.** First, an animal's nervous system receives a signal from the environment. Second, its nervous system processes the signal. Finally, its nervous system signals the muscles, which contract, causing the skeleton to move.

Animals move for many reasons. They move to obtain food, defend and protect themselves, maintain homeostasis, and find mates.

✏️ 🔁 **Relate Text and Visuals** For each photo, write a reason why the animal might be moving.

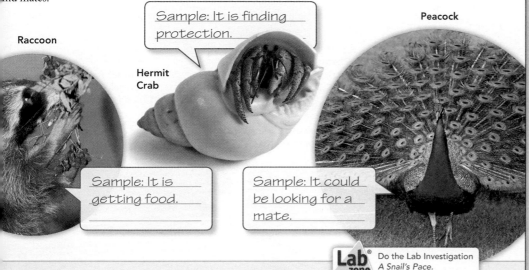

Raccoon

Hermit Crab

Peacock

Sample: It is finding protection.

Sample: It is getting food.

Sample: It could be looking for a mate.

Lab zone Do the Lab Investigation *A Snail's Pace.*

🔑 Assess Your Understanding

Got it?

○ **I get it!** Now I know that animals move about <u>when their skeletal, nervous, and muscular systems work together.</u>

○ **I need extra help with** <u>See TE note.</u>

Go to **my science 🔍 COACH** online for help with this subject.

187

Explain

Introduce Vocabulary

Tell students that the word *vascular* comes from the Latin term meaning "vessels" or "tubes." This may help them to remember that a *water vascular system* is made up of tubes that contain a watery fluid.

Teach Key Concepts 🔑

Explain that the organ systems of an animal do not work separately from one another, but work together to perform the functions necessary for life. Ask: **Which organ systems work together to make an animal move?** *(Skeletal system, nervous system, and muscular system)* **What are some reasons why an animal would move?** *(To obtain food, defend itself, maintain homeostasis, and find mates)* **What is homeostasis?** *(The maintaining of stable internal conditions)* Have students look at the photographs on this page and describe how they think each animal moves. If students have not seen a male peacock before, explain that the tail is not always held in this position. Ask: **Why do you think the male peacock is displaying its colorful tail feathers?** *(To get a peahen's attention and mate)*

🔁 **Relate Text and Visuals** Explain to students that visuals include photos and diagrams. They are often used to visually represent information in the text.

Lab Resource: Lab Investigation 🔬

L2 A SNAIL'S PACE Students will investigate how the movement of a snail varies with temperature.

Evaluate

Assess Your Understanding

Have students evaluate their understanding by completing the appropriate sentence.

RTI Response to Intervention

If students cannot describe the systems involved in movement, **then** briefly summarize what students have learned about the three systems.

my science 🔍 COACH Have students go online for help in understanding animal movement.

My Planet Diary provides an opportunity for students to explore real-world connections to animal movement.

my science online.com | Animal Movement

E L L Support

1 Content and Language
Write the term *vascular* on the board. Explain that the word *vascular* means "having or relating to vessels or tubes."

2 Frontload the Lesson
Have students brainstorm a list of ways animals move. Discuss with students how each animal's way of moving relates to its body size, structure, and habitat.

3 Comprehensible Input
Have each student make a three-column chart with the headings *Animal, Where the Animal Moves,* and *Adaptations for Movement.* Invite each student to choose three animals—one from each of the figures in the lesson—and list them in the first column of the chart. Then, have students fill in the other two columns with information from the lesson.

Explain

Teach Key Concepts

Have students think about how they move in different environments. Explain that animals can move in different ways. Ask: **How do you move in the hallway at school?** *(Walk)* **How do you move in water?** *(Swim or dive)* **Which of these movements comes more naturally to you? Why?** *(Sample: walking; because we live on land, not water; because we had to be taught to swim)* **How do you think an animal's environment is related to how the animal moves?** *(Students should explain that different environments require different kinds of locomotion.)*

Lead a Discussion

WATER VASCULAR SYSTEM Explain to students that the echinoderms move by crawling over surfaces. There can be hundreds of tiny tube feet on the underside of a sea star, but they do not all move at once. A sea star can release suction in one area while maintaining suction in other areas. When a sea star moves, it releases one arm while holding onto a surface with others. Tell students that sea stars often live along rocky shores and can be found in tide pools, areas that are under several feet of water at high tide and that are puddles at low tide.

Ask: **Why is having strong suction an important adaptation for a sea star?** *(They live along the shore where there are waves. If the sea star could not hang onto the rocks, it would be washed out to sea. Or it might be washed up too far on the beach, where it would dry out and die.)*

Explore

Build Inquiry **Lab zone**

L2 SEA STAR SUCTION

Materials plastic dropper, water

Time 10 minutes

Have students fill a plastic dropper with water. Direct students to squeeze out most of the water. Tell them to squeeze the last drop onto the inside of their arms. Then, while still squeezing the bulb, students should touch the tip of the dropper into the water drop. With the dropper tip against the skin, students should release the bulb. Students should lift the dropper slowly and observe their skin.

Ask: **What happens to your skin when you lift the dropper?** *(It is pulled a little.)* **How does the plastic dropper and water model how a sea star uses its water vascular system to move?** *(The sea star uses this type of suction to grip onto objects.)* **Besides moving, how else might sea stars use their tube feet?** *(To grasp food)*

How Do Adaptations for Movement Compare?

Animals live nearly everywhere on Earth. **Animals that live in water, on land, or in the air have different adaptations for movement.**

Moving in Water If you have ever tried to walk in a swimming pool, you know that moving in water is more difficult than moving on land. This is because water is resistant to movement through it. Many animals that swim, such as fishes, dolphins, and penguins, have streamlined bodies that help them move through water. They also have appendages for swimming. Fishes have fins, and dolphins and penguins have fleshy flippers.

Some animals that live in water do not swim but move through water in other ways. For example, sea stars and other echinoderms have a **water vascular system,** a system of fluid-filled tubes. The tubes produce suction, which enables an echinoderm to grip surfaces and move along. Look at **Figure 1** to see some different animal adaptations for moving in water.

FIGURE 1 ....

> INTERACTIVE ART Moving Through Water

Complete the activity and then answer the question.

1. **Summarize** In the table on the next page, identify each animal's adaptation for moving. Then describe how the animal moves.

2. **Make Judgments** How is a fish helped by staying at a certain depth without using a lot of energy?

   Sample: It has more energy for finding food and escaping enemies.

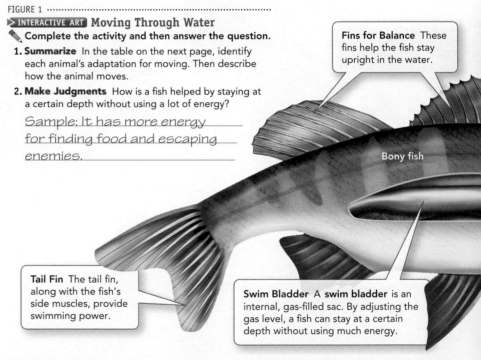

Fins for Balance These fins help the fish stay upright in the water.

Bony fish

Tail Fin The tail fin, along with the fish's side muscles, provide swimming power.

Swim Bladder A **swim bladder** is an internal, gas-filled sac. By adjusting the gas level, a fish can stay at a certain depth without using much energy.

Interactive Art shows the water vascular system of a sea star.

my science online .com | Adaptations for Movement

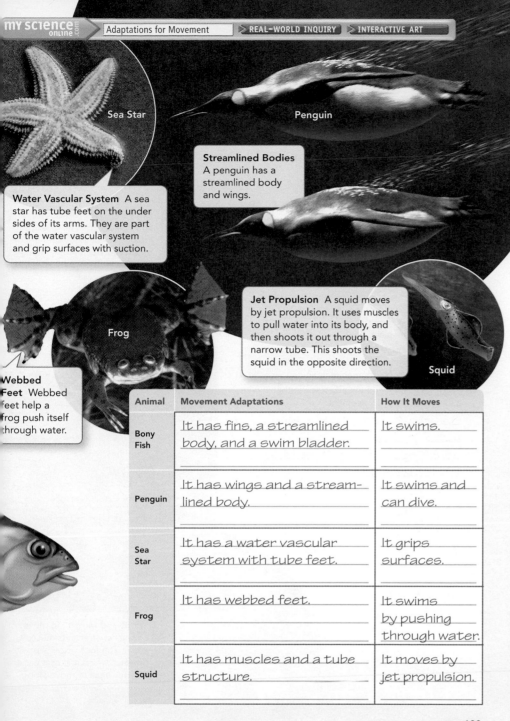

Sea Star

Penguin

Streamlined Bodies A penguin has a streamlined body and wings.

Water Vascular System A sea star has tube feet on the under sides of its arms. They are part of the water vascular system and grip surfaces with suction.

Jet Propulsion A squid moves by jet propulsion. It uses muscles to pull water into its body, and then shoots it out through a narrow tube. This shoots the squid in the opposite direction.

Frog

Squid

Webbed Feet Webbed feet help a frog push itself through water.

Animal	Movement Adaptations	How It Moves
Bony Fish	It has fins, a streamlined body, and a swim bladder.	It swims.
Penguin	It has wings and a stream-lined body.	It swims and can dive.
Sea Star	It has a water vascular system with tube feet.	It grips surfaces.
Frog	It has webbed feet.	It swims by pushing through water.
Squid	It has muscles and a tube structure.	It moves by jet propulsion.

189

Differentiated Instruction

L1 Investigate Floating Have small groups of students get three snack-size plastic bags. Tell them to fill one with water, another with both air and water, and the third with air. Ask them to seal all three bags. Challenge them to submerge the bags in a large bowl or tub filled part way with water. Ask students to figure out how the amount of air in the bag is related to whether the bag floats or sinks. Work with students to relate this investigation to a swim bladder.

L3 Compare Movement Have pairs of students use books or online sources to research fish movement. Have students choose two fishes with very different physical features, such as a shark and a catfish. Then, tell them to make simple cardboard models of the body shape and fin shape for both.

Explain
Teach With Visuals

Tell students to look at **Figure 1**. Discuss with students how each animal's body is adapted for life in the water. Have students look at the penguin, fish, and squid. Ask: **What is the advantage of a streamlined body for animals that move in water?** *(It helps them glide through the water more easily.)* **Why isn't a streamlined body important for a sea star?** *(It doesn't swim; it crawls.)* Direct students' attention to the photograph of the frog. Ask: **Have you ever used flippers when swimming or snorkeling? How do they help you swim?** *(Sample: They make your feet larger, so there is a larger area to push against the water.)* **How does the frog use its webbed feet?** *(The frog kicks out its feet and pushes against the water.)* If students ask why the frog doesn't pull itself backward when it draws its legs against its body in preparation for the next kick, point out that the webbing is between toes. The frog pulls its toes together as it draws up its legs, making the foot smaller. Then it spreads the toes for the next kick.

Elaborate

21st Century Learning

L1 CRITICAL THINKING Display a photo of one or more Olympic or similar swimmers. Try to include some with full-body swimsuits. Ask: **Other than to keep their hair dry, why do you think these swimmers wear bathing caps?** *(To make their bodies more streamlined)* **Why do their wear tight-fitting swimsuits?** *(To move through the water more smoothly)* **How do the traits of these swimmers compare to adaptations of animals that live in water?** *(The swimmers do not have natural adaptations that help them survive in water. They use bathing caps and swimsuits to mimic the adaptations of animals that live in water.)*

Teacher Demo

L1 JET PROPULSION

Materials small balloon

Time 5 minutes

Inflate a small balloon, but do not tie off the end. Release the balloon and have students observe what happens.

Ask: **What did the balloon do when I let go of it?** *(It flew around the room.)* **Which animal shown in Figure 1 swims this way?** *(The squid)* **What other animal swims this way?** *(Samples: jellyfish, octopus)*

189

Explain

Lead a Discussion

LAND ANIMALS Explain that animals on land have adaptations to help them survive. Some of these adaptations also help them to move. Ask: **How would you describe the movement of a snake?** *(It slithers.)* **How would you describe the movement of a snail?** *(It crawls.)* **How does the speed at which a snake moves compare to the speed at which a snail moves?** *(Most snakes can move much faster than snails can move.)* Review with students the differences in muscles between vertebrates and invertebrates. Most vertebrates that live on land walk on four feet. Even apes, which can walk bipedally, or on two feet, use their long arms for stability as they walk. Because they put knuckles, not the palms of the hand, on the ground, this type of gait is called "knuckle walking." Ask: **Which vertebrates do not walk on legs?** *(Snakes)* Students may find it interesting that scientists think that the ancestors of snakes did have legs. Some species of snakes, including pythons, have a vestigial pelvis, a nonfunctional version of pelvic bones.

Elaborate

21st Century Learning

L1 CREATIVITY Encourage students to draw or collect images of land animals in motion and make a poster about animal motion. Students with an interest in a particular animal, such as the horse, might collect images showing their different gaits. Students might use field guides to animals to find illustrations of animal tracks that show the length of different animals' strides.

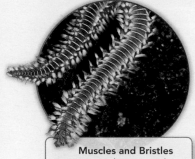

Muscles and Bristles
A segmented worm, such as this fireworm, has muscles that contract to extend the worm forward. It also has bristles that grip the soil.

Moving on Land Have you ever watched a snake slither through the grass? Perhaps you've watched ants walk across the ground. Both snakes and ants move on land, but their adaptations for moving on land are different. A snake contracts its muscles and pushes against the ground with its body. An ant uses its jointed appendages to walk. **Figure 2** shows some of the many adaptations that animals have for moving on land.

FIGURE 2

Moving on Land

The different adaptations of these animals allow them to move in different ways.

✎ **Complete these activities.**

1. **Apply Concepts** In the graphic organizer on the next page, describe an adaptation for moving that three other animals you know have.

2. **CHALLENGE** Describe the adaptations that a kangaroo has for movement.

   Sample: A kangaroo has large feet for landing, muscular upper legs for hopping, and a tail for balance.

✎

Vocabulary Identify Multiple Meanings The word *foot* has other meanings besides appendage. Write another meaning for *foot* below.

Sample: A foot is a unit of measurement.

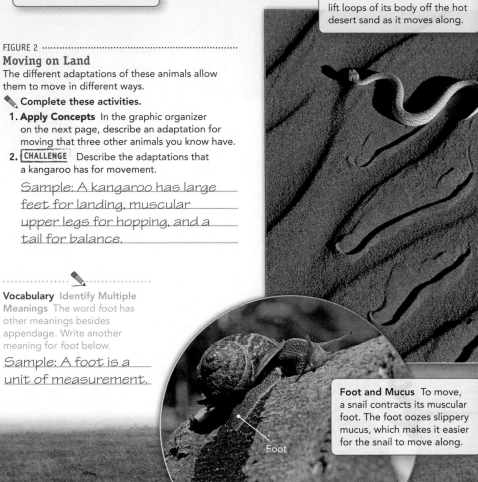

Body Muscles This sidewinding adder snake uses its muscles to lift loops of its body off the hot desert sand as it moves along.

Foot and Mucus To move, a snail contracts its muscular foot. The foot oozes slippery mucus, which makes it easier for the snail to move along.

Foot

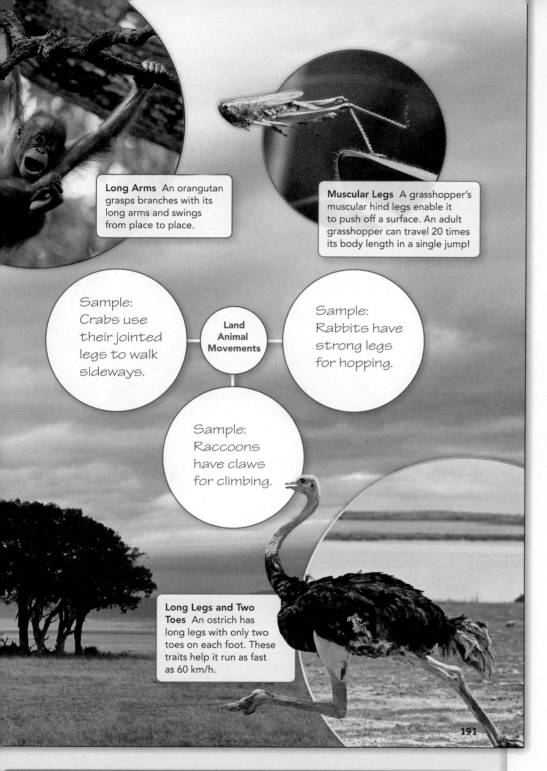

Long Arms An orangutan grasps branches with its long arms and swings from place to place.

Muscular Legs A grasshopper's muscular hind legs enable it to push off a surface. An adult grasshopper can travel 20 times its body length in a single jump!

Sample: Crabs use their jointed legs to walk sideways.

Land Animal Movements

Sample: Rabbits have strong legs for hopping.

Sample: Raccoons have claws for climbing.

Long Legs and Two Toes An ostrich has long legs with only two toes on each foot. These traits help it run as fast as 60 km/h.

191

Explain

Teach With Visuals

Tell students to look at **Figure 2.** As a class, read each caption. Encourage volunteers to describe each type of movement and then have students complete the graphic organizer. Point out that many answers are possible. Suggest that students first think of an animal that moves on land. Then, they should figure out what type of adaptation enables the animal to move. If students need help completing the graphic organizer, provide them with nature magazines or books about animals and give them time to browse through these sources of information.

21st Century Learning

INTERPERSONAL SKILLS Have students read *Marsupials* in the **Big Ideas of Science Reference Library.** Pairs should work together to write ten multiple-choice questions about marsupials and be sure to include the correct answers. Pairs can exchange their work and answer the questions.

Elaborate

Address Misconceptions

L1 **NOT ALL BIRDS CAN FLY** Students may be tempted to see the feathers of a bird and assume flight. Remind students that all birds have feathers, but not all birds can fly. Ask: **How does an ostrich move?** *(It walks or runs.)* **How does a penguin move?** *(It walks or swims.)* **How does an eagle move?** *(It flies.)*

Differentiated Instruction

L1 **Movement Words** Ask students to create a poster to show the different types of movement among land animals. Tell students to choose four to five animals, and include a picture or diagram of each. Then ask students to list words that describe the movement. They might use words such as *hop, run, glide, crawl,* or *slither.* Encourage students to be creative in their choice of verbs.

L3 **Movement Models** Some animals move in a wave-like way. Have pairs of students work together to use coiled springs to model animal movement. Challenge students to use the spring to make two different kinds of movement. One way is to move the end back and forth perpendicular to the spring. Another way is to push the spring in and out, parallel to the spring.

Explain

Lead a Discussion

ANIMALS IN AIR Invite volunteers to name some animals that fly through the air. Point out that they might include birds and insects, and even one mammal. Ask: **What structures do animals need to fly?** *(Wings)* **How is movement different when an animal is speeding up as opposed to when it is gliding?** *(An animal flaps its wings back and forth to speed up and holds its wings in place to glide.)*

Address Misconceptions

FLYING SQUIRRELS Because of the animal's common name, students may think that a flying squirrel is actually able to fly. Explain that a flying squirrel does not really fly. It has extra skin between the front and back legs that it can stretch out when it jumps. Because it cannot flap the skin and gain altitude, the flying squirrel is not truly flying. Its action is closer to that of a hang glider.

Elaborate

21st Century Learning

L3 CREATIVITY Challenge students to imagine that they can fly. Ask them to write a short story or short play describing the places they would go and the things they would see. Tell them to include information about the adaptations they have that help them to fly as well as reasons why they need to move about.

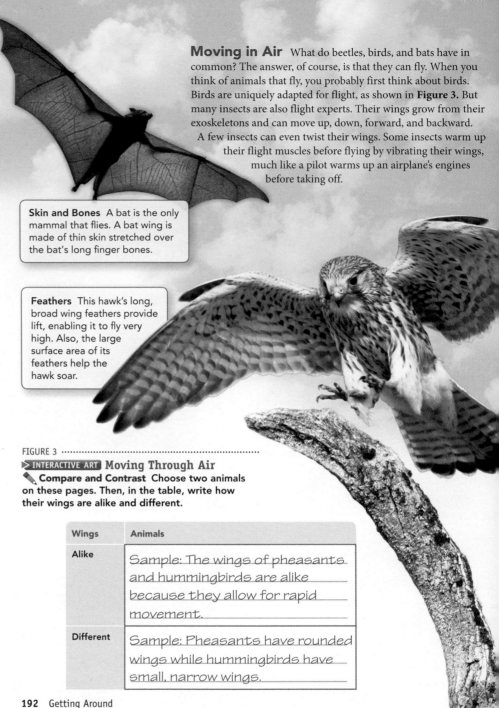

Moving in Air What do beetles, birds, and bats have in common? The answer, of course, is that they can fly. When you think of animals that fly, you probably first think about birds. Birds are uniquely adapted for flight, as shown in **Figure 3**. But many insects are also flight experts. Their wings grow from their exoskeletons and can move up, down, forward, and backward. A few insects can even twist their wings. Some insects warm up their flight muscles before flying by vibrating their wings, much like a pilot warms up an airplane's engines before taking off.

Skin and Bones A bat is the only mammal that flies. A bat wing is made of thin skin stretched over the bat's long finger bones.

Feathers This hawk's long, broad wing feathers provide lift, enabling it to fly very high. Also, the large surface area of its feathers help the hawk soar.

FIGURE 3 ....

> INTERACTIVE ART Moving Through Air

✎ **Compare and Contrast** Choose two animals on these pages. Then, in the table, write how their wings are alike and different.

Wings	Animals
Alike	Sample: The wings of pheasants and hummingbirds are alike because they allow for rapid movement.
Different	Sample: Pheasants have rounded wings while hummingbirds have small, narrow wings.

Interactive Art allows students to compare and contrast different types of movement.

Digital Lesson: Assign the *Do the Math* activity online and have students submit their work to you.

my science online.com | **Adaptations for Movement**

Paired Wings A dragonfly has two wings on each side of its body. The wings enable it to fly a long time and change direction quickly.

Wings for Hovering The small, narrow wings of this hummingbird can flap rapidly. This allows hummingbirds to fly forward, backward, and even hover like a helicopter.

Short, Round Wings Some forest birds, such as this pheasant, have short, rounded wings that enable them to take off rapidly.

Front and Hind Wings Butterflies have front and hind wings that are linked by a thin layer of cells. This helps the butterfly flap both pairs of wings at the same time.

do the math!

Different insects beat their wings at different rates, which are measured in beats per second (bps).

Insect	Wing bps
Housefly	190
Horsefly	96
Large white butterfly	12

❶ Interpret Data How many times does a housefly beat its wings in one minute?

$190 \times 60 = 11,400$

❷ ◢Calculate How many times faster does a horsefly beat its wings than a large white butterfly?

It beats them 8 times faster. ($96 \div 12$)

193

Explain
Teach With Visuals

Tell students to look at **Figure 3**. As a class, read each caption. Point out that the animals shown are different from each other in many ways, yet they all fly. Ask students to look for traits that are common to all of the animals as well as traits that are different. Ask: **What can you see silhouetted in the bat's wings?** *(Its front limbs)* Tell students that the short segments they can see near the bat's body are its arms. The long bones of the wing are actually the bones of one finger. The bones in a bird's wing are different from those of a bat's wing. The wing of a bird is more like a person's arm. Obtain a picture of a bird's skeleton to show the class. Ask: **Which two animals shown here do not have bones in their wings?** *(The dragonfly and the butterfly)*

Elaborate
Do the Math!

L1 Explain that a table is a useful way to organize and display data made up of numbers. Point out that whenever students see a data table, they should read the titles of the columns to make sure they know what is listed. This table lists types of insects in the first column and wing beats in the second column. Students must know the unit of measurement used in order to answer questions about the data. This table uses bps, which stands for beats per second.

◢**Calculate** Remind students that calculating involves determining a value using math skills, such as adding, subtracting, multiplying, or dividing.

See the *Math Skill and Problem-Solving Activities* for support.

Differentiated Instruction

L1 Airplanes Have pairs of students work together to construct a paper airplane with wings like those of a bird. Tell students to conduct trial flights and make improvements to make their airplanes fly faster or farther. Allow students to compare their designs and results with other students. Invite volunteers to relate the shape of the wings to the flight of their airplane.

L3 Wing Shape Some students may be interested in comparing most efficient wing shape and specific flight mode. Encourage students to use available resources to produce a visual presentation relating wing shape, flight type, and example species. *(Samples: narrow, pointed wings for gliding long distances—seabirds, gulls, albatross; large surface area for soaring—eagles, storks, pelicans)*

Elaborate

Explore the Big Q ❓ UbD

Direct students' attention to **Figure 4.** Begin by having volunteers describe the traits of each animal shown. Students should include observable traits, as well as information they know about where the animal lives and what it eats. Ask: **Which animal moves in water?** *(Trout)* **Which animals move on or in land?** *(Earthworm, raccoon, and moose)* **Which animals move in air?** *(Dragonfly and eagle)* **Which animals hunt for food?** *(The eagle hunts; the raccoon fishes.)* **In what way are the adaptations of all the animals similar?** *(They all help the animal move in its environment.)* **How are they different?** *(The adaptations depend on the particular environment and the requirements for moving in that environment.)*

21st Century Learning

L1 **INTERPERSONAL SKILLS** Have students make a glossary of all the boldface terms presented in the chapter. Tell them to write each term in alphabetical order, along with a definition. Ask students to draw a small diagram that represents each term. Diagrams should include labels when appropriate. When complete, have students exchange glossaries with a partner. Ask partners for suggestions to improve the glossary.

How do animals move?

FIGURE 4 ·············

▶ **REAL-WORLD INQUIRY** A raccoon scurries over rocks as a bald eagle soars above it looking for a meal. Nearby, dragonflies skim over a stream where trout surface to snatch a meal. Movement is everywhere.

✎ Answer the questions in the boxes.

Summarize What adaptations does an eagle have for moving?

It has feathers, light bones, a streamlined body, and strong chest muscles.

Describe What kind of wings does a dragonfly have and how do they help it fly?

A dragonfly has paired wings which help it fly for a long time and change direction quickly.

List What structures enable a trout to move?

The trout has muscles, an endoskeleton, a streamlined shape, fins, and a swim bladder.

Explain What are the skeletons of earthworms like?

Earthworms have fluid-filled cavities surrounded by muscle.

194 Getting Around

Real-World Inquiry allows students to explore how different animals' nervous systems are adapted to their particular environments.

my science online.com ▸ | **Adaptations for Movement**

Summarize How does a raccoon's nervous system work with its muscular system to escape an eagle?

Sample: The raccoon's brain sends a message to its muscles. This process enables the raccoon to run away.

Identify When a moose smells a leafy plant, what kinds of neurons are involved? What roles do the neurons serve?

Sensory neurons detect the plant's odor. Interneurons process the information. Motor neurons move muscles so the moose can eat.

 Do the Quick Lab *Webbing Along.*

Assess Your Understanding

1a. Explain What adaptation does a grasshopper have to move on land?

It has muscular hind legs.

b. **ANSWER** How do animals move?

The nervous, skeletal, and muscular systems interact and enable animals to use their adaptations to move.

got it?

○ **I get it!** Now I know that animals have different adaptations for movement depending on _____ *whether the animals live in water, on land, or in the air.*

○ **I need extra help with** *See TE note.* _____

Go to **MY SCIENCE COACH** *online for help with this subject.*

195

Lab Resource: Quick Lab **Lab zone**

L1 **WEBBING ALONG** Students will explore how webbing affects movement through water.

Evaluate

Assess Your Understanding

After students answer the questions, have them evaluate their understanding by completing the appropriate sentence.

Answer the Big Q ? UbD

To help students focus on the Big Question, lead a class discussion about how different animals move.

RTI Response to Intervention

1a. If students have difficulty recognizing the adaptation of a grasshopper, **then** have them first describe the movement of the grasshopper and then describe the animal's habitat.

b. If students have trouble describing the general process of movement, **then** help them review the actions of the skeletal, muscular, and nervous systems.

MY SCIENCE COACH Have students go online for help in understanding animal movement.

Differentiated Instruction

L3 **Compare Feet** Although birds fly, they do need to land. The shape of a bird's foot is an adaptation that helps it perform its functions. Have students research different types of bird feet, such as talons, webbed feet, and so on. Ask them to show the class how each type of foot helps the bird move in its particular environment.

Lab zone **After the Inquiry Warm-Up**

Animal Movement

Inquiry Warm-Up, *Hydra Doing?*
In the Inquiry Warm-Up, you investigated the body plan and motion of hydras and used your observations to classify hydras as polyps or medusas. Using what you learned from that activity, answer the questions below.

1. **COMMUNICATE** Draw a two-part diagram that shows a hydra before and after you touched it with the toothpick.

2. **USE PRIOR KNOWLEDGE** In scientific terms, what was the touch of the toothpick to the hydra?

   _____

   _____

3. **USE PRIOR KNOWLEDGE** In scientific terms, what was the reaction of the hydra's tentacles to that touch?

   _____

   _____

4. **PREDICT** Suppose a tiny water animal touched a hydra tentacle. What do you think would happen?

   _____

   _____

   _____

Assess Your Understanding

Animal Movement

What Causes Animals to Move?

got it? ··

○ **I get it!** Now I know that animals move about _____

_____

○ **I need extra help with** _____

_____

How Do Adaptations for Movement Compare?

1a. EXPLAIN What adaptation does a grasshopper have to move on land? _____

_____

b. ANSWER How do animals move? _____

_____

_____

got it? ··

○ **I get it!** Now I know that animals have different adaptations for movement

depending on _____

_____

○ **I need extra help with** _____

_____

Key Concept Summaries

Animal Movement

What Causes Animals to Move?

All animal movements have something in common. **An animal moves when its nervous system, muscular system, and skeletal system work together to make movement happen.** First, an animal's nervous system receives a signal from the environment. Second, its nervous system signals the muscles, which contract and cause the skeleton to move. Animals move for many reasons. They move to obtain food, defend and protect themselves, maintain homeostasis, and find mates.

How Do Adaptations for Movement Compare?

Animals live nearly everywhere on Earth. **Animals that live in water, on land, or in the air have different adaptations for movement.**

Many animals that swim, such as fishes, dolphins, and penguins, have streamlined bodies that help them move through the water. They also have appendages, such as flippers and fins, for swimming. Some animals that live in water do not swim, but move through water in other ways. Sea stars and other echinoderms have a **water vascular system,** a system of fluid-filled tubes that allow them to grip surfaces with suction. Some fishes have an internal, gas-filled sac called a **swim bladder.** By adjusting the gas level in the bladder, a fish can stay at a certain depth in water.

Animals have many different adaptations for moving on land. A snake contracts its muscles and pushes against the ground with its belly. An ant uses its jointed appendages to walk. Other animals have long arms to swing in trees, powerful legs to jump, or long legs to run.

When you think of animals that can fly, you probably first think of birds. Birds are uniquely adapted for flight. A hawk's long, broad wing feathers enable it to fly high and to soar. A hummingbird's small, narrow wings flap rapidly, so it can hover like a helicopter. Forest birds such as the pheasant have short, rounded wings that enable them to take off rapidly.

Many insects are also flight experts. Their wings grow from their exoskeletons and can move up, down, forward, and backward. Some, such as the dragonfly, have more than one pair of wings. The only mammal that flies is the bat. Its wings are made of thin skin stretched over its long finger bones.

On a separate sheet of paper, choose three animals, one that lives in water, one that lives on land, and one that flies. Explain how each one moves and how it is uniquely adapted for movement within its environment.

Name _____ Date _____ Class _____

Animal Movement

Understanding Main Ideas
Answer the following questions in the spaces provided.

1. How do all animals move?

_____

_____

_____

2. List three reasons for animals to move.

_____

3. Why do you think it is useful for animals that live in water to have streamlined bodies?

_____

_____

4. You see an arthropod with strong, muscular hind legs. How might this animal move on land? Explain your reasoning.

_____

5. What type of flight is enabled by large wings with long, broad feathers?

_____

Building Vocabulary
Write a definition for each of these terms on the lines below.

6. water vascular system

_____

_____

7. swim bladder

_____

_____

Name _____ Date _____ Class _____

Animal Movement

Snakes can move in several different ways. There is no shape or texture of solid surface that snakes can't cross. Two types of snake movement are serpentine motion and linear motion. Read the passage and study the diagrams below. Then, use a separate sheet of paper to answer the questions that follow.

How Snakes Get Around

- **Serpentine motion:** This is a very common way in which snakes move, and the fastest. The snake bends its body into curves. The outside rear part of each curve presses against surrounding objects, pushing the snake forward. The snake's head can easily be seen to move from side to side.

- **Linear motion:** The snake's body moves in a straight line, as if it were crawling. This is also called "caterpillar" motion. As the snake moves, small ripples of contracting muscles can be seen moving along its sides. At the same time, the broad belly scales grip against even tiny bumps or ridges on which the snake is crawling, in order to push the snake forward. A snake can't use linear motion on an extremely smooth or slippery surface, and it is only useful for moving slowly. A snake using linear motion is not easily observed.

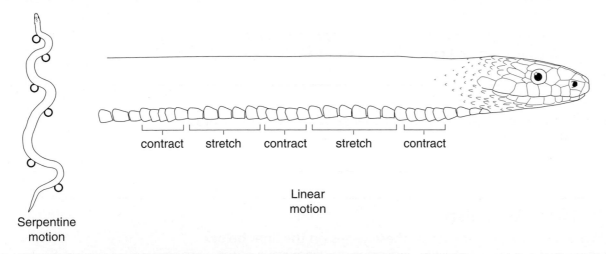

contract   stretch   contract   stretch   contract

Linear
motion

Serpentine
motion

1. Imagine that a small snake in a grassy yard sees you coming. Which type of motion would it probably use to move away quickly? Why?
2. Which type of motion would a large snake most likely use to sneak up on a motionless rabbit? Explain.
3. Which of the two kinds of motion would a snake use to move across deep water? Explain.

Name _____ Date _____ Class _____

Lesson Quiz

Animal Movement

If the statement is true, write *true*. If the statement is false, change the underlined word or words to make the statement true.

1. _____ Animals that live in <u>air</u> might have fins and flippers.

2. _____ Echinoderms have a system of fluid-filled tubes known as a(n) <u>swim bladder</u>.

3. _____ Some insects warm up their flight muscles by <u>vibrating</u> their wings.

4. _____ A snail uses a(n) <u>tail</u> and mucus to move on land.

5. _____ Webbed feet are most useful for an animal to move in <u>water</u>.

Fill in the blank to complete each statement.

6. The _____ is the only mammal that flies.

7. Animals move to obtain food, defend and protect themselves, maintain _____, and find mates.

8. A squid moves through water using _____ propulsion.

9. A dragonfly can change direction quickly because it has _____ pairs of wings.

10. The bones in a bat's wings are actually _____ bones.

Animal Movement

Answer Key

After the Inquiry Warm-Up

1. Students should show that the hydra has a vase-shaped body with tentacles extending upward from a central cavity and that the hydra's tentacles responded to touch by wrapping around the toothpick.

2. The touch of the toothpick was a stimulus.

3. The hydra tentacles curling around the toothpick was a response.

4. Answers will vary. Sample: The hydra's tentacle would immediately sting the tiny animal, stunning or killing it. Then, the tentacle would wrap around the animal and pull it into the hydra's central cavity to be digested.

Key Concept Summaries

Sample: A bony fish swims in water. It has a tail and strong side muscles for powerful swimming, fins that help it balance, and a swim bladder that helps it sty at a certain depth. A grasshopper jumps on land. It has muscular hind legs to give it a strong push off a surface and send it traveling up to 20 times its body length in a single jump. A hawk flies through the air. Its long, broad wing feathers enable it to fly high and to soar.

Review and Reinforce

1. An animal moves when its nervous system receives a signal from the environment. Its nervous system processes the signal. Then it signals muscles to contract, causing the animal's skeleton to move.

2. Answers may include obtaining food, defending themselves, finding protection, maintaining homeostasis, and finding mates.

3. Having a streamlined body allows an animal to move through the water more quickly with less resistance.

4. It probably uses the strong hind legs to jump.

5. soaring

6. a system of fluid-filled tubes that provide suction that helps grip surfaces

7. an internal, gas-filled sac that helps a fish to stay at a certain water depth

Enrich

1. serpentine motion; The snake could push off the grass easily, because it wants to get away as quickly as possible.

2. The snake would probably use linear motion because it would be less likely to be seen by the rabbit.

3. The snake would have to use serpentine motion because deep water wouldn't have any surface for its belly scales to grip. It could push off of the water, as a fish pushes through water with its fins.

Lesson Quiz

1. water
2. water vascular system
3. true
4. foot
5. true
6. bat
7. homeostasis
8. jet
9. two
10. finger

Study Guide

Review the Big Q UbD

Have students complete the statement at the top of the page. These Key Concepts support their understanding of the chapter's Big Question. Have students return to the chapter opener pages. What is different about how students view the image of the bat now that they have completed the chapter? Thinking about this will help them prepare for the *Apply the Big Q* activity in the Review and Assessment.

Partner Review

Have partners review definitions of vocabulary terms by using the Study Guide to quiz each other. Students could read the Key Concept statements and leave out words for their partner to fill in, or change a statement so that it is false and then ask their partner to correct it.

Class Activity: Concept Map

Have students develop a concept map to show how the information in this chapter is related. Have students brainstorm to identify the Key Concepts, vocabulary, details and examples. They can then write each one on a sticky note and attach it at random on chart paper or on the board. Explain that the concept map will begin at the top of the chart with the Key Concepts. Ask students to use the following questions to help them organize the information on the notes:

- What is a skeleton?
- What is the function of muscles?
- What are the functions of an animal's nervous system?
- How do animals move?
- How are different animals adapted to move in their particular environments?

My Science Coach allows students to complete the *Practice Test* online.

The Big Question allows students to complete the *Apply the Big Q* activity about how animals move.

Vocab Flash Cards offer a way to review the chapter vocabulary words.

my science online.com ▸ Getting Around

---

5 Study Guide

REVIEW THE BIG Q

An animal's <u>nervous system</u>, <u>muscles</u>, and <u>skeleton</u> work together to help the animal move.

LESSON 1 Skeletons and Muscles

🔑 A skeleton is a framework that shapes and supports an animal, protects its internal organs, and allows it to move in its environment.

🔑 Muscles help animals move their body parts.

Vocabulary
- molting
- cartilage
- joint
- muscle

LESSON 2 The Nervous System

🔑 A nervous system allows animals to detect signals in their environments, process the signals, and react to them.

🔑 The simplest nervous systems are a netlike arrangement of neurons throughout the body. The most complex systems have a nerve cord and a brain.

Vocabulary
- nervous system • stimulus • response • neuron
- impulse • sensory neuron • interneuron
- motor neuron • brain

LESSON 3 Animal Movement

🔑 An animal moves about when its nervous system, muscular system, and skeletal system work together to make movement happen.

🔑 Animals that live in water, on land, or in the air have different adaptations for movement.

Vocabulary
- water vascular system
- swim bladder

ELL Support

4 Language Production

Arrange the class in small-group circles. Introduce a question based on the essential questions from the chapter. Then have one member of each circle give a fact or detail that helps answer the question. The student to his or her right should then provide a different fact or detail. The cycle continues until there is no new information to share and all questions have been discussed.

Beginning
LOW/HIGH Students can refer to their books or notes during the discussion.

Intermediate
LOW/HIGH Allow students extra time to share their facts and details.

Advanced
LOW/HIGH Challenge students to use vocabulary terms during the discussion.

Review and Assessment

LESSON 1 Skeletons and Muscles

1. What type of skeleton is shown in the diagram below?

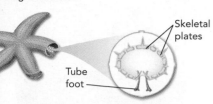

Skeletal plates

Tube foot

a. no skeleton   **b.** exoskeleton

c. a skeleton without hard parts   **(d.)** endoskeleton

2. A _joint_ is a place where two or more parts of a skeleton meet.

3. Make Generalizations List three functions of a skeleton.

It shapes and supports an animal, protects internal organs, and enables it to move.

4. Relate Cause and Effect How might an endoskeleton affect the size of an animal?

An animal might be larger because an endoskeleton is light and grows with the animal.

5. Sequence Describe how your muscles work to help you kick a ball.

Sample: A muscle pair in my thigh moves my leg backward and then forward. The muscle in the back of my thigh contracts to pull my leg back, while the muscle in front relaxes. Then the front muscle contracts to pull my leg forward.

LESSON 2 The Nervous System

6. A signal that causes an animal to react in some way is called a

a. response.   **b.** neuron.

(c.) stimulus.   **d.** impulse.

7. The most complex nervous systems have a nerve cord and a _brain._

8. Communicate Describe the nervous system of a cnidarian.

Sample: A cnidarian's nervous system is a nerve net, a network of neurons. A stimulus to one neuron sends impulses in all directions.

Use the diagrams below to answer Question 9.

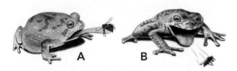

A   B

9. Interpret Diagrams Explain the stimulus in diagram A and the toad's response in diagram B.

Sample: The stimulus is probably an insect sting. The toad's response was to spit out the insect.

10. **Write About It** Write a paragraph in which you describe a complex animal's response to a specific stimulus. Explain how the three kinds of neurons work together to transfer information in your example.
See TE rubric.

Review and Assessment

Assess Understanding

Have students complete the answers to the Review and Assessment questions. Have a class discussion about what students find confusing. Write Key Concepts on the board to reinforce knowledge.

R T I Response to Intervention

5. If students have trouble relating muscles to skeletal systems, **then** review the process by which muscles relax and contract to move bones.

6. If students need help with defining _stimulus,_ **then** have them locate the highlighted term and review the definition.

Alternate Assessment

L1 **MAKE A POSTER** Have students design and create a three-panel poster that summarizes the chapter content. Each panel should depict the information covered in one lesson. Students should be sure to incorporate all the Key Concepts and vocabulary terms in their murals and to address the Big Question. The class can then use the mural as a way to review chapter material.

CHAPTER 5

Write About It	Assess student's writing using this rubric.			
SCORING RUBRIC	**SCORE 4**	**SCORE 3**	**SCORE 2**	**SCORE 1**
Describe animal's response to a stimulus	Student identifies the three and explains how they work together.	Student names the three neurons and partially explains how they work together when responding to a stimulus.	Students identifies one or two neurons but has difficulty explaining how they work when responding to a stimulus.	Students does not identify three types of neurons and does not explain how an animal responds to a stimulus.

Review and Assessment, Cont.

RTI Response to Intervention

14. If students cannot recall how adaptations are related to environment, **then** choose animals that swim, walk, and fly and compare their environments.

Apply the Big Q ? UbD

TRANSFER Students should be able to demonstrate understanding of how animals move by answering this question. See the scoring rubric below.

Connect to the Big Idea ? UbD

BIG IDEA Structures in living things are related to their functions.

Send students back to the Big Ideas of Science at the beginning of their student edition. Have them read what they wrote before they started the chapter. Lead a class discussion about how their thoughts have changed. If all chapters have been completed, have students fill in the bottom section for the Big Idea.

L3 WRITING IN SCIENCE Ask students to write a blog entry that explains to readers how different animals move. Students should be sure to discuss how different animals are adapted to move in their particular environments.

CHAPTER 5 Review and Assessment

11. An animal that moves using a water vascular system is a

 a. sea star.
b. penguin.
c. squid.
d. shark.

12. A fish can use its <u>swim bladder</u> to help it stay at a certain depth without using much energy.

13. Draw Conclusions What are three reasons why an animal might need to move about?

<u>Student answers should include any three of the following: Animals need to move about to obtain food, defend and protect themselves, maintain homeostasis, and find mates.</u>

14. Apply Concepts Why is it easier for a dolphin to move through water than it is for a horse?

<u>Sample: A dolphin's body is streamlined for swimming in the water, whereas a horse's body is not.</u>

15. [Write About It] Write a paragraph in which you describe a different adaptation that rabbits, bats, and snakes each have that enables them to move as they do.
See TE rubric.

How do animals move?

16. Suppose this ostrich's nervous system was not receiving signals properly. How might it be dangerous for the ostrich?

<u>If the ostrich's nervous system was not receiving signals properly, it would not receive information from the environment. Then the ostrich could not sense food or danger from predators.</u>
<u>See TE rubric.</u>

[Write About It] Assess student's writing using this rubric.

SCORING RUBRIC	SCORE 4	SCORE 3	SCORE 2	SCORE 1
Adaptations	Student correctly describes an adaptation of a rabbit, a bat, and a snake and relates the adaptations to the movement of each animal.	Student describes an adaptation of a rabbit, a bat, and a snake but do not relate the adaptations to the movement of each animal.	Student describes an adaptation of one animal and relates it to the movement of the animal.	Student does not describe an adaptation of any of the animals.

How do animals move?
Assess student's response using this rubric.

SCORING RUBRIC	SCORE 4	SCORE 3	SCORE 2	SCORE 1
Effects of problems with nervous system	Student accurately describes how ostrich's basic functions are adversely affected.	Student describes how most of the ostrich's function are adversely affected.	Student describes how one or two of ostrich's function are adversely affected, but makes errors in description.	Student does not describe how ostrich's functions are adversely affected.

Standardized Test Prep

Multiple Choice

Circle the letter of the best answer.

Which is true of the skeleton shown below?

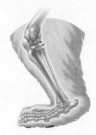

- Ⓐ It grows with the animal.
- B It molts as the animal grows.
- C It does not have hard parts.
- D It is mostly cartilage.

A rock hits a turtle on its shell. Then the turtle hides inside its shell. What is the stimulus?

- A the turtle hiding
- B the turtle's shell
- Ⓒ a rock hitting the shell
- D the turtle walking

What adaptation does a sea star have for moving in water?

- Ⓐ a water vascular system
- B a streamlined body
- C fins
- D a swim bladder

4. What enables an animal's endoskeleton to grow?

- A The animal molts.
- B The animal's joints become dislocated.
- C The animal's nervous system gets larger.
- Ⓓ The animal's bone and cartilage contain living cells.

5. Animals with nerve nets have

- Ⓐ no specialized neurons.
- B sensory neurons, but no interneurons.
- C interneurons, but no sensory neurons.
- D only motor neurons.

Constructed Response

Use the diagram below and your knowledge of science to help you answer Question 6. Write your answer on a separate sheet of paper.

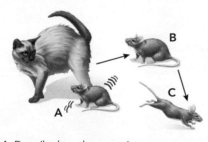

6. Describe how the mouse's nervous system is functioning in this diagram. Include the roles of the sensory neurons, interneurons, and motor neurons.

   See TE note.

199

Standardized Test Prep

Test-Taking Skills

PREVIEWING A QUESTION Explain to students that reading over a question quickly can help them better analyze an illustration. If they focus on the illustration first, they may waste time trying to figure out what it is. By reading the question first, they know that it is part of a skeleton. Then, they can look more closely at the illustration and refer to it as they consider the answer choices.

Constructed Response

6. When the mouse uses its senses to recognize the cat, its sensory neurons send a message to the brain. The information is processed and then interneurons transfer a message to the motor neurons telling them how to respond. The motor neurons cause the muscles to move the skeletal system and make the mouse run away.

Additional Assessment Resources

Chapter Test
ExamView® Computer Test Generator
Performance Assessment
Progress Monitoring Assessments
SuccessTracker™

CHAPTER 5

E L L Support

5 Assess Understanding

Have ELL students complete the Alternate Assessment. Provide guidelines on the information it must cover, and a rubric for assessment. Before beginning their posters, have ELLs discuss any questions they have with one another.

Beginning

LOW/HIGH Allow students with extra time to complete their posters.

Intermediate

LOW/HIGH Students can refer to their books or notes when completing their posters.

Advanced

LOW/HIGH Challenge students to incorporate vocabulary terms and Key Concepts from the chapter in their posters.

Remediate If students have trouble with...

QUESTION	SEE LESSON	STANDARDS
1	1	
2	2	
3	3	
4	1	
5	2	
6	2	

Science Matters

Museum of Science

Have students read *Lights, Camera, Shark Action!*
Explain that the shark submarine, named *Troy,* was
called a "Trojan Shark," because of its similarity to
the Trojan Horse. In the legend told by the poet
Virgil, Greek soldiers hid inside a giant wooden
horse that allowed them to sneak into their enemies'
city, Troy, disguised as a gift. The shark submarine
allowed Cousteau to similarly live among the sharks
without being detected. Tell students that Cousteau
was inspired to build the shark submarine when he
saw a drawing of something similar on the cover of
a Belgian comic book at age 7.

Explain that the shark submarine was a prototype,
or the first of its kind. Cousteau and his team were
not sure how well it would work when it got into
the water. The interior of the submarine was filled
with water and Cousteau had to wear a wetsuit and
breathe through scuba gear.

The Troy Project took place between 2004 and 2006.
Cousteau studied sharks in one of their favorite
feeding spots, near Isla Guadalupe off the Pacific
coast of Mexico. Cameras shot over 260 hours of
footage of Cousteau's interactions with the sharks,
which was eventually edited to make a documentary
for primetime network television.

As students research Cousteau's project, have them
consider the source of the article in their evaluation
of bias.

Ask: **What was unique about Cousteau's
project?** *(He was able to observe sharks without the
sharks knowing there were humans nearby.)* **Why
did Cousteau want to do this project?** *(To get to
see sharks as they really are, not as people imagine
they are)*

LIGHTS, CAMERA, SHARK ACTION!

In movies, sharks are often scary, toothy
costars. Although many people know
that sharks have a mean reputation, the
is a lot that we don't know about them.

To discover more about these mysteriou
creatures, Fabien Cousteau and his team
created a shark submarine. The one-
person submarine has a steel skeleton
and a thick rubber skin that makes it loc
like a great white shark. The 4.25-meter
shark sub moves through the water as
quietly and quickly as a real shark, and
can even wiggle its tail!

In the sub, Cousteau was able to observ
shark behavior up close. He saw sharks'
feeding habits, how they investigated
new things, and how they prepared to
attack. He also saw real sharks trying
to communicate with the fake one by
rolling their eyes and puffing their gills.
The submarine's cameras recorded
hours of shark action, which will help us
understand these creatures better.

Research It Find three articles describing
Cousteau's interaction with the sharks.
Write your own article comparing and
reviewing the science presented in the
articles. Describe any new information
you learned from each article, and
evaluate any bias in the articles. How
was the information presented in each
article? Did the authors balance their
discussions of the risks and benefits of
shark research?

Museum of Science

200 Getting Around

Quick Facts

Fabien Cousteau is the grandson of a very famous underwater explorer, Jacques
Cousteau. Born in France in 1910, Cousteau always had an interest in the sea
and joined the French Navy in 1933. He and French engineer Emile Gagnan
co-invented the aqualung, a device that allowed people to breathe underwater,
enabling Cousteau to explore underwater for longer periods of time. He
published many books and made films about life under the sea that financed his
expeditions aboard his ship, *Calypso.* Some of his films won Academy Awards.
He spent eight years making a television series about undersea life and founded
the Cousteau Society, a group that protects ocean life. Have students research
Cousteau and his explorations to find out why his research was important.

"feet" of engineering

Geckos are tiny lizards that live in warm climates all over the world, including the southwestern United States. If you've ever seen one, you've probably watched it scale a wall in about the time it takes for you to blink. Or you may have seen a gecko hang from one foot.

How do geckos hang from one foot? The answer is their hair! The gecko's feet are covered in millions of tiny hairs. Molecules in the hairs are attracted to molecules in the wall or on any other surface. These forces of attraction, called van der Waals forces, affect every form of matter, but they are usually so weak that you can't feel them. However, there are so many tiny hairs on a gecko's feet that geckos can cling to nearly any surface!

Gecko feet have inspired scientists to design artificial super-sticky materials that use the same principle. Maybe someday these materials could be used for surgical bandages, wall-crawling robots, or even shoes with incredible grip. For now, scientists will have to see which designs stick!

Design It Technological design inspired by biology is called biomimetic design. Research a few other examples of biomimetic design, and choose a simple problem that one of your examples could solve. Make or draw a model of your solution.

Frontiers of Technology

Have students read *"Feet" of Engineering.* Tell students that the technical name for the hair on a gecko's feet is *setae,* which means bristles. There are about 14,000 setae on every square millimeter of a gecko footpad. Each seta (singular) is a fraction of the width of a human hair. The setae on the feet of a gecko are self-cleaning and remove dirt from themselves within a few steps.

Explain that van der Waals interactions require no fluids, so theoretically a gecko could walk on the outside of a space shuttle as easily as it does up a wall. Being underwater reduces this kind of adhesion.

Explain that the amount of attraction between the gecko and a surface depends on how many setae are in contact with it. Have students look at close-up photos of gecko toes. Point out that the toes bend in the opposite direction from our fingers and toes. Explain that geckos peel their toes away from a surface from the tips inward when they walk. This reduces the number of setae in contact with the surface and allows geckos to overcome the van der Waals forces and move their feet. Explain that adhesion varies based on the roughness of the surface the gecko walks on, but, most of the time, geckos' toes work at much less than their full attractive capabilities. If all the setae are in contact with a smooth surface, a gecko can support eight times its own weight while hanging from a single toe.

Ask: **Why do scientists study van der Waals forces?** *(Sample: By studying van der Waals forces in geckos, scientists may develop materials that have similar sticky properties that can be applied in useful ways.)* **Would a gecko find it easier to climb a wet surface or a dry one?** *(A wet surface)*

201

Obtaining Energy

Introduce the Big Q ❓ UbD

Have students look at the image and read the Engaging Question and description. Ask the students to predict what happens when the frog gets to the snake's esophagus. Point out that the snake's jaws actually separate to accommodate the frog. Ask: **Why does the snake need to eat?** *(It needs energy.)* **Why might it be important for the snake to take in a large meal such as this frog?** *(One large meal can meet its energy needs for a long period of time.)* **What would happen to the snake if its jaws could not stretch to fit the frog?** *(It would be limited to eating very small prey and would need to eat more often.)*

Untamed Science Video

CEPHALIC FEEDING IS SOO MUCH FUN Before viewing, invite students to suggest ways in which animals obtain energy from their environments. Then play the video. Lead a class discussion and make a list of questions that this video raises. You may wish to have students view the video again after they have completed the chapter to see if their questions have been answered.

To access the online resources for this chapter, search on or navigate to *Obtaining Energy*.

Untamed Science Video shows how animals get and use energy.

The Big Question allows students to answer the Engaging Question about how the snake gets energy.

my science online.com ▶ **Obtaining Energy**

HOW CAN THIS SNAKE DIGEST A FROG?

❓ THE BIG

How do animals get and use energy?

You might wonder how a snake can swallow a frog that is much bigger than the snake's mouth. A snake's jaws can stretch open, allowing the snake to spread its jaws around the frog. The snake's teeth are curved backward to hold the frog, as parts of the jaw, throat, and cheek muscles work the frog into the snake's food tube, or esophagus. All the while, digestion begins in the snake's mouth as its saliva drenches the frog.

▶ **UNTAMED SCIENCE** Watch the **Untamed Science** video to learn more about how animals get and use energy.

Predict What do you think happens after the frog reaches the snake's esophagus?

Sample: The snake's muscles will move the frog into the stomach where digestion of the frog will continue.

Professional Development Note **From the Author**

I have been a runner for many years. Two years before reaching a "significant" birthday I decided to run a marathon—42 kilometers. I found a how-to book, outlined a plan, and began my training. As I built up my endurance, I was confronted with an energy surprise. I could not do my long runs—up to 32 kilometers and necessary for any marathon training—without planning how I could get food. In the end I distributed water bottles with an energy drink and energy bars along my planned route. It took me over 40 minutes to drive and hide these the night before a run. By the way, I finished the marathon in just over 4 hours.

✉ *Michael Padilla*

Obtaining Energy

CHAPTER 6

Chapter at a Glance

CHAPTER PACING: 7–10 periods or $3\frac{1}{2}$–5 blocks

INTRODUCE THE CHAPTER: Use the Engaging Question and the opening image to get students thinking about how animals obtain energy. Activate prior knowledge and preteach vocabulary using the Getting Started pages.

Lesson 1: How Animals Obtain and Digest Food

Lesson 2: How Animals Obtain Oxygen

Lesson 3: Circulation and Excretion

ASSESSMENT OPTIONS: Chapter Test, *ExamView*® Computer Test Generator, Performance Assessment, Progress Monitoring Assessments, SuccessTracker™

Preference Navigator, in the online Planning tools, allows you to customize *Interactive Science* to your own teaching style. You can also edit lesson plans by selecting the Lesson Planner option.

Digital Teacher's Edition allows you to access your Teacher's Edition and Resource online.

MY SCIENCE online.com

Differentiated Instruction

L1 Animal Diets Tell students that all animals need food to survive. Ask them to find pictures of at least three animals with which they are familiar. Have students make a poster showing what each animal eats for food.

L3 Snakes Have students research more about the eating habits and digestive systems of snakes. How often do snakes need to eat? How are snakes able to eat animals larger than themselves? What happens to the parts of their prey that snakes cannot digest? Students can write short reports and summarize their findings to the class in a presentation.

Getting Started

Check Your Understanding

This activity assesses students' understanding of the action of the heart and the exchange of gases in respiration. After students have shared their answers, point out that there are many different types of behaviors. Some behaviors are voluntary, or controlled by the animal. Other behaviors are involuntary, which means they occur without the animal having to control them consciously.

Preteach Vocabulary Skills

Explain to students that a suffix changes the meaning of the word to which it is added. Learning to identify suffixes can make it easier to learn new vocabulary words. For example, *biologist* is a noun that refers to a person who studies living things, whereas *biological* is an adjective that means "of or relating to living things." Changing the suffix *-ist* to *-ical* changes the meaning of the base word.

---

6 Getting Started

Check Your Understanding

1. **Background** Read the paragraph below and then answer the question.

> After Amy's dog ate, he curled up and fell asleep. Sleeping after eating is his normal **behavior.** His chest slowly rose and fell with each breath. The blood pumping through his heart's **chambers** helped the dog's lungs **exchange** oxygen and carbon dioxide.

> **Behavior** is the actions an animal performs.
>
> A **chamber** is an enclosed space.
>
> To **exchange** is to trade one thing for another.

- What was happening inside the dog's body as his chest rose and fell?

  Sample: Oxygen and carbon dioxide were being exchanged.

> **MY READING WEB** If you had trouble completing the question above, visit **My Reading Web** and type in *Obtaining Energy.*

Vocabulary Skill

Suffixes A suffix is a word part that is added to the end of a word to change its meaning. The table below lists suffixes that will help you learn key terms in this chapter.

Suffix	Meaning of Suffix	Example
-ory	relating to	circulatory, *adj.* relating to the movement of blood through the body
-sion	process of	diffusion, *n.* the process in which particles move from an area of high concentration to an area of low concentration

2. **Quick Check** Fill in the blank with the correct term.

- The _circulatory_ system includes blood, vessels, and a heart.

My Reading Web offers leveled readings that offer a foundation for the chapter content.

Vocab Flash Cards offer extra practice with the chapter vocabulary words.

Digital Lesson

- Assign the *Check Your Understanding* activity online and have students submit their work to you.
- Assign the *Vocabulary Skill* activity online and have students submit their work to you.

my science online.com ⟩ Obtaining Energy

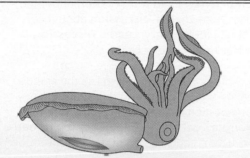

Chapter Preview

LESSON 1
- carnivore
- herbivore
- omnivore
- filter feeder
- radula
- digestion
- digestive system
- anus
- crop
- gizzard
- intestine
- esophagus
- stomach
- ◉ Identify the Main Idea
- △ Classify

LESSON 2
- cellular respiration
- diffusion
- respiratory system
- gill
- lung
- ◉ Compare and Contrast
- △ Predict

LESSON 3
- circulatory system
- heart
- open circulatory system
- closed circulatory system
- capillary
- atrium
- ventricle
- excretory system
- kidney
- urine
- ◉ Summarize
- △ Draw Conclusions

▶ **VOCAB FLASH CARDS** For extra help with vocabulary, visit **Vocab Flash Cards** and type in **Obtaining Energy**.

205

Preview Vocabulary Terms

Have students create a personalized science glossary for the vocabulary terms in this chapter. In their glossaries, students should define each term and reference the pages in the chapter that define and explain the term. Encourage students to include drawings and diagrams that help explain the meaning of the terms and concepts. A list of Academic Vocabulary for each lesson can be found in the Support All Readers box at the start of the lesson.

L1 Have students look at the images on this page as you pronounce the vocabulary word. Have students repeat the word after you. Then read the definition. Use the sample sentence in italics to clarify the meaning of the term.

carnivore *(KAHR nuh vawr)* An animal that eats only other animals. *A lion is a carnivore that feeds on wildebeest, zebras, and antelope.*

herbivore *(HUR buh vawr)* An animal that eats only plant material. *A rabbit is a herbivore that feeds on different kinds of plants.*

gills *(gilz)* Featherlike structures where gases are exchanged between water and blood. *Most animals that live in water take in oxygen through gills.*

circulatory system *(SUR kyoo luh tawr ee SIS tum)* An organ system that transports needed materials to cells and takes away wastes. *Blood flows through a grasshopper's open circulatory system.*

CHAPTER 6

ⒺⓁⓁ Support

Have students complete the Preview Vocabulary Terms activity either alone or in pairs. Before students begin creating their science glossaries, write each word and introduce it to students by pointing and saying it aloud.

Beginning
LOW Draw a picture or other visual aid for each vocabulary term in the glossary to associate the term with its definition.

HIGH Include words and phrases in the native language to help students remember specific terms they have trouble with.

Intermediate
LOW/HIGH Include English pronunciations for each term in the glossary.

Advanced
LOW/HIGH For each vocabulary term in the glossary, write a sentence that uses the term correctly.

205

1

How do animals get and use energy?

Lesson Pacing: 2–3 periods or 1–1½ blocks

🕐 **SHORT ON TIME?** To do this lesson in approximately half the time, do the Activate Prior Knowledge activity on page 206. A discussion of the Key Concepts on pages 207 and 212 will familiarize students with the lesson content. Have students do the Quick Lab. The rest of the lesson can be completed by students independently.

Preference Navigator, in the online Planning tools, allows you to customize *Interactive Science* to your own teaching style. You can also edit lesson plans by selecting the Lesson Planner option.

Digital Teacher's Edition allows you to access your Teacher's Edition and Resource materials online.

my science online.com

Lesson Vocabulary

- carnivore
- herbivore
- omnivore
- filter feeder
- radula
- digestion
- digestive system
- anus
- crop
- gizzard
- intestine
- esophagus
- stomach

Content Refresher

Professional Development Note

Adaptations For Digestion The digestive tract is similarly organized in all mammals. It includes the mouth, esophagus, stomach, small intestine, and large intestine. The simplest versions are seen in omnivores and carnivores. The food they eat is readily digested by enzymes released from the digestive glands. Herbivorous grazing mammals have more complex, very long digestive tracts. This is an adaptation to the slow and difficult task of breaking down cellulose, which is the main part of their diet.

Even herbivores cannot digest cellulose, however. They rely entirely on vast numbers of microorganisms that live in specialized chambers in the digestive tract. Herbivorous mammals fall into two categories: ruminants and nonruminants. The ruminants include cows, bison, goats, giraffes, and others that are named for the rumen, which is the first and largest chamber in their four-chambered stomachs. The rumen contains great numbers of microorganisms. It breaks down the tough cellulose material, yielding fatty acids, sugars, and starches. In nonruminants, including horses, rabbits, elephants, koalas, and others, cellulose digestion takes place in the cecum, a saclike organ found at the junction of the small and large intestine.

LESSON OBJECTIVES

🔑 Identify the different ways animals obtain food.

🔑 Compare the different ways animals digest food.

Blended Path
Active learning using Student Edition, Inquiry Path, and Digital Path

ENGAGE AND EXPLORE

Teach this lesson using a variety of resources. Begin by reading **My Planet Diary** as a class. Have students discuss how owls obtain food and what kinds of foods they eat. Then have students do the **Inquiry Warm-Up activity.** Students will use a sock and an orange to model a snake feeding. The **After the Inquiry Warm-Up worksheet** sets up a discussion about a feeding adaptation that some snake species have but lizards do not have. Have volunteers share their answers to question 4, telling which animal will take longer to digest a meal, a snake or a lizard.

EXPLAIN AND ELABORATE

Teach Key Concepts by explaining how animals use some adaptations to get the type of food they eat. **Lead a Discussion** about the mouthparts of various animals. Have students practice the inquiry skill in the **Apply It activity. Lead a Discussion** about the mouthparts of filter feeders. Then **Lead a Discussion** about how mollusks use a radula to obtain food. Finally, **Lead a Discussion** about what scientists can learn about a bird by the shape of its beak.

Teach Key Concepts by explaining that in order to use the energy and other materials stored in food, animals must digest the food. **Lead a Discussion** about digestion outside of cells. **Support the Big Q** by discussing how animals get energy from food. Then, **Lead a Discussion** about the structure and function of the digestive tube.

Hand out the **Key Concept Summaries** as a review of each part of the lesson. Students can also use the online **Vocab Flash Cards** to review key terms.

EVALUATE

Have students take the **Lesson Quiz.** For an alternate assessment, see the *ExamView®* Computer Test Generator, Progress Monitoring Assessments, or SuccessTracker™.

ELL Support

1 Content and Language
Have students add the terms in this lesson to their vocabulary notebook or science journal. Suggest that they use their own words to define the terms and incorporate visuals whenever possible.

DIFFERENTIATED INSTRUCTION KEY
L1 Struggling Students or Special Needs
L2 On-Level Students **L3** Advanced Students

LESSON PLANNER 6.1

Lab zone Inquiry Path
Hands-on learning in the Lab zone

Digital Path
Online learning at my science online.com

ENGAGE AND EXPLORE

To teach this lesson with an emphasis on inquiry, begin with the **Inquiry Warm-Up activity.** Students will use a sock and an orange to model a snake feeding. The **After the Inquiry Warm-Up worksheet** sets up a discussion about a feeding adaptation that some snake species have but lizards do not have. Have volunteers share their answers to question 4, telling which animal will take longer to digest a meal, a snake or a lizard.

EXPLAIN AND ELABORATE

Focus on the **Inquiry Skill** for the lesson. Remind students that when they classify, they organize things into groups according to how the things are alike and different. What information in the **Inquiry Warm-Up activity** could be used to classify an animal as a snake? *(Snakes have backward growing teeth.)* Before beginning the **Apply It activity,** point out that animals that eat other animals need to be able to tear flesh, while animals that eat plants need to be able to grind plant materials. **Build Inquiry** by exploring the advantage of having teeth with different shapes. Have students do the **Quick Lab** to observe how a planarian feeds.

Support the Big Q by discussing how animals get energy from food. Have students do the **Lab Investigation** in which they look at an owl's leftovers and draw conclusions about an animal's diet. Students can use the online **Vocab Flash Cards** to review key terms.

EVALUATE

Have students take the **Lesson Quiz.** For an alternate assessment, see the *ExamView®* Computer Test Generator, Progress Monitoring Assessments, or SuccessTracker™.

ENGAGE AND EXPLORE

Teach this lesson using digital resources. Begin by having students learn more about how animals obtain and digest food and explore real-world connections to the ways animals eat at **My Planet Diary** online. Have them access the Chapter Resources to find the **Unlock the Big Question activity.** There they can answer the questions and refine their responses as they continue through the lesson. You can re-assign the activity and have students submit their work so you can track their progress.

EXPLAIN AND ELABORATE

Students reading above, at, or below the lexile measure of this lesson can access basic content readings at their level at **My Reading Web.** Encourage students to use the online **Vocab Flash Cards** to preview key terms. Assign the **Apply It activity** online and have students submit their work to you. Assign the **Do the Math activity** online and have students submit their work to you. Use the **Interactive Art activity** online to allow students to match animals to their mouthparts based on what each animal eats and how it obtains food. Have students do the **Quick Lab,** observing how a planarian feeds.

Support the Big Q by discussing how animals get energy from food. The **Key Concept Summaries** online allow students to read a summary and see an image associated with each part of the lesson. Online remediation is available at **My Science Coach.**

EVALUATE

Have students take the **Lesson Quiz.** For an alternate assessment, see the *ExamView®* Computer Test Generator, Progress Monitoring Assessments, or SuccessTracker™.

2 Frontload the Lesson
Skim the headings, images, and vocabulary with students. Have them make predictions about lesson content. Stop after reading each section and compare their predictions with the lesson.

3 Comprehensible Input
Have students make a two-column chart titled "How Animals Eat." Have them list *Animals that Tear Food, Animals that Chew Food,* and *Animals that Suck Food* in one column and add examples of animals from the chapter and their own knowledge to the other column.

4 Language Production
Pair or group students with varied language abilities to complete labs collaboratively for language practice. Have each student copy the completed written lab for personal reference.

5 Assess Understanding
In teams of four, give each member a number of 1, 2, 3, or 4. Ask the essential questions from the lesson. Groups should work so all can agree on the answer. Call out a number and allow the corresponding member in each group to give the answer.

LESSON 6.1

How Animals Obtain and Digest Food

Establish Learning Objectives

After this lesson, students will be able to:

🗝 Identify the different ways animals obtain food.

🗝 Compare the different ways animals digest food.

Engage

Activate Prior Knowledge

MY PLANET DIARY Read *Owl Pellets* with the class. Explain to students that scientists can learn a lot about an animal by finding out what it eats. Ask: **How do you get food?** *(Students might mention their pantry, refrigerator, or grocery store.)* **What kinds of foods do you eat?** *(Answers will vary.)* **How do owls get food?** *(They hunt for it.)* **What kinds of foods do owls eat?** *(They eat small animals and insects.)*

BIG IDEAS OF SCIENCE REFERENCE LIBRARY 📖
Have students look up the following topics: Barracuda, Scorpion, Seals, Tasmanian Devil, Teeth.

Explore

Lab Resource: Inquiry Warm-Up 🔬

L1 **HOW DO SNAKES FEED?** Students will use a sock and an orange to model snake feeding.

LESSON
1
How Animals Obtain and Digest Food

UNLOCK THE BIG ❓

🗝 **How Do Animals Obtain Food?**

🗝 **How Do Animals Digest Food?**

MY PLANET DIARY

FUN FACTS

Owl Pellets

You chew your food before you swallow it using your teeth. Owls, however, do not have teeth. They swallow their food whole. Their food includes mice and insects. After an owl swallows, the food travels into its digestive system to be digested.

What happens to the body parts that an owl cannot digest? Any bones, teeth, and fur travel to the gizzard, a part of an owl's digestive system. Then the owl regurgitates, or spits up, the undigested parts as a pellet. Scientists can examine a pellet to find out what an owl eats.

Owl pellet

Read the following questions. Write your answers below.

1. What happens to the food that an owl eats?

   Some parts are digested and others are formed into a pellet that is regurgitated.

2. What might you learn about an owl's environment by looking at its pellet?

   Sample: I might learn what small animals live in the owl's environment.

▶ **PLANET DIARY** Go to **Planet Diary** to learn more about how animals obtain and digest food.

 Do the Inquiry Warm-Up *How Do Snakes Feed?*

How Do Animals Obtain Food?

Think about the last time you had pizza and how good it tasted. That pizza was more than just a great meal. It also gave you the energy you needed to ride a bike or use a computer. All animals—including you—need food to provide the raw materials and energy that their cells need to carry out their functions.

206 Obtaining Energy

SUPPORT ALL READERS

Lexile Measure = 890L   Lexile Word Count = 1609

Prior Exposure to Content: Many students may have misconceptions on this topic

Academic Vocabulary: *classify, identify, main idea*

Science Vocabulary: *carnivore, herbivore, omnivore*

Concept Level: Generally appropriate for most students in this grade

Preteach With: My Planet Diary "Owl Pellets" and Figure 4 activity

Go to **My Reading Web** to access leveled readings that provide a foundation for the content.

my science online.com

Vocabulary

- carnivore • herbivore • omnivore • filter feeder
- radula • digestion • digestive system • anus
- crop • gizzard • intestine • esophagus • stomach

Skills

- ⊙ Reading: Identify the Main Idea
- △ Inquiry: Classify

What Animals Eat 🔖 The different ways that an animal obtains food depends on what it eats and its adaptations for getting food.

Animals may be grouped based on what type of food they eat. Most animals, like those in **Figure 1**, are carnivores, herbivores, or omnivores. Animals that eat only other animals are **carnivores**. Animals that eat only plant material are **herbivores**. Animals that eat both plant material and other animals are **omnivores**. A few types of animals—such as earthworms, snails, and crabs—eat decaying plants and animals.

FIGURE 1 ·····················
Animal Diets
All animals need food, but they differ in what they eat and how they get it.

△ **Infer** Choose one animal from each of the three groups and write in the box what you think it eats.

Caterpillar

Raccoon

Lion

Elephant

Herbivores
Sample: A caterpillar eats leaves.

Carnivores
Sample: A lion eats other animals.

Omnivores
Sample: A bear eats fish and fruit.

Bear

Jellyfish

207

Explain

Introduce Vocabulary

Point out that the words *carnivores, herbivores,* and *omnivores* all contain the Latin root word *vor,* meaning "to eat or devour." The root word *carni* means flesh. Carnivores eat the flesh of other animals. The root word *herbi* means grass. Herbivores eat grass and other plants. The root word *omni* means all. Omnivores eat both animals and plants.

Teach Key Concepts 🔖

Remind students that an adaptation can be a physical structure an animal has or an action that it performs in order to accomplish a function. Tell students that animals use some adaptations to obtain food. Ask: **What is a carnivore?** *(An animal that eats other animals)* **What kinds of adaptations might help a carnivore obtain food?** *(Sharp teeth, rapid movement, and keen eyesight)* **What is an herbivore?** *(An animal that eats plants)* **What kinds of adaptations might help an herbivore obtain food?** *(A long neck or flat teeth)*

Teach With Visuals

Tell students to look at **Figure 1.** Have students work in pairs to complete the activity. After a few minutes, have a class discussion about their answers. Ask volunteers to name of each of the animals and describe the types of food the animal eats. Ask: **What does a bear eat?** *(It might eat fish and fruit.)* **What parts of its body does it use to get these foods?** *(It might use its paws and claws to hunt for fish in a river or pick fruit from a tree branch.)* **What does a lion eat?** *(It might eat zebra and antelope.)* **What parts of its body does it use to get these foods?** *(It might use strong legs to run, as well as claws and sharp teeth to catch animals.)* **What does an elephant eat?** *(It might eat leaves from a tree.)* **What parts of its body does it use to get these foods?** *(It might use its strong head to knock over a tree or its trunk to grab leaves.)* If students are unsure of what a raccoon eats, explain that a raccoon eats fish and fruit. Tell students that the jellyfish eats fish. Ask: **What kind of consumer is a jellyfish?** *(Carnivore)*

My Planet Diary provides an opportunity for students to explore real-world connections to the ways animals eat.

my science online.com | **How Animals Obtain Food**

ⓔⓛⓛ Support

1 Content and Language

Write *digestion* on the board. Explain that the term is derived from the Latin prefix *di-* (meaning "apart") and the Latin verb *gerere* (meaning "to carry"). Lead students to see how the meanings of these word parts relates to the scientific definition of the term.

2 Frontload the Lesson

Invite students to think about parts of the human body that play a role in obtaining and eating food. Then, discuss how humans compare and contrast with other animals in how they obtain food.

3 Comprehensible Input

Have pairs create flowcharts that show the sequence as animals digest food. Encourage some students to focus on intracellular digestion and others to focus on extracellular digestion.

LESSON 6.1

Explain

Lead a Discussion

ANIMAL MOUTHPARTS Ask students what they use to chew food. Point out that not all animals have teeth. Ask: **How does a grasshopper's mouth help it get food?** (*Its mouthparts let it tear and chew leaves.*) **How does a hummingbird's mouthparts help it get food?** (*Its mouthparts let it suck plant juices.*) **How are the teeth of carnivores different from those of herbivores?** (*Carnivores have pointed teeth for tearing meat, while herbivores have flat teeth for grinding plant material.*)

Elaborate

Apply It!

L1 Before beginning the activity, point out that animals that eat other animals need to be able to tear flesh, while animals that eat plants need to be able to grind plant materials.

△ **Classify** Tell students that when they classify, they organize things into groups according to how they are alike and different. Direct them to focus on the teeth shown in the three photos. Point out that some teeth are sharp, whereas others are more flat.

Build Inquiry Lab zone

L1 **TEETH**

Materials cracker, hand mirror

Time 15 minutes

Direct students to wash their hands before beginning the activity. Then, ask students to use the mirror to look at their teeth. Have them compare the shapes of the different teeth according to their location. Tell them to use their tongue to feel the cutting surfaces of the different teeth. Have students bite off a piece of cracker and chew it. Allow them to observe the teeth they use to bite it and the teeth they use to chew it. Direct students to wash their hands again when they are finished.

Ask: **What is the advantage of having teeth with different shapes?** (*A variety of teeth means that a variety of foods can be eaten.*)

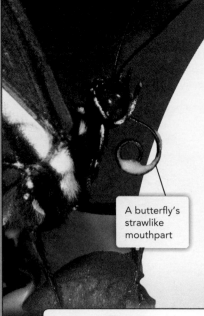

A butterfly's strawlike mouthpart

Animal Mouthparts Have you ever watched animals eating? If you have, you may have noticed some of the many different adaptations that animals have for eating. Depending on their mouthparts, animals may eat by tearing, chewing, sucking, or filtering their food.

Animals That Tear, Chew, and Suck Food Some animals have mouthparts that are specialized for tearing, chewing, or sucking food. For example, grasshoppers have sharp mouthparts that tear and chew leaves. Hummingbirds and some arthropods, such as butterflies, have mouthparts that enable them to suck plant juices from flowers, stems, and leaves.

Many other animals have teeth. Animal teeth are specialized for eating certain types of food. Carnivores, such as wolves, have pointed teeth used for tearing meat. Herbivores, such as rabbits, have flat teeth for grinding plant material. Omnivores usually have both pointed and flat teeth for eating their food.

apply it!

Many animals use teeth to eat.

1 △ **Classify** Look at the teeth of each animal. Based on its teeth, classify each animal as a carnivore, herbivore, or omnivore.

2 **Relate Evidence and Explanation** In each box, explain why you classified the animal as you did.

A bear is an omnivore. I think it is an omnivore because it has some pointed teeth for tearing meat and some flat teeth for grinding plants.

A zebra is a herbivore. I think it is a herbivore because it has flat teeth for grinding and chewing grass.

An alligator is a carnivore. I think it is a carnivore because it has pointed teeth for tea meat.

208 Obtaining Energy

Digital Lesson

• Assign the *Apply It* activity online and have students submit their work to you.
• Assign the *Do the Math* activity online and have students submit their work to you.

my science online.com | **How Animals Obtain Food**

Animals That Filter Food Some animals that live in water strain their food from the water. They are called filter feeders. Most **filter feeders** trap and eat microscopic organisms that live in the water. They have netlike structures for doing this. Filter feeders vary in size from the largest animals on Earth, blue whales, to small barnacles. You can see some filter feeders in **Figure 2**.

FIGURE 2 ....

Filter Feeders

✏ **Compare and Contrast** Write on the line below how all these animals are alike. Then write in the chart below how they are different.

Sample: All are filter feeders.

Clams

Clams have siphons that draw water into their bodies. The water passes over their gills, which filter out the microorganisms that they eat.

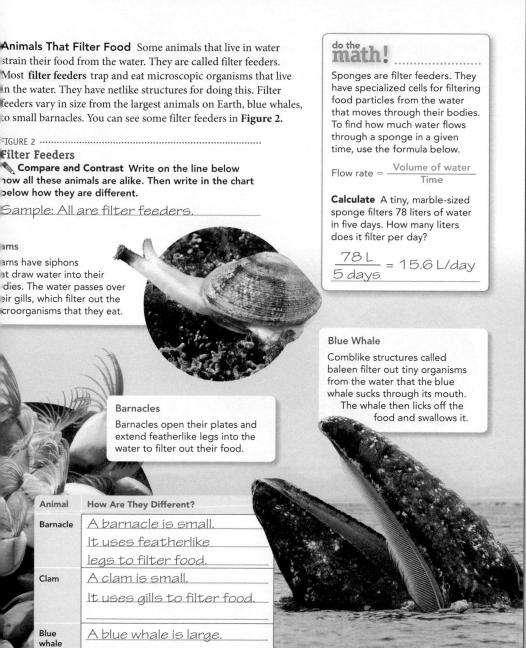

Barnacles
Barnacles open their plates and extend featherlike legs into the water to filter out their food.

Blue Whale
Comblike structures called baleen filter out tiny organisms from the water that the blue whale sucks through its mouth. The whale then licks off the food and swallows it.

Animal	How Are They Different?
Barnacle	*A barnacle is small. It uses featherlike legs to filter food.*
Clam	*A clam is small. It uses gills to filter food.*
Blue whale	*A blue whale is large. It uses its baleen to filter food.*

do the math!

Sponges are filter feeders. They have specialized cells for filtering food particles from the water that moves through their bodies. To find how much water flows through a sponge in a given time, use the formula below.

$$\text{Flow rate} = \frac{\text{Volume of water}}{\text{Time}}$$

Calculate A tiny, marble-sized sponge filters 78 liters of water in five days. How many liters does it filter per day?

$$\frac{78\ L}{5\ days} = 15.6\ L/day$$

209

Explain

Lead a Discussion

FILTER FEEDERS Show students a coffee filter or similar filter. Demonstrate that you can pour a mixture through it, but only the liquid passes through. Ask: **What do you see on the filter?** *(The solid materials are caught in the filter.)* **How are the mouthparts of filter feeders similar to the coffee filter?** *(They let water pass through, but they catch small organisms for the animal to eat.)*

Teach With Visuals

Tell students to look at **Figure 2**. Elicit from students that all these animals are filter feeders that live in water. Guide a discussion about why filtering their food is an advantage for each of these animals and how their structure enables them to filter the type of food that they eat. Ask: **What structures do you see in the whale's mouth?** *(They are comblike structures.)* **What do these structures do?** *(They filter organisms out of the water.)* **How does the clam get food?** *(It siphons water across its gills.)* **What is the purpose of the barnacles' featherlike legs?** *(They filter out organisms from the water.)*

Elaborate

Do the Math!

L1 Remind students that they can use formulas to solve certain types of problems. Explain that a formula is made up of variables that represent quantities. The formula for flow rate relates volume of water and time. Make sure that students include the appropriate units in their calculations. The unit for rate of flow is liters per day, L/day.

See the *Math Skill and Problem-Solving Activities* for support.

Differentiated Instruction

L1 **Types of Mouthparts** Ask students to make a chart relating the types of mouthparts animals have to the foods they eat. The chart should include a column for the type of mouthpart, a description of how the mouthpart helps the animals, and an example of an animal with this mouthpart. Have students share their charts with the class.

L3 **Types of Teeth** Have students choose an animal with teeth. They should research the type of teeth the animal has and how it uses its teeth to obtain and/or eat food. Students can write a short report summarizing their findings, including a discussion about how the animal's teeth are adapted to its diet.

Explain

Teach With Visuals

Tell students to look at **Figure 3** and compare the animals shown in the three photographs. Ask: **Which animal shown is a herbivore?** *(The grasshopper)* **Which animals are carnivores?** *(The spider and the sea star)* **Does the sea star look large enough to swallow the clam?** *(No)* If students have previously studied mollusks, they will know that the body of a clam is soft, but the shell is hard. Remind students that the two shells of a clam are attached along one side. The sea star cannot break the shells. But it can pull on them so that the edges that are not connected separate slightly. The sea star then turns its stomach inside-out into the space inside the clam shells. There, enzymes digest the soft tissues of the clam, and the digested material is absorbed by the sea star's stomach. Once it has finished this process, the sea star pulls its stomach back into its body, releases its hold on the clam, and moves on.

Lead a Discussion

RADULA Remind students that mollusks include snails, slugs, squids, and clams. Clams and other bivalves lack a radula, but other groups of mollusks have a radula. Ask: **If a snail uses its radula to bore through the shell of another mollusk, is the snail a carnivore, herbivore, or omnivore?** *(Carnivore)* **If a garden snail uses its radula to eat the leaves of a flowering plant, is the snail a carnivore, herbivore, or omnivore?** *(Herbivore)*

◭ **Classify** Remind students that when they classify, they put things in groups of things that are alike in some way.

Address Misconceptions

SPIDERS DO NOT HAVE TEETH Point out the fangs of the spider in **Figure 3**. Students may know that poisonous snakes have hollow teeth called fangs. Emphasize that unlike a snake's fangs, the spider's fangs are not teeth. A spider's mouthparts are modified appendages and are made of the same material that forms the exoskeleton. Spiders do, however, use their fangs to inject poison into their prey.

21st Century Learning 📖 DK

COMMUNICATION Have students read *Tasmanian Devil* in the **Big Ideas of Science Reference Library.** Ask students to use the information in the reading to write a short essay that describes and explains the Tasmanian devil's adaptations for obtaining food. Interested students can present their essays to the class.

Adaptations for Obtaining Food Animals have an amazing variety of adaptations for obtaining food. These adaptations include structures and behaviors. For example, animals have an opening through which food enters their bodies. This opening is usually called a mouth. Structures such as beaks and claws enable animals to get food into their mouths. Behaviors also help animals obtain food. For example, most spiders make webs that help them capture their prey. In **Figure 3**, you can see some adaptations that animals have for obtaining food.

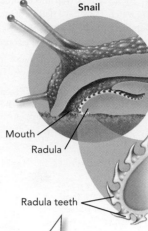

Snail
Mouth
Radula
Radula teeth

FIGURE 3 ······
▶ **INTERACTIVE ART** **Obtaining Food**
Adaptations help organisms such as a grasshopper and a spider obtain food.

✏️ **Study the photos and read the description about how each animal obtains food. Then answer the questions in the boxes.**

Grasshopper   Spider

A snail has a **radula,** or a flexible, tonguelike ribbon of tiny teeth. Some snails use their radula to tear through plant tissues. Others use it to drill through animal shells or scrape decaying material from surfaces of objects.
✏️ **Classify** Do you think a snail is a carnivore, herbivore, or omnivore? Why?

Sample: Some are carnivores and some are herbivores based on what they eat. Some eat decaying material.

Insects have different mouthparts. Grasshoppers have mouthparts for chewing grass.
✏️ **Develop Hypotheses** This spider is a carnivore. Describe how you think it uses its fangs.

Sample: It uses them to stab its food.

Sea Star

A sea star uses its tube feet like suction cups to pry open the shells of its food.
✏️ **Infer** Name two animals that a sea star might eat.

Sample: They might eat scallops and clams.

210 Obtaining Energy

Interactive Art allows students to match animals to their mouthparts based on what each animal eats and how it obtains food.

my science online.com ▷ How Animals Obtain Food

Hawk

Silversides Fish

A coral has stinging cells on its tentacles that stun its prey.
✎ **Interpret Photos** Identify how corals move their food into their mouths.

Sample: They use their tentacles.

Cup Coral

Birds use their beaks to obtain food. The shapes of beaks are specialized for eating different kinds of food.

✎ **Communicate** Look at the beaks of the hawk and pileated woodpeckers. With a partner, decide which beak shape is best for probing soft material and which is best for eating meat.

Sample: Long pointed beaks are best for probing. Hooked beaks are best for tearing meat.

Pileated Woodpeckers

type of snake stretches its jaws, opens its h very wide, and swallows its food whole.

CHALLENGE Explain how this adaptation help this type of snake survive.

mple: It can eat food larger n its own mouth.

Egg-Eating Snake

 Do the Quick Lab
Planarian Feeding Behavior.

🔑 **Assess Your Understanding**

1a. Review What types of food do carnivores, herbivores, and omnivores eat?

Carnivores eat animals, herbivores eat plants, and omnivores eat both.

b. Compare and Contrast How are the teeth of carnivores and herbivores alike and different?

Both use their teeth to eat. Carnivores have sharp teeth for tearing. Herbivores have flat teeth for grinding.

got it? ······················

○ **I get it!** Now I know that the way an animal gets food depends on _what it eats and its adaptations for getting food._

○ **I need extra help with** _See TE note._

Go to **MY SCIENCE COACH** online for help with this subject.

211

Differentiated Instruction

L1 Adaptations for Feeding Ask students to write each of the following terms on separate index cards: *mouth, radula, fang, stinging cells, beak, tube feet.* Tell students to write a definition of the term on the opposite side of the card. Then pair students together, and have one student read the sentence while the other student tries to name the term.

L3 Mosquitoes Have students research the mouthparts of mosquitoes. Then they should prepare a brief summary and drawing describing how mosquitoes bite and withdraw blood from their prey, often undetected.

Explain

Teach With Visuals

Tell students to look at **Figure 3.** Begin by reading the caption describing the hawk. Ask: **How would you describe the shape of a hawk's beak?** *(Samples: hooked, sharp)* **How does this help a hawk eat?** *(This shape is good for tearing flesh.)* Students may be aware that a hawk is a predator. Ask: **What do hawks eat?** *(Small mammals, birds)* **What adaptations do you know of that help a hawk catch its food?** *(Hawks have sharp talons for grasping their prey and holding onto it while they eat.)* Next read the caption describing the snake. Ask: **Why do you think a snake swallows its food whole?** *(Sample: It has no teeth or front limbs to hold or manipulate the food.)* **What would happen to the snake if it could not open its jaws wide enough to swallow the egg?** *(It would be limited to smaller food.)*

Lead a Discussion

BIRD BEAKS Explain that scientists can learn a lot about a bird by the shape of its beak. The shape of the beak helps a bird get food where it lives. Ask: **What kind of food do you think a bird with a long, thin beak eats?** *(It might dig into soil to get worms or it might reach into plants to get plant juices.)* **What kind of food do you think a bird with a short, thick beak eats?** *(It might eat nuts and seeds that it cracks open with its beak.)*

Elaborate

Lab Resource: Quick Lab

L3 PLANARIAN FEEDING BEHAVIORS Students will observe how a planarian feeds.

Evaluate

Assess Your Understanding

After students answer the questions, have them evaluate their understanding by completing the appropriate sentence.

RTI Response to Intervention

1a. If students have difficulty differentiating among the types of food, **then** have students identify an example of each type of animal and what it eats.

b. If students need help comparing the teeth of different types of feeders, **then** discuss how and what each animal eats.

MY SCIENCE COACH Have students go online for help in understanding animal feeding.

Explain

Teach Key Concepts 🔑

Explain that food contains stored energy along with other materials. In order to use this energy and materials, the food must be digested. Ask: **What happens during digestion?** *(Food is broken down into small molecules.)* **Where does digestion take place?** *(In some animals, it takes place inside cells. In most animals, it takes place outside cells.)*

Address Misconceptions

DIGESTION AND ENERGY Students often think that the breakdown of food that happens during digestion is the source of energy for the body. Remind them that cells get their energy from cellular respiration, which takes place inside the cells. In digestion, molecules that are too large to enter cells are broken down into smaller molecules, which the cell can take in and use. Ask: **In what order do these two processes take place?** *(Digestion takes place before cellular respiration.)*

Teach With Visuals

Tell students to look at **Figure 4.** To help students understand how food moves from the collar cells to the jellylike cells, explain that the collar cells surround the inside of the sponge's central cavity. They have whip-like structures that beat back and forth to move water through the sponge. The jellylike cells are farther inside the sponge, and they are where digestion is completed. Ask: **Through what structures does water containing food enter the sponge?** *(Through the pores)* **What is the role of collar cells?** *(They filter food out of the water and begin digestion.)* **What type of cells complete digestion?** *(Jellylike cells)*

How Do Animals Digest Food?

You already know that the food animals eat provides needed materials to their cells. However, the food that animals eat is too large to enter the cells. It must be broken down first. The process that breaks down food into small molecules is called **digestion**. 🔑 **Some types of animals digest food mainly inside their cells, but most animals digest food outside their cells.**

Digestion Inside Cells Sponges and a few other animals digest food inside specialized cells in their bodies. The digested food then diffuses into other cells, where it is used. This process is called intracellular digestion. **Figure 4** shows how intracellular digestion occurs in sponges.

FIGURE 4 ....

Intracellular Digestion

Structures surrounding the central cavity of a sponge are adapted for digestion.

✎ **Sequence** Read each box carefully. Then write a number in each circle to show the order in which intracellular digestion occurs in sponges.

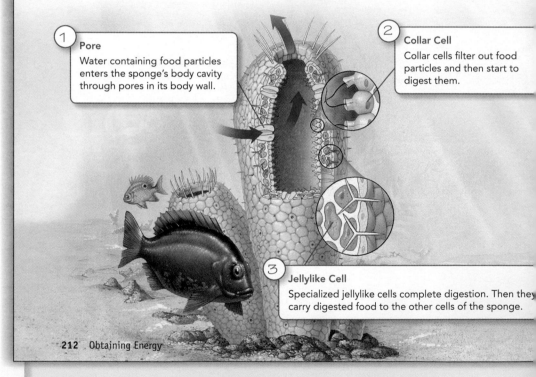

① **Pore**
Water containing food particles enters the sponge's body cavity through pores in its body wall.

② **Collar Cell**
Collar cells filter out food particles and then start to digest them.

③ **Jellylike Cell**
Specialized jellylike cells complete digestion. Then they carry digested food to the other cells of the sponge.

Digestion Outside Cells Most animals digest their food outside their cells. This process is called extracellular digestion. Digestion outside cells occurs in a digestive system. A **digestive system** is an organ system that has specialized structures for obtaining and digesting food. Most carnivores, herbivores, and omnivores have digestive systems.

Internal Body Cavity The simplest kind of digestive system has only one opening. Food enters the body and wastes exit the body through the same opening. Cnidarians and flatworms have this type of digestive system, which you can see in **Figure 5**.

FIGURE 5 ···

Extracellular Digestion
Corals are a type of cnidarian. Planarians are a type of flatworm. Both have extracellular digestion and an internal body cavity with one opening.

Compare and Contrast Write in the Venn Diagram how intracellular digestion and extracellular digestion are alike and different.

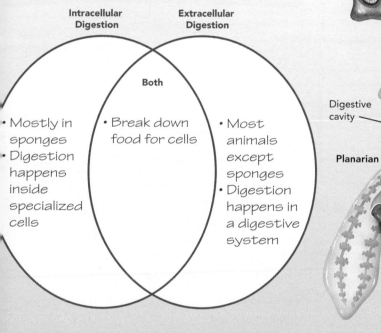

Tentacles
Digestive cavity opening
Coral
Digestive cavity

Digestive cavity
Planarian
Tubelike opening

Intracellular Digestion | **Both** | **Extracellular Digestion**

- Mostly in sponges
- Digestion happens inside specialized cells

- Break down food for cells

- Most animals except sponges
- Digestion happens in a digestive system

213

Explain

Lead a Discussion

Explain that most animals are not like sponges. They digest food outside their cells. Ask: **What body system has specialized structures for breaking down food?** (The digestive system) **What type of digestion takes place outside of cells?** (Extracellular)

Teach With Visuals

Tell students to look at **Figure 5**. Explain that the animals shown have very simple digestive systems. If students have already studied body symmetry, review radial and bilateral symmetry. Explain that the planarian's mouth is the tube-like opening on its underside. Ask: **How is the location of the planarian's mouth different from that of most animals that have bilateral symmetry?** (Most animals have the mouth at the head end of the body.) **If the coral and the planarian have digestive systems with a single opening, how do you suppose the animals get rid of wastes?** (Sample: The wastes must go out through that opening because there is nowhere else for them to go.)

Support the Big Q ❓ UbD

Remind students that all living things need energy. Ask: **Where do animals get energy?** (From food) **What kinds of food do animals eat, and what is the term used to describe each way of getting food?** (Carnivores eat animals. Herbivores eat plants. Omnivores eat both animals and plants.) **Through what process do animals break down food into a form that can be used as a source of energy?** (Digestion) **What is the body system that breaks down food?** (Digestive system)

Differentiated Instruction

L1 Draw a Diagram Ask students to use clay to make a model of **Figure 4**. Tell students to be sure to recognize the difference between the size of the pores through which water enters and leaves the sponge. Then have students present their models and explain what happens when a sponge gets and digests food.

L3 Contrast Digestion Processes Ask students to write a paragraph describing the difference between digestion in a sponge and digestion in a coral. Tell students to use the terms *intracellular, extracellular, digestion,* and *digestive system* in the paragraphs and to accompany them with drawings. Have volunteers read their paragraphs aloud.

Explain

Lead a Discussion

DIGESTIVE TUBE Hold up a cardboard tube. Place an object in one end of the tube and allow students to watch it roll out of the other end. Point out that digestive systems in complex animals have a tube shape. Ask: **How many openings does the tube have?** *(Two)* **How does a tube keep digested food separate from undigested food?** *(Undigested food goes in one end and is digested in the tube.)* **What comes out the other end?** *(Any material that could not be digested.)*

Identify the Main Idea Tell students that when they identify the main idea, they determine the most important, or biggest, idea in a paragraph or section. The other information in the paragraph or section supports or further explains the main idea.

Teach With Visuals

Tell students to look at **Figure 6.** Remind students that a digestive tube allows food to pass through in one direction. As a class, use the captions to sequence how food is digested in the earthworm. Ask: **What happens in the earthworm's crop?** *(Food is softened and stored.)* **What happens in the earthworm's gizzard?** *(Food is ground up)* **What happens in the earthworm's intestine?** *(Digested food is absorbed.)* Then, review the captions for the fish. Ask: **What happens in the fish's esophagus?** *(Food is passed from the mouth to the stomach.)* **What happens in the fish's stomach?** *(Food is partially broken down.)* **How is the fish's intestine similar to the earthworm's intestine?** *(Digested food is absorbed in the intestine.)*

Identify the Main Idea
Underline the main idea in the Digestive Tube section. Then circle the supporting details.

Digestive Tube Complex animals have digestive systems that consist of a tube with two openings. One opening is a mouth for taking in food. The other opening is an **anus** through which waste leave. A digestive tube has specialized areas where food is processe for digestion, digested, and absorbed. You can see the specialized areas of an earthworm's and a fish's digestive tubes in **Figure 6.** A digestive system with two openings is more efficient than a system with one opening. This efficiency is because digested food does not mix with undigested food.

FIGURE 6

Digestive Tubes
The digestive tubes of earthworms and fishes have specialized areas in common. These areas have the same functions.

Interpret Diagrams In each box, list the names of each area of the tube in the order through which food passes.

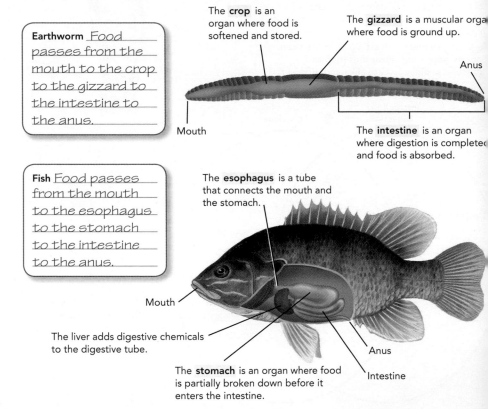

Earthworm *Food passes from the mouth to the crop to the gizzard to the intestine to the anus.*

The **crop** is an organ where food is softened and stored.

The **gizzard** is a muscular orga where food is ground up.

Anus

Mouth

The **intestine** is an organ where digestion is completed and food is absorbed.

Fish *Food passes from the mouth to the esophagus to the stomach to the intestine to the anus.*

The **esophagus** is a tube that connects the mouth and the stomach.

Mouth

The liver adds digestive chemicals to the digestive tube.

Anus

The **stomach** is an organ where food is partially broken down before it enters the intestine.

Intestine

Specialized Digestive Systems Some animals have specialized digestive systems that meet their needs. For example, birds have a crop where they can store food for long flights. A cow's stomach has four parts, each with a special function. The largest part of the cow's stomach is called the rumen. Bacteria in the rumen produce chemicals that help the cow digest plant material. The cow's digestive system is shown in **Figure 7.**

FIGURE 7 ··································

Specialized Digestive System of a Cow
The rumen is the first and largest chamber in a cow's stomach.

✎ **Complete these tasks.**

1. **Identify** Label the parts of a cow's digestive system in the diagram.

2. **Summarize** In the box, write how its rumen helps a cow digest grass.

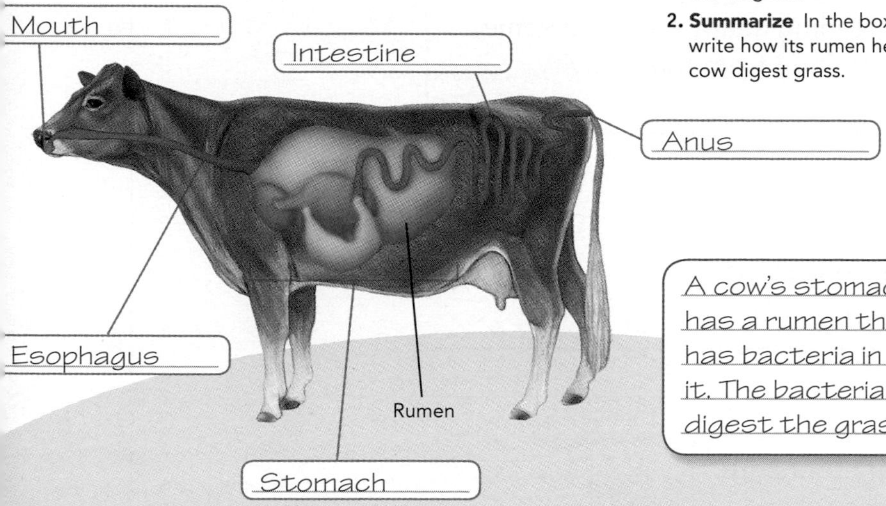

Mouth

Intestine

Anus

A cow's stomach has a rumen that has bacteria in it. The bacteria digest the grass.

Esophagus

Rumen

Stomach

 Lab zone Do the Lab Investigation *Looking at an Owl's Leftovers.*

⊟ **Assess Your Understanding**

a. Explain What is extracellular digestion?
It is digestion that happens outside cells in a digestive system.

b. Draw Conclusions How is it an advantage for an animal to have a long intestine?
Sample: A long intestine has more surface area, allowing more food to be absorbed.

ot it? ··

○ **I get it!** Now I know that the two ways animals can digest food are inside their cells or outside their cells.

○ **I need extra help with** See TE note.

Go to MY SCIENCE ⬤ COACH *online for help with this subject.*

215

Explain ———

Teach With Visuals

Tell students to look at **Figure 7.** Remind students that plant materials, such as cellulose, are difficult to digest. Ask: **How do cows digest plant material?** *(Bacteria in their digestive systems break down the plant material.)* **Where are these bacteria located?** *(In the rumen)* **How is the shape of a cow's intestine different from that of the rumen?** *(The rumen is a large pouch. The intestine is a long, narrow tube.)* Ask students to list the structures of the cow's digestive system in the order in which food passes through them. *(Mouth, esophagus, stomach, intestine, anus)*

Lab Resource: Lab Investigation **Lab zone**

L2 **LOOKING AT AN OWL'S LEFTOVERS** Students will draw conclusions about an animal's diet by examining undigested materials.

Evaluate ———

Assess Your Understanding

After students answer the questions, have them evaluate their understanding by completing the appropriate sentence.

R T I Response to Intervention

2a. If students cannot define extracellular respiration, **then** review the meaning of the prefix *extra-* as "outside."

b. If students have trouble identifying the advantage of having a long intestine, **then** remind students that food is absorbed in the intestine.

MY SCIENCE ⬤ COACH Have students go online for help in understanding digestive systems.

Differentiated Instruction

L1 **Make a Glossary** Ask students to make vocabulary cards that include the following terms: *crop, gizzard, intestine, esophagus, stomach,* and *anus.* Tell students to list each word and write a definition for it. Have students switch cards and make suggestions to improve their partner's definitions.

L3 **Explain Expressions** Tell students that there is an expression related to cows known as "chewing the cud." Have students conduct research to find out what this expression means and how it relates to a cow's digestive system.

Lab zone **After the Inquiry Warm-Up**

How Animals Obtain and Digest Food

Inquiry Warm-Up, *How Do Snakes Feed?*
In the Inquiry Warm-Up, you used a model to investigate a feeding adaptation that some snake species have but lizards do not have. Using what you learned from that activity, answer the questions below.

1. **DEVELOP HYPOTHESES** You read in the lab that snakes' teeth grow backward, pointing back toward the throat. How might this adaptation be helpful in an animal that often swallows its prey alive?

   _____

   _____

2. **INFER** Unlike a mammal, a snake does not have a muscular esophagus to move swallowed food to its stomach. How do you think a snake moves food through its esophagus to its stomach?

   _____

   _____

3. **INFER** A snake does not chew its food. What adaptation do you think a snake's stomach might have to help it digest animals that are swallowed whole?

   _____

   _____

4. **INFER** Which animal do you think will take longer to digest a meal—a snake or a lizard? Explain.

   _____

   _____

Assess Your Understanding

How Animals Obtain and Digest Food

How Do Animals Obtain Food?

1a. REVIEW What types of food do carnivores, herbivores, and omnivores eat? _____

_____

b. COMPARE AND CONTRAST How are the teeth of carnivores and herbivores alike and different? _____

_____

_____

got it? ....

O **I get it!** Now I know that the way an animal gets food depends on _____

_____

_____

O **I need extra help with** _____

_____

How Do Animals Digest Food?

2a. EXPLAIN What is extracellular digestion? _____

_____

b. DRAW CONCLUSIONS How is it an advantage for an animal to have a long intestine? _____

_____

got it? ....

O **I get it!** Now I know that the two ways animals can digest food are _____

_____

O **I need extra help with** _____

_____

How Animals Obtain and Digest Food

How Do Animals Obtain Food?

All animals need food to provide the materials and energy their cells need to function. **The different ways an animal obtains food depends on what it eats and its adaptation for getting food.** Animals that eat only other animals are **carnivores.** Animals that eat only plant material are **herbivores.** Animals that eat both plants and other animals are **omnivores.**

Animal mouthparts are often adapted to the food they eat. Butterfly mouthparts enable them to suck juices from plants. Carnivores have pointed teeth for tearing meat. Herbivores have flat teeth for grinding plant material. Omnivores usually have both pointed and flat teeth. Some animals that live in water called **filter feeders** have mouthparts that strain microscopic organisms from the water.

Animals have a variety of structural and behavioral adaptations for obtaining food. One structural adaptation is a snail's **radula,** a flexible, tonguelike ribbon of tiny teeth it uses to tear plant tissues or drill through shells. One behavioral adaptation is a spider spinning a web to catch prey.

How Do Animals Digest Food?

Digestion is the process that breaks down food into small molecules. **Some animals digest food mainly inside their cells, but most animals digest food outside their cells.** In a process called intracellular digestion, sponges digest food inside specialized cells in their bodies. Most animals digest food outside their cells in a process called extracellular digestion.

A **digestive system** is an organ system that has specialized structures for obtaining and digesting food. Complex animals' digestive systems have two openings: a mouth to take in food, and an **anus** through which wastes leave. Between the mouth and the anus, animals' digestive systems can differ. An earthworm has a **crop,** an organ where food is softened and stored; a **gizzard,** a muscular organ where food is ground up: and an **intestine,** where digestion is completed and food is absorbed. A fish has an **esophagus,** a tube that connects the mouth to the stomach. The **stomach** is an organ where food is partially broken down before it enters the intestine. Some animals have specialized digestive systems.

On a separate sheet of paper, tell how a cow is classified by the food it eats. Then explain how a cow is adapted to eat and digest that food.

Name _____ Date _____ Class _____

How Animals Obtain and Digest Food

Understanding Main Ideas
Answer the following questions on a separate sheet of paper.

1. Explain why carnivores, herbivores, and omnivores have different types of teeth.
2. Give an example of one structural adaptation and one behavioral adaptation that different animals use to obtain food.
3. What is the purpose of digestion?
4. What is the difference between intracellular digestion and extracellular digestion?
5. Describe the differences between the digestive systems of a very simple animal and a complex animal.

Building Vocabulary
Match each term with its definition by writing the letter of the correct definition in the right column on the line beside the term in the left column.

6. ___ radula   **a.** digestive opening through which wastes exit

7. ___ anus   **b.** organ where food is partially broken down

8. ___ crop   **c.** organ where food is absorbed

9. ___ gizzard   **d.** flexible, tonguelike ribbon of tiny teeth

10. ___ intestine   **e.** organ where food is softened and stored

11. ___ esophagus   **f.** tube that connects the mouth and stomach

12. ___ stomach   **g.** animal that strains and eats microscopic organisms in water

13. ___ filter feeder **h.** muscular organ where food is ground up

Enrich

How Animals Obtain and Digest Food

Movement and feeding are characteristics of animals, and animals have different methods of getting food. Read the passage and study the graphs. Then use a separate sheet of paper to answer the questions that follow.

Rushing to Eat

The amount of time an animal spends moving around and the speed with which it moves depend on its method of obtaining food. The graphs at right show the kind of data you might get if you were to record the speed at which an animal moves throughout the day. The *x*-axis shows the hours of the day, and the *y*-axis shows the speed at which the animal is moving.

1. At what speed was Animal 1 moving most of the time? What seems to be its top speed? Did it move at this top speed for very long?

2. About how fast did Animal 2 move when it was active? Was it most active during the day or during night? How often did it stop to rest?

3. When was Animal 3 active? Was it usually moving at high speed? What was its top speed? For approximately how long did it move at this speed? How far would it have traveled during this time?

4. Which of the four animals was mostly active at night? Which animal remained active through the heat of the afternoon?

5. Match each animal with the feeding method it most likely uses.

   a. ___ Animal 1   **1.** sit-and-wait predator

   b. ___ Animal 2   **2.** predator that pursues its prey long distances

   c. ___ Animal 3

   d. ___ Animal 4   **3.** herbivore or omnivore

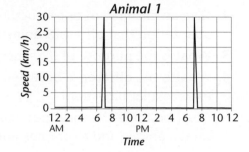

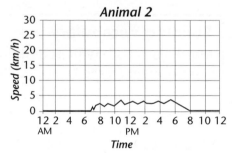

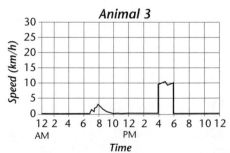

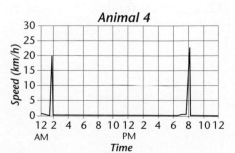

Lesson Quiz

How Animals Obtain and Digest Food

Write the letter of the correct answer on the line at the left.

1. ___ Which of the following are all filter feeders?

 A barnacles, clams, and blue whales

 B clams, sponges, and planarians

 C dolphins, otters, and blue whales

 D fish and amphibians

2. ___ A digestive tube has specialized areas where food is processed for digestion, digested, and

 A filtered

 B eaten

 C absorbed

 D broken down

3. ___ One example of a behavioral adaptation for obtaining food is

 A a hawk's sharp beak

 B a spider spinning a web

 C a coral's tentacles

 D a giraffe's long neck

4. ___ The openings of the digestive system of a complex animal are the

 A pore and intestine

 B crop and radula

 C mouth, intestine, and anus

 D mouth and anus

If the statement is true, write *true*. If the statement is false, change the underlined word or words to make the statement true.

5. _____ Earthworms, snail, and crabs eat <u>microscopic</u> plants and animals

6. _____ In <u>intracellular</u> digestion, animals digest food outside their cells.

7. _____ A digestive system with two openings is <u>more</u> efficient than a system with one opening.

8. _____ Because it is an herbivore, a horse has <u>pointed</u> teeth.

9. _____ A(n) <u>herbivore</u> eats only other animals.

10. _____ Filter feeders trap and eat <u>microscopic</u> organisms.

How Animals Obtain and Digest Food

Answer Key

After the Inquiry Warm-Up

1. Accept all reasonable answers. Students will likely say that an animal trying to pull out will get caught on the teeth.

2. Accept all reasonable answers. Students may say that movements of the snake's body push food down its esophagus to its stomach.

3. Accept all reasonable answers. Students will likely say that a snake's stomach is adapted to grind food or contains stronger acids than a mammal's stomach.

4. Accept all reasonable answers. Students will likely say that a snake will take longer to digest a meal because its meals can be much larger.

Key Concept Summaries

Because it eats only plants, a cow is an herbivore. A cow's mouth has flat teeth for grinding plant material. Chewed food passes through the esophagus to the stomach, which has four parts. In the largest part, the rumen, bacteria produce chemicals that help digest plant material. After the stomach, the cow's food passes into the intestine, where food is absorbed.

Review and Reinforce

1. Each type of animal has specialized teeth that are adapted to the animal's diet. For example, a carnivore has pointed teeth for tearing meat.

2. Sample: A bird's beak and claws are structural adaptations that help it get food into its mouth. A spider spinning a web is a behavioral adaptation that helps it catch prey.

3. Digestion breaks food down into small molecules that can be absorbed by cells.

4. Intracellular digestion takes place within special cells in an animal's body. Extracellular digestion takes place outside an animal's cells.

5. The digestive systems of very simple animals have only one opening. Complex animals' digestive systems have two openings.

6. d   7. a   8. b
9. h   10. c   11. f
12. b   13. g

Enrich

1. Most of the time it wasn't moving. Its top speed was 30 km/h, but it moved at this speed only for very short amounts of time.

2. Its average speed was about 3 km/h. It was active during the day. It stopped to rest only during the night. During the day it kept moving.

3. Animal 3 was active in the early morning and early evening. It usually moved at low speed or not at all. Its top speed was about 10 km/h. It kept that speed for close to 2 hours. It would have traveled about 20 km.

4. Animal 4 was mostly active at night; it was active around 8 P.M. and 1 A.M. Animal 2 was active in the heat of the afternoon.

5. **a.** 1
   b. 3
   c. 2
   d. 1

Lesson Quiz

1. A   2. C
3. B   4. D
5. decaying   6. extracellular
7. true   8. flat
9. carnivore   10. true

Place the outside corner, the corner away from the dotted line, in the corner of your copy machine to copy onto letter-size paper.

How Animals Obtain Oxygen

 How do animals get and use energy?

Lesson Pacing: 2–3 periods or 1–1½ blocks

SHORT ON TIME? To do this lesson in approximately half the time, do the Activate Prior Knowledge activity on page 216. A discussion of the Key Concepts on pages 218 and 219 will familiarize students with the lesson content. Have students do the Quick Labs. The rest of the lesson can be completed by students independently.

Preference Navigator, in the online Planning tools, allows you to customize *Interactive Science* to your own teaching style. You can also edit lesson plans by selecting the Lesson Planner option.

Digital Teacher's Edition allows you to access your Teacher's Edition and Resource materials online.

my science online.com

Lesson Vocabulary

- cellular respiration
- diffusion
- respiratory system
- gill
- lung

 Content Refresher

Professional Development Note

Cellular Respiration All living things need energy to survive. In most ecosystems on Earth, the ultimate source of energy is the sun. Plants absorb the sun's energy and use it to produce food, in the form of sugar, during photosynthesis. During photosynthesis, carbon dioxide and water are changed into glucose and oxygen.

Plants use some of the energy to carry out their own life functions. They store the rest in their tissues. Animals that eat plants obtain stored energy. Similarly, the animal uses some of the energy to carry out its life functions and stores the rest.

The process through which the energy stored in food is released to be used by plants and animals is known as *cellular respiration.* In general, cellular respiration is the reverse of photosynthesis. Cells combine oxygen and glucose to produce carbon dioxide and water. Energy is released during this reaction. It is for this reason that animals need to obtain oxygen. Without it, only a small amount of stored energy can be used.

LESSON OBJECTIVES

☞ Explain how animals exchange oxygen and carbon dioxide with the environment.

☞ Compare the different respiratory structures of animals.

Blended Path
Active learning using Student Edition, Inquiry Path, and Digital Path

ENGAGE AND EXPLORE

Teach this lesson using a variety of resources. Begin by reading **My Planet Diary** as a class. Have students discuss how most fish get the oxygen they need. Then have students do the **Inquiry Warm-Up activity.** Students will observe fish and how their gills work. The **After the Inquiry Warm-Up worksheet** sets up a discussion about the natural behavior of a fish, particularly how it uses its gills. Have volunteers share their answers to question 4, explaining their hypothesis and the experiments designed to test them.

EXPLAIN AND ELABORATE

Support the Big Q by explaining to students that cellular respiration is a series of chemical reactions that take place in cells. **Teach Key Concepts** by explaining that oxygen and carbon dioxide move across membranes by diffusion. Have students practice the inquiry skill in the **Apply It activity.**

Teach Key Concepts by describing the respiratory system as the organ system that exchanges gases with an animal's surroundings. **Lead a Discussion** about gills and lungs. Then **Lead a Discussion** about what the respiratory systems of all animals that live on land have in common. Continue to **Lead a Discussion** about the structures vertebrates use to breathe. Finally, **Lead a Discussion** about the air sacs that are extensions of the lungs of birds.

Hand out the **Key Concept Summaries** as a review of each part of the lesson. Students can also use the online **Vocab Flash Cards** to review key terms.

EVALUATE

Have students take the **Lesson Quiz.** For an alternate assessment, see the *ExamView®* Computer Test Generator, Progress Monitoring Assessments, or SuccessTracker™.

E L L Support

1 Content and Language

Review the definitions of the vocabulary terms. Then challenge students to write two sentences, using *cellular respiration* and *diffusion* in one sentence and *respiratory system, gill,* and *lung* in the other.

DIFFERENTIATED INSTRUCTION KEY
L1 Struggling Students or Special Needs
L2 On-Level Students **L3** Advanced Students

LESSON PLANNER 6.2

Lab zone Inquiry Path
Hands-on learning in the Lab zone

Digital Path
Online learning at my science online.com

ENGAGE AND EXPLORE

To teach this lesson with an emphasis on inquiry, begin with the **Inquiry Warm-Up activity.** Students will observe fish and how their gills work. The **After the Inquiry Warm-Up worksheet** sets up a discussion about the natural behavior of a fish, particularly how it uses its gills. Have volunteers share their answers to question 4, explaining their hypothesis and the experiments designed to test them.

EXPLAIN AND ELABORATE

Focus on the **Inquiry Skill** for the lesson. Remind students that when they predict, they use what they already know about a subject to infer what is most likely to happen in the future. How is the hypothesis made in the **Inquiry Warm-Up activity** like a prediction? *(Sample: My hypothesis was that the respiration rate of a fish would increase as the water temperature increased. This is a prediction of what I think will happen.)* **Support the Big Q** by explaining to students that cellular respiration is a series of chemical reactions that take place in cells. Before beginning the **Apply It activity,** review the meaning of *concentration.* Have students do the **Quick Lab** modeling diffusion across cell membranes.

Build Inquiry to model diffusion in the respiratory systems of animals. Have students do the **Quick Lab** to observe the breathing structures of pond organisms. Students can use the online **Vocab Flash Cards** to review key terms.

EVALUATE

Have students take the **Lesson Quiz.** For an alternate assessment, see the *ExamView®* Computer Test Generator, Progress Monitoring Assessments, or SuccessTracker™.

ENGAGE AND EXPLORE

Teach this lesson using digital resources. Begin by having students learn more about how animals obtain oxygen and explore real-world connections to the ways animals breathe at **My Planet Diary** online. Have them access the Chapter Resources to find the **Unlock the Big Question activity.** There they can answer the questions and refine their responses as they continue through the lesson. You can re-assign the activity and have students submit their work so you can track their progress.

EXPLAIN AND ELABORATE

Students reading above, at, or below the lexile measure of this lesson can access basic content readings at their level at **My Reading Web.** Encourage students to use the online **Vocab Flash Cards** to preview key terms. **Support the Big Q** by explaining to students that cellular respiration is a series of chemical reactions that take place in cells. Assign the **Apply It activity** online and have students submit their work to you. Have students do the **Quick Lab** modeling diffusion across cell membranes.

Use the **Art in Motion activity** online to show how different types of respiratory structures work. Have students do the **Quick Lab** to observe the breathing structures of pond organisms. The **Key Concept Summaries** online allow students to read a summary and see an image associated with each part of the lesson. Online remediation is available at **My Science Coach.**

EVALUATE

Have students take the **Lesson Quiz.** For an alternate assessment, see the *ExamView®* Computer Test Generator, Progress Monitoring Assessments, or SuccessTracker™.

2 Frontload the Lesson
Have students make a three-column chart to rate their knowledge of the terms, listing the terms in the first column. In the second column, they should indicate whether they can define and use the word, have heard or seen the word before, or do not know the word. As they read, they should write definitions in the third column.

3 Comprehensible Input
Have students list the respiratory structures of animals in the chapter. Urge them to write sentences that compare or contrast two structures.

4 Language Production
Pair or group students with varied language abilities to complete labs collaboratively for language practice. Have each student copy the completed written lab for personal reference.

5 Assess Understanding
Ask students to make notes about Key Concepts from the lesson and use the notes to prepare an oral presentation of the concepts. Encourage students to use the visuals in the lesson to support their presentations.

Lexile Measure = 940L

How Animals Obtain Oxygen

Establish Learning Objectives

After this lesson, students will be able to:

🔑 Explain how animals exchange oxygen and carbon dioxide with the environment.

🔑 Compare the different respiratory structures of animals.

Engage

Activate Prior Knowledge

MY PLANET DIARY Read *The Lungfish* with the class. Have students describe fish that they have seen. Ask: **Where do most fish get the oxygen they need?** *(Most get it from the water through their gills.)* **Do you know any animals that live in water but come to the surface to breathe?** *(Samples: sea turtles, dolphins, whales)*

BIG IDEAS OF SCIENCE REFERENCE LIBRARY 📖
Have students look up the following topics: Birds, Elephants.

Explore

Lab Resource: Inquiry Warm-Up 🧪

L1 **HOW DOES WATER FLOW OVER A FISH'S GILLS?** Students will observe fish and how their gills work.

LESSON

2 How Animals Obtain Oxygen

🔑 **How Do Animals Obtain Oxygen?**

🔑 **How Do Animal Respiratory Systems Compare?**

my planet diary

FUN FACTS

The Lungfish

What fish lives in water but must come up for air? It is the African lungfish. Like many fish, it has gills. But it also has two lungs. Though the African lungfish can use its gills, it breathes mostly with its lungs. It rises to the surface, pokes its mouth out of the water, and gulps in air. If it cannot obtain air this way, it can drown. Imagine that—a fish drowning!

Sometimes the bodies of water that African lungfish live in can dry up. When this happens, the fish digs a hole in the mud. Then mucus oozes out of its body and lines the hole. The mucus keeps the fish from drying out. The lungfish clears the area around its nostrils so it can still breathe. Lungfish can survive this way for months until the area fills with water again.

Answer the following questions.

1. What are two ways lungfish differ from other fishes you know about?
   Sample: They use lungs to breathe, and they can live in mud.

2. What is another animal you know that lives in water and must come to the surface for air?
   Sample: Whales live in water but go to the surface to breathe air.

▶ **PLANET DIARY** Go to **Planet Diary** to learn more about how animals obtain oxygen.

Lab zone Do the Inquiry Warm-Up *How Does Water Flow Over a Fish's Gills?*

216 Obtaining Energy

SUPPORT ALL READERS

Lexile Measure = 940L   Lexile Word Count = 1285

Prior Exposure to Content: May be the first time students have encountered this topic

Academic Vocabulary: *compare, contrast, predict*

Science Vocabulary: *cellular respiration, diffusion, gill, lung*

Concept Level: Generally appropriate for most students in this grade

Preteach With: My Planet Diary "The Lungfish" and Figure 1 activity

Go to **My Reading Web** to access leveled readings that provide a foundation for the content.

my science online.com

Vocabulary
- cellular respiration • diffusion
- respiratory system • gill • lung

Skills
- Reading: Compare and Contrast
- Inquiry: Predict

How Do Animals Obtain Oxygen?

What happens when you try to hold your breath? It is not easy after a while, is it? It is difficult because you must breathe to exchange two important gases with your surroundings. Your body cannot function without constantly taking in oxygen and getting rid of carbon dioxide.

Why Animals Need Oxygen Just like you, all other animals need a constant supply of oxygen. Animals need oxygen for a process called cellular respiration. **Cellular respiration** is the process in which cells use oxygen and digested food molecules to release the energy in food. Cellular respiration occurs in every cell in an animal's body. Carbon dioxide is a waste product of the process.

Breathing and cellular respiration are not the same process. Some animals breathe to get oxygen into their bodies. But other animals do not breathe. Instead, they get oxygen into their bodies in different ways. Cellular respiration cannot occur until oxygen is inside an animal's cells. All animals have cellular respiration, but not all animals breathe.

Breathing | **Cellular Respiration**

Breathing brings oxygen into an animal's body and lets carbon dioxide out of it.

Both
Both involve oxygen and carbon dioxide.

Cells use oxygen and digested food molecules to release the energy in food. Carbon dioxide is produced as waste.

Compare and Contrast
In the Venn diagram, compare and contrast breathing and cellular respiration.

217

Explain

Introduce Vocabulary

Remind students that they will often encounter related forms of a word in science texts. For example, *diffuse* is a verb, but the process by which a substance diffuses is called *diffusion*, which is a noun.

Support the Big Q ? UbD

RESPIRATION Explain to students that cellular respiration is a series of chemical reactions that take place in cells. Ask: **What gas does an animal use in cellular respiration?** *(Oxygen)* **What does the animal get out of the food molecules?** *(Energy)* **What gas does the animal give off as a waste product of cellular respiration?** *(Carbon dioxide)* Tell students to take a deep breath. Ask: **What just happened?** *(I took air into my lungs.)* **Is this cellular respiration?** *(No)* **How is it related to cellular respiration?** *(It brings air, which contains oxygen needed for cellular respiration, into the lungs. The oxygen enters the bloodstream where it is brought to cells all over the body.)*

Compare and Contrast Explain to students that when they compare two things, they tell how the things are alike. When students contrast two things, they tell how the things are different. Point to the graphic organizer. Explain that in a Venn diagram, points of similarity are put in the overlapping section of the circles, while points of difference are put in the other sections of the diagram.

21st Century Learning

CRITICAL THINKING Ask students to sequence digestion, cellular respiration, and breathing. Students should be able to defend their answers. *(Sample: Breathing and digestion must take place before cellular respiration. Breathing is necessary in order to deliver oxygen to the body. Digestion is necessary to break down food molecules into molecules the cell can take in and use.)*

My Planet Diary provides an opportunity for students to explore real-world connections to the ways that animals breathe.

E L L Support

1 Content and Language
Write *respiration* on the board. Tell students that the noun *respiration* comes from the Latin prefix *re-*, meaning "again," and the verb *spirare*, meaning "to breathe."

2 Frontload the Lesson
Invite students to visualize what happens during the process of inhaling and exhaling air. Ask them to think about whether various other animals breathe the same way that humans do.

3 Comprehensible Input
Have students create cluster diagrams or spider maps to organize information about the respiratory systems of animals living in water and animals living on land. Remind students to include specific terms for structures that animals use to exchange gases.

Explain

Teach Key Concepts 🔑

Explain that oxygen and carbon dioxide move across cell membranes by diffusion. Ask: **What causes particles to diffuse from one place to another?** *(They move from regions of high concentration to regions of lower concentration.)* **Is the concentration of oxygen higher or lower inside a cell than outside the cell?** *(Lower)* **Is the concentration of carbon dioxide higher or lower inside a cell than outside the cell?** *(Higher)*

Elaborate

Apply It!

L1 Before beginning the activity, review the meaning of *concentration*. Note that the exact number of Xs on the diagram is not important as long as the student shows more Xs inside the circle than outside.

🔺 **Predict** Remind students that when they predict, they use what they already know about a subject to infer what is most likely to happen in the future.

Lab Resource: Quick Lab

L2 **HOW DO ANIMALS GET OXYGEN?** Students will model diffusion across cell membranes.

Evaluate

Assess Your Understanding

After students answer the questions, have them evaluate their understanding by completing the appropriate sentence.

RTI Response to Intervention

1a. If students have trouble recalling the importance of breathing, **then** have students draw a simple diagram to show the movement of oxygen and carbon dioxide into and out of an animal.

b. If students cannot explain the reason for diffusion, **then** have them reread the Key Concept statement for this section.

MY SCIENCE COACH Have students go online for help in understanding breathing.

Exchanging Gases Animals exchange oxygen and carbon dioxide with their surroundings by diffusion. In the process of **diffusion**, particles move from an area of high concentration to an area of low concentration. 🔑 **Animal cells exchange oxygen and carbon dioxide with their surroundings by diffusion across the outer coverings, or membranes, of cells.** Cell membranes are moist and thin, which enable efficient diffusion.

Cells use oxygen in the process of cellular respiration. Therefore the concentration of oxygen inside cells is usually lower than it is outside cells. So, oxygen tends to diffuse into cells. Because cellular respiration produces carbon dioxide, there is usually a higher concentration of carbon dioxide inside cells than outside cells. As a result, carbon dioxide tends to diffuse out of cells.

apply it!

Use this model of an animal's muscle cell to complete the activity.

① Identify Is the concentration of oxygen greater inside or outside the cell?

It is greater outside the cell.

② Predict Draw X's to represent the concentration of carbon dioxide inside and outside the cell. Explain what you drew.

Sample: I drew more carbon dioxide inside the cell because it is produced in cellular respiration.

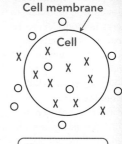

Cell membrane

Cell

Key
O Oxygen
X Carbon dioxide

Lab zone® Do the Quick Lab How Do Animals Get Oxygen

🔑 Assess Your Understanding

1a. Review What does breathing do for an animal?

Breathing gets oxygen into and carbon dioxide out of its body.

b. Relate Cause and Effect Why does oxygen tend to diffuse into cells?

The amount of oxygen in a cell is often lower than it is outside.

got it?

○ I get it! Now I know that animals exchange oxygen and carbon dioxide with their surroundings by means of diffusion across cell membranes.

○ I need extra help with See TE note.

Go to **MY SCIENCE COACH** online for help with this subject.

Digital Lesson: Assign the *Apply It* activity online and have students submit their work to you.

 MY SCIENCE online .com | **Animals and Oxygen**

How Do Animal Respiratory Systems Compare?

The structures that an animal uses to exchange gases with its surroundings make up the **respiratory system**. Respiratory systems include structures such as skin, gills, and lungs. The type of respiratory system an animal has depends on how complex the animal is and where it lives.

Animals that exchange gases across their skin live in water or moist places on land. However, most animals that live in water, which contains dissolved oxygen, have gills. **Gills** are featherlike structures where gases are exchanged between water and blood. In contrast, most animals that breathe air, which contains oxygen, have lungs. **Lungs** are saclike structures made up of a thin layer of cells where gases are exchanged between air and blood. Lungs are located inside the body where they can stay moist. Animals with these structures can be seen in **Figure 1**.

FIGURE 1 ························

ART IN MOTION **Respiratory Structures**
Animals exchange gases with their environment through gills, lungs, or skin.

Make Generalizations Explain what you think is different about where dolphins are found and where lobsters are found in the water.

Sample: Dolphins are found closer to the water's surface because they need air. Lobsters are on the ocean floor because they use gills to breathe.

A lobster is an arthropod that has gills under its body near its legs.

A frog is an amphibian that exchanges gases through the skin that covers its body.

A dolphin is a mammal that has lungs inside its body.

219

Differentiated Instruction

L1 Describe Respiratory Systems
Ask pairs of students to list the three structures through which animals can exchange gases. Have students create their own version of **Figure 1** by identifying animals that breathe with lungs, gills, and through the skin.

L3 Show Diffusion Ask pairs of students to make a model to represent diffusion. Students can use common household items, such as marbles or dry pasta. They should mount their models on poster board or other material so they can present them to the class. Each model should indicate some type of change over time.

Explain

Teach Key Concepts

Describe the respiratory system as the organ system that exchanges gases with an animal's surroundings. Ask: **What structures are found in the respiratory system of most animals that live in water?** *(Gills)* **What structures are found in the respiratory system of most animals that live on land?** *(Lungs)*

Teach With Visuals

Tell students to look at **Figure 1**. Read the descriptions of each animal as a class. Ask: **What is most likely true about animals, such as dolphins, that have lungs?** *(They breathe air.)* **What is most likely true about animals that have gills, such as lobsters?** *(They stay under water all the time.)* Point out the frog. Tell students that the main respiratory structure of most adult amphibians, including frogs and salamanders, is their skin. However, these animals also have lungs where gas exchange may occur between air and blood.

Explore

Build Inquiry 🧪

L1 DIFFUSION

Materials clock or watch with a second hand, food coloring, large plastic beaker, plastic dropper, water

Time 20 minutes

Have student groups fill a beaker three-quarters full of water and allow the water to stand for 2 minutes. Then, put eight drops of food coloring into the water. Ask students to note what the food coloring looks like as it enters the water? *(It is dark and concentrated.)* Have students observe the water every 2 minutes over a 10-minute period.

Ask: **What happened to the food coloring?** *(It spread evenly through the water.)* **How is this similar to what happens in the respiratory systems of animals?** *(Oxygen and carbon dioxide move across cell membranes from regions where they are more concentrated to regions where they are less concentrated.)*

Art in Motion shows how different types of respiratory structures work.

MY SCIENCE online .com | Animal Respiratory Systems

Explain

Lead a Discussion

LIVING UNDERWATER Describe a scuba diver exploring a coral reef. Ask: **Why can't the scuba diver breathe underwater?** *(The scuba diver has lungs and needs to breathe air.)* **What does the scuba diver need to bring so he or she can breathe?** *(A tank of air)* **What structures do fishes, mollusks, and arthropods that live in water use to breathe?** *(Gills)* **What structures do dolphins, whales, and alligators use to breathe?** *(Lungs)*

Teach With Visuals

Tell students to look at **Figure 2.** Review with students the classification group that each animal represents. Ask: **Does the coral have gills?** *(No)* **How does the coral get oxygen?** *(By diffusion through its outer body covering)* **Where are the gills of a fish?** *(On the sides of its head)* Point out the covering over the fish's gills. Explain that the fish draws water in through its mouth and then expels the water over the gills. Help students locate the gill in the diagram of the squid. Also point out the body opening shown in the diagram. Explain that this is one of the animal's siphons, structures through which water is moved, causing a stream of water to flow over the gills. Ask: **Why is it important for the squid and the fish to keep water moving over the gills?** *(As oxygen diffuses into the gills and carbon dioxide diffuses out of the gills, the concentrations in the water near the gills becomes similar to that of the gills. Diffusion exchanges gases only when the concentrations are different.)*

21st Century Learning

CRITICAL THINKING Explain that water contains less oxygen than air does, so gills need to be very efficient. One way to make gas exchange more efficient is to increase the surface area across which diffusion occurs. Gills usually have a folded surface, somewhat like a fan. Ask: **How does a folded structure affect surface area?** *(It increases surface area.)* **How does an increased surface area affect gas exchange?** *(A greater surface area means that more oxygen can enter the gills and more carbon dioxide can leave the gills.)*

Animals Living in Water Think about animals that live in water, such as jellyfishes, clams, sharks, and whales. Just as these animals are diverse, so are their respiratory structures. Most of these animals use either their outer body coverings or gills as respiratory structures, as shown in **Figure 2.** For example, cnidarians use their outer body coverings for gas exchange. Fishes, mollusks, and arthropods use their gills. However, some animals that live in water have lungs and get oxygen from the air. Whales, dolphins, and alligators breathe air at the surface and hold their breath when they dive.

FIGURE 2 ....

Respiration Without Lungs
Animals that live in water and do not have lungs use their outer body covering or gills to exchange gases.

✏ **Relate Text and Visuals** In each box, identify the animal's respiratory structure.

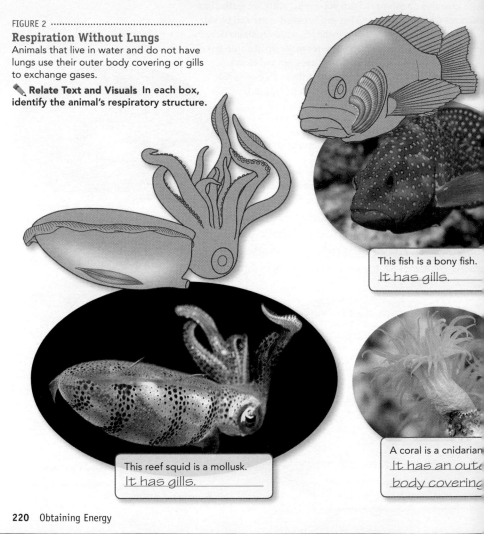

This fish is a bony fish.
It has gills.

This reef squid is a mollusk.
It has gills.

A coral is a cnidarian
It has an oute
body covering

Professional Development Note — Teacher to Teacher

Activity A little competition with posters can be fun. Give student teams specific parameters for the posters—size, materials to be used, minimum of two examples of how different invertebrates obtain oxygen, and whether or not Internet or photocopied pictures are allowed. Remind students to cite sources of images and information. Each team's poster should be divided into categories of how oxygen is obtained, such as gills versus breathing tubes. Students can draw or paste copied illustrations in each category. Brief descriptions gain more points. Design a good rubric to help guide the students throughout the project. Oral presentations of final products as well as peer scoring are additional ideas to consider.

✎ *Susan M. Pritchard, Ph.D.*
Washington Middle School
La Habra, California

nimals Living on Land You might think that all
nimals living on land use their lungs to exchange gases. Some
nimals do use lungs, but others do not. For example, amphibians
ay use their skin as their main respiratory structure. Arthropods
d other invertebrates have some unique respiratory structures.
lthough the respiratory structures of land-dwelling animals are
verse, they do have something in common. They all are made up
thin layers of moist cells. In addition, in more complex animals,
e layers have folds or pockets that increase the surface area for
s exchange. The respiratory structures of invertebrates and
rtebrates are different.

vertebrate Structures Just a few of the invertebrates that live
land are shown in **Figure 3**. Their respiratory structures include
in, book lungs, and tracheal tubes.

GURE 3 ························

vertebrate Respiration
in, book lungs, and tracheal tubes are
spiratory structures of invertebrates.

Summarize In the chart, list each
imal shown, and write the name of its
spiratory structure.

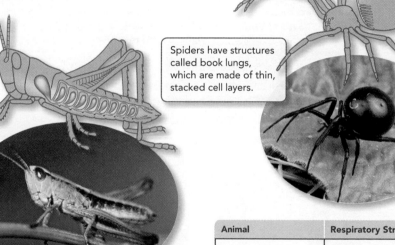

Earthworms
exchange gases
through their
moist skin.

Spiders have structures
called book lungs,
which are made of thin,
stacked cell layers.

asshoppers have tracheal tubes,
ich have openings for gases
enter and leave the body.

Animal	Respiratory Structure
Earthworm	Skin
Spider	Book lung
Grasshopper	Tracheal tubes

221

Explain

Lead a Discussion

LIVING ON LAND Point out that animals that live
on land have a variety of adaptations that help them
to exchange gases. Ask: **What do the respiratory
systems of all animals that live on land have
in common?** *(They are all made up of thin layers
of moist cells, and the layers have folds or pockets.)*
How do folded layers affect respiration? *(They
increase the surface area, which means that more
cells are exposed for diffusion.)*

Teach With Visuals

Tell students to look at **Figure 3.** As a class, read
the descriptions next to each animal. Ask: **What
structure do earthworms use to exchange
gases?** *(Moist skin)* **What structure do spiders use
to exchange gases?** *(Book lungs)* **What structure
do insects use to exchange gases?** *(Tracheal
tubes)* **Why do you think earthworms spend
much of their time during the day in the soil?**
(They must stay moist, so they stay out of the sun.)

21st Century Learning

L3 **CREATIVITY** Challenge pairs of students to write
a script for to a brief interview. The interviewer
should ask questions to an insect, a spider, and an
earthworm to learn about their respiratory structures.
Once written, have students take the role of the
interviewer or the animals and present the interview
to the class.

Differentiated Instruction

L1 **Cooperative Review** Have
students work in groups of three. Each
student should choose one type of
invertebrate and describe its respiratory
structures to the others. Encourage the
students who are listening to ask
questions and make suggestions as to
how to improve the description.

L3 **Time Underwater** Have students
research the length of time different
animals that breathe air can stay under
water. Encourage them to investigate
at least three different animals. Ask
students to make a graph showing
their results.

Explain

Lead a Discussion

VERTEBRATE STRUCTURES Explain that, with the exception of fishes, most vertebrates use lungs to breathe. Ask: **What are two ways in which the lungs of vertebrates differ?** *(In size and number of folds)* **How is the efficiency of the lungs related to the number of folds?** *(Efficiency increases with the number of folds.)*

Teach With Visuals

Tell students to look at **Figure 4.** Help students identify each of the animals shown. They should easily recognize the chimpanzee as a mammal, but they may have difficulty distinguishing the reptile (lizard) from the amphibian (newt). Remind students that reptiles have scaly skin, while amphibians have smooth, moist skin. Then direct students' attention to the three drawings of vertebrate lungs. Point out that the three drawings are not to scale. Ask: **Which lungs are the most complex?** *(Mammal lungs)* **Which lungs have the fewest pockets or folds?** *(Amphibian lungs)* **How are pockets related to efficiency?** *(The more pockets a lung has, the more efficient it is.)*

Elaborate

Make Analogies

MODEL A LUNG Partially blow up a balloon. Then allow some, but not all, of the air to escape. Blow up the balloon once more and allow the some of the air to escape again. Ask: **What type of respiratory structure is similar to the balloon?** *(Students should say lungs.)* **What process is like filling the balloon with air?** *(Breathing in, or inhaling)* **What process is like letting the air out of the balloon?** *(Breathing out, or exhaling)*

21st Century Learning

L1 CRITICAL THINKING Discuss with students the effect of physical activity on a person's breathing. Ask: **Do you breathe faster or more slowly when you are exerting yourself, such as when you run?** *(Faster)* **How does breathing faster affect the amount of oxygen you take in?** *(Breathing faster takes in more oxygen.)* **What does this tell you about your cells during physical activity?** *(They need more energy to be active so they need more oxygen.)*

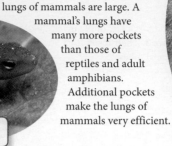

Vertebrate Structures Most vertebrates, including reptiles, birds, mammals, and most adult amphibians, use lungs to breathe. However, as you can see in **Figure 4,** lungs are not all the same. Because some lungs have more pockets or folds than others, the amount of surface area for gas exchange differs. For example, adult amphibian lungs are small and do not have many pockets. Therefore, the main respiratory structure for an adult amphibian is its skin. In contrast, the lungs of mammals are large. A mammal's lungs have many more pockets than those of reptiles and adult amphibians. Additional pockets make the lungs of mammals very efficient.

FIGURE 4 ......

Lungs

✎ Complete these tasks.

1. **Relate Text and Visuals** Label each animal above with the correct letter of the lungs below that belong to it. Then answer the question.

2. **CHALLENGE** How do pockets increase a lung's surface area?

   <u>Sample: Similar to pant pockets, a lung's pockets add a layer. More pockets in the lungs allow for more gas exchange.</u>

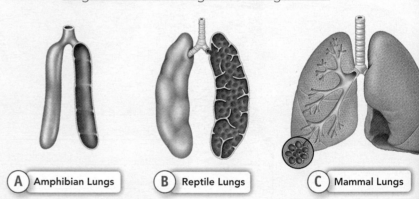

| **A** Amphibian Lungs | **B** Reptile Lungs | **C** Mammal Lungs |

Specialized Respiratory Structures Birds require a lot of energy to fly. Therefore, their cells must receive plenty of oxygen to release the energy contained in food. To obtain more oxygen from each breath of air, birds have a system of air sacs in their bodies. Most birds have nine air sacs. As you can see in Figure 5, air sacs connect to the lungs.

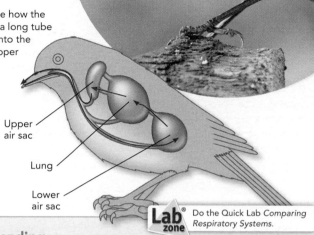

FIGURE 5 ....

A Bird's Lungs
In this simplified diagram, you can see how the fresh air a bird inhales flows through a long tube into the lower air sacs. It then flows into the lungs. From there, it flows into the upper air sacs until it is exhaled.

✎ Observe On the diagram, draw arrows to trace the path of air through the bird's respiratory structures.

Upper air sac

Lung

Lower air sac

Lab zone
Do the Quick Lab *Comparing Respiratory Systems.*

Assess Your Understanding

a. Explain What do all respiratory structures have in common?

They all have moist surfaces where diffusion can occur efficiently.

b. Apply Concepts Why is having several air sacs an advantage for a bird?

It provides the bird with the oxygen it needs to release energy from food to fly.

got it? ....

○ I get it! Now I know that the type of respiratory structure an animal has depends on how complex the animal is, where it lives, and may include skin, gills, and lungs.

○ I need extra help with See TE note.

Go to MY SCIENCE ⚲ COACH online for help with this subject.

223

Differentiated Instruction

L1 Model Lungs Have students make a model of lungs using clay. Tell them to gently push pockets into the clay to increase its surface area. Ask students to write a few sentences describing how increasing the surface area can increase the rate of diffusion.

L3 Surface Area Have students draw a diagram of a cube. Tell them to find the area of one side of the cube and then multiply it by the number of sides. Challenge students to show how cutting the cube in half and then half again increases the total surface area.

Explain ——————————
Lead a Discussion

AIR SACS Explain that air sacs are extensions of the lungs in birds. Birds have several pairs of air sacs that always remain inflated. Gas exchange does not occur in the air sacs. Ask: **How might inflated air sacs be an advantage to a bird?** *(They always provide a source of fresh air.)* **How do you think the portion of a bird's body made up of respiratory structures compares to that a mammal's body?** *(A much greater portion of a bird's body is filled by respiratory structures.)*

Lab Resource: Quick Lab Lab zone

L1 COMPARING RESPIRATORY SYSTEMS Students will observe the breathing structures of pond organisms.

21st Century Learning

INFORMATION LITERACY Have students read *Birds* in the **Big Ideas of Science Reference Library.** Ask students to research the breathing rates of five different birds. They should record this information in a chart that lists the breathing rates from slowest to fastest and display their charts in the classroom. Then, ask students draw conclusions about a bird's breathing rate and its body size.

Evaluate ——————————
Assess Your Understanding

After students answer the questions, have them evaluate their understanding by completing the appropriate sentence.

RTI Response to Intervention

2a. If students have trouble recognizing the similarities among respiratory structures, **then** review the role these structures play in living things.

b. If students need help understanding why frogs need to live near water, **then** review examples of diffusion through moist skin.

MY SCIENCE ⚲ COACH Have students go online for help in understanding respiratory structures.

Lab zone **After the Inquiry Warm-Up**

How Animals Obtain Oxygen

Inquiry Warm-Up, *How Does Water Flow Over a Fish's Gills?*
In the Inquiry Warm-Up, you investigated the natural behavior of a fish, particularly how it uses its gills. Using what you learned from that activity, answer the questions below.

1. **COMMUNICATE** Draw a multi-step diagram to show the movement of the fish's mouth and gill flaps that you observed.

2. **COMMUNICATE** In the lab, you developed a hypothesis about how water was moving through the fish's mouth and gills. To your diagram for question 1, add arrows and labels indicating how you believe water flows.

3. **CALCULATE** In the lab, you compared your data on how many times a minute the gill flaps open with your classmates' data. Find the average.

   _____

4. **DESIGN EXPERIMENTS** In the lab, you were asked what affect you thought changing the water temperature would have on the respiration rate of a fish. Explain how you could conduct an experiment to test your hypothesis.

   _____

   _____

   _____

   _____

Name _____ Date _____ Class _____

How Animals Obtain Oxygen

How Do Animals Obtain Oxygen?

1a. **REVIEW** What does breathing do for an animal? _____
_____

b. **RELATE CAUSE AND EFFECT** Why does oxygen tend to diffuse into cells? _____
_____

got it? ....

○ **I get it!** Now I know that animals exchange oxygen and carbon dioxide with their
surroundings _____
_____

○ **I need extra help with** _____
_____

How Do Animal Respiratory Systems Compare?

1a. **EXPLAIN** What do all respiratory structures have in common? _____
_____
_____

b. **APPLY CONCEPTS** Why is having several air sacs an advantage for a bird? _____
_____
_____

got it? ....

○ **I get it!** Now I know that the type of respiratory structure an animal has depends
on _____
_____
_____

○ **I need extra help with** _____
_____

Name _____ Date _____ Class _____

How Animals Obtain Oxygen

How Do Animals Obtain Oxygen?

All animals need oxygen for **cellular respiration,** or the process in which cells use oxygen and digested food molecules to release the energy in food. Cellular respiration occurs in every cell. Carbon dioxide is a waste product of the process. Breathing and cellular respiration are not the same process. Cellular respiration is carried out in all animals, but not all animals breathe.

Animal cells exchange oxygen and carbon dioxide with their surroundings by diffusion

across the outer coverings, or membranes, of cells. In the process of **diffusion,** particles move from an area of high concentration to an area of low concentration. Cells use oxygen in cellular respiration, so the concentration of oxygen is usually lower inside cells than outside. So, oxygen tends to diffuse into cells. A high concentration of carbon dioxide inside cells means carbon dioxide tends to diffuse outside.

How Do Animal Respiratory Systems Compare?

The structures that an animal uses to exchange gases with its surroundings make up the **respiratory system. Respiratory systems include structures such as skin, gills, and lungs. The type of respiratory system an animal has depends on how complex the animal is and where it lives.**

Most animals that live in water have **gills,** featherlike structures where gases are exchanged between water and blood. Not all water-dwellers have gills, though. Cnidarians exchange gases through their outer body coverings. Dolphins, whales, and alligators have lungs to breathe air.

All land animals have respiratory structures made of thin layers of moist cells. Most air-breathing animals

have **lungs,** saclike structures made of a thin layer of cells where gases are exchanged between air and blood.

The respiratory structures of invertebrates and vertebrates are different. The varied respiratory structures of invertebrates include skin, book lungs, and tracheal tubes. Most vertebrates use lungs to breathe, but lungs are not all the same. Because some lungs have more pockets or folds than others, the amount of surface area for gas exchange differs. Extra pockets make the lungs of mammals very efficient. Because birds require a lot of energy to fly, birds have a system of air sacs connected to their lungs.

On a separate sheet of paper, explain why a mammal needs oxygen and how it obtains it.

Name _____ Date _____ Class _____

How Animals Obtain Oxygen

Understanding Main Ideas

Answer the following questions on a separate sheet of paper.

1. How is cellular respiration different from breathing?
2. How do animal cells exchange oxygen and carbon dioxide with their surroundings?
3. Why does carbon dioxide tend to diffuse out of animal cells?
4. What determines the type of respiratory system an animal has?
5. Explain why a mammal's lungs are more efficient than the lungs of an adult amphibian.

Building Vocabulary

Match each term with its definition by writing the letter of the correct definition in the right column on the line beside the term in the left column.

6. ___ cellular respiration

7. ___ diffusion

8. ___ respiratory system

9. ___ gills

10. ___ lungs

a. the process in which particles move from an area of high concentration to an area of low concentration

b. structures where gases are exchanged between air and blood

c. the structures an animal uses to exchange gases with its surroundings

d. the proc ess in which cells use oxygen to release energy from digested food molecules

e. structures where gases are exchanged between water and blood

How Animals Obtain Oxygen

Respiratory systems allow gas exchanges in the bodies of organisms. Oxygen and carbon dioxide are exchanged. Read the passage and study the table. Then use a separate sheet of paper to answer the questions that follow.

Breathing Methods

Animals have different respiratory organs and obtain oxygen from different sources. The table below shows how some animals breathe.

Animal	Respiratory Organ	Obtains Oxygen From
Fish	gills	water
Amphibians	gills/skin/lungs	water/air
Reptiles	lungs	air
Birds	lungs	air
Mammals	lungs	air

Amphibians may have the most interesting respiratory system of the animal world. Young amphibians, such as tadpoles, use gills. Adult amphibians use both lungs and moist skin as respiratory organs. Their moist skin allows rapid gas exchange. For example, when a frog is in a dormant state, it requires very little oxygen and that oxygen is acquired through its skin.

Amphibians usually begin life in water and move to land as adults. As adults, most amphibians have a three-chambered heart and two lungs. They are cold-blooded, becoming more active in warm environments. Amphibians are vertebrates with double lives—one in water and another on land.

1. Which animals obtain oxygen and release carbon dioxide through lungs?
2. Why is water so essential for amphibians?
3. Explain how an amphibian leads a double life.
4. Research the amphibian's metamorphosis as it applies to the amphibian's respiratory system. Write a short summary.

Name _____ Date _____ Class _____

How Animals Obtain Oxygen

Fill in the blank to complete each statement.

1. All animals need a constant supply of _____.

2. Earthworms use their _____ for gas exchange.

3. Carbon dioxide tends to _____ out of animal cells.

4. Extra _____ make the lungs of mammals very efficient.

5. Cellular _____ is the process by which cells release the energy in digested food molecules.

If the statement is true, write *true*. If the statement is false, change the underlined word or words to make the statement true.

6. _____ <u>All</u> animals breathe.

7. _____ <u>Gills</u> are respiratory structures located inside the body where they can stay moist.

8. _____ Because cells make carbon dioxide in cellular respiration, the concentration of carbon dioxide inside cells is usually <u>greater</u> than it is outside cells.

9. _____ <u>Gills</u> are structures where gases are exchanged between air and blood.

10. _____ <u>All</u> animals that live in water have gills.

How Animals Obtain Oxygen

Answer Key

After the Inquiry Warm-Up

1. Students should show that the fish's mouth and gill flaps open at the same time.

2. Students should indicate that water is flowing into the fish's mouth and passing back out through the gills.

3. Answers will vary.

4. I would fill several bowls with water at slightly different temperatures. I would place the fish in each bowl, allow it time to get used to the water, and count how many times its gills open per minute. Then I would compare my data to see if the fish's breathing rate consistently increased or decreased as the water temperature increased or decreased.

Key Concept Summaries

Like all animals, a mammal needs oxygen for cellular respiration, a process in which every body cell uses oxygen to release energy from digested food molecules. A mammal gets oxygen by breathing air into its lungs. Inside cells in the lung, gases are exchanged between the air and blood through the process of diffusion. Oxygen moves into the blood to be used by all the body's cells and carbon dioxide moves into the lungs to be exhaled.

Review and Reinforce

1. Cellular respiration is the process in which all animal cells use oxygen to release energy from digested food molecules. Breathing is the process some animals use to take oxygen into their bodies.

2. by diffusion across cell membranes

3. Cellular respiration usually leaves higher levels of carbon dioxide inside cells than outside. During diffusion, particles move from an area of higher concentration to an area of lower concentration.

4. how complex it is and where it lives

5. A mammal's lungs have more pockets and folds, which increase their surface area. Greater surface area enables more gas exchange.

6. d   7. a   8. c
9. e   10. b

Enrich

1. mammals, birds, reptiles, adult amphibians

2. Amphibians are born and reproduce in water and water keeps their skin moist, which is necessary for breathing.

3. Amphibians start out living in water and then live on land as adults. They first breathe through gills and then through lungs and moist skin.

4. Amphibian larvae use gills to obtain oxygen from the water they live in. During metamorphosis, they lose their gills and develop lungs. Their skin remains moist to allow them to receive oxygen from air.

Lesson Quiz

1. oxygen   2. skin
3. diffuse   4. pockets (or folds)
5. respiration   6. Some
7. Lungs   8. true
9. Lungs   10. Most

Place the outside corner, the corner away from the dotted line, in the corner of your copy machine to copy onto letter-size paper.

Circulation and Excretion

Blended Path Active learning using Student Edition, Inquiry Path, and Digital Path

Lesson Pacing: 2–3 periods or 1–1½ blocks

🕐 **SHORT ON TIME?** To do this lesson in approximately half the time, do the Activate Prior Knowledge activity on page 224. A discussion of the Key Concepts on pages 225, 228, and 231 will familiarize students with the lesson content. Explore the Big Q by using the photograph of a bear eating a fish in Figure 6 to discuss how animals get and use energy. Have students do the Real-World Inquiry and the Quick Labs. The rest of the lesson can be completed by students independently.

> **Preference Navigator,** in the online Planning tools, allows you to customize *Interactive Science* to your own teaching style. You can also edit lesson plans by selecting the Lesson Planner option.
>
> **Digital Teacher's Edition** allows you to access your Teacher's Edition and Resource online.

Lesson Vocabulary

- circulatory system
- heart
- open circulatory system
- closed circulatory system
- capillary
- atrium
- ventride
- excretory system
- kidney
- urine

Content Refresher

Professional Development Note

Open and Closed Circulatory Systems In open circulatory systems, a heart pumps blood into short blood vessels that empty into open spaces. In these low-pressure systems, the blood percolates along, delivering oxygen and nutrients and collecting wastes, until the cavities narrow into vessels that direct the blood back to the heart. In closed systems, blood remains within vessels, and all exchanges are carried out through the capillary walls. Blood pressure is generally much higher in closed systems.

The kind of circulatory system that an animal has generally relates to its oxygen demands. If the demands are low, the animal is probably sedentary or moves slowly and a low-pressure, more sluggish flow of blood is sufficient. If the oxygen demands are high and the animal is very active, it often has the oxygen-efficient, high-pressure closed system. But there are exceptions to these generalizations.

Most vertebrates are active animals. So, they have closed circulatory systems. There is no clear pattern in invertebrates. Many have open systems and are comparatively sluggish, but others with open systems, including insects, are quite active. Some slow-moving invertebrates, such as segmented worms, have closed systems.

LESSON OBJECTIVES

🔑 Describe the two types of circulatory systems.

🔑 Explain how closed circulatory systems differ among vertebrates.

🔑 Compare how different animals get rid of waste products.

ENGAGE AND EXPLORE

Teach this lesson using a variety of resources. Begin by reading **My Planet Diary** as a class. Have students discuss the heart's role in circulation. Then have students do the **Inquiry Warm-Up activity.** Students will model the one-loop circulatory system found in fishes and the exchange of gases in a fish's body. The **After the Inquiry Warm-Up worksheet** sets up a discussion about the exchange of gases in a fish's body. Have volunteers share their answers to question 4, telling from where the fish's gills get oxygen.

EXPLAIN AND ELABORATE

Teach Key Concepts by explaining the two types of circulatory systems and the parts of a circulatory system. **Lead a Discussion** about an open circulatory system. Then **Lead a Discussion** about a closed circulatory system.

Teach Key Concepts by pointing out that closed circulatory systems can be further classified according to how the blood circulates: in a single loop or in a double-loop. **Lead a Discussion** about single-loop circulation. Then **Lead a Discussion** about double-loop circulation.

Teach Key Concepts by explaining the structures animals have to remove wastes. **Lead a Discussion** about how the structures of some excretory systems also control the water level in the animals' bodies. Have students practice the inquiry skill in the **Apply It activity. Lead a Discussion** explaining that animals use energy to perform their functions. **Explore the Big Q** by using the photograph of a bear eating a fish in **Figure 6** to discuss how animals get and use energy. **Answer the Big Q** by leading a class discussion about how animals get and use energy.

Hand out the **Key Concept Summaries** as a review of each part of the lesson. Students can also use the online **Vocab Flash Cards** to review key terms.

EVALUATE

Have students take the **Lesson Quiz.** For an alternate assessment, see the *ExamView*® Computer Test Generator, Progress Monitoring Assessments, or SuccessTracker™.

(ELL) Support

1 Content and Language

Have students continue adding the terms to their vocabulary notebook or science journal. Suggest that they use their own words to define the terms and incorporate visuals whenever possible

Lab zone Inquiry Path
Hands-on learning in the Lab zone

ENGAGE AND EXPLORE

To teach this lesson with an emphasis on inquiry, begin with the **Inquiry Warm-Up activity.** Students will model the one-loop circulatory system found in fishes and the exchange of gases in a fish's body. The **After the Inquiry Warm-Up worksheet** sets up a discussion about the exchange of gases in a fish's body. Have volunteers share their answers to question 4, telling from where the fish's gills get oxygen.

EXPLAIN AND ELABORATE

Focus on the **Inquiry Skill** for the lesson. Remind students that when you draw conclusions, you use what you have learned or read to make a statement about your observations. What conclusion could be drawn about the function of the fish's gills in the **Inquiry Warm-Up activity?** (Sample: Since all animals need oxygen to survive, I was able to draw the conclusion that the fish used its gills to get oxygen from the water that passes over them.) Have students do the **Quick Lab** using plastic tubing, a pump, and a plastic container to model an open circulatory system.

Have students do the **Quick Lab** to model a double-loop circulatory system.

Review the importance of removing wastes from animals before beginning the **Apply It activity. Explore the Big Q** by using the photograph of a bear eating a fish in **Figure 6** to discuss how animals get and use energy. Have students do the **Quick Lab** modeling the functions of a kidney. **Answer the Big Q** by leading a class discussion about how animals get and use energy. Students can use the online **Vocab Flash Cards** to review key terms.

EVALUATE

Have students take the **Lesson Quiz.** For an alternate assessment, see the *ExamView®* Computer Test Generator, Progress Monitoring Assessments, or SuccessTracker™.

Digital Path
Online learning at my science online.com

ENGAGE AND EXPLORE

Teach this lesson using digital resources. Begin by having students learn more and explore real-world connections to circulatory systems at **My Planet Diary** online. Have them access the Chapter Resources to find the **Unlock the Big Question activity.** There they can answer the questions and refine their responses as they continue through the lesson. You can re-assign the activity and have students submit their work so you can track their progress.

EXPLAIN AND ELABORATE

Students reading above, at, or below the lexile measure of this lesson can access basic content readings at their level at **My Reading Web.** Encourage students to use the online **Vocab Flash Cards** to preview key terms. Have students do the **Quick Lab** using plastic tubing, a pump, and a plastic container to model an open circulatory system.

Have students do the **Quick Lab** to model a double-loop circulatory system. Use the **Interactive Art activity** online to allow students to compare and contrast the circulatory systems found in fishes, adult amphibians, and birds.

Assign the **Apply It activity** online and have students submit their work to you. **Explore the Big Q** by using the photograph of a bear eating a fish in **Figure 6** to discuss how animals get and use energy. Have students do the **Quick Lab,** modeling the functions of a kidney. **Answer the Big Q** by leading a class discussion about how animals get and use energy. The **Key Concept Summaries** online allow students to read a summary and see an image associated with each part of the lesson. Online remediation is available at **My Science Coach.**

EVALUATE

Have students take the **Lesson Quiz.** For an alternate assessment, see the *ExamView®* Computer Test Generator, Progress Monitoring Assessments, or SuccessTracker™.

2 Frontload the Lesson
Discuss the illustration on page 228. Have students identify how the artist demonstrated the location of the heart in the fish's body. Then look at Figure 5. Discuss why the artist uses arrows in the drawings of the circulatory systems. Have students trace the direction of circulation in each system as you describe it.

3 Comprehensible Input
Have students use an outline to better understand the information in this lesson. Have them use the blue and red heads to help organize.

4 Language Production
Pair or group students with varied language abilities to complete labs collaboratively for language practice. Have each student copy the completed written lab for personal reference.

5 Assess Understanding
Have students keep a content area log for this lesson using a two-column format with the headings "What I Understand" and "What I Don't Understand." Follow up so that students can move items from the "Don't Understand" to the "Understand" column.

Circulation and Excretion

Establish Learning Objectives

After this lesson, students will be able to:

🔑 Describe the two types of circulatory systems.

🔑 Explain how closed circulatory systems differ among vertebrates.

🔑 Compare how different animals get rid of waste products.

Engage

Activate Prior Knowledge

MY PLANET DIARY Read *Octopus Hearts* with the class. Ask students what a heart looks like. Point out that a heart does not look like the hearts drawn for holidays and greeting cards. Ask: **How many hearts do you have?** *(One)* **Where is your heart located?** *(In the chest)* **What does your heart do?** *(It beats and pumps blood in the body.)*

BIG IDEAS OF SCIENCE REFERENCE LIBRARY 📖
Have students look up the following topic: Octopus.

Explore

Lab Resource: Inquiry Warm-Up 🔬

L2 **GETTING OXYGEN** Students will model the one-loop circulatory system found in fishes and the exchange of gases in a fish's body.

3 Circulation and Excretion

UNLOCK THE BIG ?

🔑 **What Are the Two Types of Circulatory Systems?**

🔑 **How Do Vertebrate Circulatory Systems Differ?**

🔑 **How Do Animals Get Rid of Wastes?**

MY PLANET DIARY

DISCOVERY

Octopus Hearts

How many hearts do you think an octopus has? One? Two? No, it has three! An octopus has one main heart and two smaller hearts, one for each gill. The two smaller hearts pump blood through each gill, where the blood picks up oxygen. The main heart then pumps this oxygen-rich blood through the rest of the body of the octopus. To make things even stranger, all this blood pumping through the octopus is not red, it is blue!

Answer the questions below.

1. What is the function of the octopus's two smaller hearts?

   They pump blood through the gills, which enables the octopus to obtain oxygen.

2. What other facts do you know about an octopus?

   Sample: It has eight arms and it squirts ink.

▶ PLANET DIARY Go to **Planet Diary** to learn more about circulation and excretion.

🔬 Lab zone Do the Inquiry Warm-Up *Getting Oxygen.*

SUPPORT ALL READERS

Prior Exposure to Content: Many students may have misconceptions on this topic

Academic Vocabulary: *conclusions, summarize*

Science Vocabulary: *heart, capillary, atrium, ventricle, kidney*

Concept Level: Generally appropriate for most students in this grade

Preteach With: My Planet Diary "Octopus Hearts" and Figure 2 activity

Go to **My Reading Web** to access leveled readings that provide a foundation for the content.

my science online.com

Vocabulary
- circulatory system • heart • open circulatory system • closed circulatory system • capillary • atrium • ventricle • excretory system • kidney • urine

Skills
- ⟳ Reading: Summarize
- △ Inquiry: Draw Conclusions

What Are the Two Types of Circulatory Systems?

You have probably seen ants coming and going from their nest. Did you know that ants work as a team? Each ant has a specific job. While worker ants are out searching for food, other ants are protecting the nest. A soldier ant may even put its head in the nest's opening to stop enemies from entering. By working together, these ants are able to get food and stay safe. What teamwork!

Getting materials to an animal's cells and taking away wastes also takes teamwork. The circulatory system must work with both the digestive and respiratory systems to do so. The **circulatory system** transports needed materials to cells and takes away wastes.

🔑 **Complex animals have one of two types of circulatory systems: open or closed.** Both types of systems include blood, vessels, and a heart. A **heart** is a hollow, muscular structure that pumps blood through vessels. Blood vessels are a connected network of tubes that carries blood. Blood transports digested food from the digestive system and oxygen from the respiratory system to the cells. In addition, blood carries carbon dioxide and other wastes from cells to the organs that eliminate them from the body.

Ants working together

⟳ **Summarize** On the clipboard, write in your own words how the digestive, respiratory, and circulatory systems work as a team.

Sample: The digestive system digests food. The respiratory system exchanges gases. The circulatory system transports digested food and oxygen to body cells and carries carbon dioxide and other wastes to the respiratory structures and other organs for elimination.

225

LESSON 6.3

Explain

Introduce Vocabulary

Explain to students that they may encounter the word *atrium* when studying buildings. An atrium is an open chamber that is connected to passageways. In science, an *atrium* is a chamber that makes up part of the heart.

Teach Key Concepts 🔑

Explain to students that circulatory systems can be described as open or closed. Ask: **What is the function of a circulatory system?** *(To transport needed materials to cells and take away wastes)* **What needed materials are carried to cells?** *(Oxygen and nutrients)* **What are the parts of a circulatory system?** *(Blood, vessels, and a heart)* **What is a heart?** *(A hollow, muscular structure that pumps blood through vessels)* **What are blood vessels?** *(A network of tubes through which blood flows)* **What other systems work with the circulatory system to provide cells with needed materials and take away wastes?** *(Digestive system and respiratory system)*

⟳ **Summarize** Tell students that when they summarize, they briefly restate the main ideas of what they have read. In addition to the main ideas, a summary can contain the most important supporting details. Students can use their summaries to review what they have learned.

My Planet Diary provides an opportunity for students to explore real-world connections to circulatory systems in animals.

my science ONLINE.COM ▶ | Animal Circulatory Systems

E L L Support

1 Content and Language
Explain that the term *circulatory* comes from the Latin word *circulus,* meaning "circle or ring." Then, explain that *excretory* comes from the Latin word *cernere,* meaning "to sift," and the prefix *ex-,* meaning "out."

2 Frontload the Lesson
Ask volunteers to use their own words to explain what the circulatory and excretory systems do. Getting students

to speculate about what would happen if either system were missing will give students another way to think about its function.

3 Comprehensible Input
Invite groups to work on large, colorful illustrations showing the similarities and differences between open and closed circulatory systems. Have each group choose a different animal as the basis for its diagram.

Explain

Lead a Discussion

OPEN SYSTEMS Point out that in some circulatory systems, blood is not always found in vessels. Ask: **What pumps the blood in an open circulatory system?** *(One or more hearts)* **Where does the blood flow?** *(In spaces around the organs)* **How does oxygen get into cells?** *(Diffusion)* **What kinds of animals have open circulatory systems?** *(Arthropods, mollusks, and many other invertebrates)*

Teach With Visuals

Tell students to look at **Figure 1.** Ask: **What do the grasshopper's hearts do?** *(They pump blood throughout the body.)* **Where does blood go after it leaves the hearts?** *(Around organs)* **What happens to the blood after it exchanges materials with cells?** *(It returns to the hearts.)*

Elaborate

21st Century Learning

CRITICAL THINKING Hold an inflated balloon in front of the class. Gently push on one part of the balloon. Explain to students that when you push on the balloon you increase the pressure of the air inside. If the balloon pops, the air spreads throughout the room. The pressure decreases because the air is no longer held in the balloon. Ask: **Do you think the pressure of the fluid in an open circulatory system is high or low?** *(Low because there is no pressure after it leaves the hearts)* **Why do you think that small animals, such as insects, have an open circulatory system, but large animals, such as horses, do not?** *(In a small animal, the blood does not have to travel far to get back to the heart, so the low pressure is not a problem. In a larger animal, more pressure is needed to push blood back to the heart.)*

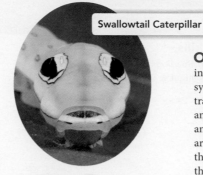

Swallowtail Caterpillar

did you know?

Did you know that many insects have green blood? Their blood is clear or yellowish green because of the food they eat, usually plants. Unlike your blood, insect blood does not contain the protein that makes it red.

Open Circulatory Systems Many invertebrates, including arthropods and most mollusks, have open circulatory systems. In an **open circulatory system,** blood does not always travel inside vessels. One or more hearts pump blood to the head and organs. Then the blood flows into the spaces around the animal's organs. There, food particles, oxygen, water, and wastes are exchanged between the blood and cells directly. Eventually, the blood moves back into the heart or hearts to be pumped out to the body again. You can see this type of circulatory system in the grasshopper shown in **Figure 1.**

FIGURE 1

An Open Circulatory System

Grasshoppers have several hearts that pump blood into short vessels. These vessels open into the body spaces containing the internal organs. The blood washes over the organs and eventually returns to the hearts.

✎ **Sequence** In the graphic organizer, describe the flow of blood in the grasshopper's body. Start with blood in the hearts.

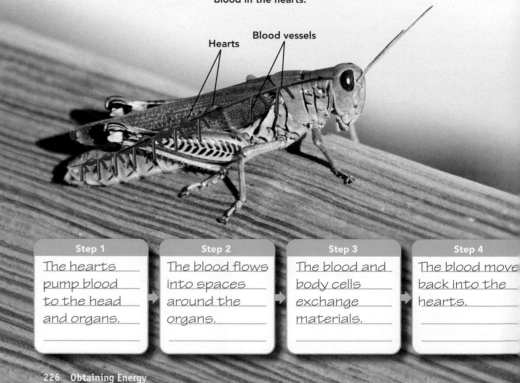

Hearts

Blood vessels

Step 1	Step 2	Step 3	Step 4
The hearts pump blood to the head and organs.	The blood flows into spaces around the organs.	The blood and body cells exchange materials.	The blood move back into the hearts.

226 Obtaining Energy

Closed Circulatory Systems Segmented worms, some mollusks, and all vertebrates have closed circulatory systems. In a **closed circulatory system,** blood always stays inside vessels and the heart. Large vessels lead away from the heart to the organs. In the organs, vessels called capillaries surround cells. **Capillaries** are tiny, thin-walled blood vessels where the blood and body cells exchange substances. Digested food molecules and oxygen in the blood pass through the capillary walls into the cells. At the same time, carbon dioxide and other wastes pass from the cells into the capillaries. The capillaries merge and form large vessels that lead back to the heart. You can see an earthworm's closed circulatory system in **Figure 2.**

CHALLENGE Why is an earthworm's circulatory system more efficient than that of an insect?

Sample: Capillaries surround the organs, which allows more oxygen to reach the cells.

FIGURE 2 ···

A Closed Circulatory System
An earthworm's body is divided into more than 100 segments. The earthworm's circulatory system runs through all of the segments.

✎ **Compare and Contrast** On the notebook page, write how open and closed circulatory systems are alike and different.

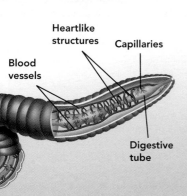

Heartlike structures

Capillaries

Blood vessels

Digestive tube

Both systems include a heart and blood. However, blood stays inside vessels in a closed circulatory system but not in an open system.

Lab zone Do the Quick Lab *Comparing Circulatory Systems.*

Assess Your Understanding

1a. Describe What are the parts of a circulatory system?
The parts are blood, vessels, and a heart.

b. Draw Conclusions What happens in a circulatory system if the heart stops functioning?
Sample: Blood stops moving through the system.

got it? ···

○ **I get it!** Now I know that the two types of circulatory systems are _open and closed_ _systems._

○ **I need extra help with** _See TE note._

Go to **MY SCIENCE** 💬 **COACH** online for help with this subject.

227

Differentiated Instruction

L3 Sequence Blood Flow Have students draw flowcharts showing the path of blood in both open and closed circulatory systems. Students should use arrows to show where the blood

flows. For example, the diagram should show where blood flows after it leaves the heart. Encourage students to be creative in their diagrams.

Explain ————————
Lead a Discussion

CLOSED SYSTEMS Explain that in a closed circulatory system, blood always stays inside vessels or the heart. Ask: **What role do capillaries play in closed circulatory systems?** *(They are thin vessels across which diffusion takes place.)* **Does blood have more oxygen when it enters a capillary in a muscle or when it leaves?** *(When it enters)*

Teach With Visuals

Tell students to look at **Figure 2.** Ask: **What kind of circulatory system does an earthworm have?** *(Closed)* **How many main blood vessels can you see?** *(Two, running the length of the worm's body.)* **What happens to blood vessels as they approach the digestive tube?** *(Sample: They branch into smaller vessels.)* **What are the smallest blood vessels called?** *(Capillaries)* **Why do you think there are many capillaries in the digestive tube?** *(Food enters the blood through capillaries, so many capillaries are needed to pick up digested food molecules from the food tube.)*

Elaborate ————————
Lab Resource: Quick Lab

L1 COMPARING CIRCULATORY SYSTEMS Students will use plastic tubing, a pump, and a plastic container to model an open circulatory system.

Evaluate ————————
Assess Your Understanding

After students answer the questions, have them evaluate their understanding by completing the appropriate sentence.

RTI Response to Intervention

1a. If students cannot identify the parts of a circulatory system, **then** help them review the parts.

b. If students need help predicting what would happen if the heart stops functioning, **then** ask volunteers to describe the function of the heart.

MY SCIENCE 💬 **COACH** Have students go online for help in understanding circulatory systems.

Explain

Teach Key Concepts

Point out that closed circulatory systems can be further classified according to how the blood circulates. Ask: **What are the two types of closed circulatory systems?** *(Single loop and double-loop)* **What do both types have in common?** *(They rely on a heart to pump blood. The blood is always contained in the heart or blood vessels.)* **What are two types of chambers in the heart?** *(Atrium and ventricle)* **How are the two chambers different?** *(An atrium receives blood from the body, whereas a ventricle pumps blood out to the body.)*

Teach With Visuals

Tell students to look at **Figure 3.** Point out the arrows in the highlighted portion of the diagram. Ask: **Where does blood enter the heart?** *(Atrium)* **From where does leave the heart?** *(Ventricle)* **Where does blood go after it leaves the heart?** *(It travels to the cells of the body.)* Tell students that the small bulge to the right of the atrium in the diagram is called the *sinus venosus.* It is part of the fish's heart, but it is not a heart chamber. Unlike the atrium and ventricle, it does not have muscle tissue and it does not contract.

Summarize Tell students that when they summarize, they briefly restate the main ideas of what they have read in their own words. In addition to the main ideas, a summary can contain the most important supporting details. However, a summary must be short and concise.

How Do Vertebrate Circulatory Systems Differ?

All vertebrates have closed circulatory systems. However, these circulatory systems are not all the same. There are two patterns for circulating blood in a closed circulatory system. **Some closed systems have a single-loop circulation pattern. Others have a double-loop circulation pattern.**

Both circulation patterns rely on a heart to pump blood through the body. All vertebrate hearts have two types of hollow areas called chambers. One type of chamber is called an atrium (plural *atria*). An **atrium** receives blood from the body. The other type of chamber is called a ventricle. A **ventricle** receives blood from an atrium and pumps it to the body. You can see the two chambers of fish's heart in **Figure 3.**

Vocabulary Suffixes The suffix *-tion* means "process of." Use this meaning to write a definition of *circulation* in your own words.

Sample: Circulation means the process of moving or transporting.

FIGURE 3 ·······························

Heart Chambers

In fishes, the heart has two chambers—one atrium and one ventricle.

Summarize In the boxes, write the function of each type of heart chamber.

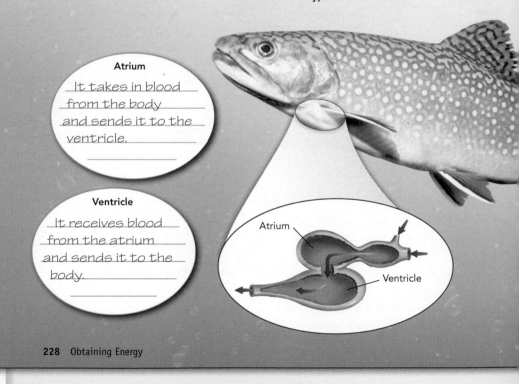

Atrium

It takes in blood from the body and sends it to the ventricle.

Ventricle

It receives blood from the atrium and sends it to the body.

Atrium

Ventricle

A Single-Loop Pattern

Sharks, some of Earth's most fearsome hunters, have a single-loop circulation pattern, as do most vertebrates with gills. A single-loop circulation pattern forces blood around an animal's body in one direction. <u>The ventricle of a two-chambered heart pumps blood to capillaries in the gills.</u> Here, carbon dioxide diffuses out of the blood and oxygen diffuses into the blood. <u>The oxygen-rich blood moves into vessels that lead to capillaries in the animal's organs.</u> There, oxygen diffuses from the blood into the cells, and waste products diffuse from the cells into the blood. <u>The oxygen-poor blood flows from the organs back to the heart's atrium.</u> <u>Then the blood moves from the atrium to the ventricle, completing the pattern.</u> The pattern is shown in **Figure 4.**

1 2 3 4

> ✏️ **Sequence** Underline the text that describes the steps involved in blood flow in a single-loop pattern. Number the steps.

FIGURE 4

A Single-Loop Pattern

Water flows into the mouth of this fish and then over its gills. Oxygen moves into the blood and is delivered to the cells of the fish. Blood is pumped around the body in one direction.

✏️ **Interpret Diagrams** Label the atrium and ventricle. In the boxes, write what happens to oxygen and carbon dioxide in the gills and body organs.

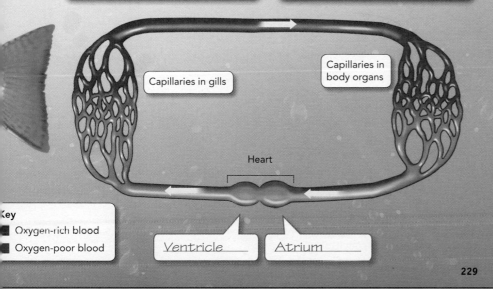

Gills
Oxygen diffuses into the blood and carbon dioxide diffuses out.

Body Organs
Oxygen diffuses into cells and carbon dioxide diffuses into the blood.

Capillaries in gills

Capillaries in body organs

Heart

Key
- Oxygen-rich blood
- Oxygen-poor blood

Ventricle   Atrium

229

Explain

Lead a Discussion

SINGLE LOOP CIRCULATION Explain that a single-loop circulation pattern moves blood in one direction around the body. Ask: **When would blood be oxygen-poor?** (After it has transferred its oxygen to cells.) **Where does oxygen-poor blood go after it has transferred oxygen to cells?** (To the gills) **What happens to the blood in the gills?** (It picks up oxygen.) **Where does the blood go next?** (To all parts of the body)

Teach With Visuals

Tell students to look at **Figure 4.** Trace the parts of the diagram with students. Ask: **What exchange of materials takes place in the gills?** (Oxygen diffuses into blood and carbon dioxide diffuses out.) **What exchange of materials takes place at body organs?** (Oxygen diffuses out of blood and carbon dioxide diffuses in.) **How many chambers does the heart have?** (Two) **What part of the heart pumps blood to the gills?** (Ventricle) **What part of the heart takes blood from the organs?** (Atrium)

Elaborate

Address Misconceptions

L1 **BLUE BLOOD** Point out to students that blood is never actually blue. Blood is described as dark red or bright red. Dark red blood sometimes looks blue when it is seen through the vessels it travels in. Ask: **Why does blood take on different appearances?** (It depends on the amount of oxygen it contains.) **When might blood be described as dark in color?** (When it is low in oxygen.) **What causes blood to appear bright red?** (It is rich in oxygen.)

Differentiated Instruction

L1 **Trace a Loop** Ask students to reread the paragraph describing a single-loop pattern. Have students write the sentences describing the flow of blood through the loop. They should copy the sentence, but write them as a numbered list that shows the sequence of events. As an alternative, write the series of steps out of order on the board. Work with students to sequence the steps in their correct order.

Explain

Lead a Discussion

DOUBLE LOOP CIRCULATION Explain that many animals have a double-loop circulatory system. Ask: **What are the two loops of this type of system?** *(One loop is between the heart and the lungs. The other loop is between the heart and the body.)* **Why must hearts in these systems have more than one atrium?** *(One atrium receives blood from the lungs and the other atrium receives blood from the body.)* **How is the blood that enters each atrium different?** *(Blood is rich in oxygen when it returns from the lungs and poor in oxygen when it returns from the body.)*

Teach With Visuals

Tell students to look at **Figure 5.** Begin by tracing the flow of blood in the three-chambered heart. Ask: **From which part of the heart does blood flow to the lungs?** *(Ventricle)* **To where does blood return from the lungs?** *(Left atrium)* **What happens in the lungs?** *(Oxygen is transferred to blood and carbon dioxide is transferred out of blood.)* Remind students that a salamander can exchange gases through its skin, so some of the blood returning to the heart from the body is oxygen rich. Then, trace the flow of blood in the four-chambered heart. **From which part of the heart does blood flow to the lungs?** *(Right ventricle)* **To where does blood return from the lungs?** *(Left atrium)* **From which part of the heart is blood pumped to the body?** *(Left ventricle)* **To which part of the heart does blood return from the body?** *(Right atrium)* **What happens in the lungs?** *(Oxygen is transferred to blood and carbon dioxide is transferred out of blood.)*

Lab Resource: Quick Lab Lab°

L2 DOUBLE-LOOP CIRCULATION Students will model a double-loop circulatory system.

Evaluate

Assess Your Understanding

Have students evaluate their understanding by completing the appropriate sentence.

RTI Response to Intervention

If students need help describing the two types of circulatory systems, **then** have volunteers use the visuals to summarize an example of each.

MY SCIENCE **s** **COACH** Have students go online for help in understanding circulatory systems.

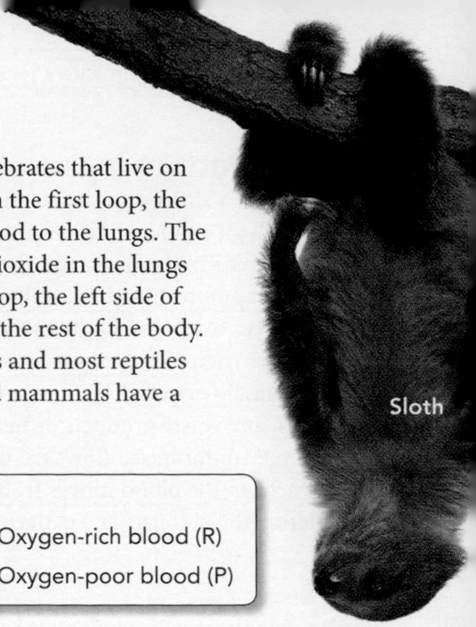

A Double-Loop Pattern Most vertebrates that live on land have a double-loop circulation pattern. In the first loop, the right side of the heart pumps oxygen-poor blood to the lungs. The blood picks up oxygen and drops off carbon dioxide in the lungs and then returns to the heart. In the second loop, the left side of the heart pumps the oxygen-rich blood out to the rest of the body. In **Figure 5,** you can see that adult amphibians and most reptiles have a three-chambered heart, while birds and mammals have a four-chambered heart.

Sloth

FIGURE 5 ·················

▶ INTERACTIVE ART **A Double-Loop Pattern**

✎ **Classify** Look at the key. On the lines, write an *R* or a *P* to describe the type of blood in each heart chamber. If blood is mixed, use both letters. The first one is done for you.

Key
- ■ Oxygen-rich blood (R)
- ■ Oxygen-poor blood (P)

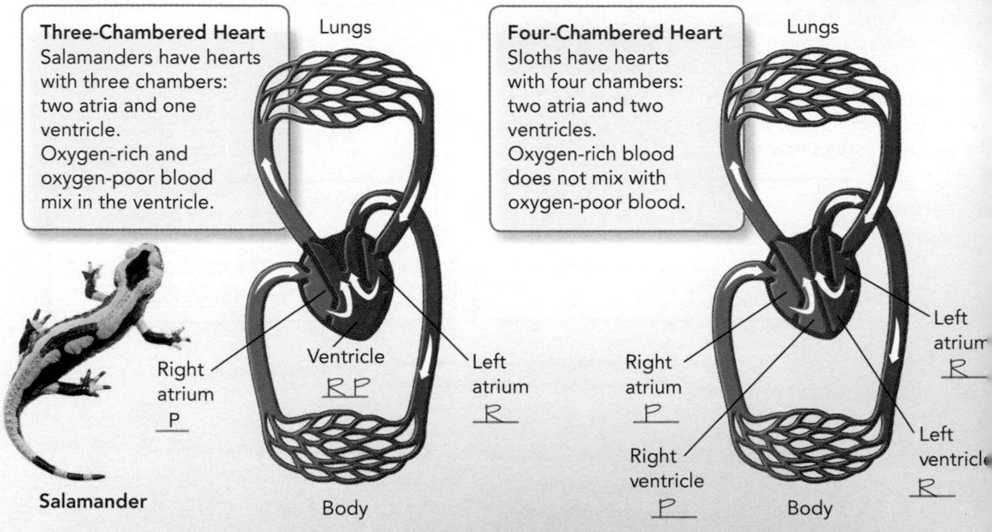

Three-Chambered Heart
Salamanders have hearts with three chambers: two atria and one ventricle. Oxygen-rich and oxygen-poor blood mix in the ventricle.

Lungs

Salamander

Right atrium **P**

Ventricle **R P**

Left atrium **R**

Body

Four-Chambered Heart
Sloths have hearts with four chambers: two atria and two ventricles. Oxygen-rich blood does not mix with oxygen-poor blood.

Lungs

Right atrium **P**

Right ventricle **P**

Left atrium **R**

Left ventricle **R**

Body

 Do the Quick Lab *Double-Loop Circulation.*

🔑 **Assess Your Understanding**

got**it?**

○ **I get it!** Now I know that vertebrate circulatory systems differ because they have either a single-loop or a double-loop pattern.

○ I need extra help with See TE note.

Go to **MY SCIENCE** **s** **COACH** online for help with this subject.

Interactive Art allows students to compare and contrast the circulatory systems found in fishes, adult amphibians, and birds.

MY SCIENCE online.com ▷ | Vertebrate Circulatory Systems |

How Do Animals Get Rid of Wastes?

Many animals have specialized structures to get rid of wastes. As you know, most animals use their respiratory systems to take in oxygen and to get rid of carbon dioxide. However, cells produce other wastes that the respiratory system cannot eliminate. For example, breaking down certain foods during cellular respiration produces wastes that contain nitrogen. Some animals also have excess water or salt in their bodies, depending on where they live or what they eat. For example, planarians live in fresh water and have excess water in their cells. Fishes that live in oceans have excess salt in their cells.

In animals, the **excretory system** is the system that rids a body of nitrogen-containing wastes, and excess salt and water. Depending on the animal, this system includes different structures. In vertebrates, **kidneys** are the main organs that filter nitrogen-containing wastes from the blood. They produce **urine**, a watery fluid that holds those wastes.

apply it!

A marine iguana spends hours feeding in ocean water every day. It has a specialized structure in its nose that helps it "sneeze out" the excess salt that gets into its body.

① Identify What other wastes does a marine iguana need to get rid of?

Sample: It needs to get rid of
nitrogen-containing wastes and
carbon dioxide.

② △ Draw Conclusions Look at the marine iguana. What do you think the white crusty material is on its head? Explain.

It is excess salt because it
sneezes salt out of its nose.

231

Differentiated Instruction

L1 Excretory System Ask students to explain in their own words why animals need excretory systems. Students should practice their explanations with a partner. Then, once they have refined it, students can present their explanations to the class. Challenge students to explain how the excretory system is related to the circulatory system.

L3 Kidneys Ask students to find out how the kidneys act as filters. Tell them to find out what structures inside kidneys increase surface area. Then, have students create a diagram and present their findings to the class.

Explain

Teach Key Concepts 🔑

Remind students that carbon dioxide and other wastes are produced during cellular respiration. If those wastes are not removed, they will prevent the cells and organs from working properly. Ask: **What system removes wastes that contain nitrogen, salt, and water?** (Excretory system) **What organs filter nitrogen-containing wastes from the blood of vertebrates?** (Kidneys) **What do kidneys produce to remove the filtered wastes?** (Urine)

Lead a Discussion

WATER The structures of some excretory systems also control the water level in the body. Ask: **How will the amount of urine produced be affected if an animal drinks an excess of water?** (More urine will be produced.) **How will the amount of urine produced be affected if an animal performs physical activity and loses water by sweating or panting?** (Less urine will be produced.) **How is skin involved in the excretory system?** (Water and salts are removed through sweating.)

Elaborate

Apply It!

L1 Review the importance of removing wastes from animals before beginning the activity.

△ Draw Conclusions Explain to students that when you draw conclusions, you use what you have learned or read to make a statement about your observations.

Digital Lesson: Assign the *Apply It* activity online and have students submit their work to you.

my science online | Animal Excretory Systems

231

Lead a Discussion

ENERGY Remind students that animals get and use energy. Explain that energy is the ability to do work or cause change. Animals require energy to perform all of their functions—walking, running, jumping, and even yawning. Direct students' attention to **Figure 6.** Ask: **How does energy get into the fish's body?** *(The fish ate other food, such as other fishes.)* **Where did those fish get energy?** *(At some point, they got it from plants that got energy from the sun.)* **Through what process does the bear release energy from the fish's body?** *(Cellular respiration)* **What gas is needed for this process and what gas is released as waste from it?** *(Oxygen is needed and carbon dioxide is released as waste.)* **What will happen if the bear cannot find enough food to eat?** *(It will not have enough energy to perform its functions.)*

Elaborate

21st Century Learning

L1 CREATIVITY Ask students to imagine they are a particle of oxygen in the air that the bear breathes in. Write a short story describing the path the oxygen takes in the bear's body.

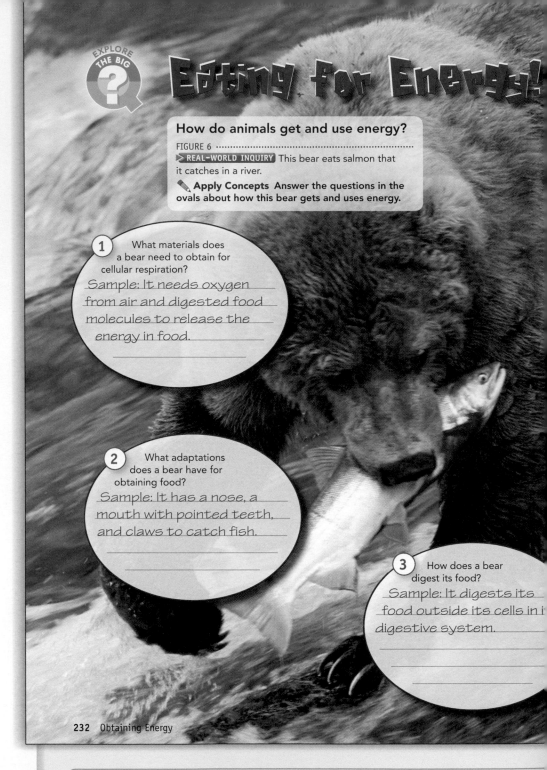

EXPLORE THE BIG ?

Eating for Energy!

How do animals get and use energy?

FIGURE 6 ·······························

> REAL-WORLD INQUIRY This bear eats salmon that it catches in a river.

✎ **Apply Concepts** Answer the questions in the ovals about how this bear gets and uses energy.

1 What materials does a bear need to obtain for cellular respiration?
Sample: It needs oxygen from air and digested food molecules to release the energy in food.

2 What adaptations does a bear have for obtaining food?
Sample: It has a nose, a mouth with pointed teeth, and claws to catch fish.

3 How does a bear digest its food?
Sample: It digests its food outside its cells in i digestive system.

232 Obtaining Energy

Real-World Inquiry allows students to explore how frogs obtain energy and oxygen very differently over their life cycles.

my science online.com | **Animal Excretory Systems**

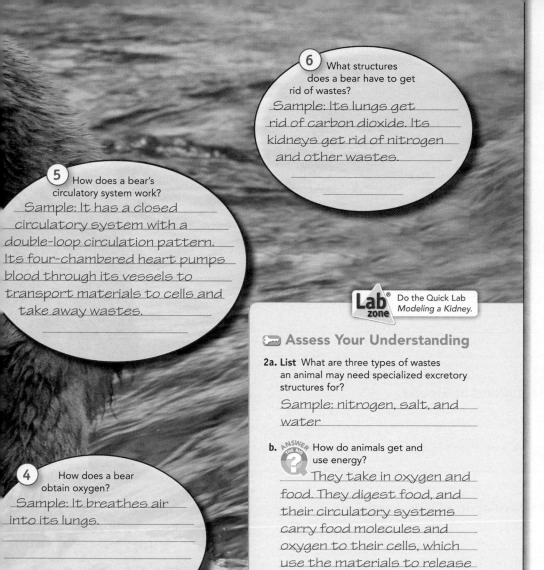

6 What structures does a bear have to get rid of wastes?

Sample: Its lungs get rid of carbon dioxide. Its kidneys get rid of nitrogen and other wastes.

5 How does a bear's circulatory system work?

Sample: It has a closed circulatory system with a double-loop circulation pattern. Its four-chambered heart pumps blood through its vessels to transport materials to cells and take away wastes.

4 How does a bear obtain oxygen?

Sample: It breathes air into its lungs.

Lab zone Do the Quick Lab Modeling a Kidney.

Assess Your Understanding

2a. List What are three types of wastes an animal may need specialized excretory structures for?

Sample: nitrogen, salt, and water

b. ANSWER THE BIG **?** How do animals get and use energy?

They take in oxygen and food. They digest food, and their circulatory systems carry food molecules and oxygen to their cells, which use the materials to release the food's energy.

got it? ....

○ I get it! Now I know that to get rid of wastes animals have __specialized structures.__

○ I need extra help with __See TE note.__

Go to MY SCIENCE ⓢ COACH online for help with this subject.

233

Explore the Big Q **?** **UbD**

Discuss with students the scene shown in **Figure 6.** Ask: **What animals do you see?** *(A bear and a fish.)* **What is the bear doing and why?** *(It is eating the fish to get energy.)* **What happens to the fish after the bear swallows it?** *(It is broken down into smaller molecules that can diffuse into the bear's blood.)* **What does the bear need in order to release the energy stored in the fish?** *(Oxygen)* **Where does the bear get this gas?** *(From the air it breathes in)* **How are gases and nutrients transported throughout the bear's body?** *(Blood in the circulatory system carries oxygen and nutrients to cells, and carries carbon dioxide and other wastes away from cells.)* **What happens to wastes, other than gases, that the bear's cells produce?** *(They are removed by the bear's excretory system.)*

Lab Resource: Quick Lab

L1 **MODELING A KIDNEY** Students will model how the kidneys of a vertebrate work.

Evaluate

Assess Your Understanding

After students answer the questions, have them evaluate their understanding by completing the appropriate sentence.

Answer the Big Q **?** **UbD**

To help students focus on the Big Question, lead a class discussion about how animals get and use energy.

R T I Response to Intervention

2a. If students cannot summarize the three types of waste, **then** list them on the board with input from volunteers.

b. If students have difficulty tying all of the concepts together, **then** work together to make a flowchart to show the path of energy through the body.

MY SCIENCE ⓢ COACH Have students go online for help in understanding how animals get and use energy.

Differentiated Instruction

L1 **Summarize** Ask students to explain the meaning of the word *specialized* as it pertains to the structures in the bear's body. Have students cite examples from this situation and throughout the chapter.

L3 **System Relationships** Have students explain how the bear's respiratory, circulatory, and excretory systems are related. Tell students they can describe the relationship by drawing and labeling a picture, acting it out, writing a paragraph, or in other ways.

Circulation and Excretion

> **Inquiry Warm-Up, *Getting Oxygen***
> In the Inquiry Warm-Up, you used a model to investigate the exchange of gases in a fish's body. Using what you learned from that activity, answer the questions below.

1. **INFER** What did the students in Group C represent?

   _____

   _____

2. **INFER** What did the regular clapping of the students in Group D represent?

   _____

   _____

3. **COMMUNICATE** Draw a diagram to show the circulation of blood and exchange of gases in the model.

4. **USE PRIOR KNOWLEDGE** Where are the fish's gills getting oxygen?

   _____

   _____

Name _____ Date _____ Class _____

Circulation and Excretion

What Are the Two Types of Circulatory Systems?

1a. DESCRIBE What are the parts of a circulatory system? _____

_____

b. DRAW CONCLUSIONS What happens in a circulatory system if the heart

stops functioning? _____

_____

got it? ··

○ **I get it!** Now I know that the two types of circulatory systems are _____

_____

○ **I need extra help with** _____

_____

How Do Vertebrate Circulatory Systems Differ?

got it? ··

○ **I get it!** Now I know that vertebrate circulatory systems differ because _____

_____

○ **I need extra help with** _____

_____

Assess Your Understanding

Circulation and Excretion

> ### How Do Animals Get Rid of Wastes?

2a. **LIST** For what are three types of wastes an animal may need specialized excretory structures? _____

_____

b. **ANSWER** 🅱 How do animals get and use energy? _____

_____

_____

_____

_____

got it? ···

○ **I get it!** Now I know that to get rid of wastes animals have _____

_____

○ **I need extra help with** _____

_____

Circulation and Excretion

What Are the Two Types of Circulatory Systems?

The **circulatory system** transports needed material to cells and takes away wastes. **Complex animals have one of two types of circulatory systems: open or closed.** Both types of systems include blood, vessels, and a heart. A **heart** is a hollow, muscular structure that pumps blood through vessels.

In an **open circulatory system,** blood does not always travel inside vessels. One or more hearts pump blood into the spaces around the organs. There, food particles, oxygen, water, and wastes are exchanged between the blood and cells directly. Eventually, blood returns to the heart or hearts.

In a **closed circulatory system,** blood always stays inside vessels and the heart. Large vessels lead away from the heart to the organs. In the organs, vessels called capillaries surround the cells. **Capillaries** are tiny, thin-walled blood vessels where blood and body cells exchange substances. The capillaries merge and form large vessels that return to the heart.

How Do Vertebrate Circulatory Systems Differ?

Some closed systems have a single-loop circulating pattern. Others have a double-loop circulation pattern. All vertebrate hearts have two types of hollow areas called *chambers*. An **atrium** receives blood from the body. A **ventricle** receives blood from an atrium and pumps it to the body.

Most vertebrates with gills have a single-loop circulation pattern that forces blood around the body in one direction. Most vertebrates that live on land have a double-loop circulation pattern. In the first loop, the right side of the heart pumps oxygen-poor blood to the lungs. There, blood picks up oxygen and then returns to the heart. In the second loop, the left side of the heart pumps the oxygen-rich blood to the rest of the body.

How Do Animals Get Rid of Wastes?

Many animals have specialized structures to get rid of wastes. Cells produce wastes that the respiratory system cannot eliminate. In animals, the **excretory system** is the system that rids a body of nitrogen-containing wastes, and excess salt and water. In vertebrates, **kidneys** are the main organs that filter nitrogen-containing wastes from the blood. They produce **urine,** a watery fluid that holds those wastes.

On a separate sheet of paper, tell whether a salamander has an open or closed circulatory system and what kind of circulation pattern it has. Then explain how the salamander's circulatory system functions.

Circulation and Excretion

Understanding Main Ideas
Answer the following questions on a separate sheet of paper.

1. How does an open circulatory system work?
2. How does a closed circulatory system work?
3. How does a single-loop circulatory pattern work?
4. How does a double-loop circulatory pattern work?
5. Why is a four-chambered heart more efficient than a three-chambered heart?

Building Vocabulary
Fill in the blank to complete each statement.

6. The _____ is a hollow, muscular structure that pumps blood.

7. Nitrogen-containing wastes, and excess salt and water are removed by a vertebrate's _____ system.

8. In the heart, a(n) _____ receives blood from the body.

9. _____ are tiny, thin-walled blood vessels.

10. _____ is a watery fluid that holds wastes.

11. A chamber called a(n) _____ pumps blood to the body.

12. An animal's _____ system transports needed material to cells and takes away wastes.

13. The _____ filters nitrogen-containing wastes from the blood.

Enrich

Circulation and Excretion

> Read the passage below. Then answer the questions that follow in the spaces provided.

Nitrogenous Wastes: Ammonia, Urea, or Uric Acid?

Ammonia is a toxic byproduct resulting from metabolic removal of nitrogen wastes. Animals that live in water usually excrete ammonia in dilute solutions. Although the excretion of ammonia works for water-dwelling animals, it doesn't work well for animals that live on land. Land-dwelling animals, such as mammals and most amphibians when they are on land, excrete urea. Urea is produced by the liver in a metabolic cycle that combines ammonia with carbon dioxide. Insects, birds, and some reptiles excrete uric acid. Uric acid is often excreted as a precipitate (paste-like solid). Uric acid dissolves far less easily than ammonia or urea.

Both urea and uric acid are adaptations that allow animals that live on land to excrete nitrogen wastes without losing too much water. If land-dwelling animals excreted these wastes as ammonia, they would need to pass very large amounts of urine. Ammonia would be so toxic that it could only be transported within the animal and excreted in a very dilute solution; thus the large amounts of urine.

1. What are the three forms of nitrogen wastes excreted by animals?

   _____

   _____

2. Which animals excrete each form of nitrogenous wastes?

   _____

   _____

   _____

3. Why don't mammals excrete ammonia?

   _____

   _____

4. Most amphibians live in water first and then, after metamorphosis, live on land. Do you think their excretions change? Explain.

   _____

   _____

Lesson Quiz

Circulation and Excretion

If the statement is true, write *true*. If the statement is false, change the underlined word or words to make the statement true.

1. _____ Blood carries carbon dioxide and other wastes from <u>lungs</u> to the organs that eliminate them from the body.

2. _____ In the heart, a ventricle receives blood from a(n) <u>atrium</u>.

3. _____ <u>Capillaries</u> filter nitrogen-containing wastes from the blood.

4. _____ An animal's excretory system rids its body of nitrogen-containing wastes, and excess <u>carbon dioxide</u> and water.

5. _____ In a three-chambered heart, oxygen-rich blood and oxygen-rich blood mix in the <u>ventricle</u>.

Fill in the blank to complete each sentence.

6. The _____ system transports needed material to cells and takes away wastes.

7. In a closed circulatory system, blood always stays inside vessels and

   the _____.

8. Both open and closed circulatory systems include blood, _____, and a heart.

9. _____ and mammals have a four-chambered heart.

10. Planarians live in fresh water and have excess _____ in their cells.

Circulation and Excretion

Answer Key

After the Inquiry Warm-Up

1. The students in Group C represented blood circulating in the fish's bloodstream.

2. The clapping represented the beating of the fish's heart, pumping blood throughout its body.

3. Students should show a circular or oval path with *Gills* and *Body* at opposite ends and *Heart* halfway between. They should indicate blood flowing from *Heart* to *Gills,* where it picks up oxygen and gives up carbon dioxide, then to *Body,* where it picks up carbon dioxide and gives up oxygen, then back to *Heart.*

4. The fish's gills are getting oxygen from the water that passes over them.

Key Concept Summaries

A salamander has a closed circulatory system. Blood flows both to and from its heart inside vessels. The salamander has a double-loop circulation pattern. In the first loop, the right side of the heart pumps oxygen-poor blood to the lungs, where it picks up oxygen before returning to the heart. In the second loop, the left side of the heart pumps the oxygen-rich blood to the rest of the body.

Review and Reinforce

1. In an open circulatory system, blood does not always travel inside vessels. The hearts pump blood into spaces around the organs. Substances are exchanged, and eventually blood returns to the heart.

2. In a closed circulatory system, blood always stays inside vessels and the heart. Large vessels lead away from the heart to the organs, where blood and body cells exchange substances through thin-walled capillaries. Capillaries merge to form large vessels that return to the heart.

3. A single-loop circulation pattern forces blood around the body in one direction.

4. In the first loop, the right side of the heart pumps blood to the lungs to pick-up oxygen. In the second loop, the left side of the heart pumps the oxygen-rich blood to the rest of the body.

5. Oxygen-rich blood does not mix with oxygen-poor blood in a four-chambered heart.

6. heart
7. excretory
8. atrium
9. Capillaries
10. Urine
11. ventricle
12. circulatory
13. kidney

Enrich

1. The three forms of nitrogenous wastes are ammonia, urea, and uric acid.

2. ammonia: animals that live in water; urea: animals that live on land, such as mammals and most amphibians when they are on land; uric acid: insects, birds, some reptiles

3. Ammonia is too toxic to mammals' internal systems. It would need to be excreted in very dilute solution, resulting in large amounts of urine.

4. Yes, most amphibians excrete ammonia in water and urea as land-dwelling animals.

Lesson Quiz

1. cells
2. true
3. Kidneys
4. salt
5. true
6. circulatory
7. heart
8. vessels
9. Birds
10. water

Study Guide

Review the Big Q

Have students complete the statement at the top of the page. These Key Concepts support their understanding of the chapter's Big Question. Have students return to the chapter opener pages. What is different about how students view the image of the snake eating the frog now that they have completed the chapter? Thinking about this will help them prepare for the *Apply the Big Q* activity in the Review and Assessment.

Partner Review

Have partners review definitions of vocabulary terms by using the Study Guide to quiz each other. Students could read the Key Concept statements and leave out words for their partner to fill in. They may also change a statement so that it is false and then ask their partner to correct it.

Class Activity: Concept Map

Have students develop a concept map to show how the information in this chapter is related. Have students brainstorm to identify the Key Concepts, vocabulary, details, and examples. They can then write each one on a sticky note and attach it at random on chart paper or on the board. Explain that the concept map will begin at the top of the chart with Key Concepts. Ask students to use the following questions to help them organize the information on the notes:

- How do different animals obtain and digest food?
- How do different animals obtain oxygen?
- What are the functions of the circulatory and excretory systems in animals?
- How do open and closed circulatory systems differ?
- What specialized structures do animals have in order to get rid of waste?

My Science Coach allows students to complete the *Practice Test* online.

The Big Question allows students to complete the *Apply the Big Q* activity about how animals get and use energy.

Vocab Flash Cards offer a way to review the chapter vocabulary words.

my science online.com ▸ Obtaining Energy

CHAPTER
6 Study Guide

REVIEW THE BIG ?

An animal's _digestive_ , _respiratory_ , and _circulatory_ systems help it obtain food and use the food as _energy_ .

LESSON 1 How Animals Obtain and Digest Food

🔑 The different ways that an animal obtains food depends on what it eats and its adaptations for getting food.

🔑 Some types of animals digest food mainly inside their cells, but most animals digest food outside their cells.

Vocabulary
- carnivore • herbivore
- omnivore • filter feeder
- radula • digestion • digestive system
- anus • crop • gizzard • intestine
- esophagus • stomach

LESSON 2 How Animals Obtain Oxygen

🔑 Animal cells exchange oxygen and carbon dioxide with their surroundings by diffusion across the outer coverings, or membranes, of cells.

🔑 Respiratory systems include structures such as skin, gills, and lungs. The type of respiratory system an animal has depends on how complex the animal is and where it lives.

Vocabulary
- cellular respiration • diffusion
- respiratory system • gill • lung

LESSON 3 Circulation and Excretion

🔑 Complex animals have one of two types of circulatory systems: open or closed.

🔑 Some closed systems have a single-loop circulation pattern. Others have a double-loop circulation pattern.

🔑 Many animals have specialized structures to get rid of wastes.

Vocabulary
- circulatory system • heart • open circulatory system
- closed circulatory system • capillary • atrium
- ventricle • excretory system • kidney • urine

ELL Support

4 Language Production

Divide the class into three groups and do a Gallery Walk. Post three large sheets of paper with essential questions from each lesson at the top of each sheet. Position each group at one poster. Have them write responses to the questions. Then have them rotate to the other posters to add information.

Beginning
LOW/HIGH Allow students to answer with drawings or short phrases.

Intermediate
LOW/HIGH Have students draft sentences to answer the questions.

Advanced
LOW/HIGH Have students assist and/or edit the work of classmates with lower language proficiency.

Review and Assessment

LESSON 1 How Animals Obtain and Digest Food

1. Animals that eat only plant material are
   a. omnivores.
   b. filter feeders.
   c. carnivores.
   d. herbivores.

2. The process of breaking down food into small molecules is called _digestion._

3. **Compare and Contrast** How are the digestive systems of a flatworm and an earthworm alike? How are they different?

   Sample: Both digest food
   outside their cells. A flatworm's
   digestive system has one
   opening, and an earthworm's
   digestive system has two
   openings.

4. **Relate Cause and Effect** Explain how a butterfly uses its mouthparts to obtain food.

   The butterfly has a strawlike
   mouthpart that enables it to
   suck plant juices from flowers.

5. **Make Generalizations** What type of teeth would you expect an omnivore to have? How do they help the animal eat its food?

   An omnivore has pointed and
   flat teeth. The pointed teeth
   help the animal tear the meat
   it eats. The flat teeth help it
   grind the plants it eats.

LESSON 2 How Animals Obtain Oxygen

6. The process in which an animal's cells use oxygen and digested food molecules to release the energy in food is
   a. breathing.
   b. cellular respiration.
   c. diffusion.
   d. gas exchange.

7. When particles move from an area of high concentration to an area of low concentration, _diffusion_ occurs.

8. **Apply Concepts** Describe the function of the main respiratory structure of the dolphin shown below.

   Its lungs enable it to exchange
   gases between air and blood.

9. **Draw Conclusions** How is having moist skin an advantage for a frog?

   Sample: The frog exchanges
   oxygen that is dissolved in
   water across its skin. Moist
   skin enables it to obtain
   enough oxygen.

10. **Write About It** Describe three structures that an animal's respiratory system may have. Name one animal that has each structure.
   See TE rubric.

235

Review and Assessment

Assess Understanding

Have students complete the answers to the Review and Assessment questions. Have a class discussion about what students find confusing. Write Key Concepts on the board to reinforce knowledge.

RTI Response to Intervention

3. If students have difficulty comparing ways that animals digest food, **then** review the graphic organizer they completed to compare intracellular and extracellular digestion.

7. If students cannot explain the process of diffusion, **then** have them locate the highlighted term and review the definition.

Alternate Assessment

L3 **PRESENTATION** Have students work in small groups to plan and give a presentation that uses the chapter content to explain how animals get and use energy. Have them create visual aids and props that they can use in their presentations. Students should address essential Questions and the Big Question in their presentations.

Write About It Assess student's writing using this rubric.

SCORING RUBRIC	SCORE 4	SCORE 3	SCORE 2	SCORE 1
Describe possible structures of respiratory system and provide examples	Student identifies skin, gills, and lungs as three possible structures, and provides examples of animals for each.	Student identifies two of the three structures and gives an example of an animal that uses each.	Student identifies one or two structures but does not provide any examples of animals.	Student does not identify any structures or animals.

235

Review and Assessment, Cont.

ℝ𝕋𝕀 Response to Intervention

13. If students cannot explain what would happen if a kidney stopped functioning, **then** ask them to think about the effects of waste not being removed from an organism's blood.

Apply the Big Q ② UbD

TRANSFER Students should be able to demonstrate understanding of how animals get and use energy by answering this question. See the scoring rubric below.

Connect to the Big Idea ② UbD

BIG IDEA: Living things grow, change, and reproduce during their lifetimes.

Send students back to the Big Ideas of Science at the beginning of their student edition. Have them read what they wrote before they started the chapter. Lead a class discussion about how their thoughts have changed. If all chapters have been completed, have students fill in the bottom section for the Big Idea.

L3 WRITING IN SCIENCE Ask students to write a television interview with a biologist that explains to viewers how animals get and use energy.

LESSON 3 Circulation and Excretion

11. A heart chamber that receives blood from body structures is called
   a. a capillary.   **b.** a ventricle.
   c. an atrium.   **d.** a vessel.

12. Blood always stays inside the heart and blood vessels in a __closed__ circulatory system.

13. Predict What would happen if a kidney stopped functioning?
   Sample: The kidney would not filter nitrogen-containing wastes from the blood. Wastes would build up and cause illness or death.

14. Interpret Diagrams How does blood move in a fish's circulatory system shown below?

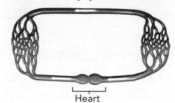

Heart

   The heart pumps blood to the gills, from the gills to the body organs, and back to the heart.

15. **Write About It** When visiting a pond, you see a fish and a frog. Describe how the single-loop circulation pattern of the fish is similar to and different from the double-loop circulation pattern of the frog.
   See TE rubric.

 How do animals get and use energy?

16. This pileated woodpecker eats insects that liv in trees. Explain how its beak helps it obtain its food. Then describe how its body digests the food into molecules, obtains oxygen, and transports these materials to body cells. Include how the body cells use the materials.

   The long beak can probe inside the tree. Food enters the woodpecker through the mout then passes to the esophagus and into the stomach, where it is partially broken down. It the moves to the intestine where it is absorbed. Wastes are eliminated through the anus. Oxygen is obtained through its lungs. Blood is circulated in a double-loop pattern by a four-chambered heart. The blood obtains oxygen from the lungs and delivers it and digested food molecules to th body cells. The cells use these materials to release the energ in the food.
   See TE rubric.

Write About It Assess student's writing using this rubric.

SCORING RUBRIC	SCORE 4	SCORE 3	SCORE 2	SCORE 1
Types of circulation	Student accurately compares and contrasts the two types of patterns.	Student adequately compares and contrasts the two types of patterns.	Student partially compares and contrasts the two types of patterns.	Student does not compare and contrast the two types of patterns.

 How do animals get and use energy? Assess student's response using this rubric.

SCORING RUBRIC	SCORE 4	SCORE 3	SCORE 2	SCORE 1
How a beak helps it obtain food	Student offers accurate explanation.	Student provides adequate explanation.	Student offers partial explanation.	Student does not offer an explanation.
How body digests, obtains oxygen, and transports	Student accurately describes what happens to food after eaten.	Student describes what happens to food after eaten.	Student partially describes what happens to food after eaten.	Student does not describe what happens to food after eaten.

tandardized Test Prep

ultiple Choice

rcle the letter of the best answer.

Based on the type of teeth you see in the diagram below, make an inference about what type of animal it is.

A omnivore   **B** herbivore
C carnivore   D filter feeder

Which organs do mollusks use to obtain oxygen from their environments?

A radula
B lungs
C gills
D legs

Of the following digestive tube structures, which one stores food?

A bill
B crop
C gizzard
D stomach

4. Animals get rid of nitrogen-containing wastes through the

   A respiratory system.
   B digestive system.
   C circulatory system.
   D excretory system.

5. What is an adult amphibian's main respiratory structure?

   A skin
   B gills
   C lungs
   D tracheal tubes

Constructed Response

Use the diagrams below and your knowledge of science to help you answer Question 6. Write your answer on a separate sheet of paper.

Cell membrane

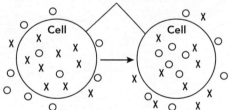

6. The diagram above shows a process that occurred in the same cell. The Os represent oxygen particles. The Xs represent carbon dioxide particles. Identify the process. Describe how the concentrations of particles changed.
See TE note.

237

Standardized Test Prep

Test-Taking Skills

MAKING INFERENCES Remind students that when they make an inference, they have to draw a conclusion that is not stated or shown explicitly. In this question, they are not given any direct information that shows what type of animal it is. Students must infer the animal is an herbivore based on information about the teeth and skull in the diagram.

Constructed Response

6. Sample: The process is diffusion. The cell had a lower concentration of oxygen inside than outside. It had a higher concentration of carbon dioxide outside than inside. Because of diffusion, the particles moved from an area of high concentration to an area of low concentration. So, some oxygen moved into the cell and some carbon dioxide moved out of the cell. As a result, the cell has equal concentrations of oxygen and carbon dioxide inside and outside it.

Additional Assessment Resources

Chapter Test
ExamView® Computer Test Generator
Performance Assessment
Progress Monitoring Assessments
SuccessTracker™

ELL Support

5 Assess Understanding

Have ELL students complete the Alternate Assessment. Provide guidelines on the information it must cover, and a rubric for assessment. You may wish to have them complete the activity in small groups of varying language proficiencies.

Beginning

LOW/HIGH Allow students extra time to complete their presentations.

Intermediate

LOW/HIGH Allow students to refer to their books or notes when completing their presentations.

Advanced

LOW/HIGH Challenge students to use vocabulary terms from the lesson in their presentations.

Remediate If students have trouble with...

QUESTION	SEE LESSON	STANDARDS
1	1	
2	2	
3	1	
4	3	
5	2	
6	2	

Science Matters

Think Like a Scientist

Have students read *A Free Lunch?* Point out that the Sacculina have a symbiotic relationship with crabs. Explain that in a symbiotic relationship between a parasite and a host, the parasite benefits from the relationship while the host is harmed by it.

Tell students that one of the ways that Sacculina harm their host crabs is by making them infertile. Sacculina attach themselves to host crabs on their underside, toward the back end of the body. When the host crab is female, the location of the attachment blocks where she would normally carry her egg sac. When the host crab is male, the hormone changes the Sacculina to induce the male crab to behave like a female, rendering the host infertile. Instead, the Sacculina themselves are only able to reproduce when attached to crabs. Remarkably the crabs take care of the Sacculina larvae like their own young because of the hormone changes induced by the parasite.

Explain that Sacculina harm their host crabs in other ways as well. Sacculina prevent crabs from going through the natural process of molting, or losing their outer shell when they out grow it. The ability of crabs to regrow a claw that has been severed or damaged is also impaired by Sacculina.

As students write their hypotheses, ask them to think about what would happen to the Sacculina if they did kill their host crabs.

Ask: **How do Sacculina benefit from their host crabs?** *(The crabs provide nourishment, a body to grow and reproduce in, and protection while the larvae gestate.)* **How are the host crabs harmed by Sacculina?** *(They are made infertile and they cannot molt or regrow damaged claws.)*

A FREE LUNCH?

A *Sacculina* infection looks like a white lump on a crab's body. But it's more than a lumpy infection. ▽

Is there really "no free lunch"? All animals are consumers. They eat other organisms. This usually means that they have to gather or hunt their food. That's a lot of work! But you could say the parasite *Sacculina* gets it lunch for free.

Sacculina begins its life as a tiny organism that drifts in the ocean. Eventually, it finds its host, a crab. It injects itself into the crab's body and absorbs nutrients from the crab's bloodstream.

Many animals, including crabs, produce hormones. These hormones, produced in the brain, control the animals' behavior and development. Over time, *Sacculina* alters the way its host produces hormones. At first, the crab is not affected. As the hormone levels change, the crab's behavior and development change. In fact, the crab behaves as if the eggs of the *Sacculina* parasite are crab eggs.

When the parasite eggs are ready to hatch, the crab releases the larvae in pulses. The crab will even wave its claws to help the *Sacculina* parasite larvae spread out to find other victims!

Think About It *Sacculina* and other parasites often make their hosts very sick. But they do not usually kill the host. In one or two paragraphs, describe your hypothesis for why this might be true.

238 Obtaining Energy

Quick Facts

Tiger salamanders are a unique member of the amphibian family as are caecilians, a family of legless, tailless amphibians that live in tropical habitats. They often look like snakes and can be mistaken for earthworms because they mostly live underground. They have rings on the outside of their body, which sometimes contain scales and sensory tentacles, on the sides of their heads which are retractable. Some species have eyes, but do not use them to see. They live on a diet of insects and earthworms. Some species live entirely in water and can be mistaken for eels. Their habitats are generally warm, swampy places. Have students research caecilians and create a chart that compares and contrasts them with other amphibians.

SKIN OR GILLS?

Like most other living things, tiger salamanders need oxygen to get energy from food stored in their cells. Cells use this energy to function. But unlike most living things, tiger salamanders can change the way they get oxygen.

Tiger salamanders breed and lay eggs in water. Their larvae also live in water and have large, feathery external gills that absorb oxygen from the water. When a larva matures, it goes through a change, or metamorphosis. Normally, the larva loses its gills and becomes a land-dweller. The adult salamander absorbs oxygen from the air through its moist skin and mouth.

Sometimes, though, a tiger salamander keeps its gills into adulthood. It stays under water and never becomes a land dweller. How might keeping its gills benefit the adult salamander? The answer is in its environment.

Tiger salamanders eat insects and other small animals. Salamander larvae find food in the ponds in which they live. Adult salamanders eat insects that they find on land. In very dry areas, there may be very few insects on land. So, in these areas, tiger salamanders do not go through metamorphosis. The larvae keep their gills and continue to live in the water, where they can find food and reproduce.

▲ Adult tiger salamanders usually live on land. They absorb oxygen through their skin and mouth.

Research It Salamanders are known as "environmental indicator" species. This means that when there are dangerous chemicals, or toxins, in the environment, salamanders are among the first species to show ill effects. Find out what feature of salamanders makes them more likely to be harmed by toxins. Make a poster to tell people in your school about why it is important to monitor the health of salamander populations.

239

Hot Science

Have students read *Skin or Gills?* Explain that tiger salamanders are native to North America and can be found from the Rocky Mountains to the Atlantic coast and from the southern United States into parts of Canada. Salamander and frog larvae look a lot alike, but the external gills on the salamander sets them apart.

Tell students that, although tiger salamanders all have the unique ability to lose their external gills and become land-dwellers, several different subspecies have unique coloring, habitats, and breeding periods. The gray tiger salamander has dark green to gray coloring and lives in the northern parts of the United States and Canada. Blotched tiger salamanders have more of a dull, yellow coloring and live somewhat south of the gray tiger salamander habitat. Both the gray and blotched subspecies breed in early spring. Barred tiger salamanders live mostly in Texas, Oklahoma, Kansas, and Nebraska and tend to breed in the winter, especially towards the southern part of their habitat. The eastern tiger salamander lives in the eastern half of the United States. The Arizona tiger salamander looks much like the one pictured in the article and lives in desert areas. The Sonoran tiger salamander lives on the border of Mexico in Arizona and is considered an endangered species.

Ask: **Based on their habitats both on land and in water, what kind of animals are tiger salamanders?** (amphibians) **Why do some adult tiger salamanders keep their gills?** (to allow them live in water when food on land is scarce) **What subspecies do you think is most likely to keep its gills?** (Sample: Arizona)

Animal Reproduction and Behavior

Introduce the Big Q UbD

Have students look at the image and read the Engaging Question and description. Ask them to draw a conclusion about how the armadillo's body parts might help it to survive. Point out that animals have physical body structures and behaviors that help them survive. Ask: **How does the armadillo's back look like a suit of armor?** *(It looks tough and it protects the armadillo's body.)* **How might they use their thick skin for protection?** *(They might wrap it around their bodies like a ball.)* **In what way is the armadillo similar to a turtle?** *(The turtle has a thick shell for protection. It can hide inside for protection.)*

Untamed Science Video

IS THAT DANCE JUST FOR ME? Before viewing, invite students to discuss what they know about animal behavior. Then play the video. Lead a class discussion and make a list of questions that this video raises. You may wish to have students view the video again after they have completed the chapter to see if their questions have been answered.

To access the online resources for this chapter, search on or navigate to *Animal Reproduction and Behavior.*

Untamed Science Video shows the mating dance of the sharptail grouse.

The Big Question allows students to answer the Engaging Question about what body parts help the armadillos survive.

 my science online.com ▸ Animal Reproduction & Behavior

WHAT
BODY PARTS
HELP THESE
ARMADILLOS
SURVIVE?

How does an animal's behavior help it survive and reproduce?

These nine-banded armadillo pups are well adapted to survive where they live. Armadillos have a great sense of smell, which they use to find insects. Armadillos dig into an insect nest using their sharp claws, and then scoop up the insects with their long tongues. If they are threatened by a predator, armadillos use their claws to defend themselves. They also have tough, scaly skin that acts like armor.

▸ UNTAMED SCIENCE Watch the **Untamed Science** video to learn more about behavior.

Draw Conclusions **What body parts will help these young armadillos survive?**

The armadillos' long tongues and sharp claws help them find food. Claws and tough skin help protect armadillos against predators.

 **Professional Development Note** ## From the Author

In many parts of the US, we can observe migration. Ask students to consider their region of the country: Is it a place that animals would migrate to or from during winter? Have them compare fall and spring: Do they hear fewer or more birds singing? They may see flocks of geese traveling in a classic "V" formation across the skies. Point out that some species of migratory waterfowl, such as Canada Geese, have begun to "stay put" during the migrating season. This may be a result of people feeding waterfowl. If the waterfowl have a steady source of nutrition during the cold winter months, they have no need to migrate.

✆ *Zipporah Miller*

Animal Reproduction and Behavior

CHAPTER 7

Chapter at a Glance

CHAPTER PACING: 8–12 periods or 4–6 blocks

INTRODUCE THE CHAPTER: Use the Engaging Question and the opening image to get students thinking about animal reproduction and behavior. Activate prior knowledge and preteach vocabulary using the Getting Started pages.

Lesson 1: Animal Reproduction and Fertilization

Lesson 2: Development and Growth

Lesson 3: What Is Behavior?

Lesson 4: Patterns of Behavior

ASSESSMENT OPTIONS: Chapter Test, *ExamView®* Computer Test Generator, Performance Assessment, Progress Monitoring Assessments, SuccessTracker™

Preference Navigator, in the online Planning tools, allows you to customize *Interactive Science* to your own teaching style. You can also edit lesson plans by selecting the Lesson Planner option.

Digital Teacher's Edition allows you to access your Teacher's Edition and Resource online.

my science online.com

CHAPTER 7

Differentiated Instruction

L1 Armadillos There are 20 different species of armadillos in existence, and their closest living relatives are anteaters and sloths. Have students work in small groups to research more about armadillos. Different groups can find out more about different aspects of the animal, such as its habitat, diet, anatomy, and behavior. Encourage groups to present their findings to the class.

L3 Word Analysis Have students use a dictionary to determine the scientific meaning and origin of the term *metamorphosis*. Students should break down the word into its component parts and explain how the different parts contribute to the term's overall meaning. Then, have students identify and discuss animals that undergo this process.

Getting Started

Check Your Understanding

This activity assesses students' understanding of how animals can be classified into groups based on their characteristics. After students have shared their answers, point out that the key to classifying animals is to place them into smaller and smaller groups. The smaller the groups become, the more similar the animals in that group are.

Preteach Vocabulary Skills

Explain to students that knowing high-use academic words will help them to understand new concepts. Learning high-use academic words can make it easier to learn new vocabulary words. Also point out that academic words do not necessarily have to be long or complex words. They are simply words that are useful to know when learning new concepts in school.

Check Your Understanding

1. **Background** Read the paragraph below and then answer the question.

> Sal and Kai are at the zoo, trying to decide where to go. Sal wants to see the birds, reptiles, and **mammals.** Kai has a completely different plan. She doesn't understand why Sal only wants to see **vertebrates.** Kai would rather go directly to the **invertebrate** exhibit.

> **Mammals** are vertebrates whose body temperatures are regulated by their internal heat, and that have skin covered with hair or fur and glands that produce milk to feed their young.
>
> **Vertebrates** are animals with backbones.
>
> **Invertebrates** are animals without backbones.

• Circle the correct word to complete the following sentence. A bird is an example of a (vertebrate)/invertebrate).

> **MY READING WEB** If you had trouble completing the question above, visit **My Reading Web** and type in *Animal Reproduction and Behavior.*

Vocabulary Skill

High-Use Academic Words High-use academic words appear frequently in textbooks and are often used in classrooms. As you read this chapter, look for the words in the table below.

Word	Definition	Example Sentence
aquatic	*adj.* related to or living in water	Caesar has a large tank filled with fish and other *aquatic* animals.
demonstrate	*v.* to show	Will you *demonstrate* how to ride that bicycle?

2. **Quick Check** Fill in the word that best completes the following sentence.

• Whales, sharks, and eels live in an _aquatic_ environment.

My Reading Web offers leveled readings that offer a foundation for the chapter content.

Vocab Flash Cards offer extra practice with the chapter vocabulary words.

Digital Lesson

• Assign the *Check Your Understanding* activity online and have students submit their work to you.
• Assign the *Vocabulary Skill* activity online and have students submit their work to you.

my science online.com | Animal Reproduction and Behavior

external fertilization

amniotic egg

instinct

courtship behavior

Chapter Preview

LESSON 1
- larva • polyp • medusa
- external fertilization
- internal fertilization
- gestation period
- Compare and Contrast
- Calculate

LESSON 2
- amniotic egg • placenta
- metamorphosis
- complete metamorphosis
- pupa
- incomplete metamorphosis
- nymph • tadpole
- Summarize
- Interpret Data

LESSON 3
- behavior • instinct • learning
- imprinting • conditioning
- trial-and-error learning
- insight learning
- Relate Cause and Effect
- Predict

LESSON 4
- pheromone • aggression
- territory • courtship behavior
- society • circadian rhythm
- hibernation • migration
- Identify the Main Idea
- Communicate

> VOCAB FLASH CARDS For extra help with vocabulary, visit **Vocab Flash Cards** and type in *Animal Reproduction and Behavior.*

Preview Vocabulary Terms

Have students work together to create a word wall to display the vocabulary terms for the chapter. Be sure to discuss and analyze each term before posting it on the wall. As the class progresses through the chapter, the words can be sorted and categorized in different ways. A list of Academic Vocabulary for each lesson can be found in the Support All Readers box at the start of the lesson.

L1 Have students look at the images on this page as you pronounce the vocabulary word. Have students repeat the word after you. Then read the definition. Use the sample sentence in italics to clarify the meaning of the term.

external fertilization *(ek STUR nul fur tih lih ZAY shun)* The joining of a sperm cell and an egg cell outside the female's body. *Many fish reproduce using external fertilization by releasing eggs and sperm into the water.*

amniotic egg *(am nee AHT ik eg)* An egg covered with membranes and a leathery shell while inside the parent's body. *A baby eagle develops from an amniotic egg.*

instinct *(IN stingkt)* A response to a stimulus that is inborn and that an animal performs correctly the first time. *Many spiders have an instinct to spin complex webs.*

courtship behavior *(KAWRT ship bee HAYV yur)* The behavior in which males and females of the same species prepare for mating. *A male peacock spreads its colorful feathers as part of his courtship behavior.*

243

CHAPTER 7

(ELL) Support

Have students work together to sort and categorize the words on the word wall. As the class progresses through the chapter and new words are introduced, be sure to say each word aloud and have students repeat it.

Beginning
LOW/HIGH Have students add definitions for the words in their native languages.

Intermediate
LOW/HIGH Have students write down words for you to define and post.

Advanced
LOW/HIGH Challenge students to come up with new categories to classify the words.

Animal Reproduction and Fertilization

1 ❓ **How does an animal's behavior help it survive and reproduce?**

Lesson Pacing: 2–3 periods or 1–1½ blocks

🕐 **SHORT ON TIME?** To do this lesson in approximately half the time, do the Activate Prior Knowledge activity on page 244. A discussion of the Key Concepts on pages 245 and 250 will familiarize students with the lesson content. Have students do the Quick Labs. The rest of the lesson can be completed by students independently.

> **Preference Navigator,** in the online Planning tools, allows you to customize *Interactive Science* to your own teaching style. You can also edit lesson plans by selecting the Lesson Planner option.
>
> **Digital Teacher's Edition** allows you to access your Teacher's Edition and Resource materials online.

my science online.com

Lesson Vocabulary

- larva
- polyp
- medusa
- external fertilization
- internal fertilization
- gestation period

 Content Refresher

Professional Development Note

Parthenogenesis Parthenogenesis is the development of an offspring from an egg that has not been fertilized by a sperm. This process takes place in several invertebrate groups, most often in insects. In a honeybee hive, only the queen bee lays eggs. She mates once, and stores sperm for the rest of her life. Some of the eggs she lays are fertilized, and become worker bees, which are sterile females. Some of the eggs are not fertilized. They develop by parthenogenesis and become drones, fertile males. In aphids, parthenogenesis is an adaptation that helps the species take advantage of available food supplies in spring and summer. Aphids feed on plant sap, which is abundant during the growing season for plants. Parthenogenetic offspring of aphids are all female, and are born live, as opposed to hatching from eggs that are laid and left to develop on their own. Some species of aphid can double their population in two days.

Among vertebrates, parthenogenesis is seen in some species of lizards, including the Komodo dragon, and some species of whiptail lizard. The parthenogenetic whiptails are unusual species because they reproduce only asexually and all the individuals are female. In the Komodo dragon, a female will reproduce by parthenogenesis when a male is not present. When a male is present, the female will not reproduce by parthenogenesis. When the male and female mate and reproduction is sexual, with the egg being fertilized by a sperm.

LESSON OBJECTIVES

☞ Compare asexual and sexual reproduction in invertebrates and vertebrates.

☞ Explain how internal fertilization and external fertilization differ.

Blended Path
Active learning using Student Edition, Inquiry Path, and Digital Path

ENGAGE AND EXPLORE

Teach this lesson using a variety of resources. Begin by reading **My Planet Diary** as a class. Have students share ideas about things they have learned from their own experiments and others' experiments. Then have students do the **Inquiry Warm-Up activity.** Students will investigate two methods of reproduction. Discuss the difference in the amount of beans put down by Team A and B. The **After the Inquiry Warm-Up worksheet** sets up a discussion about the number of beans Team B would produce if the experiment went on for five minutes. Have volunteers share their answers to question 4 about how the reproductive process would continue for each example.

EXPLAIN AND ELABORATE

Teach Key Concepts by explaining asexual reproduction and then ask students how the offspring of asexual reproduction compare to their parent. Use **Figure 1** to illustrate the type of asexual reproduction known as budding. **Lead a Discussion** about sexual reproduction. Use **Figure 2** to identify similarities and differences between parent and offspring from the vertebrate classes. **Lead a Discussion** about the advantages and disadvantages of sexual and asexual reproduction. **Lead a Discussion** about organisms that reproduce sexually and asexually. Use **Figure 4** to show students how a sponge reproduces sexually. In **Figure 5** the life cycle of a moon jellyfish is shown to demonstrate which body form reproduces asexually and which form reproduces sexually.

Continue to **Teach Key Concepts** by asking students where external fertilization usually takes place and then ask students to identify organisms that have external fertilization. Use the **Support the Big Q** to describe how various aquatic organisms handle their developing fish eggs. **Lead a Discussion** about internal fertilization. Hand out the **Key Concept Summaries** as a review of each part of the lesson. Students can also use the online **Vocab Flash Cards** to review key terms.

EVALUATE

Have students take the **Lesson Quiz.** For an alternate assessment, see the *ExamView®* Computer Test Generator, Progress Monitoring Assessments, or SuccessTracker™.

E L L Support

1 Content and Language

The terms *internal fertilization* and *external fertilization* both contain prefixes. The prefix *in-* means "in or into" while the prefix *ex-* means "out." Remind students that *internal fertilization* occurs inside the body while *external fertilization* occurs outside of the body.

DIFFERENTIATED INSTRUCTION KEY
L1 Struggling Students or Special Needs
L2 On-Level Students **L3** Advanced Students

LESSON PLANNER 7.1

Lab zone Inquiry Path
Hands-on learning in the Lab zone

Digital Path
Online learning at my science online.com

ENGAGE AND EXPLORE

To teach this lesson with an emphasis on inquiry, begin with the **Inquiry Warm-Up activity.** Students will investigate two methods of reproduction. Discuss why students think Team A put down each set of beans more often than Team B. Have students do the **After the Inquiry Warm-Up worksheet.** Talk about how many beans Team B would have if the experiment continued for five minutes. Have volunteers share their answers to question 4 about how the reproductive process would continue for both Teams.

EXPLAIN AND ELABORATE

Focus on the **Inquiry Skill** for the lesson. Point out that when you calculate, you use mathematical skills to determine a value. What was calculated in the **Inquiry Warm-Up activity?** *(Number of beans Team B would produce if the experiment continued for five minutes)* Do the **Teacher Demo** to help students understand the value of variations in a population. Have students do the **Quick Lab** to observe and sketch the stages of hydra budding.

Support the Big Q by describing the reproductive behaviors in various fishes. Do the **Quick Lab** to reinforce understanding of external and internal fertilization. Students can use the online **Vocab Flash Cards** to review key terms.

EVALUATE

Have students take the **Lesson Quiz.** For an alternate assessment, see the *ExamView*® Computer Test Generator, Progress Monitoring Assessments, or SuccessTracker™.

ENGAGE AND EXPLORE

Teach this lesson using digital resources. Begin by having students explore real-world connections to animal reproduction at **My Planet Diary** online. Have them access the Chapter Resources to find the **Unlock the Big Question activity.** There they can answer the questions and refine their responses as they continue through the lesson. You can re-assign the activity and have students submit their work so you can track their progress.

EXPLAIN AND ELABORATE

Students reading above, at, or below the lexile measure of this lesson can access basic content readings at their level at **My Reading Web.** Have students use the online **Vocab Flash Cards** to preview key terms. Do the **Quick Lab** and then ask students to share their observations and sketches.

Use the **Support the Big Q** to illustrate the reproductive behavior in fishes. Assign the **Do the Math activity** online and have students submit their work to you. Have students do the **Quick Lab** to model internal and external fertilization. The **Key Concept Summaries** online allow students to read a summary and see an image associated with each part of the lesson. Online remediation is available at **My Science Coach.**

EVALUATE

Have students take the **Lesson Quiz.** For an alternate assessment, see the *ExamView*® Computer Test Generator, Progress Monitoring Assessments, or SuccessTracker™.

2 Frontload the Lesson
Preview the lesson visuals, labels, and captions. Ask students what they know about the terms *larva, polyp,* and *medusa.* Explain the specific meanings these words have in science.

3 Comprehensible Input
Have students study the visuals and their captions on pages 245, 246, 247, 248, 249, and 250 to support the key concepts of the lesson.

4 Language Production
Pair or group students with varied language abilities to complete labs collaboratively for language practice. Have each student copy the completed written lab for personal reference.

5 Assess Understanding
Have students keep a content area log for this lesson using a two-column format with the headings "What I Understand" and "What I Don't Understand." Follow up so that students can move items from the "Don't Understand" to the "Understand" column.

Lexile Measure = 950L

Animal Reproduction and Fertilization

Establish Learning Objectives

After this lesson, students will be able to:

🔑 Compare asexual and sexual reproduction in invertebrates and vertebrates.

🔑 Explain how external fertilization and internal fertilization differ.

Engage

Activate Prior Knowledge

MY PLANET DIARY Read *A Nutty Experiment* with the class. Point out to students that scientists in large laboratories are not the only people who discover information. Ask: **How is a scientific question different from other types of questions?** *(Scientific questions can be tested to find out if they can be proven false.)* **What is a suggested answer to a scientific question?** *(A hypothesis)*

BIG IDEAS OF SCIENCE REFERENCE LIBRARY Have students look up the following topics: Courtship Rituals, Sea Horse, Worms.

Explore

Lab Resource: Inquiry Warm-Up

L1 **MAKING MORE** Students will model two methods of reproduction.

LESSON
1

Animal Reproduction and Fertilization

🔑 **How Do Animals Reproduce?**

🔑 **How Do External and Internal Fertilization Differ?**

MY PLANET DIARY

PROFILE

A Nutty Experiment

Did you know that moths have favorite foods? The navel orangeworm moth lays its eggs inside of nuts, such as pistachios, walnuts, and almonds. The young that hatch out of the eggs look like worms, and eat their way out of the nuts. This causes damage to crops on nut farms.

Navel orangeworm moths were thought to prefer almonds over other nuts—that is, until California middle school student Gabriel Leal found evidence to the contrary. Gabriel conducted a science project to investigate whether the young of navel orangeworm moths preferred pistachios, walnuts, or almonds. He put equal amounts of each type of nut into three different traps. A fourth trap was left empty. All four traps were placed into a cage with young navel orangeworms. Most worms went to the pistachio trap. No worms went to the empty trap. Gabriel's research could help scientists control worm damage to walnut and almond crops.

Control Variables Read the paragraphs and answer the questions below.

1. Write a one-sentence conclusion of Gabriel's research.

   Sample: Young navel orangeworms prefer pistachios over almonds and walnuts.

2. What was the purpose of the empty trap in Gabriel's experiment?

   He needed to find out if worms were attracted to traps or preferred nuts.

▶ **PLANET DIARY** Go to **Planet Diary** to learn more about animal reproduction and fertilization.

Lab Do the Inquiry Warm-Up *Making More.*

SUPPORT ALL READERS

Lexile Measure = 950L   Lexile Word Count = 1279

Prior Exposure to Content: May be the first time students have encountered this topic

Academic Vocabulary: *calculate, compare, contrast*

Science Vocabulary: *external fertilization, internal fertilization, gestation period*

Concept Level: Generally appropriate for most students in this grade

Preteach With: My Planet Diary "A Nutty Experiment" and Figure 5 activity

Go to **My Reading Web** to access leveled readings that provide a foundation for the ontent.

my science online.com

Vocabulary
• larva • polyp • medusa • external fertilization
• internal fertilization • gestation period

Skills
◉ Reading: Compare and Contrast
△ Inquiry: Calculate

How Do Animals Reproduce?

Whether they wiggle, hop, fly, or run, have backbones or no backbones—all animal species reproduce. Elephants make more elephants, grasshoppers make more grasshoppers, and sea stars make more sea stars. Some animals produce offspring that are identical to the parent. Most animals, including humans, produce offspring that are different from the parents. ⌐ **Animals undergo either asexual or sexual reproduction to make more of their own kind or species.** Because no animal lives forever, reproduction is essential to the survival of a species.

Asexual Reproduction Imagine you are digging in the soil with a shovel, and accidentally cut a worm into two pieces. Most animals wouldn't survive getting cut in two—but the worm might. Certain kinds of worms can form whole new worms from each cut piece. This is one form of asexual reproduction. Another example of asexual reproduction is called budding. In budding, a new animal grows out of the parent and breaks off. In asexual reproduction, one parent produces a new organism identical to itself. This new organism receives an exact copy of the parent's set of genetic material, or DNA. Some animals, including sponges, jellyfish, sea anemones, worms, and the hydra in **Figure 1,** can reproduce asexually.

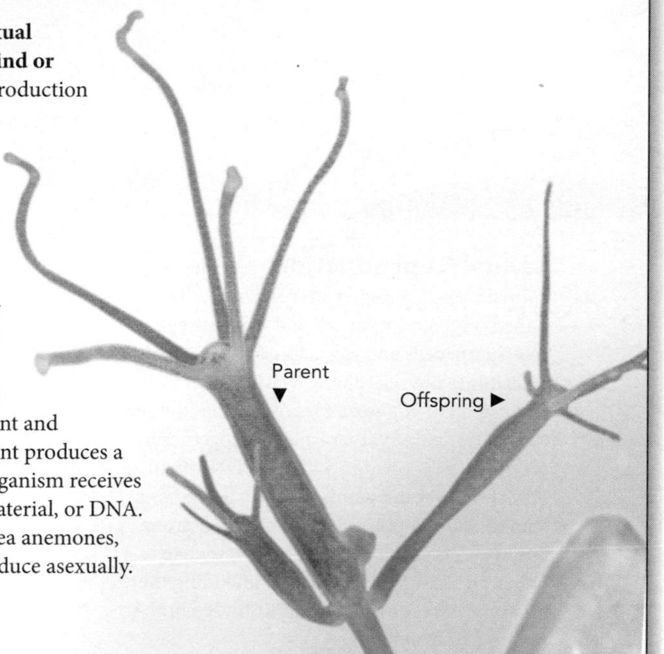

Parent ▼

Offspring ►

FIGURE 1 ·····················
A Chip off the Old Block
Budding is the most common form of asexual reproduction for this hydra, a type of cnidarian.

✎ **Relate Text to Visuals** How does this photo show asexual reproduction?

The offspring is growing out of the parent and looks just like the parent, except smaller.

245

Explain

Introduce Vocabulary

Students may have heard of polyps as abnormal growths in the body, often in the colon or nasal passages. Explain that, in this lesson, the term *polyp* refers to the body shape of some cnidarians.

Teach Key Concepts ⌐

Explain to students that all animals reproduce, or make more of their own kind. Ask: **What are the two types of reproduction?** (*Sexual reproduction and asexual reproduction*) Make sure students understand that asexual reproduction is, by definition, reproduction that involves only one parent. If students have previously studied protists, then they have seen that many protists reproduce by dividing. There is one parent, so this is asexual reproduction. **How do the offspring of asexual reproduction compare to the parent? Why?** (*They are identical because they have the same DNA.*)

Teach With Visuals

Tell students to look at **Figure 1.** If students have previously studied cnidarians, explain the hydra is a small cnidarian found in freshwater environments. The structures at the top of the hydra are tentacles, and the circular structure at the base of the tentacles is the animal's mouth. Ask: **Is this an example of sexual reproduction or asexual reproduction?** (*Asexual*) **What is this kind of asexual reproduction called?** (*Budding*) **How do you think it got this name?** (*The offspring grow off the side of the parent's body, much as buds produce side shoots on a plant.*)

My Planet Diary provides an opportunity for students to explore real-world connections to animal reproduction.

 | Reproduction

1 Content and Language
Write the term *gestation period* on the board. Explain that the noun *gestation* comes from the Latin *gestare,* meaning "to bear." Point out that *period* means "a portion of time." So, a *gestation period* is the portion of time between fertilizing an egg and bearing offspring.

2 Frontload the Lesson
Invite students to think of an example of a person who looks similar to one or

both parents. Tell students that many animals reproduce in pairs of males and females, but some animals reproduce without finding a mate.

3 Comprehensible Input
Have students create a Venn diagram to organize information about reproduction. Urge students to include examples of species and parts of each reproductive process.

Explain

Lead a Discussion

SEXUAL REPRODUCTION Explain to students that sexual reproduction involves two parents. Ask: **What are the two sex cells called?** *(Sperm and egg)* **What is the joining of these two sex cells called?** *(Fertilization)* **What do these cells contribute to the new organism?** *(DNA)* **How does the DNA of the offspring compare to that of the parents?** *(It is a combination of DNA from both parents, so the offspring is not identical to the parents.)*

Teach With Visuals

Tell students to look at **Figure 2.** Point out that the wolves and guinea pigs are mammals. Explain that mammals are not the only group of animals that reproduce by sexual reproduction. All vertebrate classes (fishes, amphibians, reptiles, birds, and mammals) reproduce only sexually. As students compare the parents and offspring, also ask them to compare the two wolf cubs. Ask: **How do these cubs look different?** *(One has black fur and the other has a combination of black and brown fur.)* **What do you think the other parent looks like?** *(Sample: It has black fur.)* Have students note that the wolf cubs have blue eyes and the parent has golden eyes. Explain that, like many puppies, wolf cubs may have blue eyes when they are born, but the eyes will change color as they get older.

Sexual Reproduction Like many animals, you developed after two sex cells joined—a male sperm cell and a female egg cell. Sperm cells and egg cells carry DNA that determines physical characteristics such as size and color. During sexual reproduction, the sex cells of two parent organisms join together to produce a new organism that has DNA that differs from both parents. The offspring has a combination of physical characteristics from both parents and may not look exactly like either parent. Most vertebrates, including the mammals in **Figure 2,** and most invertebrates reproduce sexually.

In some animals, including some worms, mollusks, and fishes, a single individual may produce both eggs and sperm. Individuals of these species will usually fertilize the eggs of another individual, not their own eggs. Recall that fertilization is the joining of sperm and egg cells.

FIGURE 2
Sexual Reproduction
These wolf cubs and guinea pig pups are products of sexual reproduction.

✎ **Use the photos to answer the questions.**

1. Interpret Photos How do the offspring in each photo differ from their parent?
The fur colors are different and the offspring are smaller

2. Explain Why do the parent and the offspring look different?
Because the offspring have a combination of physical characteristics from two parents

246 Animal Reproduction and Behavior

Professional Development Note | **Teacher to Teacher**

Activity A great way to study animal diversity is through the use of graphic organizers. Break your students into collaborative groups. Give each group a list and pictures of animals such as a frog, worm, chicken, dog, and so on. Provide each student with a chart containing the following column titles: *Organism, Method of Movement* and *Reproduction.* Allow the students to work together to complete the chart and answer the questions: *Why do animals reproduce? What is an environmental factor that may affect animal reproduction?* Using the information recorded in the chart, you may demonstrate the similarities and differences between two to three of the assigned animals using a Venn diagram.

✍ *Treva Jeffries*
Scott High School
Toledo, Ohio

Comparing Asexual and Sexual Reproduction

Asexual and sexual reproduction are different survival methods. Each method has advantages and disadvantages. An advantage of asexual reproduction is that one parent can quickly produce many identical offspring. But a major disadvantage is that the offspring have the same DNA as the parent. The offspring have no variation from the parent and may not survive changes in the environment. In contrast, sexual reproduction has the advantage of producing offspring with new combinations of DNA. These offspring may have characteristics that help them adapt and survive changes in the environment. However, a disadvantage of sexual reproduction is that it requires finding a mate, and the development of offspring takes a longer time.

did you
know?..............

Some fishes, such as this anemone clownfish, can change from male to female during their lifetime!

FIGURE 3 ·······································
Asexual and Sexual Reproduction

Compare and Contrast Write an advantage and a disadvantage of each type of reproduction in the table.

	Asexual Reproduction	Sexual Reproduction
Advantage	One parent can quickly produce many identical offspring.	The offspring may have characteristics that help them survive changes in the environment.
Disadvantage	The offspring have the same DNA as the parent and may not survive changes in the environment.	Parents must find a mate, and the development of offspring takes a longer time.

These aphids can reproduce asexually and sexually. They reproduce asexually when environmental conditions are favorable. If conditions worsen, they reproduce sexually. ▼

247

Differentiated Instruction

L3 Aphids Have interested students research aphids to find out about the conditions under which these insects reproduce sexually and the conditions under which they reproduce asexually. Students can share what they have learned in the form of a poster or multimedia presentation.

L1 Compare and Contrast To help students compare and contrast the two types of reproduction, draw a Venn diagram on the board. Ask students how the two types of reproduction differ based on the number of parents and the genetic makeup of the offspring. Record this information in the appropriate spots of the diagram. Then, ask students how the two types of reproduction are similar. Lead students to see that both types result in offspring. Record this information in the overlapping section of the diagram.

Explain ─────────

Lead a Discussion

ASEXUAL AND SEXUAL Review with students the difference between sexual reproduction and asexual reproduction. If students have already studied natural selection, then they should recognize the value of genetic variety among offspring. If not, review the main points of natural selection. Stress that the variations are present before the environment selects the best variations. Ask: **Why is sexual reproduction important for adaptation?** *(Sexual reproduction produces new combinations of characteristics, which increases variation in the population.)* **What are drawbacks to sexual reproduction?** *(It requires finding a mate. It takes longer than asexual reproduction.)*

Compare and Contrast Explain that when students compare and contrast, they explain how two objects or events are similar and different.

Elaborate ─────────

21st Century Learning

CRITICAL THINKING Tell students that earthworms and many other worms are hermaphrodites, organisms that have both male and female reproductive organs. Although a worm may produce both sperm and eggs, they do not use their sperm to fertilize their own eggs. Instead, many hermaphrodites cross-fertilize. That is, the sperm of one individual fertilizes the eggs of the second individual. The sperm of the second individual fertilizes the eggs of the first individual. Ask: **What is the value of cross-fertilization?** *(It is true sexual reproduction with two parents, produces offspring that have a different combination of characteristics than either parent has.)*

Teacher Demo Lab zone

L2 VARIATION AND SELECTION

Materials none

Time 5 minutes

To help students understand the value of variations in a population, draw 20 red circles in one area on the board. Then draw 5 red circles, 5 blue circles, 5 green circles, and 5 yellow circles in another area. Tell students that a new disease can wipe out red individuals. Ask students to predict what will happen in each population. Then erase all the red circles.

Ask: **Which population had more variation?** *(The one with several colors)* **Was being red a dangerous trait before the disease arrived in the area?** *(No)* **Was being blue or green a valuable trait before the disease arrived in the area?** *(No)* Emphasize that a healthy population includes many variations.

247

Explain

Lead a Discussion

BUDDING Review the definition of *budding*. Make sure students understand that there are no buds shown in **Figure 4**. Buds would look like bumps growing out from the sides of the sponges. Ask: **What animal did you see budding in Figure 1?** *(Hydra)* **What kind of animal is the hydra?** *(Cnidarian)* Point out that sponges are simpler organisms than cnidarians. Ask: **Why do you think budding happens in simpler organisms?** *(Sample: They have relatively few body structures to duplicate, so a bud is not difficult to produce.)*

Teach With Visuals

Tell students to look at **Figure 4**. Remind students that sponges do not have separate male and female individuals. Ask: **How do sperm get from one sponge to another?** *(They are released into the water and swim to another sponge.)* **Where does a sperm fertilize an egg?** *(Inside the sponge)* **What does a fertilized egg develop into?** *(A larva)* **What is a larva?** *(An immature form of an animal that looks very different from the adult)*

Elaborate

21st Century Learning

CREATIVITY Have students look again at **Figure 4**. Ask them to write a description of a sponge and how it lives. Students should include in their descriptions the fact that a sponge lives attached to a rock or other surface. Remind students to use descriptive words and phrases that help the reader visualize what is being described. Then, ask students to explain the value of a free-swimming larva to such a species. *(Samples: Sponges cannot get up and move to a new place, so the swimming larva can extend the population to new places. By settling in new places, the larvae develop away from the parents, which reduces competition between individuals.)*

Reproductive Cycles Several aquatic invertebrates, such as sponges and cnidarians, have life cycles that alternate between asexual and sexual reproduction.

A Sponges

Sponges reproduce both asexually and sexually. Sponges reproduce asexually through budding. Small new sponges grow, or bud, from the sides of an adult sponge. Eventually, the buds break free and begin life on their own. Sponges reproduce sexually, too, but they do not have separate sexes. A sponge can produce both sperm cells and egg cells. After a sponge egg is fertilized by a sperm, a larva develops. A **larva** (plural *larvae*) is an immature form of an animal that looks very different from the adult. **Figure 4** shows sponge reproduction.

B Cnidarians

Many cnidarians alternate between two body forms: a **polyp** (PAHL ip) that looks like an upright vase and a **medusa** (muh DOO suh) that looks like an open umbrella. Some polyps reproduce asexually by budding. Other polyps just pull apart, forming two new polyps. Both kinds of asexual reproduction rapidly increase the number of polyps in a short time. Cnidarians reproduce sexually when in the medusa stage. The medusas release sperm and eggs into the water. A fertilized egg develops into a swimming larva. In time, the larva attaches to a hard surface and develops into a polyp that may continue the cycle. The moon jelly in **Figure 5** undergoes both asexual and sexual reproduction.

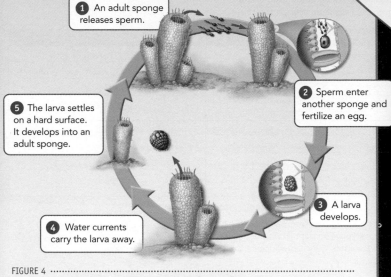

1 An adult sponge releases sperm.

2 Sperm enter another sponge and fertilize an egg.

3 A larva develops.

4 Water currents carry the larva away.

5 The larva settles on a hard surface. It develops into an adult sponge.

FIGURE 4 ·······
Reproduction of a Sponge

These sponges are reproducing sexually. ✎ **Complete these tasks.**

1. **Identify** A budded sponge is a product of (asexual/sexual) reproduction and a larva is a product of (asexual/sexual) reproduction.
2. **Interpret Diagrams** How do the sponge larva and adult differ?

   They have different shapes and sizes. The larva moves through water; the adult is stationary.

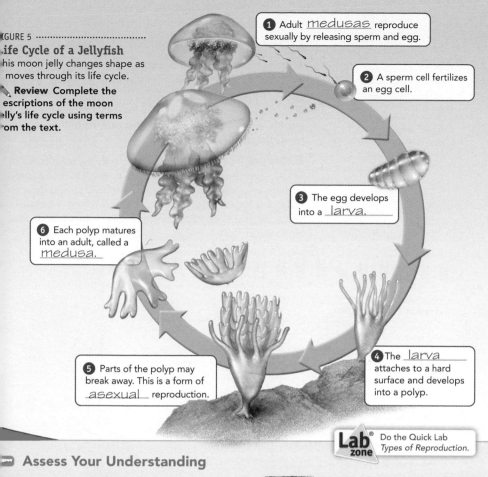

FIGURE 5 ....

Life Cycle of a Jellyfish
This moon jelly changes shape as it moves through its life cycle.

✍ **Review** Complete the descriptions of the moon jelly's life cycle using terms from the text.

1 Adult <u>medusas</u> reproduce sexually by releasing sperm and egg.

2 A sperm cell fertilizes an egg cell.

3 The egg develops into a <u>larva</u>.

4 The <u>larva</u> attaches to a hard surface and develops into a polyp.

5 Parts of the polyp may break away. This is a form of <u>asexual</u> reproduction.

6 Each polyp matures into an adult, called a <u>medusa.</u>

Lab zone Do the Quick Lab *Types of Reproduction.*

⬚ Assess Your Understanding

a. Define (Asexual/(Sexual)) reproduction involves the joining of sperm and eggs.

b. Summarize How are the reproductive cycles of sponges and cnidarians similar?
<u>Both have forms that</u>
<u>reproduce asexually and</u>
<u>sexually.</u>

c. CHALLENGE In rare cases, female sharks born in captivity that have never been exposed to male sharks have become pregnant. Is this an example of asexual or sexual reproduction? Explain your answer.
<u>This is an example of asexual</u>
<u>reproduction because only one</u>
<u>parent is involved.</u>

got it? ....

◯ **I get it!** Now I know that the two ways animals can reproduce are <u>asexually or sexually.</u>

◯ **I need extra help with** <u>See TE note.</u>

Go to **MY SCIENCE** ⬤ **COACH** *online for help with this subject.*

249

Differentiated Instruction

L1 Asexual Reproduction of a Polyp Help students understand reproduction of the polyp stage of the moon jelly by comparing it to budding in the hydra. In both cases, large offspring break off the parent. Contrast this with reproduction by the medusa stage in which a small larva is formed.

L3 Gemmules In addition to forming buds, sponges can reproduce sexually by forming gemmules. Encourage students to research gemmules, including how they form and when they are released. Students can prepare a poster showing what they have learned.

Explain

Teach With Visuals

Tell students to look at **Figure 5.** Ask: **Which body form reproduces sexually?** *(The medusa)* **Which body form reproduces asexually?** *(The polyp)* **How are polyps produced?** *(The male medusas release sperm, which fertilize eggs of female medusas. A fertilized egg develops into a larva, which then develops into a polyp.)* Make sure students understand that polyps are produced sexually, but they themselves reproduce asexually. The opposite is true for medusas, which are produced asexually, but reproduce sexually.

Elaborate

21st Century Learning

L3 INFORMATION LITERACY The medusa body form is named after a figure from Greek mythology. Invite interested students to research Medusa and share their information with the class.

Lab Resource: Quick Lab

L1 TYPES OF REPRODUCTION Students will observe and sketch the stages of a hydra budding.

Evaluate

Assess Your Understanding

After students answer the questions, have them evaluate their understanding by completing the appropriate sentence.

R T I Response to Intervention

1a. If students have trouble contrasting asexual and sexual reproduction, **then** review with them the definitions of these two terms.

  b. If students cannot identify the similarities between the two reproductive cycles, **then** have them review **Figure 4** and **Figure 5.**

  c. If students have difficulty relating a new situation to the definitions they learned, **then** review examples of asexual and sexual reproduction.

MY SCIENCE ⬤ **COACH** Have students go online for help in understanding types of reproduction.

249

Explain

Teach Key Concepts 🔑

Remind students that fertilization is the joining of a sperm and an egg. Depending on the organism, this can take place inside or outside the female's body. Ask: **What is external fertilization?** *(The joining of an egg and sperm outside the body of the female)* **Why does external fertilization usually take place in water?** *(To keep the eggs and sperm from drying out)* **What are some organisms that have external fertilization?** *(Fishes, amphibians, and aquatic invertebrates)*

Support the Big Q ❓ UbD

REPRODUCTIVE BEHAVIOR IN FISHES Many aquatic organisms deposit eggs and sperm in the water and then leave. This includes fishes such as salmon, pike, and brook trout. Some fishes, however, show complex behavior patterns that involve protection of their offspring. Sunfish and black bass prepare nests where eggs and sperm are deposited. The adults stay near the nest and chase away fishes and other animals that might eat the eggs. Ask: **Why are developing fish eggs vulnerable to predators?** *(Samples: They have no shells for protection. They can't swim away and hide.)* Ask students if they have ever seen a photograph of a seahorse. This organism is a kind of fish. Tell students that the male seahorse has a pouch on its body into which the female deposits her eggs. The male fertilizes the eggs in his pouch, and the eggs develop there. (Remind students that this is an example of external fertilization because it still takes place outside the *female's* body.) Ask: **Which fertilized eggs get better protection, those of a salmon, a sunfish, or a seahorse?** *(The eggs of a seahorse)* **Which of these fishes do you think produces more eggs? Why?** *(Sample: The salmon; its eggs have no protection, so a lot of them probably are eaten by fishes or other animals.)*

How Do External and Internal Fertilization Differ?

Sexual reproduction involves fertilization, or the joining of a sperm cell and an egg cell. Fertilization may occur either outside or inside of the female organism's body. **External fertilization occurs outside of the female's body, and internal fertilization occurs inside the female's body.**

External Fertilization For many fishes, amphibians, and aquatic invertebrates, fertilization occurs outside the body. Usually external fertilization must take place in water to prevent the eggs and sperm from drying out. First, the female releases eggs into the water. Then the male releases sperm nearby. **Figure 6** shows trout fertilization.

FIGURE 6 ·····
External Fertilization
This male trout is depositing a milky cloud of sperm over the round, white eggs.

✎ Use the text to answer the following questions.
1. **Identify** (Land/Water) is the best environment for external fertilization.
2. **CHALLENGE** What might be a possible disadvantage of external fertilization?
   Sample: The water current may wash away the eggs or the sperm. The fertilized eggs are out in the open and may be eaten by predators.

Digital Lesson: Assign the *Do the Math* activity online and have students submit their work to you.

MY SCIENCE online.com ▸ Fertilization

LESSON 7.1

Internal Fertilization Fertilization occurs inside the body in many aquatic animals and all land animals. The male releases sperm directly into the female's body, where the eggs are located.

Most invertebrates and many fishes, amphibians, reptiles, and birds lay eggs outside the parent's body. The offspring continue to develop inside the eggs. For other animals, including most mammals, fertilized eggs develop inside the female animal. The female then gives birth to live young. The length of time between fertilization and birth is called the **gestation period.** Opossums have the shortest gestation period—around 13 days. African elephants have the longest gestation period—up to 22 months.

✏️ **Compare and Contrast**
Describe how external and internal fertilization are alike and different.

Both involve sexual reproduction. But external fertilization occurs outside the female's body and internal fertilization occurs inside the female's body.

do the math!

Study the graph and answer the questions below.

1 Calculate About how many days longer is the giraffe's gestation period than the fox's?

About 400 days

2 Make Generalizations How do you think an animal's size relates to the length of its gestation period?

Larger animals generally have a longer gestation period.

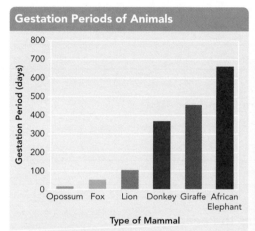

Gestation Periods of Animals

Gestation Period (days): 0, 100, 200, 300, 400, 500, 600, 700, 800

Type of Mammal: Opossum, Fox, Lion, Donkey, Giraffe, African Elephant

 Lab zone Do the Quick Lab *Types of Fertilization.*

🦴 **Assess Your Understanding**

got it?

⃝ **I get it!** Now I know that external fertilization occurs _outside of the female's body_ and internal fertilization occurs _inside the female's body._

⃝ **I need extra help with** _See TE note._

Go to **my science COACH** online for help with this subject.

251

Explain

Lead a Discussion

INTERNAL FERTILIZATION Explain that internal fertilization takes place inside the body of the female. Ask: **In which animals does internal fertilization take place?** *(Most invertebrates, many fishes, amphibians, reptiles, birds, and mammals)* **How is reproduction in mammals different from reproduction by most of the other groups of animals you listed?** *(In most of the other animals, the fertilized eggs develop outside the body of the female. In most mammals, the fertilized eggs develop inside the body of the female.)* **What is a gestation period?** *(The time between fertilization and birth)*

Elaborate

Do the Math!

L1 Explain that a bar graph is a way to display data that compares numbers of different categories. In this graph, the height of each bar represents the number of days of gestation. Tell students that they can quickly compare different types of animals by comparing the heights of the bars that represent them.

△ **Calculate** Remind students that calculating involves determining a value using math skills, such as adding, subtracting, multiplying, or dividing.

See the *Math Skill and Problem-Solving Activities* for support.

Lab Resource: Quick Lab **Lab zone**

L1 TYPES OF FERTILIZATION Students will model external and internal fertilization using flour and peppercorns.

Evaluate

Assess Your Understanding

Have students evaluate their understanding by completing the appropriate sentence.

R T I Response to Intervention

If students have difficulty comparing and contrasting types of fertilization, **then** review the meanings of the prefixes *ex-* and *in-*.

my science COACH Have students go online for help in understanding external and internal fertilization.

Differentiated Instruction

L1 Gestation and Incubation
Students may note that all the animals listed in the *Do the Math* activity are mammals, and wonder if the term *gestation period* applies to birds. Tell them that the time from egg laying to hatching in birds is called the *incubation period.*

L3 Internal Fertilization in Fishes
Some species of fishes and reptiles have internal fertilization and the eggs develop inside the body of the female. Encourage interested students to research how this development is different from that of mammals. Students should also find examples of species in which eggs develop this way.

Lab zone **After the Inquiry Warm-Up**

Animal Reproduction and Fertilization

Inquiry Warm-Up, *Making More*

In the Inquiry Warm-Up, you investigated two methods of reproduction. Using what you learned from that activity, answer the questions below.

1. **INFER** Why do you think Team A put down each set of beans more often than Team B?

   _____

   _____

2. **DRAW CONCLUSIONS** What do the first bean for Team A and the first two beans for Team B represent?

   _____

   _____

3. **CALCULATE** For Team B, you can find how many times the beans would produce another offspring by multiplying the number of minutes by 60 and then dividing that total by 20. How many beans would Team B have if the experiment continued for five minutes?

   _____

4. **INFER** Explain how the reproductive process would continue for each example.

   _____

   _____

   _____

Assess Your Understanding

Animal Reproduction and Fertilization

How Do Animals Reproduce?

1a. **DEFINE** (Asexual/Sexual) reproduction involves the joining of sperm and eggs.

b. **SUMMARIZE** How are the reproductive cycles of sponges and cnidarians similar? _____

_____

c. [CHALLENGE] In rare cases, female sharks born in captivity that have never been exposed to male sharks have become pregnant. Is this an example of asexual or sexual reproduction? Explain your answer. _____

_____

_____

gotit?··

○ **I get it!** Now I know that the two ways animals can reproduce are _____

_____

○ **I need extra help with** _____

_____

How Do External and Internal Fertilization Differ?

gotit?··

○ **I get it!** Now I know that external fertilization occurs _____
_____ and internal fertilization occurs _____

_____

○ **I need extra help with** _____

_____

Name _____ Date _____ Class _____

Animal Reproduction and Fertilization

How Do Animals Reproduce?

Animals undergo either asexual or sexual reproduction to make more of their own kind or species. In asexual reproduction, one parent produces a new organism identical to itself. This new organism receives an exact copy of the parent's set of genetic material, or DNA. During sexual reproduction, the sex cells of two parent organisms join together to produce a new organism that has DNA from both parents. Most vertebrates and most invertebrates reproduce sexually.

In asexual reproduction, one parent can produce many offspring quickly but there is not variation in the offspring's DNA and it may not survive changes to its environment. Sexual reproduction produces offspring with new combinations of DNA, but requires finding a mate and more time to develop offspring.

Several aquatic invertebrates have life cycles that alternate between asexual and sexual reproduction. Sponges reproduce asexually by budding, or having offspring grow out of and break off from the parent. Sponges also reproduce sexually but they do not have separate sexes. A sponge can produce an egg cell and the sperm cells to fertilize it, after which a **larva,** or immature form of the animal that looks very different from the parent, develops. Many cnidarians alternate between two body forms. In a **polyp** form that looks like an upright vase, they reproduce asexually. In a **medusa** form that looks like an open umbrella, they reproduce sexually.

How Do External and Internal Fertilization Differ?

Sexual reproduction involves either **external fertilization** or **internal fertilization. External fertilization occurs outside the female's body, and internal fertilization occurs inside the female's body.** For many fishes, amphibians, and aquatic invertebrates, fertilization occurs outside the body in water to prevent the eggs and sperm from drying out. Fertilization occurs inside the body in many aquatic animals and all land animals. Offspring develop, either inside an egg or inside the female animal. The length of time between fertilization and birth is called the **gestation period.**

On a separate sheet of paper, compare and contrast asexual and sexual reproduction.

Review and Reinforce

Animal Reproduction and Fertilization

Understanding Main Ideas
Answer the following questions in the spaces provided.

1. Why do animals reproduce?

_____

2. How do animals reproduce asexually?

_____

_____

3. How do animals reproduce sexually?

_____

_____

4. What is the difference between external and internal fertilization?

_____

_____

Building Vocabulary
Match each term with its definition by writing the letter of the correct definition in the right column beside the term in the left column.

5. ___ larva

6. ___ polyp

7. ___ medusa

8. ___ external fertilization

9. ___ internal fertilization

10. ___ gestation period

a. fertilization that takes place inside the female organism's body

b. a body form that looks like an open umbrella

c. an immature form of an animal that looks different from the adult

d. the length of time between fertilization and birth

e. a body form that looks like an upright vase

f. fertilization that takes place outside the female organism's body

Enrich

Animal Reproduction and Fertilization

The eggs of most vertebrates including many amphibians, reptiles, and birds are fertilized inside the body. The females lay the fertilized eggs, which continue to grow outside the body. Read the passage below. Then use a separate sheet of paper to answer the questions that follow.

The Emperor Penguin, A "Good Daddy"

Birds take care of their eggs. Often the eggs are laid in a protective nest and a parent, usually the female, keeps the eggs warm in a process called incubation or brooding.

However, there is an interesting exception: the emperor penguin from Antarctica. This large penguin has a mass of about 16 kilograms. The male penguin is the caretaker from right after the egg is laid. The female lays one large egg each year using up most of her resources. Then she goes fishing to replace these resources. The male stays on Antarctica's ice and keeps the egg warm on his feet covered by a fold of skin.

This process goes on for about 8 weeks in the Antarctic cold. About the time the egg hatches the female returns with food and the male can go for food. He returns with food to share in about two weeks. The emperor penguin chick is truly Daddy's little boy or girl.

1. Do birds reproduce sexually or asexually? Explain.
2. Where does fertilization take place for a bird?
3. How are bird eggs usually cared for?
4. How is the emperor penguin an exception?

Name _____ Date _____ Class _____

Animal Reproduction and Fertilization

Fill in the blank to complete each statement.

1. _____ reproduction requires only one parent organism.

2. Most vertebrates and most invertebrates reproduce _____.

3. Sponges reproduce asexually when a new sponge grows from a parent and breaks off in a process called _____.

4. _____ may occur either inside or outside the female organism's body.

5. External fertilization usually occurs in _____ so that the egg and sperm cells do not dry out.

If the statement is true, write *true*. If the statement is false, change the underlined word or words to make the statement true.

6. _____ <u>Sexual</u> reproduction requires a mate.

7. _____ Offspring from <u>asexual</u> reproduction have different DNA than the parent(s).

8. _____ A(n) <u>polyp</u> is a cnidarian body form that looks like an open umbrella.

9. _____ <u>Internal</u> fertilization occurs inside the female organism's body.

10. _____ The length of time between fertilization and birth is called the <u>fertilization</u> period.

Animal Reproduction and Fertilization

Answer Key

After the Inquiry Warm-Up

1. Team A's method of reproduction produces offspring more quickly than Team B's method.

2. The first beans represent the parent generation.

3. $5 \times 60 = 300$; $300 \div 20 = 15$; Team B will have 15 beans.

4. Team A: Each offspring bean can produce one pair of offspring beans of its own for each reproductive cycle.
Team B: Each offspring bean can pair with another offspring bean to create one offspring bean for each reproductive cycle.

Key Concept Summaries

In asexual reproduction, one parent can produce many offspring quickly but the offspring has no variation in its DNA from the parent's DNA; they are genetically identical. Sexual reproduction produces offspring with new combinations of DNA, but takes a longer amount of time because it requires time for finding a mate and allowing the offspring to develop before birth.

Review and Reinforce

1. because reproduction is essential to the survival of a species

2. A parent organism produces a new organism, identical to itself.

3. The sex cells of two parent organisms join together to produce a new organism that has DNA from both parents.

4. External fertilization occurs outside the female organism's body. Internal fertilization occurs inside the female organism's body.

5. c

6. e

7. b

8. f

9. a

10. d

Enrich

1. Birds reproduce sexually. A male sperm cell and a female egg cell join together to produce a new organism.

2. Fertilization takes place inside the female bird's body.

3. The eggs are laid in a nest and kept warm by the female bird until hatching.

4. The male emperor penguin is a caretaker for the egg, keeping it warm on his feet, wrapped in a skin fold.

Lesson Quiz

1. Asexual

2. sexually

3. budding

4. Fertilization

5. water

6. true

7. sexual

8. medusa

9. true

10. gestation

Place the outside corner, the corner away from the dotted line, in the corner of your copy machine to copy onto letter-size paper.

Development and Growth

How does an animal's behavior help it survive and reproduce?

Lesson Pacing: 3–4 periods or 1½–2 blocks

🕐 **SHORT ON TIME?** To do this lesson in approximately half the time, do the Activate Prior Knowledge activity on page 252. A discussion of the Key Concepts on pages 253, 255, and 259 will familiarize students with the lesson content. Have students do the Quick Labs. The rest of the lesson can be completed by students independently.

> **Preference Navigator,** in the online Planning tools, allows you to customize *Interactive Science* to your own teaching style. You can also edit lesson plans by selecting the Lesson Planner option.
>
> **Digital Teacher's Edition** allows you to access your Teacher's Edition and Resource materials online.

Lesson Vocabulary

- amniotic egg
- placenta
- metamorphosis
- complete metamorphosis
- pupa
- incomplete metamorphosis
- nymph
- tadpole

Content Refresher

Professional Development Note

Altricial and Precocial Birds Birds are often characterized as either altricial or precocial, according to the condition of the newly hatched birds. An altricial bird is naked when it hatches. Its eyes are closed and it is completely dependent on its parents for food. It is also dependent on its parents for warmth. Although all birds are endotherms as adults, newly hatched altricial birds cannot maintain a constant body temperature. Until this ability develops, a parent stays in the nest most of the time, keeping the chicks warm.

Precocial birds hatch with a covering of down. Their eyes are open, and they are able to walk and follow their parents right away. Precocial birds vary in the extent to which their parents feed them. Precocial species often nest on the ground, and are vulnerable to predators. The precocial development allows the baby bird to be mobile and less vulnerable. It also means that the parent does not have to commute between a food source and the nest. Although precocial species can walk soon after hatching, the birds cannot fly until their wing feathers develop.

LESSON OBJECTIVES

- Compare and contrast embryonic development in different vertebrates.
- Describe life cycles in invertebrates and vertebrates.
- Describe how different vertebrates care for their young.

Blended Path
Active learning using Student Edition, Inquiry Path, and Digital Path

ENGAGE AND EXPLORE

Teach this lesson using a variety of resources. Begin by reading **My Planet Diary** as a class. Have students share ideas about why it is important for some animals to find a mate. Then have students do the **Inquiry Warm-Up activity.** Students will observe an egg and discuss its various parts. The **After the Inquiry Warm-Up worksheet** sets up a discussion about the functions of the parts of a chicken egg. Have volunteers share their answers to question 4 about how a chicken egg and a human embryo are alike and different.

EXPLAIN AND ELABORATE

Teach Key Concepts by explaining that development of offspring takes place inside or outside of the parent's body. Use **Figure 1** to identify the structures and functions of parts of an amniotic egg. **Lead a Discussion** about egg-retaining animals. Use **Figure 2** to illustrate how a placental mother provides the embryo with everything it needs during development.

Continue to **Teach Key Concepts** by explaining that young animals undergo changes in their bodies between birth and maturity, when they are able to reproduce. **Lead a Discussion** about complete metamorphosis and incomplete metamorphosis. Have students identify the stages of complete metamorphosis in **Figure 4. Lead a Discussion** about the three stages of incomplete metamorphosis. The process of frog metamorphosis is visible in **Figure 5.**

Describe the different amounts of care that animals provide to their offspring to **Teach Key Concepts.** Compare how the snakes in **Figure 6** are protected during development versus how fish eggs are protected. Use the **Support the Big Q** to illustrate the advantages and disadvantages of ground-nesting and tree-nesting birds. Hand out the **Key Concept Summaries** as a review of each part of the lesson. Students can also use the online **Vocab Flash Cards** to review key terms.

EVALUATE

Have students take the **Lesson Quiz.** For an alternate assessment, see the *ExamView®* Computer Test Generator, Progress Monitoring Assessments, or SuccessTracker™.

ELL Support

1 Content and Language

Remind students that in some cases the prefix *in-* means "in." Point out that the prefix *in-* is used in the term *incomplete metamorphosis.* However in this case, *in-* means "not." *Incomplete metamorphosis* lacks the larval stage, so it is not considered *complete metamorphosis.*

| DIFFERENTIATED INSTRUCTION KEY |
| L1 Struggling Students or Special Needs |
| L2 On-Level Students L3 Advanced Students |

LESSON PLANNER 7.2

Lab zone Inquiry Path
Hands-on learning in the Lab zone

Digital Path
Online learning at my science online.com

ENGAGE AND EXPLORE

To teach this lesson with an emphasis on inquiry, begin with the **Inquiry Warm-Up activity.** Students will examine a chicken egg. Discuss what students observed about the chicken egg. Have students do the **After the Inquiry Warm-Up worksheet.** Talk about the function of the yolk and the shell. Have volunteers share their answers to question 4 about the similarities and differences between a human embryo and a chicken egg.

ENGAGE AND EXPLORE

Teach this lesson using digital resources. Begin by having students explore real-world connections to how animals develop and grow at **My Planet Diary** online. Have them access the Chapter Resources to find the **Unlock the Big Question activity.** There they can answer the questions and refine their responses as they continue through the lesson. You can re-assign the activity and have students submit their work so you can track their progress.

EXPLAIN AND ELABORATE

Focus on the **Inquiry Skill** for the lesson. Point out that when you interpret data, you use facts, figures, and information to draw conclusions. What conclusions could be drawn about the chicken egg based on the data interpreted in the **Inquiry Warm-Up activity?** *(Answers will vary.)* Have students do the **Quick Lab** to compare the protection provided to an embryo by an egg shell and a mother's body and then share their results.

Do the **Teacher Demo** to give children the opportunity to see insect metamorphosis. Do the **Quick Lab** to model complete and incomplete metamorphosis.

Support the Big Q by identifying some of the advantages of ground-nesting birds. Do the **Build Inquiry activity** to illustrate the importance of the nutrients found in milk. Do the **Quick Lab** to reinforce understanding of how parental care can influence the survival of offspring. Students can use the online **Vocab Flash Cards** to review key terms.

EXPLAIN AND ELABORATE

Students reading above, at, or below the lexile measure of this lesson can access basic content readings at their level at **My Reading Web.** Have students use the online **Vocab Flash Cards** to preview key terms. Do the **Quick Lab** and then ask students to share their comparisons.

The online **Interactive Art activity** will allow students to explore the life cycles of an insect, a parasite, a mollusk, and a human. Do the **Quick Lab** to model complete and incomplete metamorphosis.

Use the **Support the Big Q** to illustrate why some birds are able to move around as soon as they hatch. Assign the **Do the Math activity** online and have students submit their work to you. Have students complete the **Quick Lab** to better understand how the survival of offspring can be influenced by parental support. The **Key Concept Summaries** online allow students to read a summary and see an image associated with each part of the lesson. Online remediation is available at **My Science Coach.**

EVALUATE

Have students take the **Lesson Quiz.** For an alternate assessment, see the *ExamView®* Computer Test Generator, Progress Monitoring Assessments, or SuccessTracker™.

EVALUATE

Have students take the **Lesson Quiz.** For an alternate assessment, see the *ExamView®* Computer Test Generator, Progress Monitoring Assessments, or SuccessTracker™.

2 Frontload the Lesson
Preview the lesson visuals, labels, and captions. Ask students what they know about the terms *amniotic egg* and *placenta.* Explain the specific meanings these words have in science.

3 Comprehensible Input
Have students study the visuals and their captions on pages 253, 254, 255, 256, 257, 258, 259, and 260 to support the key concepts of the lesson.

4 Language Production
Pair or group students with varied language abilities to complete labs collaboratively for language practice. Have each student copy the completed written lab for personal reference.

5 Assess Understanding
Have students create a portfolio of their notes and then do oral presentations of lesson content.

LESSON 7.2

Development and Growth

Establish Learning Objectives

After this lesson, students will be able to:

 Compare and contrast embryonic development in different vertebrates.

 Describe life cycles in invertebrates and vertebrates.

 Describe how different vertebrates care for their young.

Engage

Activate Prior Knowledge

MY PLANET DIARY Read *Beware of Glass* with the class. Ask: **What would happen if an animal could not locate a mate?** *(It could not produce offspring.)* **How might a species be harmed if certain objects tricked some animals into thinking they were possible mates?** *(The animal would waste its time trying to attract or mate with the object so the population of the species would decrease.)*

BIG IDEAS OF SCIENCE REFERENCE LIBRARY 📖
Have students look up the following topics: Gorillas, Penguins, Sea Horse, Sloth.

Explore

Lab Resource: Inquiry Warm-Up 🧪

L2 **"EGGS-AMINATION"** Students will observe a chicken egg.

LESSON

2 Development and Growth

 Where Do Embryos Develop?

 How Do Young Animals Develop?

 How Do Animals Care for Their Young?

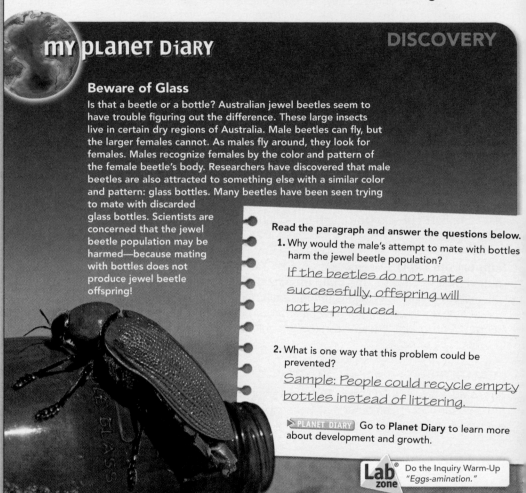

MY PLANET DIARY   DISCOVERY

Beware of Glass

Is that a beetle or a bottle? Australian jewel beetles seem to have trouble figuring out the difference. These large insects live in certain dry regions of Australia. Male beetles can fly, but the larger females cannot. As males fly around, they look for females. Males recognize females by the color and pattern of the female beetle's body. Researchers have discovered that male beetles are also attracted to something else with a similar color and pattern: glass bottles. Many beetles have been seen trying to mate with discarded glass bottles. Scientists are concerned that the jewel beetle population may be harmed—because mating with bottles does not produce jewel beetle offspring!

Read the paragraph and answer the questions below.

1. Why would the male's attempt to mate with bottles harm the jewel beetle population?

   If the beetles do not mate successfully, offspring will not be produced.

2. What is one way that this problem could be prevented?

   Sample: People could recycle empty bottles instead of littering.

> PLANET DIARY Go to **Planet Diary** to learn more about development and growth.

🧪 Lab zone Do the Inquiry Warm-Up "Eggs-amination."

252 Animal Reproduction and Behavior

SUPPORT ALL READERS

Lexile Measure = 960L   Lexile Word Count = 1701

Prior Exposure to Content: Many students may have misconceptions on this topic

Academic Vocabulary: *data, interpret, summarize*

Science Vocabulary: *amniotic egg, placenta, metamorphosis, pupa, nymph*

Concept Level: May be difficult for students who struggle with math

Preteach With: My Planet Diary "Beware of Glass" and Figure 1 activity

Go to **My Reading Web** to access leveled readings that provide a foundation for the content.

my science online.com

Vocabulary
- amniotic egg • placenta • metamorphosis
- complete metamorphosis • pupa
- incomplete metamorphosis • nymph • tadpole

Skills
- Reading: Summarize
- Inquiry: Interpret Data

Where Do Embryos Develop?

Turtles, sharks, and mice all reproduce sexually. But after fertilization occurs, the offspring of these animals develop in different ways. **The growing offspring, or embryo, may develop outside or inside of the parent's body.**

Egg-Laying Animals The offspring of some animals develop inside an egg laid outside of the parent's body. Most animals without backbones, including worms and insects, lay eggs. Many fishes, reptiles, and birds lay eggs, too. The contents of the egg provide all the nutrients that the developing embryo needs. The eggs of land vertebrates, such as reptiles and birds, are called **amniotic eggs.** Amniotic eggs are covered with membranes and a leathery shell while still inside the parent's body. **Figure 1** shows some of the structures of an amniotic egg.

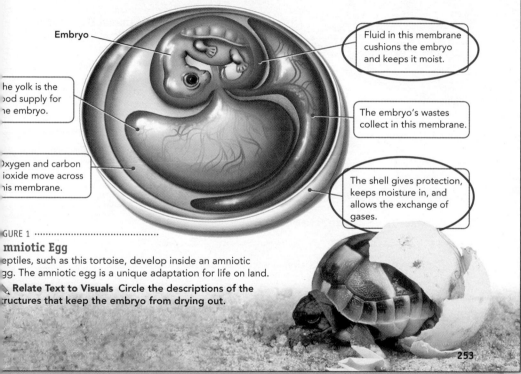

Embryo

The yolk is the food supply for the embryo.

Oxygen and carbon dioxide move across this membrane.

Fluid in this membrane cushions the embryo and keeps it moist.

The embryo's wastes collect in this membrane.

The shell gives protection, keeps moisture in, and allows the exchange of gases.

FIGURE 1
Amniotic Egg
Reptiles, such as this tortoise, develop inside an amniotic egg. The amniotic egg is a unique adaptation for life on land.

Relate Text to Visuals Circle the descriptions of the structures that keep the embryo from drying out.

253

1 Content and Language
Explain that the word *metamorphosis* combines the prefix *meta-,* meaning "change," the Greek root *morph,* meaning "form," and the suffix *-osis,* meaning "process." It is the process of a body changing its form.

2 Frontload the Lesson
Encourage students to think of examples of animals that lay eggs to produce offspring. Help students identify an essential difference between this method of developing an embryo and the method used by dogs, cats, and human beings.

3 Comprehensible Input
Have small groups of students contribute to a classroom mural that shows the metamorphoses of crustaceans, insects, and amphibians. Students could illustrate details of each version of the process using a cycle diagram or a flowchart.

Explain

Introduce Vocabulary
Teach Key Concepts 🔑
Remind students that eggs can be fertilized inside the female's body or outside the female's body. Explain that development of the offspring takes place inside or outside the female's body. Ask: **Why are the eggs of fishes able to develop outside the body of the female?** *(The eggs are laid in water and develop there. They will not dry out.)* **What would happen to fish eggs if they were laid on land?** *(They would dry out and die.)* **Which two groups of vertebrates produce shelled eggs?** *(Reptiles and birds)* **Why is the shelled egg important?** *(It allows the offspring to grow and develop without drying out.)* Explain to students that a few mammals lay eggs. Egg-laying mammals are called *monotremes* and include the duck-billed platypus and four species of echidna (spiny anteaters).

Teach With Visuals

Tell students to look at **Figure 1.** This illustration shows a turtle egg. Explain to students that a bird's egg has a similar structure. Ask: **What is the developing offspring called when it is inside the egg?** *(An embryo)* **What is the function of the shell?** *(To protect the embryo and keep moisture inside the egg)* **What is the function of the yolk?** *(To provide food for the growing embryo)* Tell students that, in some species of turtle, part of the yolk remains attached to the underside of the animal. There it provides nourishment for a time after hatching. Direct students' attention to the newly hatched tortoise, or land turtle. Point out the fragments of membrane attached to the broken edges of the shell. Although the shell looks like the shell of a chicken egg, it is not as hard.

21st Century Learning

CREATIVITY Have students read *Penguins* in the **Big Ideas of Science Reference Library** and research more information about the physical development of a penguin chick from birth to its juvenile stage to adulthood. Ask students to create a poster that visually displays the information about the chick's development and the changes it undergoes.

My Planet Diary provides an opportunity for students to explore real-world connections to how animals develop and grow.

my science online | Developing Embryos

Explain

Lead a Discussion

EGG-RETAINING ANIMALS Animals whose eggs develop inside the female include sharks, guppies, and garter snakes. Emphasize that, while development inside the parent's body provides extra protection for the eggs, there is no connection to the parent. Ask: **In egg-retaining animals, where does the embryo's nourishment come from?** *(The yolk of the egg)* **When does the egg hatch?** *(Either before or after being released from the parent's body)*

Summarize Tell students that when they summarize, they briefly restate the main ideas of what they have read or heard in their own words. In addition to the main ideas, a summary can contain the most important supporting details. However, a summary must be short and concise.

Teach With Visuals

Tell students to look at **Figure 2.** Explain that most mammals are placental mammals like the cat shown here. Ask: **What is a placenta?** *(The organ through which materials are exchanged between the embryo and the mother)* **What materials move into the embryo?** *(Oxygen and food)* **What materials move out of the embryo?** *(Carbon dioxide and wastes)* Emphasize that the blood of the mother and the blood of the embryo do not mix. Materials move across the placenta by diffusion. If students have not previously learned about diffusion, you may wish to briefly explain this process. Remind students that in some mammals, called *marsupials,* the young are born at an early stage of development and usually continue to develop in a pouch on the mother's body.

Lab Resource: Quick Lab

L1 **"EGGS-TRA" PROTECTION** Students will compare the protection that an egg's shell and a mother's body provide to an embryo.

Evaluate

Assess Your Understanding

Have students evaluate their understanding by completing the appropriate sentence.

RTI Response to Intervention

If students do not recall what they learned about embryos, **then** review the three types of animals—egg-laying, egg-retaining, and placental mammals.

my science coach Have students go online for help in understanding embryos.

254 Animal Reproduction and Behavior

Summarize Read the text about egg-retaining animals. Then summarize how the embryo develops in these animals.

The embryo is kept in the parent's body. The yolk provides all the nutrients.

Mother's placenta

To Embryo *Food and oxygen*

Embryo

Blood

To Mother *Waste and carbon dioxide*

Egg-Retaining Animals In certain animals, an embryo develops inside an egg that is kept, or retained, within the parent's body. The developing embryo gets all its nutrients from the egg's yolk, just like the offspring of egg-laying animals. The young do not receive any extra nutrients from the parent. The egg hatches either before or after being released from the parent's body. This type of development is found in fishes, amphibians, and reptiles.

Placental Mammals In dogs, horses, humans, and other placental mammals, the embryo develops inside the mother's body. The mother provides the embryo with everything it needs during development. Materials are exchanged between the embryo and the mother through an organ called the **placenta,** shown in **Figure 2.** Blood carrying food and oxygen from the mother flows to the placenta and then to the embryo. Blood carrying wastes and carbon dioxide from the embryo flows to the placenta and then to the mother. The mother's blood does not mix with the embryo's blood. A placental mammal develops inside its mother's body until its body systems can function on their own.

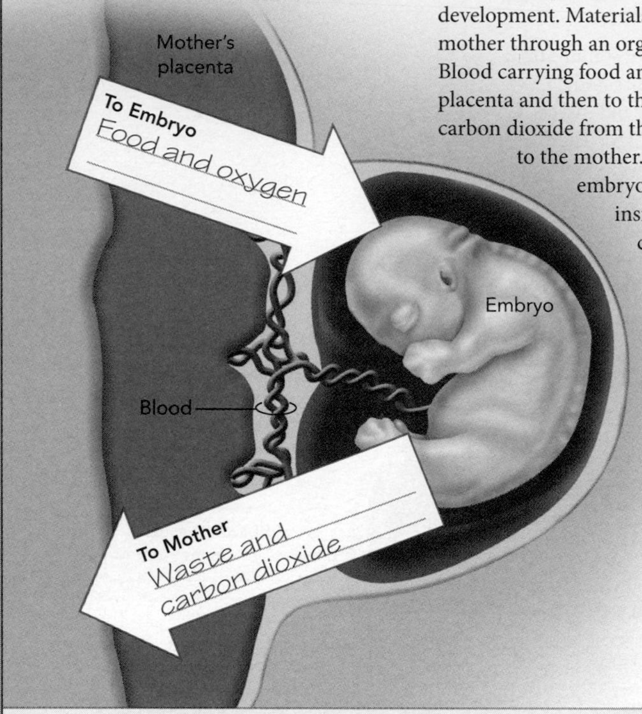

FIGURE 2 ·······························
Placental Mammal Development
This cat embryo develops inside its mother for about two months.

Complete these tasks.

1. **Identify** Write which materials pass to the embryo and which materials pass to the parent on the lines in the arrows.

2. **Explain** Why is the placenta such an important structure in development?
   The placenta allows materials to be exchanged

 **Lab zone** Do the Quick Lab "Eggs-tra" Protection

Assess Your Understanding

got it? ·······························

○ **I get it!** Now I know that the places embryos can develop are *outside or inside of the parent's body.*

○ **I need extra help with** *See TE note.*

Go to **my science coach** online for help with this subject.

How Do Young Animals Develop?

Living things grow, change, and reproduce during their lifetimes. Some young animals, including most vertebrates, look like small versions of adults. Other animals go through the process of metamorphosis, or major body changes, as they develop from young organisms into adults. 🔑 **Young animals undergo changes in their bodies between birth and maturity, when they are able to reproduce.** As you read, notice the similarities and differences among the life cycles of crustaceans, insects, and amphibians.

Crustaceans Most crustaceans, such as lobsters, crabs, and shrimp, begin their lives as tiny, swimming larvae. The bodies of these larvae do not resemble those of adults. Larvae may swim or drift in the water as they grow and change. Eventually, through metamorphosis, crustacean larvae develop into adults. **Figure 3** shows three stages of a lobster's life cycle.

FIGURE 3

Lobster Metamorphosis

Lobster larvae are only 8 millimeters long. Adults can reach lengths of 1 meter!

✎ Use the photos to help you complete the tasks.

1. **Sequence** Write the correct order of the lobster's development in the circles above each photo.

2. **Interpret Photos**
Which structures changed as the lobster developed and grew?

   Sample: The antennae, tails, and claws grew larger at each stage.

255

Explain

Teach Key Concepts 🔑

Remind students that all animals begin as a fertilized egg. During the time between fertilization and hatching or being born, growth and development take place. In most vertebrates, the offspring that is hatched or born looks like the parent. Emphasize that all offspring go through some amount of change between the time they are born or hatched and the time they are mature adults. The amount of change is different in different species. Ask: **Can you name some animals whose offspring look a lot like the adults?** *(Samples: cats, dogs, guppies, turtles)* Ask students if they have ever seen a baby bird. Ask volunteers to describe it. A newly hatched bird may have very few feathers, but it has feet and a beak like the parents. Ask students what changes they would expect the baby bird to go through in the first month or two of its life. *(Samples: The bird will grow feathers. It will get larger and its wings will get stronger.)* Ask: **What is metamorphosis?** *(Major body changes as an animal develops from a young organism into an adult)* **Do kittens, puppies, and baby birds go through metamorphosis? Explain.** *(No; they have the same body shape as the adults, so the changes that occur as they grow up will not be major changes.)*

Elaborate

21st Century Learning

INFORMATION LITERACY Direct students' attention to **Figure 3,** and remind them that shrimp and crabs also go through a similar metamorphosis. Tell students that many shrimp are farmed, or raised in captivity. Ask students to suggest the kinds of information that a shrimp farmer would need to know in order to successfully raise shrimp. Discuss ways this information could be obtained.

Differentiated Instruction

L1 Baby Animals Have students look through nature catalogs or do online research to find pictures of baby mammals. Encourage them to find a sequence of images of a species to show how the animal changes from birth to maturity. If students need guidance, suggest they look for changes in coat color or pattern, changes in facial features, or the development of adult structures, such as antlers. After students have done their research, have them work in small groups to share what they have learned. You may wish to have student groups prepare posters or a bulletin board display for the whole class to enjoy. If students do research on the Internet, remind them to follow prescribed guidelines for Internet use.

Explain

Lead a Discussion

TWO KINDS OF METAMORPHOSIS Remind students that in order to grow, insects must shed their exoskeleton (molt) and grow a new one. Tell students that every insect species undergoes either complete metamorphosis or incomplete metamorphosis. Ask: **What is complete metamorphosis?** *(Metamorphosis process that includes four stages: egg, larva, pupa, adult)* **What is a larva?** *(An immature form of an animal)* **What is a pupa?** *(A stage in which the insect is enclosed in a protective covering while it changes into the adult form)*

Teach With Visuals

Tell students to look at **Figure 4.** Point out the small diagram of the ladybug life cycle. Explain that, although the diagram shows a ladybug and the photographs show a butterfly, the stages have the same names and take place in the same order. Ask: **What is the first stage in complete metamorphosis?** *(Egg)* **What is the name for the larva of a butterfly?** *(Caterpillar)* Ask: **What stage follows the larva stage?** *(Pupa)* **What structures develop while the insect is in the pupa stage?** *(Wings, legs, antennae)*

Address Misconceptions

THE PUPA IS NOT RESTING Because the pupa does not move or eat, it seems to be inactive. Students may think that this is a resting stage. However, the pupa is active during the period, as its body changes from the larva form to an adult. Tell students that toward the end of the pupa stage, the pupa may appear to wiggle as the insect inside moves.

Insects Have you ever seen an insect egg? You might find one on the underside of a leaf. After an insect hatches from the egg, it begins metamorphosis as it develops into an adult. Insects such as butterflies, beetles, and grasshoppers undergo complete metamorphosis or incomplete metamorphosis.

Complete Metamorphosis The cycle to the right shows a ladybug going through **complete metamorphosis,** which has four different stages: egg, larva, pupa, and adult. An egg hatches into a larva. A larva usually looks something like a worm. It is specialized for eating and growing. After a time, a larva enters the next stage of the process and becomes a **pupa** (PYOO puh). As a pupa, the insect is enclosed in a protective covering. Although the pupa does not eat and moves very little, it is not resting. Major changes in body structure take place in this stage, as the pupa becomes an adult.

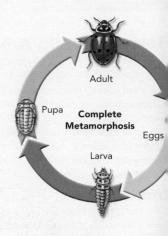

Adult

Pupa

Complete Metamorphosis

Eggs

Larva

A monarch butterfly egg develops on a milkweed plant.

A larva, or a caterpillar, hatches from the egg. The caterpillar grows larger as it feeds on plants. Then it enters the pupa stage.

Inside the pupa case adult structures such as wings, antennae, and legs form.

256   Animal Reproduction and Behavior

Interactive Art allows students to explore the life cycles of an insect, a parasite, a mollusk, and a human.

my science online.com   **Animal Development**

Incomplete Metamorphosis In contrast, [the] second type of metamorphosis, called **incomplete metamorphosis**, has no distinct [la]rval stage. Incomplete metamorphosis has [th]ree stages: egg, nymph, and adult. An egg [ha]tches into a stage called a **nymph** (nimf), [wh]ich usually looks like the adult insect [wi]thout wings. As the nymph grows, it may [sh]ed its outgrown exoskeleton several times [be]fore becoming an adult. The chinch bug [to] the right is going through incomplete [m]etamorphosis.

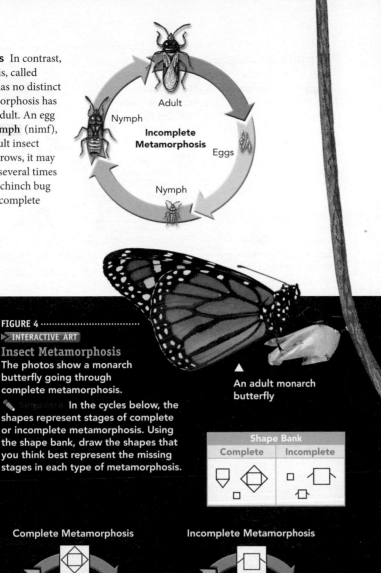

FIGURE 4

▶ **INTERACTIVE ART**

Insect Metamorphosis
The photos show a monarch butterfly going through complete metamorphosis.

✎ **Sequence** In the cycles below, the shapes represent stages of complete or incomplete metamorphosis. Using the shape bank, draw the shapes that you think best represent the missing stages in each type of metamorphosis.

An adult monarch butterfly

The adult butterfly comes out of the pupa case and the butterfly's wings expand as the blood flows into them.

Shape Bank			
Complete		Incomplete	

257

Explain

Lead a Discussion

INCOMPLETE METAMORPHOSIS Have students look at the cycle diagram for incomplete metamorphosis. Tell students that, in addition to the chinch bug shown here, grasshoppers, cockroaches, and termites go through incomplete metamorphosis. Ask: **What is incomplete metamorphosis?** *(Metamorphosis with three stages: egg, nymph, adult)* **What is a nymph?** *(An immature stage that looks like an adult without wings)* **Which stage of incomplete metamorphosis is not part of complete metamorphosis?** *(Nymph)* **Which stage of complete metamorphosis is not part of incomplete metamorphosis?** *(Larva)* **What structure do adults have that nymphs do not?** *(Wings)*

Address Misconceptions

NOT UNFINISHED Because students may have received a grade of "Incomplete" that had to be made up, they may see incomplete metamorphosis as a process that has been left unfinished. Explain that the term *incomplete metamorphosis* is used to contrast with *complete metamorphosis,* in which the adult is *completely* different from the larva. A nymph and its adult form are not completely different. They are only somewhat, or incompletely, different.

Elaborate

21st Century Learning

CRITICAL THINKING Tell students that incomplete metamorphosis is sometimes called *gradual metamorphosis.* Ask them why this term is appropriate. *(Sample: The nymph looks like a smaller wingless version of the adult. It does not change dramatically as it becomes an adult.)*

Teacher Demo

L2 BUTTERFLY LIFE CYCLE

Materials butterfly kit

Time 20 minutes to set up, a few minutes each day for observation

Butterfly kits are available from scientific supply houses and various online sources. Choose a species that you may release in your area if the weather is warm enough. Set up the kit and allow students to observe the caterpillars. Students should note feeding behavior and locomotion as well as body structure. Give students time to make subsequent observations as the caterpillars pupate and then emerge as adults.

Differentiated Instruction

L1 Growth of a Larva Remind students that insects are arthropods, and a characteristic of this phylum is the presence of an exoskeleton. If necessary, review how arthropods molt in order to grow. Point out that this is true of the caterpillar shown in **Figure 4.** The caterpillar of a monarch butterfly molts five times as it grows. The adult butterfly does not molt or grow.

L3 Gypsy Moths Many insects, including the gypsy moth, are pests. Understanding the life cycle of a pest is important in controlling the insect population. Have students research the gypsy moth and the methods that are used to control the population at different stages in the life cycle.

Explain

Teach With Visuals

Tell students to look at **Figure 5.** Remind students that frogs reproduce asexually and fertilize their eggs in water. Point out the larva shown in step 3. Ask: **What is a frog larva called?** *(Tadpole)* **How does a tadpole differ from an adult frog?** *(The tadpole has no legs, but it has a tail. The adult has no tail, but it has legs.* Tell students that there are additional differences not shown on the diagram. Tadpoles have gills and get oxygen from the water. Adult frogs have lungs and get oxygen from the air. Both stages can also absorb oxygen from the water through their skins.

Elaborate

21st Century Learning

L1 CRITICAL THINKING Tell students that tadpoles are herbivores, which means they eat algae and plant material. Adult frogs are carnivores, eating mainly insects and other small arthropods. Some frogs catch and eat fish. Have students contrast the lifestyles of the tadpole and the adult frog. Ask them to infer how these differences are good for the species. *(Sample: By living in different parts of the pond and eating different foods, the two stages reduce competition, which allows more individuals to survive.)*

Lab Resource: Quick Lab

L2 CYCLES OF LIFE Students will model complete and incomplete metamorphosis.

Evaluate

Assess Your Understanding

After students answer the questions, have them evaluate their understanding by completing the appropriate sentence.

RTI Response to Intervention

1a. If students have trouble differentiating between complete and incomplete metamorphosis, **then** ask them to copy the diagrams of each onto a sheet of paper.

b. If students cannot contrast a nymph and a larva, **then** have students describe an example of each.

c. If students need help recognizing the changes that occur during a frog's life cycle, **then** have volunteers point to each part of the diagram showing a frog's life cycle.

MY SCIENCE COACH Have students go online for help in understanding life cycles.

Amphibians Frogs begin their life cycle as fertilized eggs in water. After a few days, larvae wriggle out of the eggs and begin swimming. The larva of a frog is called a **tadpole.** Tadpoles look very different from adult frogs. You can follow the process of frog metamorphosis in **Figure 5.**

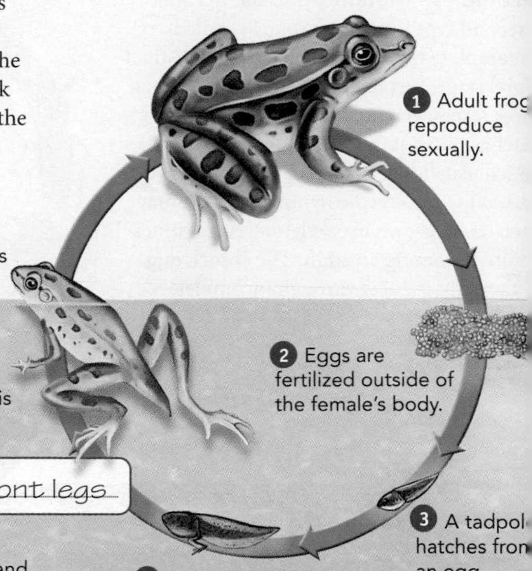

1 Adult frog reproduce sexually.

6 The tail is absorbed, and development is completed.

2 Eggs are fertilized outside of the female's body.

5 Front legs

3 A tadpole hatches from an egg.

4 Hind legs develop.

FIGURE 5 ·········
Frog Life Cycle
Important structures form during metamorphosis that help the frog live in water and on land.

 Use the frog life cycle diagram to complete each task.

1. **Name** In the space provided, write the structures that grew at stage 5.

2. **Infer** How do the structures in stages 3, 4, and 5 help the frog live in water and on land?

   <u>The tadpole has a fishlike body</u>
   <u>for swimming; the adult frog has</u>
   <u>hind and front legs for jumping.</u>

Lab zone Do the Quick Lab Cycles of Life.

🔑 Assess Your Understanding

1a. Define (Complete/**Incomplete**) metamorphosis has three stages: egg, nymph, and adult.

b. Apply Concepts Why is a nymph more likely than a larva to eat the same food as an adult?
<u>A nymph has many of the same</u>
<u>structures as an adult and so</u>
<u>is able to eat the same food.</u>

c. Compare and Contrast How are the life cycles of crustaceans and amphibians similar?
<u>Both cycles begin in water.</u>
<u>Both larvae can swim.</u>

got it? ·········

○ **I get it!** Now I know that as young animals develop they <u>undergo changes in their</u> <u>bodies between birth and maturity, when they are able to reproduce</u>

○ I need extra help with <u>See TE note.</u>

Go to **MY SCIENCE COACH** online for help with this subject.

How Do Animals Care for Their Young?

Have you seen a caterpillar, tadpole, puppy, duckling, or other baby animal recently? You may have noticed that different animals care for their offspring in different ways. ⚊ **Most amphibians and reptiles do not provide parental care, while most birds and mammals typically care for their offspring.**

No Parental Care Not all animals take care of their young. Most aquatic invertebrates, fishes, and amphibians release many eggs into water and then completely ignore them! Most amphibian larvae, or tadpoles, develop into adults without parental help. Similarly, the offspring of most reptiles, such as the snakes in **Figure 6,** are independent from the time they hatch. Offspring that do not receive parental care must be able to care for themselves from the time of birth.

FIGURE 6 ....

Checklist for Survival

These hognose snakes have just hatched from their eggs. They may stay inside the shell for several days for safety.

✎ **List** Make a list of what you think these snakes must be able to do to survive their first few days of life.

Sample: find food, find
water, find shelter, and
protect themselves

259

Explain ─────────

Teach Key Concepts ⚊

Explain to students that the amount of care that animals give to their offspring varies. Ask: **Which groups of vertebrates typically do not care for offspring?** *(Fishes, amphibians, and reptiles)* **What do you think happens to these offspring?** *(Most of them are probably eaten by predators.)* **Which groups of vertebrates usually do care for their offspring?** *(Birds and mammals)* **How do you think this affects the survival of the offspring?** *(If they are protected and cared for, they are more likely to survive.)*

Teach With Visuals

Tell students to look at **Figure 6.** Ask: **How were these snakes protected during development?** *(They were enclosed in a shell.)* Tell students that, although most reptiles do not protect their eggs, many do bury them in an area that will provide shelter and food for the hatchlings. Ask: **How does this compare to the protection that fish eggs and frog eggs receive?** *(The eggs of fishes and amphibians are not protected by a shell and are not buried or hidden from predators.)*

LESSON 7.2

Differentiated Instruction

L3 Crocodile Mothers While most reptiles do not show any parental care for the young, some species do. Invite interested students to research how crocodiles build nests, protect them, and care for the hatchlings. Ask students to share the results of their research with the class, either in the form of an oral presentation, a poster, or a multimedia presentation.

Explain

Support the Big Q ❓ UbD

CARE OF BABY BIRDS Explain to students that baby birds fall into two categories: those that can move around and feed themselves right after hatching and those that cannot. Species that nest on the ground have babies that hatch with their eyes open and are able to walk. In most cases, the baby birds follow their parents around, but soon learn to find their own food. Birds that nest and perch in trees have babies that are helpless when they hatch. Their eyes are closed and they have little or no feathers. Ask: **Why is it an advantage for ground-nesting birds to be able to move around as soon as they hatch?** *(Sample: They are vulnerable to predators; if they can move, they have a better chance to run away.)*

Elaborate

Build Inquiry 🧪 Lab zone

L1 WHAT'S IN MILK?

Materials nutrition labels from milk cartons (whole milk)

Time 10 minutes

Review with students the major nutrient groups: proteins, fats, carbohydrates, and minerals. Have students work in groups and give each group a label from a milk carton. Students should read the label and identify the nutrients found in milk. Point out that Vitamin D is added to milk, but the other nutrients on the label are not added.

Ask: **What nutrients are found in milk?** *(Proteins, fats, carbohydrates, calcium)* **Why is protein important for a baby animal?** *(The animal needs protein to grow.)* **Why is calcium important?** *(For developing strong teeth and bones)* **What do you think the carbohydrates provide?** *(Energy)* Because of the emphasis on low-fat foods as part of a healthy diet, students may be surprised that something "healthy" like milk has fat in it. Point out that fat provides building materials for a growing animal and is also a source of energy.

Parental Care You've probably never seen a duckling walking by itself. That's because most birds and all mammals typically spend weeks to years under the care and protection of a parent.

Birds Most bird species lay their eggs in nests that one or both parents build. Then one or both parents sit on the eggs, keeping them warm until they hatch. Some species of birds can move around and find food right after they hatch. Others are helpless and must be fed by the parent, as shown in **Figure 7**. Most parent birds feed and protect their young until they are able to care for themselves.

Mammals Whether a monotreme, a marsupial, or a placental mammal, young mammals are usually quite helpless for a long time after they are born. After birth, all young mammals are fed with milk from the mother's body. One or both parents may continue caring for their offspring until the young animals are independent.

FIGURE 7 ....
Parental Care
The parent bird shown above cares for its hungry offspring until they are ready to fly. The mother polar bear at the right stays with her cubs for up to two years.

✏️ Answer each question.

1. **Interpret Photos** How are the parents in these two photos caring for their young?

   The bird is feeding its young. The
   polar bear is protecting her cubs.
   _____
   _____

2. **Communicate** What is one way that a family member cares for you?

   Sample: My parents make
   sure that I have enough
   food to eat.

260 Animal Reproduction and Behavior

Digital Lesson: Assign the *Do the Math* activity online and have students submit their work to you.

my science online.com ▶ **Parental Care**

do the math! Analyzing Data

Suppose that you are a scientist researching how many fox and turtle offspring survive the first year of life. Foxes provide parental care, but turtles do not.

Calculate Using the information in the second and fourth columns of the table, calculate the number of offspring that survive the first year. Put your answer in the third column of the table.

Graph Use the data from the table to construct a double bar graph in the space provided. Label the vertical axis. Then provide a key for the data in the graph.

Interpret Data How do you think parental care is related to the percentage of offspring that survive the first year of life?

Offspring that receive parental care are more likely to survive the first year of life.

CHALLENGE Why do you think animals that provide parental care have fewer offspring?

Sample: Parental care takes time and energy. Parents can only give time and energy to a limited number of offspring.

Type of Animal	Number of Offspring	Number That Survive the First Year	Percentage That Survive the First Year
Fox	5	3	60%
Turtle	20	4	20%

Survival of Offspring

Number of Offspring vs. At birth / After the first year (Fox, Turtle)

Lab zone — Do the Quick Lab To Care or Not to Care.

Assess Your Understanding

Got it?

○ I get it! Now I know that parental care occurs in some animals such as birds and mammals, and not in others, such as fishes, amphibians, and reptiles.

○ I need extra help with See TE note.

Go to MY SCIENCE COACH online for help with this subject.

261

Elaborate

Do the Math!

L1 Explain to students that scientists often organize the data they collect in a table. The data can be displayed in a graph. A double-bar graph is a type of graph that can be used to display two sets of data in the same place. Putting both sets of data on the same graph makes comparisons easier.

△ **Interpret Data** Tell students that data are facts, figures, and other information gathered through observations. When students interpret data, they look it over carefully and use what they have learned to draw conclusions.

See the *Math Skill* and *Problem-Solving Activities* for support.

Lab Resource: Quick Lab

L2 **TO CARE OR NOT TO CARE** Students will model how parental care can influence the survival of offspring.

Evaluate

Assess Your Understanding

Have students evaluate their understanding by completing the appropriate sentence.

RTI Response to Intervention

If students cannot describe parental care in vertebrates, **then** ask volunteers to give examples of care for baby animals in the different vertebrate classes.

MY SCIENCE COACH Have students go online for help in understanding parental care.

Differentiated Instruction

L1 **Analyze Data** If students have difficulty understanding the calculations required in the *Do the Math* activity, review with them how to multiply by percents. Point out that the fox in this research had five offspring, and 60 percent of those offspring survived after the first year. Model the calculation by multiplying 5 by 0.6. Then supervise students as they calculate 20 percent of 20.

L3 **Cowbirds** Not all species of birds build nests in which to lay their eggs. Some leave their eggs in the nest of another species. These birds are referred to as *nest parasites* or *brood parasites*. Cowbirds and many species of European cuckoos are brood parasites. Invite interested students to research the brown-headed cowbird or other species of cowbird to learn about its behavior and host species.

261

Lab zone **After the Inquiry Warm-Up**

Development and Growth

Inquiry Warm-Up, *"Eggs-amination"*

In the Inquiry Warm-Up, you investigated the structure and function of parts of a chicken egg. Using what you learned from that activity, answer the questions below.

1. **INFER** Think about the consistency of the egg white. What do you think is the function of the membrane?

   _____

   _____

2. **ANALYZE SOURCES OF ERROR** Many people mistakenly think that the yolk is the part of the egg that becomes a chicken. Explain why this is incorrect.

   _____

   _____

   _____

3. **PREDICT** What would happen if, in Step 3, the shell did not hold water?

   _____

   _____

   _____

4. **COMPARE AND CONTRAST** How is a chicken egg like a human embryo? How is it different?

   _____

   _____

Development and Growth

> ### Where Do Embryos Develop?

got_{it}? ....

○ **I get it!** Now I know that the places embryos can develop are _____

_____

○ **I need extra help with** _____

_____

> ### How Do Young Animals Develop?

1a. DEFINE (Complete/Incomplete) metamorphosis has three stages: egg, nymph, and adult.

b. APPLY CONCEPTS Why is a nymph more likely than a larva to eat the

same food as an adult? _____

_____

c. COMPARE AND CONTRAST How are the life cycles of crustaceans and

amphibians similar? _____

_____

got_{it}? ....

○ **I get it!** Now I know that as young animals develop they _____

_____

_____

○ **I need extra help with** _____

_____

Assess Your Understanding

Development and Growth

> ## How Do Animals Care for Their Young?

got it? ··

○ **I get it!** Now I know that parental care occurs _____

_____

_____

○ **I need extra help with** _____

_____

Key Concept Summaries

Development and Growth

Where Do Embryos Develop?

The growing offspring, or embryo, may develop outside or inside of the parent's body. The offspring of some animals develop inside an egg laid outside of the parent's body. The eggs of land vertebrates, such as reptiles and birds, are called **amniotic eggs.** In some animals, such as some fishes, amphibians, and reptiles, the embryo develops within an egg that is kept in the parent's body. In placental mammals, the embryo develops inside the mother's body. Materials are exchanged between the embryo and the mother through an organ called the **placenta.**

How Do Young Animals Develop?

Some young animals look like small versions of adults, but others go through major body changes or, **metamorphosis. Young animals undergo changes in their bodies between birth and maturity, when they are able to reproduce.** its body undergoes significant changes. In **incomplete metamorphosis,** there is no distinct larval stage, an insect goes directly from an egg to a **nymph,** which looks like a young adult insect without wings.

Insects can undergo complete or incomplete metamorphosis. **Complete metamorphosis** has four stages: egg, larva, pupa, and adult. A **pupa** becomes enclosed in a protective covering while Amphibians, such as frogs, begin life as fertilized eggs in water and go through early stages of the life cycle in water. The larval stage of a frog is called a **tadpole.** When frogs become adults, they emerge onto land.

How Do Animals Care for Their Young?

Most amphibians and reptiles do not provide parental care, while most birds and mammals typically care for their offspring. Most aquatic invertebrates, fishes, and amphibians release eggs in the water. Those offspring are independent from the time they hatch. Birds build a nest in which to lay their eggs, after which one parent sits on the eggs until they hatch. Parent birds must then feed and protect their young until they are able to care for themselves. Young mammals feed on milk from their mother's body and are cared for by their parents until they are independent.

On a separate sheet of paper, describe the ways an embryo can develop.

Review and Reinforce

Development and Growth

Understanding Main Ideas
Answer the following questions in the spaces provided.

1. What are the three places an embryo can develop?

   _____

2. What is the difference between complete metamorphosis and incomplete metamorphosis?

   _____

   _____

3. What is the difference in parental care between reptiles, fishes, and amphibians and birds and mammals?

   _____

Building Vocabulary
Match each term with its definition by writing the letter of the correct definition in the right column on the line beside the term in the left column.

4. ___ amniotic egg

5. ___ placenta

6. ___ complete metamorphosis

7. ___ pupa

8. ___ incomplete metamorphosis

9. ___ nymph

10. ___ tadpole

a. larval stage of a frog

b. stage at which an insect undergoes major body changes

c. the egg of a land vertebrate

d. young insect that looks like a small adult without wings

e. type of metamorphosis that has no larval stage

f. organ in mammals through which materials are exchanged between a mother and an embryo

g. metamorphosis with four stages: egg, larva, pupa, adult

Name _____ Date _____ Class _____

Enrich

Development and Growth

> Did you know the production of silk is related to metamorphosis? Read the passage below. Then answer the questions that follow in the spaces provided.

Silk Production

Silk is produced by caterpillars. The nurture of the caterpillars and the collection of the silk is called *sericulture.* Sericulture requires attention and hard work.

Caterpillars hatch from eggs called *grains* on silkworm farms at temperatures of 23–25°C. Both the temperature and humidity must be maintained for 8–10 days while the caterpillars form small larvae.

The larvae are placed on feeding racks covered with mulberry leaves, that are fresh and dry. In about one month the larvae become grown caterpillars. Next they are placed in straw boxes to produce silk cocoons. The caterpillar spins a protective cocoon around itself. To complete the cocoon takes about 4 days. Usually one cocoon produces between 1,000 and 2,000 feet of silk filament. Three thousand cocoons are needed to produce one square yard of silk material. Unfortunately, in the past, to preserve the cocoon, sericulturists destroyed the worm before it broke through the silk filaments.

Techniques used in India and also in Oregon allow the silkworms to survive the silk collection process. However, the method of silk production that does not allow the silkworms to live is about 60% cheaper than the new, more humane process.

1. About how many feet of silk filament are used to produce one square yard of silk material? Explain.

   _____

   _____

2. Why do you think real silk is expensive?

   _____

   _____

3. Do you think producing silk more humanely is worth the extra cost?

   _____

   _____

4. Find out which two countries produce the most silk.

   _____

   _____

Lesson Quiz

Development and Growth

Write the letter of the correct answer on the line at the left.

1. ___ Which stage is **NOT** a part of incomplete metamorphosis?

   A egg

   B larva

   C nymph

   D adult

2. ___ The stage at which a young insect is enclosed in a protective covering is

   A egg

   B larva

   C pupa

   D adult

3. ___ What stage of life does a frog spend partly on land?

   A egg

   B tadpole

   C as legs develop

   D adult

4. ___ Which type of animal provides parental care for their young?

   A birds

   B reptiles

   C fishes

   D amphibians

If the statement is true, write *true*. If the statement is false, change the underlined word or words to make the statement true.

5. _____ The organ through which materials pass between the mother and an embryo is called the placenta.

6. _____ The larva stage of a frog is called a(n) pupa.

7. _____ Complete metamorphosis does not include a larva stage.

8. _____ Mammals provide parental care to their young until they are independent.

9. _____ Most crustaceans begin life as tiny swimming nymphs.

10. _____ Amniotic eggs are eggs kept inside a parent's body.

Development and Growth

Answer Key

After the Inquiry Warm-Up

1. The membrane holds the white in place around the yolk.

2. The yolk provides the nourishment for the embryo, but it is not the part that becomes the chicken. The white spot in the egg white becomes fertilized and grows into a chicken.

3. Sample: The shell would lose water quickly and the embryo inside would not survive.

4. Sample: They are alike because they are both fertilized egg forms of their species and they both have parts that protect and nourish them. They are different because the chicken egg has a hard shell and the embryo develops outside the mother's body, while a human embryo does not have a shell and develops inside the mother's body.

Key Concept Summaries

The growing embryo can develop outside or inside of the parent's body. The offspring of some animals develop inside an egg laid outside of the parent's body. In some fishes, amphibians, and reptiles, the embryo develops within an egg that is kept in the parent's body. In placental mammals, the embryo develops inside the mother's body.

Review and Reinforce

1. in an amniotic egg outside the mother's body, in an egg kept inside the mother's body, inside the mother's body

2. Complete metamorphosis has four stages: egg, larva, pupa and adult. Incomplete metamorphosis has no larva stage.

3. Reptiles, fishes, and amphibians do not provide parental care. Birds and mammals care for their young until they are independent.

4. c
5. f
6. g
7. b
8. e
9. d
10. a

Enrich

1. from 1,000 × 3,000 to 2,000 × 3,000, or 3,000,000 to 6,000,000 feet of silk filament

2. Silk is expensive because it is very time-consuming to produce. Temperature and timing must be carefully monitored. Many silkworms are needed to make a small amount of silk material.

3. Answers will vary. Sample: Treating the silkworms humanely is more important than the additional costs incurred in making silk material.

4. China and Japan are the two main producers of silk. They produce more than 50% of the world's silk.

Lesson Quiz

1. B
2. C
3. D
4. A
5. true
6. tadpole
7. Incomplete
8. true
9. larvae
10. laid outside

What Is Behavior?

 How does an animal's behavior help it survive and reproduce?

Lesson Pacing: 1–2 periods or $\frac{1}{2}$–1 blocks

🕐 **SHORT ON TIME?** To do this lesson in approximately half the time, do the Activate Prior Knowledge activity on page 262. A discussion of the Key Concepts on pages 263 and 264 will familiarize students with the lesson content. Have students do the Quick Labs. The rest of the lesson can be completed by students independently.

Preference Navigator, in the online Planning tools, allows you to customize *Interactive Science* to your own teaching style. You can also edit lesson plans by selecting the Lesson Planner option.

Digital Teacher's Edition allows you to access your Teacher's Edition and Resource materials online.

my science online.com

Lesson Vocabulary

- behavior
- instinct
- learning
- imprinting
- conditioning
- trial-and-error learning
- insight learning

 ## Content Refresher

Different Stimuli Animals respond to a variety of stimuli that are detected by specific sensory receptors, such as light, heat, vibrating air, gravity, chemicals, and temperature. Sensory receptors can be as complex as the eye, which perceives light through photoreceptors. Mechanoreceptors are also complex and are located in the inner ear to sense air waves (sounds) and gravity. Other receptors, called chemoreceptors, are organized in clusters to perceive chemicals in the environment. Hot and cold temperatures are detected by thermoreceptors and are distributed throughout the body of many animals. The simplest receptors, pain receptors, are plain nerve endings in the skin that perceive heat, touch, and pain. Stimulation of the receptors initiates nerve impulses that pass along neurons to specific centers in the brain where they are analyzed, and reactions are initiated.

LESSON OBJECTIVES

- Explain what causes animal behavior.
- Describe instincts and four kinds of learned behavior.

Blended Path
Active learning using Student Edition, Inquiry Path, and Digital Path

ENGAGE AND EXPLORE

Teach this lesson using a variety of resources. Begin by reading **My Planet Diary** as a class. Have students share ideas about training pets. Then have students do the **Inquiry Warm-Up activity.** Students will observe behaviors of small vertebrates. Discuss the way an animal's nervous system functions. The **After the Inquiry Warm-Up worksheet** sets up a discussion about what things could impact the animal's natural behavior. Have volunteers share their answers to question 4 about how students think the animal's behavior might be different if you observed it in the wild.

EXPLAIN AND ELABORATE

Teach Key Concepts by explaining the term *behavior* and asking students to define stimuli and response. Use **Figure 1** to illustrate how eyespots are both a stimulus and a response.

Continue to **Teach Key Concepts** by describing instinctive behaviors and by determining how you know if a behavior is instinctive. Then have students practice the inquiry skill in the **Apply It activity.** **Lead a Discussion** about learned behavior. Have students identify instinctive and learned behavior displayed by the cheetah cubs in **Figure 3.** Use the **Support the Big Q** to illustrate that imprinting involves both learned and instinctive behavior and can be important for the survival of offspring. Use **Figure 5** to describe how an animal's behavior can be conditioned. **Lead a Discussion** about trial-and-error learning. Show students how the bird used insight learning in **Figure 7** to get the bucket of food. Hand out the **Key Concept Summaries** as a review of each part of the lesson. Students can also use the online **Vocab Flash Cards** to review key terms.

EVALUATE

Have students take the **Lesson Quiz.** For an alternate assessment, see the *ExamView*® Computer Test Generator, Progress Monitoring Assessments, or SuccessTracker™.

E L L Support

1 Content and Language
The term *imprinting* comes from the Latin word *imprimere* meaning "to press into."

DIFFERENTIATED INSTRUCTION KEY
L1 Struggling Students or Special Needs
L2 On-Level Students **L3** Advanced Students

LESSON PLANNER 7.3

 **Inquiry Path** Hands-on learning in the Lab zone

ENGAGE AND EXPLORE

To teach this lesson with an emphasis on inquiry, begin with the **Inquiry Warm-Up activity.** Students will investigate an animal's behavior through observation. Discuss the actions of the animal. Have students do the **After the Inquiry Warm-Up worksheet.** Talk about why an animal's behavior may be different in the lab than in nature. Have volunteers share their answers to question 4 about how an animal's behavior may be different if you observed it in the wild.

EXPLAIN AND ELABORATE

Focus on the **Inquiry Skill** for the lesson. Point out that when you predict, you use your prior knowledge to infer what might happen in the future. In the **Inquiry Warm-Up activity** what could be predicted about how the animal's behavior may be different in the wild? *(Answers will vary.)* Have students do the **Quick Lab** to record and analyze their responses to stimuli and then share their results.

Review the concepts of instincts and learned behavior before beginning the **Apply It activity.** Ask volunteers to share what information they used to make their predictions. Do the **Teacher Demo** to show students an example of an automatic response in most mammals. **Support the Big Q** by describing how imprinting can be partially learned behavior and partially instinctive behavior. To **Build Inquiry** allow students to design an experiment in order to investigate a particular animal's response to a stimulus. Do the **Quick Lab** to reinforce understanding of why some things are more difficult to learn than others. Students can use the online **Vocab Flash Cards** to review key terms.

EVALUATE

Have students take the **Lesson Quiz.** For an alternate assessment, see the *ExamView®* Computer Test Generator, Progress Monitoring Assessments, or SuccessTracker™.

Digital Path
Online learning at my science online.com

ENGAGE AND EXPLORE

Teach this lesson using digital resources. Begin by having students explore real-world connections to how animals behave at **My Planet Diary** online. Have them access the Chapter Resources to find the **Unlock the Big Question activity.** There they can answer the questions and refine their responses as they continue through the lesson. You can re-assign the activity and have students submit their work so you can track their progress.

EXPLAIN AND ELABORATE

Students reading above, at, or below the lexile measure of this lesson can access basic content readings at their level at **My Reading Web.** Have students use the online **Vocab Flash Cards** to preview key terms. Do the **Quick Lab** and then ask students to share their results.

Review the concepts of instincts and learned behavior before assigning the online **Apply It activity.** Ask volunteers to share which shadows they circled and why. Have students submit their work to you. **Support the Big Q** by helping students to understand that imprinting involves both learned and instinctive behavior. Assign the **Do the Math activity** online and have students submit their work to you. Have students do the online **Art in Motion activity** to see examples of animal learning. During the **Quick Lab** students will consider why some things may be harder to learn than others. The **Key Concept Summaries** online allow students to read a summary and see an image associated with each part of the lesson. Online remediation is available at **My Science Coach.**

EVALUATE

Have students take the **Lesson Quiz.** For an alternate assessment, see the *ExamView®* Computer Test Generator, Progress Monitoring Assessments, or SuccessTracker™.

2 Frontload the Lesson
Preview the lesson visuals, labels, and captions. Ask students what they know about the terms *learning, imprinting,* and *conditioning.* Explain the specific meanings these words have in science.

3 Comprehensible Input
Have students divide a sheet of paper into four sections. Ask them to describe the four types of learned behavior using examples.

4 Language Production
Pair or group students with varied language abilities to complete labs collaboratively for language practice. Have each student copy the completed written lab for personal reference.

5 Assess Understanding
Make true or false statements using lesson content. Have students indicate if they agree or disagree with a thumbs up or thumbs down gesture to check whole-class comprehension.

What Is Behavior?

Establish Learning Objectives

After this lesson, students will be able to:

- Explain what causes animal behavior.
- Describe instincts and four kinds of learned behavior.

Engage

Activate Prior Knowledge

MY PLANET DIARY Read *Chris's Blog* with the class. Ask students if they have ever had a young pet. Invite volunteers to describe experiences they had trying to train the animal. Ask: **What kinds of things might you do to train a puppy?** *(Sample: You might reward the puppy for good behaviors.)* **Why can it be difficult to train a puppy?** *(They have to learn the behaviors that they are not born knowing.)*

BIG IDEAS OF SCIENCE REFERENCE LIBRARY Have students look up the following topics: Bush Baby, Instinct.

Explore

Lab Resource: Inquiry Warm-Up

L1 WHAT BEHAVIORS CAN YOU OBSERVE?
Students will observe behaviors of small vertebrates.

LESSON

3 What Is Behavior?

- What Causes Animal Behavior?
- What Are the Types of Animal Behavior?

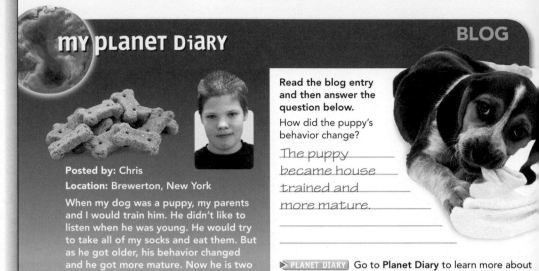

my planet diary

BLOG

Read the blog entry and then answer the question below.
How did the puppy's behavior change?

The puppy became house trained and more mature.

Posted by: Chris
Location: Brewerton, New York

When my dog was a puppy, my parents and I would train him. He didn't like to listen when he was young. He would try to take all of my socks and eat them. But as he got older, his behavior changed and he got more mature. Now he is two years old, and he is fully house trained.

> **PLANET DIARY** Go to **Planet Diary** to learn more about behavior.

Lab zone Do the Inquiry Warm-Up *What Behaviors Can You Observe?*

What Causes Animal Behavior?

Have you ever heard a bird call, or seen a dog bark at a stranger? These are examples of animal behavior. An animal's **behavior** consists of all the actions it performs. For example, behaviors include actions an animal takes to obtain food, avoid predators, and find a mate. Like body structures, the behaviors of animals are adaptations that have evolved over long periods of time.

262 Animal Reproduction and Behavior

SUPPORT ALL READERS
Lexile Measure = 920L   Lexile Word Count = 1818

Prior Exposure to Content: Many students may have misconceptions on this topic
Academic Vocabulary: *cause, effect, predict, relate*
Science Vocabulary: *behavior, instinct, imprinting, conditioning*
Concept Level: Generally appropriate for most students in this grade
Preteach With: My Planet Diary "Chris's Blog" and Figure 5 activity
Go to **My Reading Web** to access leveled readings that provide a foundation for the content.

my science online

Vocabulary

- behavior • instinct • learning • imprinting
- conditioning • trial-and-error learning • insight learning

Skills

- Reading: Relate Cause and Effect
- Inquiry: Predict

FIGURE 1 ....

A Moth's "Eyes"

Certain moths have markings on their underwings that look like the eyes of an owl. When the moth is frightened by a predator, it raises its forewings to reveal the "eyes."

✐ **Predict** How is this behavior important to the moth's survival?

The "eyes" on the moth look like the eyes of a much larger animal and may scare a predator.

Most behavior is a complex process in which different parts of an animal's body work together. Consider what happens when a water current carries a small animal to a hydra's tentacles. After stinging cells on the tentacles catch the prey, the tentacles bend toward the hydra's mouth. At the same time, the hydra's mouth opens to receive the food.

Behavior as Response In the previous situation, the touch of the prey on the tentacles acts as a stimulus to the hydra. Recall that a stimulus (plural *stimuli*) is a signal that causes an organism to react in some way. The organism's reaction to the stimulus is called a response. The hydra's response to the prey is to sting it. 🔑 **All animal behaviors are responses to stimuli.**

Some stimuli, such as prey brushing a hydra's tentacles, are outside the animal. Other stimuli, such as hunger, come from inside. An animal's responses are either external actions or internal changes (such as a faster heartbeat), or both.

The Functions of Behavior Most behaviors help an animal survive or reproduce. When an animal looks for food or hides to avoid a predator, it is doing something that helps it stay alive. When animals search for mates and build nests for their young, they are behaving in ways that help them reproduce.

Lab zone Do the Quick Lab *Animal Behavior.*

🔑 Assess Your Understanding

got it? ....

○ I get it! Now I know that animal behaviors are *responses to stimuli.*

○ I need extra help with *See TE note.*

Go to **MY SCIENCE** ⒮ **COACH** *online for help with this subject.*

263

E L L Support

1 Content and Language

Point out that the scientific meaning of *imprinting*—relating to the behavior of newborn offspring—is less than 100 years old. Explain that this meaning derives from an earlier definition of *imprint,* "to fix permanently on the memory."

2 Frontload the Lesson

Invite students to brainstorm a list of words and phrases that they associate

with the term *behavior.* As you write their responses on the board, encourage students to think about which behaviors relate in some way to reproduction or to survival.

3 Comprehensible Input

Have students create a cluster diagram organized around the terms *instincts* and *learned behaviors.* Remind students to include information about all four types of learned behavior.

Explain

Introduce Vocabulary

Students may have some idea of what the term *instinct* means, but they may not be able to state a clear definition. Explain that an instinct is an inborn behavior that an animal performs without being taught.

Teach Key Concepts 🔑

Explain to students that behaviors are actions that an animal performs. Behavior is a response to a stimulus. Ask: **What is a stimulus?** *(A signal that causes an organism to react)* **What is a response?** *(The reaction to a stimulus)* **Where can stimuli come from?** *(Inside the animal or outside the animal)* **What are the two main functions of behavior?** *(To help an animal survive or reproduce)*

Teach With Visuals

Tell students to look at **Figure 1.** Point out that the display of the eyespots is a response on the part of the moth, but it is a stimulus to the predator. Ask: **How do you think a predator will respond to this stimulus?** *(Samples: It will leave the moth alone; it will run away.)*

△ **Predict** Remind students that when they predict, they use what they already know about a subject to infer what is likely to happen in the future.

Elaborate

Lab Resource: Quick Lab 🔑

L1 ANIMAL BEHAVIOR Students will record and analyze their responses to various stimuli.

Evaluate

Assess Your Understanding

Have students evaluate their understanding by completing the appropriate sentence.

R T I Response to Intervention

If students have trouble explaining the cause of animal behavior, **then** review examples of stimuli.

MY SCIENCE ⒮ **COACH** Have students go online for help in understanding animal behavior.

My Planet Diary provides an opportunity for students to explore real-world connections to how animals behave.

Explain

Teach Key Concepts

Explain that instinctive behavior is inborn, which means that the animal is born with the ability to carry out that behavior. Ask: **What is one way that you can tell if a behavior is instinctive?** *(If the animal performs it correctly the first time without being taught, the behavior is instinctive.)* **What are some examples of instinctive behavior?** *(A spider spinning a web, a newborn kangaroo crawling into the mother's pouch)*

Address Misconceptions

INSTINCTIVE BEHAVIOR Some students may think that only simple behaviors are instinctive. Explain to students that many instinctive behaviors are complex. Spiders that spin orb-webs do so using different types of silk secreted by spinning glands. Some of the threads are not sticky, while the threads in the center of the web are sticky. When prey is trapped in the web, the spider responds to the stimulus of vibrations it feels in the web. The spider moves along the threads that are not sticky to inject venom into the prey. This behavior is instinctive. Tell students that bats use ultrasonic signals to hunt moths. Some species of moth automatically fold their wings and drop to the ground in response to an ultrasonic signal. Ask: **How is this instinctive behavior helpful to the moths?** *(Sample: The moths are less likely to be caught and eaten by the bat.)*

Elaborate

Apply It!

L1 Review the concepts of instincts and learned behavior before beginning the activity.

FIGURE 2 ·····
Survival Instinct
This spider has trapped a butterfly in the sticky strands of its silky web.

✎ **Explain** Read the text below about instincts. Could the spider survive without the instinct to spin a web? Why or why not?

<u>No; the spider would not be able</u>
<u>to catch food.</u>

What Are the Types of Animal Behavior?

Animals perform some behaviors correctly without practice. Other behaviors are learned through experience.
 The types of animal behavior are instincts and learned behaviors.

Instincts Animals perform some behaviors without being taught. An **instinct** is a response to a stimulus that is inborn and that an animal performs correctly the first time. For example, spiders, such as the one in **Figure 2,** spin complicated webs on their first try without making mistakes in the pattern. Most birds build their nests without ever being taught how.

Instincts are important for an animal's survival. For example, a newborn kangaroo crawls into its mother's pouch and attaches itself to a nipple. Without this instinct, baby kangaroos could not obtain the milk they need to live.

apply it!

Hawks, which have short necks, prey on gull chicks. Geese, which have long necks, do not prey on gull chicks. Newly-hatched gull chicks instinctively crouch down when they see any bird's shadow. As the chicks become older, they still crouch when they see a hawk's shadow, but they learn not to crouch when they see a goose's shadow.

⬧**Predict** Circle the bird shadows that will cause an older gull chick to crouch when it sees them.

264 Animal Reproduction and Behavior

Digital Lesson: Assign the *Apply It* activity online and have students submit their work to you.

MY SCIENCE ONLINE.COM | **Types of Animal Behavior**

Learned Behaviors Think about the first time you rode a bicycle. It probably took a few tries before you did it well—you had to learn how. **Learning** is the process that leads to changes in behavior based on practice or experience. In general, the larger an animal's brain, the more the animal can learn. Because learned behaviors result from an animal's experience, they are not usually done perfectly the first time.

All learned behaviors depend in part on characteristics that have passed from parents to offspring. For example, the cheetah cubs in **Figure 1** were born with physical characteristics and instincts that are necessary for hunting. They have claws that help them capture prey. They also have an instinct to pounce on any object that attracts their attention. However, only through experience can they learn hunting skills. Learned behaviors include imprinting, conditioning, trial-and-error learning, and insight learning.

FIGURE 3 ....

Learned Behavior
These cheetah cubs are practicing their hunting skills on a young gazelle.

✎ **Interpret Photos** In this photo, what action shows instinct behavior, and what action shows learned behavior?

The pouncing is an instinct, but capturing prey is a learned behavior.

265

Explain

Lead a Discussion

LEARNED BEHAVIOR Invite volunteers to describe a behavior they learned in the past week. *(Students may cite examples of athletic activities, learning to sing or play a new song, improving skills at a computer game.)* Ask: **What is learning?** *(The process that leads to changes in behavior based on practice or experience)* **How is learning related to the size of an animal's brain?** *(In general, the larger the brain, the more the animal can learn.)* **What are some examples of learned behavior?** *(Imprinting, conditioning, trail-and-error learning, and insight learning)*

Teach With Visuals

Tell students to look at **Figure 3.** Explain that what looks like play in young animals often is practice of important behaviors. Discuss with students how hunting is partly instinctive and partly learned. Ask: **What behavior of a cheetah is instinctive?** *(Pouncing)* Ask students how they think the cubs shown in the photograph got the gazelle. If students cannot suggest an answer, explain that a parent may catch a small animal and give it to the cubs to practice on. Cubs also learn by watching their parents hunt.

Elaborate

Teacher Demo Lab zone

L1 AUTOMATIC RESPONSES

Materials clear plastic sheet, foam ball

Time 10 minutes

Explain to students that some responses to stimuli are reflexive, or automatic. The automatic "blink" response is common among most mammals. Have several volunteers come to the front of the classroom. Each volunteer should hold a clear plastic sheet in front of his or her face while another volunteer gently tosses the soft foam ball at the sheet. Most students will involuntarily blink, even though they know the ball can't hit them. Encourage students to try to teach themselves to not blink. Some students may be able to do this. Others will find it more difficult.

Ask: **How can this automatic response aid a mammals survival?** *(Sample: It avoids injury to the eyes.)* **If a student was able to avoid blinking when the ball was thrown at the plastic sheet, what kind of behavior was this?** *(Learned behavior)*

Explain

Support the Big Q ❓ UbD

IMPRINTING Help students understand that imprinting is a combination of instinctive behavior and learned behavior. Ask: **What part of imprinting in geese is instinctive?** *(Following the first thing they see move)* **What part of imprinting in geese is learned?** *(Which thing to follow)* **How does following a parent help a young animal?** *(It keeps the young animal close to parents who will protect them and feed them or help them find food. It helps them learn what individuals of their own species look like.)* Tell students that nest building also involves imprinting. How to build a nest is instinctive. But in many species of birds the kind of site in which a nest is built is imprinted. Some individual birds may build nests in unusual places, either because a typical nest site is not available or because they are less strongly imprinted on the usual type of site. Students may have seen English (house) sparrows nesting in convenient niches buildings or on top of signs on stores. These are not "natural" nest sites for sparrows. Ask students to speculate on where the hatchlings are likely to build their nests when they mate. *(Students will likely say that these birds will nest on buildings, rather than in trees.)* Discuss how this kind of behavior has allowed sparrows to thrive in urban habitats.

⤵ Relate Cause and Effect Explain to students that a cause is an event that makes an effect happen. An effect happens as a result of a cause. The cause comes first and is followed by the effect.

Elaborate

Build Inquiry 🧪Lab zone

L2 DESIGN A BEHAVIOR EXPERIMENT

Materials none

Time 15 minutes

Before students begin the activity, remind them of the important steps in experimental design, such as posing a question, developing a hypothesis, controlling variables, and forming operational definitions. Divide the class into cooperative groups. Instruct each group to design an experiment to investigate a particular animal's response to a stimulus, such as a dog's response to the ringing of a doorbell. Groups can assign the tasks of the designing process to specific students. Inform students that they must write a description of the procedure, and remind them to think of ethical considerations, such as animal treatment and safety. Have groups present their experimental designs to the rest of the class. Have the class review the experiments and ask questions. If possible, allow students to do their experiments.

266 Animal Reproduction and Behavior

⤵ Relate Cause and Effect Underline why the birds imprinted on Konrad Lorenz, and circle the effect.

Imprinting Imprinting is a learned behavior. In **imprinting**, certain newly hatched birds and newborn mammals recognize and follow the first moving object they see. This object is usually the parent. But imprinting also involves instinct. The young animal has an instinct to follow a moving object, but is not born knowing what its parent looks like. The young animal learns from experience what object to follow.

Once imprinting takes place, it cannot be changed. That is true even if the young animal has imprinted on something other than its parent. Young animals have imprinted on moving toys and even humans. Konrad Lorenz, an Austrian scientist, conducted experiments in which he, rather than the parent, was the first moving object that newly hatched birds saw. **Figure 4** shows how young geese that had imprinted on Lorenz followed him around.

For young animals, imprinting on a parent is valuable for two reasons. First, it keeps offspring close to their parents, who know where to find food and how to avoid predators. Second, imprinting allows young animals to learn what other animals of their own species look like. This knowledge protects the animals while they are young. In later life, this knowledge is important when the animals search for mates.

FIGURE 4
Follow the Leader
These geese ignored other members of their species and trailed after Dr. Lorenz.

✏ **Answer the following questions.**

1. **Infer** What might happen if geese imprinted on the wrong species?

   Sample: The young animals would not follow their parents. They may not be able to find food or avoid predators.

2. **CHALLENGE** Why might imprinting be important for the offspring of animals that live in large groups?

   Sample: Offspring could become separated from their parents, who provide food and protection.

266 Animal Reproduction and Behavior

Response

Stimulus

When a hungry dog sees or smells food, it produces saliva. Dogs do not usually salivate in response to other stimuli, such as the sound of a ringing bell.

Two Stimuli Together

For many days, the scientist Ivan Pavlov rang a bell every time he fed a dog. The dog learned to associate the ringing of the bell with the sight and smell of food.

New Stimulus Only

In time, when Pavlov rang a bell but did not feed the dog, the dog still produced saliva. The new stimulus produced the response that normally only food would produce.

FIGURE 5 ·······················

Teaching a Dog New Tricks

Pavlov conditioned a dog to salivate at the sound of a ringing bell.

✎ Read the text about conditioning and complete each task.

1. ⟳ **Relate Cause and Effect** In the first panel, label the stimulus and the response.

2. ⊿ **Predict** What might the dog do if the doorbell rang?

   It might salivate because it heard a bell.

Conditioning When a dog sees its owner approaching with a leash, the dog may jump up, eager to go for a walk. The dog has learned to associate the leash with a pleasant event—a brisk walk. Learning that a particular stimulus or response leads to a good or a bad outcome is called **conditioning.**

Pets are often trained using conditioning. At first, a puppy rarely comes when you call. But every now and then, the puppy runs to you in response to your call. Each time the puppy comes, you give it a dog biscuit. Your puppy will soon learn to associate the desired response—coming when called—with the good outcome of a food reward. After a while, the puppy will come to you even if you don't give it a dog biscuit.

During the early 1900s, the Russian scientist Ivan Pavlov performed experiments involving one kind of conditioning. **Figure 5** shows the steps that Pavlov followed in his experiments.

Vocabulary High-Use Academic Words An *outcome* is defined as a result or as the way something turns out. What *outcome* did the puppy associate with training?

The puppy associated a food reward with coming when called.

267

Explain

Teach With Visuals

Tell students to look at **Figure 5.** Ask students who have a dog or cat if they have ever seen the animal drool. Although less visible in cats, salivation does begin when they see or smell food. Ask: **What was the original stimulus in the experiment?** (The smell of food) **What was the response?** (Salivating) **What stimulus was added to the smell of food?** (Ringing a bell) **What response did the bell cause?** (Salivation) **What kind of learning is this?** (Conditioning) **Household pets often become conditioned to expect food when certain stimuli are present. What kinds of stimuli can make a pet expect food?** (Samples: the sound of a can opener, the clink of the pet's dish, the opening of the container or cabinet where food is stored)

⊿ **Predict** Remind students that when they predict, they use what they already know about a subject to infer what is most likely to happen in the future.

21st Century Learning

COMMUNICATION Invite students who have ever trained a pet to describe the process. Remind students to include information about the behaviors that were taught, the treats that were used, and the commands that serve as stimuli to make the animal respond with the desired behavior. Sometimes animals learn to respond to a stimulus without being specifically taught to do so. Ask students if a pet has learned to recognize words that it associates with something pleasant, like *walk, ride, car, biscuit.* Ask how the humans changed their behavior to avoid getting the animal excited. (Sample: We now spell certain words so the pet won't know what we are talking about.)

Differentiated Instruction

L3 Research Reintroduced Birds Have students research the process of reintroducing captive-reared birds, such as whooping cranes, California condors, or peregrine falcons to the wild. Tell students to consider these questions: *How does the reintroduction plan incorporate behaviors such as imprinting into the process? How do other behaviors of the birds affect how they are handled by humans?* Students should share the results of their research with the rest of the class in the form of a news report.

L3 Operant Conditioning B. F. Skinner, an American psychologist specialized in the study of learning. Have students who are interested in training animals research his work on operant conditioning. Students can report to the class how this method of modifying behavior is based on rewarding correct behavior.

Explain

Lead a Discussion

TRIAL AND ERROR Ask students if they have heard the expression, "If at first you don't succeed, try again." The example used in the text describes learning to ride a bicycle. If students practiced on their own, the learning was trial and error. But often people have help learning difficult behaviors. A parent or coach can help a child by suggesting things to try to improve performance. Discuss how an element of chance is involved in trial-and-error learning in animals. Nobody tells a bird to look for food in one place and not another. Ask: **What happens if a bird finds tasty berries on a particular kind of bush?** (The bird will learn to go back to that bush and look for more berries.) **What happens if a bird looks for berries on a different kind of bush and gets stuck by thorns?** (The bird will learn to avoid that kind of bush in the future.) **If someone puts out a bird feeder, how do birds find it at first?** (Sample: Birds happen to see it, possibly if they stopped to rest in a tree that is near the feeder.) **What makes the birds return to the yard that has the feeder?** (They found food there, so they associate going to the feeder with getting food.)

Make Analogies

LEARN FROM MISTAKES Students may not understand the idea of making errors as part of learning. In school, the goal always seems to be to get the right answer on a quiz or a test. But if students make mistakes and think about what went wrong and how to avoid that consequence, they are learning from their mistakes. Ask students to imagine they have a new computer game, but the instructions were lost and there is no "help" function in the game. How would they learn to play the game? (Sample: Try playing it and see what happens. If you do something that makes you lose, you will know to avoid doing that again. If you find a move that helps you advance in the game or win it, you will remember to do that the next time you play.)

Elaborate

Do the Math!

L1 Explain to students that before they attempt to answer questions about a graph, they need to read the title and all labels. They also need to take a look at the key. In this graph, for example, students need to know the meaning of the orange and blue colors.

See the *Math Skill* and *Problem-Solving Activities* for support.

Trial-and-Error Learning Another type of learned behavior is **trial-and-error learning**. In trial-and-error learning, an animal learns to do a behavior through repeated practice. An animal learns to repeat behaviors that result in rewards and avoid behaviors that result in punishment. When you learned to ride a bicycle, you did it by trial and error. You may have wobbled at first, but eventually you got better. You learned to move in ways that adjusted your balance and kept you from falling over.

Many animals learn by trial and error which methods are best for obtaining food. They also learn which methods to avoid. Think of what happens when a predator tries to attack a skunk. The skunk sprays the predator with a substance that stings and smells awful. In the future, the predator is likely to avoid skunks. The predator has learned to associate the sight of a skunk with its terrible spray.

FIGURE 6
A Tough Lesson
This dog has a mouthful of porcupine quills.
Infer Why will this dog avoid porcupines in the future?
The dog attacked a porcupine and learned that the quills are painful.

do the math! Analyzing Data

A scientist conducted an experiment to find out if mice would learn to run a maze more quickly if they were given rewards. The scientist set up two identical mazes. She put a cheese reward at the end of one maze and not at the end of the other maze. Use the graph to answer the questions.

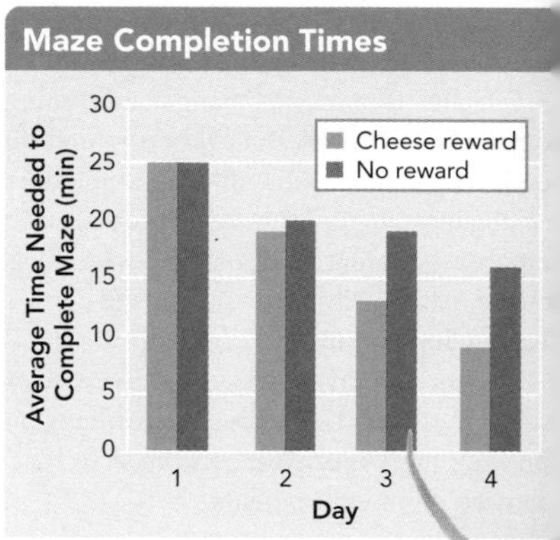

1 Read Graphs On Day 1, how long on average did it take mice with a cheese reward to complete the maze?
25 minutes

2 Calculate On Day 4, how much faster did mice with a reward complete the maze than mice without a reward?
7 minutes faster

3 Interpret Data What was the manipulated variable in this experiment?
Whether or not a reward was given

Maze Completion Times

Digital Lesson: Assign the *Do the Math* activity online and have students submit their work to you.

Art in Motion shows examples of animal learning.

my science online.com **Types of Animal Behavior**

Betty learned to use a curved wire to pull up a bucket of food from a narrow plastic tube.

A larger crow stole the curved wire. Betty found a straight wire and bent it into a curved shape.

Betty then used the curved wire to get the bucket of food.

Insight Learning The first time you try out a new video game, you may not need someone to explain how to play it. Instead, you may use what you already know about other video games to figure out how the new one works. When you solve a problem or learn how to do something new by applying what you already know, without a period of trial and error, you are using **insight learning.**

Insight learning is most common in primates, such as gorillas, chimpanzees, and humans. For example, chimpanzees use twigs to probe into the nests of termites and other insects that they eat. The chimps use insight to bend or chew their twig "tools" into a shape that will best fit the holes. Other animals, such as the crow in **Figure 7,** have also shown insight learning.

FIGURE 7 ·······························
▶ ART IN MOTION **Insight Learning**
Read the panels above to learn how a crow named Betty was able to use a wire to obtain food.

✎ **Interpret Diagrams**
How was Betty's behavior an example of insight learning?

Betty knew that by
making a curved wire
she could get the food.

 Do the Quick Lab *Become a Learning Detective.*

💬 **Assess Your Understanding**

a. Define An inborn response to a stimulus that is performed correctly the first time is called a(n) (instinct/learned behavior).

b. Compare and Contrast How are instincts and learned behaviors different?

Instincts are inborn, but
learned behaviors result from
experience.

c. Apply Concepts Right after hatching, a duckling sees a child riding a tricycle. What will probably happen the next time the child rides on the tricycle by the duckling? Explain.

The duckling will follow the
tricycle because it has
imprinted on it.

got it? ·······························

◯ **I get it!** Now I know that the types of animal behavior are _instincts and learned_
behaviors.

◯ **I need extra help with** _See TE note._

Go to **MY SCIENCE 💬 COACH** online for help with this subject.

269

Differentiated Instruction

L1 Compare and Contrast Have students construct a chart that compares and contrasts trial-and-error learning with insight learning. Students should contrast the way the animal learns a new behavior and give an example of each.

L3 Getting at Food Have interested students research examples of animals

that use surprising ways to get food. An octopus can open a bottle and remove food. A sea otter can use a rock to crack open a sea urchin. Gulls carry clams as they fly and drop them on hard surfaces to crack them. Have students record different examples and identify whether each example is instinctive or learned.

Explain
Teach With Visuals

Tell students to look at **Figure 7.** Review the meaning of insight learning. Discuss with students times they have figured out the solution to a problem without practice or trial-and-error. Then discuss the example of insight learning shown here. Ask: **What did Betty know how to do?** (*She knew how to use a bent wire to get food.*) **When she looked for the bent wire, what did Betty find?** (*She found only a straight wire.*) **Who taught Betty to bend the straight wire?** (*Nobody; she figured it out by herself.*) Explain that Betty is a New Caledonian crow. So far, this is the only species of crow that has been found to exhibit insight learning. New Caledonian crows can be found in New Caledonia, a self-governing territory of France situation in the South Pacific ocean between Australia and New Zealand.

Elaborate

Lab Resource: Quick Lab

L2 BECOME A LEARNING DETECTIVE Students will consider why some things may be harder to learn than others.

Evaluate

Assess Your Understanding

After students answer the questions, have them evaluate their understanding by completing the appropriate sentence.

RTI Response to Intervention

1a. If students cannot recall what an instinct is, **then** review the definition together.

b. If students have trouble differentiating between instincts and learned behaviors, **then** work as a class to make a table listing examples of each.

c. If students have difficulty making a prediction, **then** review the concept of imprinting.

MY SCIENCE 💬 COACH Have students go online for help in understanding types of behavior.

Lab zone **After the Inquiry Warm-Up**

What Is Behavior?

Inquiry Warm-Up, *What Behaviors Can You Observe?*
In the Inquiry Warm-Up, you investigated an animal's behavior through observing its actions and then predicted what is likely to cause the animal's behavior to change. Using what you learned from that activity, answer the questions below.

1. **USE PRIOR KNOWLEDGE** Recall how an animal's nervous system functions. What term would you use to describe the things that caused the animal's behavior to change?

   _____

2. **USE PRIOR KNOWLEDGE** Consider your answer to question 1. What term would you use to describe each change in the animal's behavior?

   _____

3. **ANALYZE SOURCES OF ERROR** In the lab, you were asked to think about observing the animal in its natural habitat. What factor in the lab might make your observations of the animal's actions an inaccurate description of its behavior in the wild?

   _____

   _____

4. **PREDICT** How do you think the animal's behavior might be different if you observed it in the wild?

   _____

   _____

   _____

Assess Your Understanding

What Is Behavior?

> ## What Causes Animal Behavior?

gotit? ···

○ **I get it!** Now I know that animal behaviors are _____

_____

○ **I need extra help with** _____

_____

> ## What Are the Types of Animal Behavior?

1a. **DEFINE** An inborn response to a stimulus that is performed correctly the first time is called a(n) (instinct/learned behavior).

b. **COMPARE AND CONTRAST** How are instincts and learned behaviors

different? _____

_____

c. **APPLY CONCEPTS** Right after hatching, a duckling sees a child riding a tricycle. What will probably happen the next time the child rides on

the tricycle by the duckling? Explain. _____

_____

_____

gotit? ···

○ **I get it!** Now I know that the types of animal behavior are _____

_____

○ **I need extra help with** _____

_____

What Is Behavior?

What Causes Animal Behavior?

An animal's **behavior** consists of all the actions it performs. These behaviors are adaptations that have evolved over long periods of time. **All animal behaviors are responses to stimuli.** Some stimuli, such as prey coming into view, are outside the animal. Other stimuli, such as hunger, come from inside. Most behaviors help an animal survive or reproduce.

What Are the Types of Animal Behavior?

The types of animal behavior are instincts and learned behaviors. An **instinct** is a response to stimulus that is inborn and that an animal performs correctly the first time. Most birds build nests without being taught how.

Learning is the process that leads to changes in behavior based on practice or experience. In general, the larger an animal's brain, the more it can learn. All learned behaviors depend in part on characteristics that have passed from parents to offspring. For example, cheetah cubs are born with physical characteristics, such as claws, and instincts, such as the instinct to pounce, that are necessary for hunting. However, only through experience can cheetah cubs learn hunting skills. Learned behaviors include imprinting, conditioning, trial-and-error learning, and insight learning.

In **imprinting,** certain newly hatched birds and newborn mammals recognize and follow the first moving object they see—usually a parent. Imprinting

on a parent is valuable. It keeps offspring safe and fed by keeping them close to their parents. It also allows young animals to learn what animals of their species look like, which later helps them find mates.

Learning that a certain stimulus or response leads to a good or a bad outcome is called **conditioning.** If you give a dog a treat every time it sits when told to, after a while the dog will sit when told, even if you don't have a treat.

In **trial-and-error learning,** an animal learns to do a behavior through repeated practice. A predator that has been sprayed by a skunk usually learns to avoid skunks.

When you solve a problem or learn how to do something new by applying what you already know, without a period of trial and error, you are using **insight learning.** Insight learning is most common in primates.

On a separate sheet of paper, explain how a cheetah hunting a gazelle uses both instincts and learned behaviors. Then describe what type or types of learned behavior you think are involved.

Review and Reinforce

What Is Behavior?

Understanding Main Ideas
Fill in the blank to complete each statement.

1. Like body structures, the behaviors of animals are _____ _____

2. Stimuli that affect an animal's behavior can come from two places: _____

3. Most behaviors help an animal to either _____

4. The difference between an instinct and a learned behavior is _____ _____ _____

5. Two ways that imprinting on a parent is valuable to an animal are: _____ _____ _____

Building Vocabulary
Match each term with its definition by writing the letter of the correct definition in the right column beside the term in the left column.

6. ___ behavior

7. ___ imprinting

8. ___ conditioning

9. ___ trial-and-error learning

10. ___ insight learning

a. learning a behavior through repeated practice

b. recognizing and following the first moving object an animal sees

c. learning that a certain stimulus or response leads to a good or a bad outcome

d. learning how to do something new by applying what you already know

e. all the actions an animal performs

What Is Behavior?

Insight learning involves the ability to apply what you already know to solve a new problem. Read the passage, look at the diagram, and study the table below. Then use a separate sheet of paper to answer the questions that follow.

A Simple Insight

The biologist L. V. Krushinsky tested animals' insight learning in a simple experiment, shown below. Animals looked through an opening in a partition and saw one empty dish and one full of food. Both dishes were then pulled behind swinging doors, where they were no longer visible.

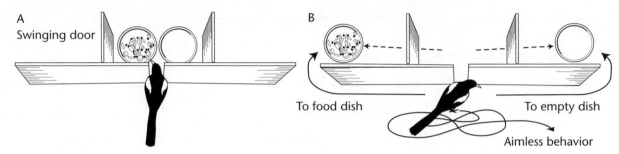

In this experiment, the animal already knows, "Follow moving food to get it." The new situation is, "The moving food goes out of sight." Any animal that used insight to walk around the correct side of the partition could get food. Krushinsky recorded how many animals walked around the correct side, how many walked to the wrong side, and how many wandered aimlessly. The table shows his results with several kinds of animals.

Species	Number of animals tested	Walked to food side	Walked to wrong side	Walked aimlessly
Pigeons	27	7%	0%	93%
Chickens	129	27%	25%	48%
Rabbits	33	24%	3%	73%
Cats	42	50%	36%	14%
Dogs	18	78%	11%	11%

1. Which animals found the food most often? Which animals found it least often?

2. Which animals walked to the correct and incorrect sides of the partition almost equally often? Do you think these animals understood how to find the food?

3. What situation might cause an animal that had achieved the insight of how to find the food to still not walk toward it? How would you design the experiment to prevent this from happening?

Lesson Quiz

What Is Behavior?

Fill in the blank to complete each statement.

1. Animal behaviors are _____ that have evolved over long periods of time.

2. Most behaviors help an animal to survive or _____.

3. Learning is the process that leads to changes in behavior based on _____ or experience.

4. All learned behaviors depend in part on _____ that have passed from parents to offspring.

5. A(n) _____ is a response to stimulus that is inborn and that an animal performs correctly the first time.

6. All animal behaviors are responses to _____.

Write the letter of the correct answer on the line at left.

7. ___ A soccer player kicking a field goal in his first football game is an example of
   A imprinting
   B conditioning
   C trial-and-error learning
   D insight learning

8. ___ A trainer using fish to reward a dolphin that jumps through a hoop is an example of
   A imprinting
   B conditioning
   C trial-and-error learning
   D insight learning

9. ___ A gymnast learning how to do a cartwheel is an example of
   A imprinting
   B conditioning
   C trial-and-error learning
   D insight learning

10. ___ A chick following a lawnmower because it was the first moving object it ever saw is an example of
   A imprinting
   B conditioning
   C trial-and-error learning
   D insight learning

What Is Behavior?

Answer Key

After the Inquiry Warm-Up

1. stimuli

2. response

3. The fact that the animal was in a cage or aquarium could make its actions different from what they would be in the wild.

4. Answers will vary. Students may say that the animal would be more alert if it were in the wild, or that it might be less quick to accept food from humans.

Key Concept Summaries

When a cheetah hunts gazelles it uses both instincts and learned behaviors. Pouncing on objects that draw its attention is an instinct. Cheetah cubs naturally pounce. But hunting also involves skills that a cheetah must learn. To hunt a gazelle, a cheetah uses trial-and-error learning, in which the hunting skills are learned through repeated practice. The cheetah may also use insight learning if, for example, it takes a skill it learned hunting another animal and uses that same skill to hunt the gazelle.

Review and Reinforce

1. adaptations that have developed over long periods of time.

2. inside or outside the animal.

3. survive or reproduce.

4. while an instinct is an inborn response that an animal performs correctly the first time, a learned behavior requires practice or experience.

5. It keeps a young animal safe and fed by keeping it close to its parents, and because it also allows a young animal to learn what animals of its species look like, it later helps the animal find mates.

6. e

7. b

8. c

9. a

10. d

Enrich

1. Dogs moved to the food side most often. Pigeons moved to the food side least often.

2. Chickens. They did not seem to understand how to find the food. If they had, they would have walked to the food side more often.

3. If an animal were not hungry, it might not go after the food, even if it knew how. To avoid this, one might withhold food from the animals for a while before testing them.

Lesson Quiz

1. adaptations

2. reproduce

3. practice

4. characteristics

5. instinct

6. stimuli

7. D

8. B

9. C

10. A

Place the outside corner, the corner away from the dotted line, in the corner of your copy machine to copy onto letter-size paper.

Patterns of Behavior

 How does an animal's behavior help it survive and reproduce?

Lesson Pacing: 1–2 periods or $\frac{1}{2}$–1 block

🕐 **SHORT ON TIME?** To do this lesson in approximately half the time, do the Activate Prior Knowledge activity on page 270. A discussion of the Key Concepts on pages 271, 272, and 274 will familiarize students with the lesson content. Use the Explore the Big Q to help students understand how an animal's behavior helps it survive and reproduce. Do the Quick Labs and have students do the online Real-World Inquiry. The rest of the lesson can be completed by students independently.

Preference Navigator, in the online Planning tools, allows you to customize *Interactive Science* to your own teaching style. You can also edit lesson plans by selecting the Lesson Planner option.

Digital Teacher's Edition allows you to access your Teacher's Edition and Resource materials online.

Lesson Vocabulary

- pheromone
- aggression
- territory
- courtship behavior
- society
- circadian rhythm
- hibernation
- migration

 Content Refresher
Professional Development Note

Circadian Rhythms The cues for circadian rhythms can be both internal or external. Many circadian rhythms are determined by an internal biological clock that "keeps time." Experiments have shown that certain behaviors will continue on a regular cycle in the absence of any external cues. Even when kept in total darkness, almost all fruit fly larvae will hatch in the early morning. A single gene acts as the internal clock. Light is the most common external cue that influences daily rhythms. Under controlled conditions with no external cues, most human biological clocks run on a 25-hour daily schedule. The internal clocks can be easily reset to 24 hours with exposure to light.

Tagging Devices Improvements to the tags used to track monarch butterfly migration have led to better tracking with less impact on the butterflies. The old tagging method involved removing the scales on a portion of the forewing and placing an oblong or rectangular adhesive tag on that area. The new tagging method, which uses new all-weather polypropylene tags, involves placing the adhesive tag on the underside of the butterfly's hind wing. No scales need to be removed to attach the tag. The new tags are round and only 9 millimeters in diameter. The recapture rate is two to three times higher with the new tags compared to rates with the old tags.

LESSON OBJECTIVES

🔑 List the three ways animals communicate.

🔑 Give examples of competitive and cooperative behaviors.

🔑 Describe cyclic behavior.

Blended Path
Active learning using Student Edition, Inquiry Path, and Digital Path

ENGAGE AND EXPLORE

Teach this lesson using a variety of resources. Begin by reading **My Planet Diary** as a class. Have students share ideas about sign language as a means of communication. Then have students do the **Inquiry Warm-Up activity.** Students will communicate without words. Discuss the ways people communicate a wide range of emotions. The **After the Inquiry Warm-Up worksheet** sets up a discussion about which senses are used and not used to communicate. Have volunteers share their answers to question 4 about other animals that use different senses than humans do to communicate.

EXPLAIN AND ELABORATE

Teach Key Concepts by describing the three ways that animals communicate.

Teach Key Concepts by explaining that animals compete with one another for limited resources, such as food, water, shelter, and mates. **Lead a Discussion** about how males and females of the same species prepare for mating. Continue to **Teach Key Concepts** by identifying some advantages and disadvantage for animals living in a group. **Lead a Discussion** about how animals in societies work together in an organized manner. Then have students practice the inquiry skill in the **Apply It activity.**

Teach Key Concepts by asking students to describe some examples of cyclic behaviors. Use **Figure 5** to illustrate the migration routes of some animals. Have students look at the birds in **Figure 6** as they discuss the courtship and survival behaviors of the black-browed albatross. **Explore the Big Q** by identifying examples of behaviors associated with getting food, claiming and defending territory, and reproduction. **Answer the Big Q** by leading a discussion on how an animal's behavior helps it to survive and reproduce. Hand out the **Key Concept Summaries** as a review of each part of the lesson. Students can also use the online **Vocab Flash Cards** to review key terms.

EVALUATE

Have students take the **Lesson Quiz.** For an alternate assessment, see the *ExamView*® Computer Test Generator, Progress Monitoring Assessments, or SuccessTracker™.

ⒺⓁⓁ Support

1 Content and Language

The word *pheromone* comes from the Greek words *pherein* meaning "convey." Have students use this word meaning to define the word *pheromone.*

Lab zone Inquiry Path
Hands-on learning in the Lab zone

Digital Path
Online learning at my science online.com

ENGAGE AND EXPLORE

To teach this lesson with an emphasis on inquiry, begin with the **Inquiry Warm-Up activity.** Students will observe nonverbal communication. Discuss the senses students used with speaking and when using body language to communicate. Have students do the **After the Inquiry Warm-Up worksheet.** Talk about which senses are consciously used in human communication and those that are not consciously used. Have volunteers share their answers to question 4 about what senses other animals use to communicate that humans do not use to communicate.

EXPLAIN AND ELABORATE

Focus on the **Inquiry Skill** for the lesson. Point out that when you communicate, you share information with others in an organized manner. Describe the senses you used to communicate in the **Inquiry Warm-Up activity?** *(Hearing and sight.)* Have students do the **Quick Lab** to investigate ways to communicate with body movement and sound and then share their results.

Do the **Teacher Demo** to show students how aggressive and competitive males of some species can be. To **Build Inquiry** have students examine photos of large groups of animals and discuss why there is safety in groups. Review cooperative behavior and communication in societies of animals before beginning the **Apply It activity.** Ask volunteers to share how they cooperated with friends at school. The **Lab Investigation** will illustrate how an ant society shows organization and cooperative behavior.

The **Real-World Inquiry** allows students to explore an animal in its environment and then to predict the animal's behavior. **Explore the Big Q** by sharing examples of behaviors associated with getting food, claiming and defending territory, and reproduction. Do the **Quick Lab** to help students understand how Pacific salmon guide themselves back to their home rivers to breed. Discuss how an animal's behavior helps it to survive and reproduce to help students **Answer the Big Q.** Students can use the online **Vocab Flash Cards** to review key terms.

EVALUATE

Have students take the **Lesson Quiz.** For an alternate assessment, see the *ExamView®* Computer Test Generator, Progress Monitoring Assessments, or SuccessTracker™.

ENGAGE AND EXPLORE

Teach this lesson using digital resources. Begin by having students explore real-world connections to patterns of animal behavior at **My Planet Diary** online. Have them access the Chapter Resources to find the **Unlock the Big Question activity.** There they can answer the questions and refine their responses as they continue through the lesson. You can re-assign the activity and have students submit their work so you can track their progress.

EXPLAIN AND ELABORATE

Students reading above, at, or below the lexile measure of this lesson can access basic content readings at their level at **My Reading Web.** Have students use the online **Vocab Flash Cards** to preview key terms. Do the **Quick Lab** and then ask students to share their results.

Review cooperative behavior and communication in societies of animals before assigning the online **Apply It activity.** Ask volunteers to share an example of when they cooperated with a friend at school. Have students submit their work to you.

Have students do the online **Real-World Inquiry** to explore an animal in its environment and then to predict the animal's behaviors. **Explore the Big Q** by asking students to give examples of behaviors associated with animal survival. Do the **Quick Lab** to model how Pacific salmon guide themselves back to their home rivers to breed. To **Answer the Big Q** discuss how an animal's behavior helps it to survive and reproduce. The **Key Concept Summaries** online allow students to read a summary and see an image associated with each part of the lesson. Online remediation is available at **My Science Coach.**

EVALUATE

Have students take the **Lesson Quiz.** For an alternate assessment, see the *ExamView®* Computer Test Generator, Progress Monitoring Assessments, or SuccessTracker™.

2 Frontload the Lesson
Preview the lesson visuals, labels, and captions. Ask students what they know about the terms *hibernation* and *migration*. Explain the specific meanings these words have in science.

3 Comprehensible Input
Have students study the visuals and their captions on pages 271, 272, 273, 274, 275, and 277 to support the key concepts of the lesson.

4 Language Production
Pair or group students with varied language abilities to complete labs collaboratively for language practice. Have each student copy the completed written lab for personal reference.

5 Assess Understanding
Divide the class into small groups, and assign them a key concept to discuss. Have each student in the group write one related idea around the key concept and, if selected, be prepared to share these notes with the class.

Lexile Measure = 940L

Patterns of Behavior

Establish Learning Objectives

After this lesson, students will be able to:

🔑 List the three ways animals communicate.

🔑 Give examples of competitive and cooperative behaviors.

🔑 Describe cyclic behavior.

Engage

Activate Prior Knowledge

MY PLANET DIARY Read *Do You Speak Gorilla?* with the class. Ask students if they have every communicated with a young child who was not yet old enough to talk. Ask: **How did you get the child to understand your ideas?** (*Students may suggest that they pointed to objects or acted out what they wanted to show.*) **How did the child communicate with you?** (*Answers will vary.*)

BIG IDEAS OF SCIENCE REFERENCE LIBRARY 📖
Have students look up the following topics: Animal Communication, Echolocation, Gorillas.

Explore

Lab Resource: Inquiry Warm-Up 🧪

L1 **COMMUNICATING WITHOUT WORDS** Students will consider ways of communicating information that do not involve speaking words.

LESSON

4 Patterns of Behavior

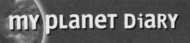

🔑 **What Are Three Ways That Animals Communicate?**

🔑 **What Are Examples of Competitive and Cooperative Behaviors?**

🔑 **What Is Cyclic Behavior?**

MY PLANET DIARY

FUN FACTS

Do You Speak Gorilla?

Animals communicate in many ways, but they don't usually say things like, "My tooth hurts." That's more or less what Koko the gorilla said in 2004, when she needed to go to the dentist. Koko uses hand signals, based on American Sign Language, to communicate with humans.

Koko was born in 1971 at the San Francisco Zoo. When she was just one year old, she began to learn how to sign words, working with Dr. Francine Patterson. Through signs, Koko has shown emotion, creativity, and intelligence. Koko can make around 1,000 signs. She can also understand around 2,000 spoken words—but she herself can't speak. Gorillas can make noises, but they don't have the mouth structures necessary to form spoken words.

Read the text and then answer the questions below.

1. Once, Koko was trying to describe an object but did not know the word. She signed "bracelet" and "finger" together. What do you think she was trying to say?

   <u>She was trying to say "ring."</u>

2. If you could talk to Koko, what would you ask her?

   <u>Sample: What is your favorite food?</u>
   <u>Do you like using sign language?</u>

🧪 Do the Inquiry Warm-Up *Communicating Without Words.*

▶ PLANET DIARY Go to **Planet Diary** to learn more about patterns of behavior.

270 Animal Reproduction and Behavior

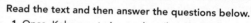

SUPPORT ALL READERS

Lexile Measure = 940L   **Lexile Word Count = 2031**

Prior Exposure to Content: May be the first time students have encountered this topic

Academic Vocabulary: *communicate, identify, main idea*

Science Vocabulary: *pheromone, aggression, circadian rhythm, hibernation*

Concept Level: Generally appropriate for most students in this grade

Preteach With: My Planet Diary "Do You Speak Gorilla?" and Figure 2 activity

Go to **My Reading Web** to access leveled readings that provide a foundation for the content.

my science online.com ▶

Vocabulary
- pheromone • aggression • territory
- courtship behavior • society • circadian rhythm
- hibernation • migration

Skills
- Reading: Identify the Main Idea
- Inquiry: Communicate

What Are Three Ways That Animals Communicate?

Animal communication comes in many forms. Perhaps you've seen a cat hissing and arching its back. It is using sound and body posture to send a message that says, "Back off!" **Animals use sounds, scents, and body movements to communicate with one another.** An animal's ability to communicate helps it interact with other animals. Notice the gecko's body movements in **Figure 1.**

Animals communicate many kinds of messages using sound. Some animals use sound to attract mates. Female crickets, for example, are attracted to the sound of a male's chirping. Animals may also communicate warnings using sound. When a prairie dog sees a coyote or other predator approaching, it makes a yipping sound that warns other prairie dogs to hide in their burrows.

Animals also communicate with chemical scents. A chemical released by one animal that affects the behavior of another animal of the same species is called a **pheromone** (FEHR uh mohn). For example, perhaps you have seen a male house cat spraying a tree. The musky scent he leaves contains pheromones that advertise his presence to other cats in the neighborhood.

FIGURE 1

Body Language
This giant leaf-tailed gecko opens its mouth when it senses danger.

Infer What might the gecko be communicating with its body movement?

Sample: "Don't get
any closer!" or
"I'm dangerous!"

Lab zone ® Do the Quick Lab Modeling Animal Communication.

Assess Your Understanding

got it?

I get it! Now I know that animals communicate using *sounds, scents, and body movements.*

I need extra help with *See TE note.*

Go to MY SCIENCE COACH online for help with this subject.

271

ELL Support

1 Content and Language
Write the term *hibernation* on the board. Point out the suffix *-ation*, meaning "state" or "action." Explain that *hibernation* comes from the Latin word *hibernus*, meaning "wintry."

2 Frontload the Lesson
Invite students to describe situations in which they observed animals communicating. Have students identify specifically what the animal did to convey a message. Tell students that they will learn about three ways that animals communicate.

3 Comprehensible Input
Invite students to work in groups to develop demonstrations of competitive behaviors used by animals. Students can use movements, gestures, sounds, and brief vignettes to portray aggression or defending a territory.

Explain

Introduce Vocabulary
Students may be familiar with the term *territory* from social studies class. Explain that the political use of the term and the scientific term are similar. In science, *territory* is defined as an area that is occupied and defended by an animal or group of animals.

Teach Key Concepts
Tell students that animals have three ways by which they can communicate with each other. Ask: **What are the ways animals communicate?** (*Through sounds, scents, and body movements*) **What is a pheromone?** (*A chemical released by one animal that affects the behavior of another animal*) **What are some ways animals communicate with sounds?** (*Crickets chirp; prairie dogs yip.*) **What are some ways animals communicate with body movements?** (*A cat arches its back; a lizard opens its mouth wide.*) You may wish to allow students who have observed animals communicating to share their experiences with the class.

Elaborate

Lab Resource: Quick Lab
L1 MODELING ANIMAL COMMUNICATION
Students will investigate ways to communicate with body movement and sound.

Evaluate

Assess Your Understanding
Have students evaluate their understanding by completing the appropriate sentence.

RTI Response to Intervention
If students need help describing ways that animals communicate, **then** have them reread the Key Concept statement for this section.

MY SCIENCE COACH Have students go online for help in understanding animal communication.

My Planet Diary provides an opportunity for students to explore real-world connections to patterns of animal behavior.

MY SCIENCE online | Animal Communication

Explain

Teach Key Concepts 🔊

Explain that competition can take place within a species and among species. Ask: **For what resources might animals compete?** *(Food, water, space, shelter, mates)* **What is aggression?** *(Threatening behavior that one animal uses to gain control over another)* **Why is establishing control in this way helpful for the species?** *(Each animal in a group knows its position. Threatening behavior is less damaging to the population than fighting.)* **Why do animals have to compete for resources?** *(Resources are limited in most habitats.)* **What is a territory?** *(An area that is occupied and defended by an animal or group of animals)* **How does establishing territory help an animal survive and reproduce?** *(Within the territory, the animal has access to the resources, which include food, water, and shelter. In many species, a male cannot attract a mate unless he holds a territory.)*

Elaborate

21st Century Learning

INFORMATION LITERACY Students may have heard a man described as being an "alpha male," meaning that he was the type of person to be a leader. In a primate troop, the alpha male is the dominant animal. But in other animal groups, the dominant member may be female. In a herd of wild horses, the dominant animal is the alpha mare. In chickens, there is a distinct order of dominance, from the alpha hen, that gets first access to water, food, and good roosting positions, down to the lowest hen in the pecking order.

Encourage students to do research to learn more about dominance order in animals. Students should evaluate the sources they find to determine which are likely to have the best information. Encourage students to report back to the class about what they have learned. If students do their research on the Internet, remind them to follow prescribed guidelines for Internet use.

FIGURE 2

Fighting in the Forest
This forest is full of competing animals.

✏️ **Identify** Select which type of competition is happening in each of the four photos. There may be more than one correct answer.

This older black bear is pushing and clawing at a younger black bear.

- ◉ Showing aggression
- ◉ Establishing territory
- ○ Attracting a mate

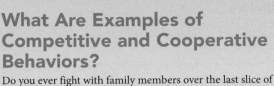

What Are Examples of Competitive and Cooperative Behaviors?

Do you ever fight with family members over the last slice of pizza? Is it easier to do chores by yourself or with other people? Sometimes you compete with people and sometimes you cooperate. Animals in the wild also compete and cooperate.

Competitive Behavior Have you ever fed pigeons in the park? They fight over every crumb because there usually isn't enough food to go around. 🔊 **Animals compete with one another for limited resources, such as food, water, shelter, and mates.** Competition can occur among different species of animals or within the same species. For example, a pride of lions might steal prey from a troop of hyenas. Or a female aphid might kick and shove another female aphid for the best leaf on which to lay eggs.

Showing Aggression When they compete, animals may display aggression. **Aggression** is a threatening behavior that one animal uses to gain control over another. Before a pack of wolves settles down to eat its prey, individual wolves demonstrate, or show aggression by snapping, clawing, and snarling. The most aggressive members of the pack eat first. The less aggressive and younger members of the pack feed on the leftovers.

Aggression between members of the same species rarely results in serious injury or death. Typically, the loser communicates "I give up" with its behavior. For example, when attacked by an older dog, a puppy will roll onto its back, showing its belly. This signal calms the older dog. The puppy can then move away.

Establishing a Territory On an early spring day, you may hear a male oriole singing. He is alerting other orioles that he "owns" a particular territory. A **territory** is an area that is occupied and defended by an animal or group of animals. If another animal of the same species enters the territory, the owner will attack the newcomer to drive it away. Birds use songs and aggressive behaviors to maintain their territories. Other animals may use calls, scratches, droppings, or pheromones.

By establishing a territory, an animal protects important resources such as food and possible mates. A territory can also provide a safe area for animals to raise young without competition from other members of their species. Most male songbirds cannot attract a mate unless they have a territory.

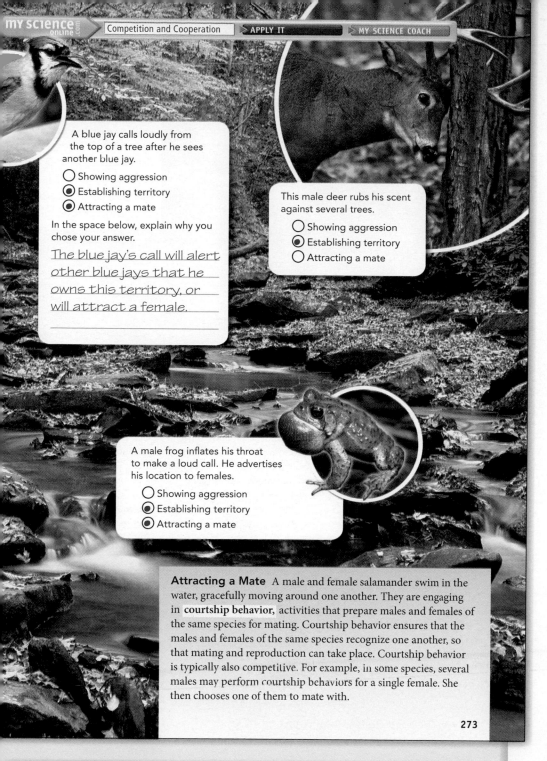

A blue jay calls loudly from the top of a tree after he sees another blue jay.

○ Showing aggression
◉ Establishing territory
◉ Attracting a mate

In the space below, explain why you chose your answer.

The blue jay's call will alert other blue jays that he owns this territory, or will attract a female.

This male deer rubs his scent against several trees.

○ Showing aggression
◉ Establishing territory
○ Attracting a mate

A male frog inflates his throat to make a loud call. He advertises his location to females.

○ Showing aggression
◉ Establishing territory
◉ Attracting a mate

Attracting a Mate A male and female salamander swim in the water, gracefully moving around one another. They are engaging in **courtship behavior,** activities that prepare males and females of the same species for mating. Courtship behavior ensures that the males and females of the same species recognize one another, so that mating and reproduction can take place. Courtship behavior is typically also competitive. For example, in some species, several males may perform courtship behaviors for a single female. She then chooses one of them to mate with.

273

Explain

Lead a Discussion

COURTSHIP BEHAVIOR Explain to students that animals show a wide variety of behaviors to attract a mate. Ask: **Why is courtship behavior an important part of the reproductive process?** *(Courtship ensures that males and females of the same species recognize one another so that mating and reproduction can take place.)* **Why is courtship behavior another example of competition?** *(In some species, males have to compete with one another to attract a female.)*

Elaborate

Teacher Demo [Lab zone]

L1 COMPETITION AND AGGRESSION

Materials 2 glass jars, 2 male bettas (Siamese fighting fish), opaque card, water

Time 10 minutes

Explain to students that males of this species are very aggressive toward other males. Place each fish in its own jar of water. Place the jars next to each other with the opaque card between the jars. Begin by allowing students time to observe the behavior of the fish. Do not allow students to tap on the jars. Remove the card. Be sure the fish can clearly see each other. Have students record and observe the behaviors of the fish.

Ask: **How do you think these behaviors benefit the bettas?** *(The strongest and most aggressive males will be able to survive and find mates.)*

21st Century Learning

CRITICAL THINKING Explain to students that frogs call to establish and defend a territory and to attract a mate. Most species do this in the spring or early summer. Each species has its own call, from a deep bullfrog croak to the high-pitched peep of the spring peeper. Ask: **Why do you think each species has a different call?** *(Sample: so that a male attracts a female of his own species)* **What do you think would happen if you sat near a pond on a spring evening and imitated frog calls? Explain** *(Sample: If I got the call right, the male frogs would answer. I would sound like a frog entering the area declaring a territory, and males would call to define and defend their territories.)*

Differentiated Instruction

L1 Use Visuals Have students use the images on these pages to help them define and understand the concepts of competitive behavior, aggression, and courtship behavior. For each image, have students write a description that tells what each animal is doing. Then have them identify the type of behavior demonstrated.

L3 Establishing a Territory Invite interested students to research how an animal of their choice establishes and defends it territory. Students should be able to answer such questions as: *What is the size of its territory? What factors influence how the animal chooses its territory?* Have students share the results of their research with the class in the form of a multimedia presentation.

Explain

Teach Key Concepts 🔑

LIVING IN A GROUP Tell students that animals such as fish, insects, and hoofed mammals often live in groups. Ask: **What are some advantages to living in a group?** *(Group members protect each other and work together to find food.)* **What disadvantage might there be for animals living in a group?** *(Samples: the group members must share resources; individuals that are low in the order of dominance may not get enough food.)*

⏺ **Identify the Main Idea** Tell students that when they identify the main idea, they determine the most important, or biggest, idea in a paragraph or section. The other information in the paragraph or section supports or further explains the main idea.

Elaborate

Build Inquiry

L2 **GROUP SAFETY**

Materials photos of groups of animals, including large schools of fishes, a herd of zebra, and a herd of antelope

Time 10 minutes

Tell students that when many individuals of the same species are in a large group, it may be confusing for a predator to see and select a single individual. Allow students to examine the photos of the groups of animals. Have them describe the markings of coloration of the animals in the group.

Ask: **When a large group of individuals are together, what happens to individual markings? How might this confuse a predator?** *(The markings of an individual animal would blend in with the rest of the group. It might be difficult for a predator to pick out an individual in the group.)* **An albino animal lacks color. Do you think an albino animal would stay close to the others, even though it doesn't blend in? Would the other animals let it stay with them? Explain.** *(Sample: The albino would stay with the group. Group behaviors are mainly instinctive, so they are the same under all conditions.)*

21st Century Learning   DK

CRITICAL THINKING Have students read *Animal Communication* in the **Big Ideas of Science Reference Library.** Draw a concept map on the board. In the center circle, write *Animal Communication*. In outer circles, write the following: *Movement, Sound, Color,* and *Scent.* Ask students to copy the concept map and have them add specific examples to each of the four categories.

274 Animal Reproduction and Behavior

FIGURE 3 ························
Safety in Numbers
When threatened by a grey reef shark, these fish form tight groups called bait balls.

✎ **Interpret Photos** How does the bait ball help an individual fish escape from being eaten by a predator?

The individual fish blends in and it is hard for a predator to target a single fish.

⏺ **Identify the Main Idea**
Living in the wild is hard work! Some animals cooperate in order to survive. In your own words, write three important reasons why animals show cooperative behaviors.

Sample: Living in a group can protect animals from predators. Finding food can be easier in a group. Dividing up work makes it easier to do.

Cooperative Behavior Not all animal behaviors are competitive. 🔑 **Animals living in groups cooperate to survive.** Although many animals live alone and only rarely meet one of their own kind, other animals live in groups. Some fishes form schools, and some insects live in large groups. Hoofed mammals, such as bison and wild horses, often form herds. Living in a group helps some animals stay alive. For example, group members may protect one another or work together to find food.

How can group members help one another? If an elephant gets stuck in a mudhole, for example, other members of its herd will dig it out. When animals such as lions hunt in a group, they can often kill larger prey than a single hunter can.

Safety in Groups Living in groups often protects animals against predators. Fish that swim in schools, such as the ones in **Figure 3,** are often safer than fish that swim alone. It is harder for predators to see and select an individual fish in a large group.

Animals in a group sometimes cooperate to fight off a predator. For example, North American musk oxen form a defensive circle against a wolf or other predator. Their calves are sheltered in the middle of the circle. The adult musk oxen stand with their horns lowered, ready to charge. The predator often gives up rather than face a whole herd of angry musk oxen.

274 Animal Reproduction and Behavior

Digital Lesson: Assign the *Apply It* activity online and have students submit their work to you.

my science online.com ▶ | **Competition and Cooperation**

FIGURE 4 ·····················
The Hive Is Alive!
A hive may have tens of thousands of worker bees.

✏ **Explain** Why do you think a honeybee society has more worker bees than any other type?

Sample: Without worker bees, the hive would not be built, defended, or maintained.

Queen bee

Worker bees

apply it!

 Communicate Discuss with your classmates one way that you have cooperated with your friends at school. Then describe how the cooperative behavior helped you.

Sample: My friend and I worked together on a project. We divided the work so it didn't take as long.

Animal Societies Some animals, including termites, honeybees, ants, and naked mole rats, live in groups called societies. A **society** is a group of closely related animals of the same species that work together in a highly organized way. In a society, there is a division of labor—different individuals perform different tasks. A honeybee society, for example, has only one egg-laying queen. But there are thousands of worker bees that build, defend, and maintain the hive. Some workers feed larvae. Some bring back nectar and pollen from flowers as food for the hive. Other worker bees guard the entrance to the hive. **Figure 4** shows a honeybee society.

Lab zone Do the Lab Investigation One for All.

🔑 **Assess Your Understanding**

1a. List What are two cooperative behaviors?
Safety in groups and societies

b. Explain How are aggression and establishing a territory related?
An animal may use aggression to scare off another animal from its territory.

c. Apply Concepts Male red-winged blackbirds display red patches on their shoulders to defend their territory. What would happen if these red patches were dyed black?
The male would not be able to defend its territory and it may lose it.

got it? ···

O **I get it!** Now I know that examples of competitive and cooperative behavior are aggression, establishing a territory, courtship behavior, and living in groups.

O **I need extra help with** See TE note.

Go to MY SCIENCE 🗨 COACH online for help with this subject.

Differentiated Instruction

L1 Group Names Have students work in small groups to make a list of names given to groups of animals, such as a pride of lions, pack of wolves, gaggle of geese. Students may find sources on the Internet at Web sites of zoos or other organizations that deal with animals. Remind students to follow prescribed guidelines for Internet use. Encourage students to make illustrated posters to share with the rest of the class.

L3 Drones In addition to the queen and worker bees, honeybee societies include drones, which are male bees. Encourage students to do research to learn about drones and their functions.

L3 Dancing Bees Honeybees communicate the location of a good source of pollen and nectar by doing a dance. Have students research how scientists decoded this dance.

Explain
Lead a Discussion

HONEYBEE SOCIETY Explain to students that honeybees live in a group called a *society*. Ask: **What is a society?** (*A group of closely related animals that work together in a highly organized way*) **What are some other examples of animal societies?** (*Ants, termites*) **In a honeybee society, what is the role of the queen?** (*To lay eggs*) **What are the roles of worker bees?** (*They build, maintain, and defend the hive. They feed larvae. They collect nectar and pollen and bring it back to the hive.*)

Address Misconceptions

INSECT SOCIETIES Students may confuse human societies and animal societies. Explain to students that human societies may consist of associations of unrelated individuals. In animal societies, such as those of ants, termites, and honeybees, all individuals are close relatives, usually siblings. In addition, while roles in animal societies are usually rigid, roles in human societies are much more flexible. Ask: **What aspects of human society differ from those of an insect society?** (*Samples: In a human society, each individual can define his or her own role and complete a variety of tasks related to survival.*)

Elaborate
Apply It!

L1 Before beginning the activity, review cooperative behavior and communication in societies of animals.

△ **Communicate** Remind students that they communicate when they talk to a classmate or write the answer to a question.

Lab Resource: Lab Investigation **Lab** zone

L2 **ONE FOR ALL** Students will explain how an ant society shows organization and cooperative behavior.

Evaluate
Assess Your Understanding

After students answer the questions, have them evaluate their understanding by completing the appropriate sentence.

R T I Response to Intervention

1. If students have trouble with different animal behaviors, **then** review the section titled *What Are Examples of Competitive and Cooperative Behaviors?*

MY SCIENCE COACH Have students go online for help in understanding competition and cooperation.

Explain

Teach Key Concepts

CYCLIC BEHAVIOR Tell students that some animals have behaviors that change over time in regular patterns—usually over the course of a day or a season. Ask: **What is a circadian rhythm?** *(A cycle of behavior that occurs over a period of approximately one day)* **What are some examples of daily behavior cycles in your own life?** *(Samples: Being awake during the day and asleep at night; being hungry at the same time each day)* **What are some examples of animal behaviors that are related to seasons?** *(Hibernation and migration)* **What is hibernation?** *(A state of greatly reduced body activity that occurs during the winter when food is scarce)* **How does hibernation help animals survive?** *(Hibernation slows down an animal's processes, so it needs less food at a time when less food is available.)* **What is migration?** *(The regular, seasonal journey of an animal from one place to another and back again)* **How does migration help animals to survive?** *(Migration allows animals to move to favorable conditions when the seasons change.)*

21st Century Learning

L3 CREATIVITY *Crepuscular, diurnal,* and *nocturnal* are terms used to describe the period of the day in which an animal is active. A crepuscular animal is active during the twilight hours at dawn and dusk. Rabbits and cats are crepuscular animals. Diurnal animals are active during the daylight hours. Humans are diurnal animals. Nocturnal animals are active at night, and include bats and owls. Have students choose a variety of familiar animals and use what they know about each animal's behavior to determine if it is crepuscular, diurnal, or nocturnal.

did you know?

Every November on Christmas Island, located in the Indian Ocean, about 120 million red crabs migrate from their forest home to breeding grounds on the coast. Sometimes, the crabs must pass through towns to get to the ocean. The people who live on this small island find crabs in the roads, schools, and even their homes!

276 Animal Reproduction and Behavior

What Is Cyclic Behavior?

Some animal behaviors, called cyclic behaviors, occur in regular, predictable patterns. **Cyclic behaviors usually change over the course of a day or a season.**

Daily Cycles Behavior cycles that occur over a period of approximately one day are called **circadian rhythms** (sur KAY dee un). For example, blowflies search for food during the day and rest at night. In contrast, field mice are active during the night and rest by day. Animals that are active during the day can take advantage of sunlight, which makes food easy to see. On the other hand, animals that are active at night do not encounter predators that are active during the day.

Hibernation Other behavior cycles are related to seasons. For example, some animals, such as woodchucks and chipmunks, are active during warm seasons but hibernate during the cold winter. **Hibernation** is a state of greatly reduced body activity that occurs during the winter when food is scarce. During hibernation, all of an animal's body processes, such as breathing and heartbeat, slow down. This slowdown reduces the animal's need for food. In fact, hibernating animals do not eat. Their bodies use stored fat to meet their reduced nutrition needs.

Migration While many animals live their lives in one area, others migrate. **Migration** is the regular, seasonal journey of an animal from one place to another and back again. Some animals migrate short distances. Dall's sheep, for example, spend summers near the tops of mountains and move lower down for the winters. Other animals migrate thousands of kilometers. Arctic terns fly more than 17,000 kilometers between the North and South poles.

Animals usually migrate to an area that provides a lot of food or a good environment for reproduction. Most migrations are related to the changing seasons and take place twice a year, in the spring and in the fall. American redstarts, for example, are insect-eating birds that spend the summer in North America. There, they mate and raise young. In the fall, insects become scarce, so the redstarts migrate south to areas where they can find plenty of food.

Scientists have discovered that migrating animals find their way using sight, taste, and other senses, including some that humans do not have. Some birds and sea turtles, for example, have a magnetic sense that acts something like a compass needle. Migrating birds also seem to navigate by using the positions of the sun, moon, and stars. Salmon use scent and taste to locate the streams where they were born, and return there to mate.

276 Animal Reproduction and Behavior

FIGURE 5 ·····················

On the Move

The migration route of monarch butterflies is sometimes as long as 3,600 kilometers. In the fall, monarchs fly south from Canada and the United States and spend the winter in the mountains of Mexico.

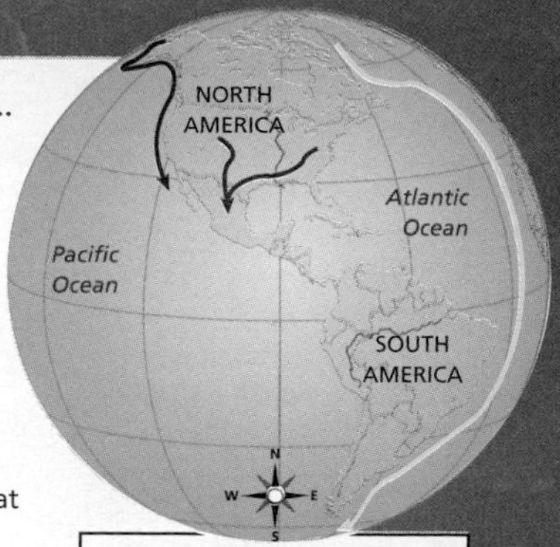

✐ **Use the map to answer the following questions.**

1. **Interpret Maps** Circle the animal that has a migration route that passes more than one continent. Then, write the name of the animal on the line below.

 A.   B.   C.

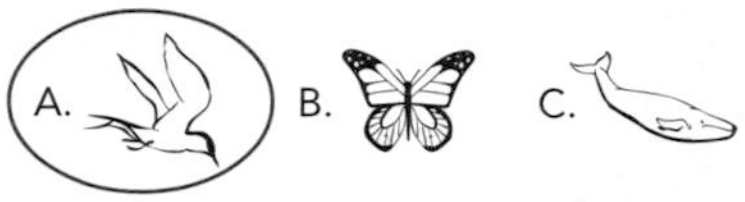

Arctic tern

2. CHALLENGE Why do you think gray whales travel to warm, southern waters to give birth to their calves?

Sample: It is easier for the calves to survive in southern waters because they don't need to use as much energy to stay warm.

NORTH AMERICA

Pacific Ocean

Atlantic Ocean

SOUTH AMERICA

N W E S

Key to Migration Routes

◻ Arctic tern

◼ Monarch butterfly

◼ Gray whale

▲ This gray whale and her calf will travel for two to three months to return to their feeding grounds in the north.

277

Teach With Visuals

Tell students to look at **Figure 5.** Ask them to compare the migration routes shown on the map. If students have previously studied Earth's movements and the seasons, they should be aware that when it is winter in the Northern Hemisphere, it is summer in the Southern Hemisphere. Review this information and ask students to relate it to the migration of the arctic tern. *(The bird spends the Northern Hemisphere summer in the Arctic region and the Southern Hemisphere summer in the Antarctic region.)* Point out that the migratory route shown on the map has been simplified. The birds actually fly south along the west coasts of Europe and Africa, and fly north along the west coasts of South America and North America. Help students trace this route on a classroom map. Ask them why they think the birds follow this route and not a more direct route. If students say it is to find places to rest, explain that these birds rarely land. Help students understand that the small fish and crustaceans the birds eat are more available near coastlines than in the middle of the ocean.

Elaborate

21st Century Learning

INFORMATION LITERACY Provide students with field guides to birds. Make sure the guides show maps of the birds' winter range and summer range. Help students locate your area on the maps. If you have guides from more than one source or from different publication dates, have students compare the maps to see if there are any differences. Discuss how continuing research can yield new data that result in a redrawn map. Then have students work in small groups to identify a bird that is a year-round resident, a bird that is a summer resident, and a bird that is a winter resident. Compile a class list of birds in each category.

Differentiated Instruction

L3 Finding Their Way Have students look at the map of migrations in **Figure 5.** Encourage interested students to find out how these or other animals find their way along their routes.

Students can create posters that trace the routes and provide additional information about the animal's migration.

Explain ——————

Teach With Visuals

Tell students to look at **Figure 6.** Tell them that the black-browed albatross lives in the Southern Hemisphere, with the largest populations on the Falklands Islands. Ask students to compare the postures of the two birds shown in the courtship behavior photograph. *(One bird appears to be approaching the other with its head extended.)* **How can you tell that this is not an aggressive behavior?** *(Samples: The posture does not look threatening. If one bird were threatening the other, it would probably have its mouth open as if it were going to bite the other bird.)* Point out the tail, which is fanned out and raised. This is part of the bird's courtship display. Ask students to look at the bird with the egg. The black-browed albatross produces only one egg per season. Help students see that the bird and the egg appear to be on top of a small column. These columns can be more easily seen in the larger image. Birds return to these nests year after year. Ask: **Do you think these birds are territorial? Explain.** *(Sample: Yes; if they return to the same nest, they must consider it "theirs," so they would claim and defend it.)*

EXPLORE THE BIG ?

Birds of a Feather...

How does an animal's behavior help it survive and reproduce?

FIGURE 6 ·······························

▶ REAL-WORLD INQUIRY Black-browed albatrosses live in colonies that can number close to 500,000 birds. Albatrosses behave in ways that enable them to reproduce and successfully raise their chicks.

✎ Interpret Photos Read the descriptions of black-browed albatross reproduction and behavior. Then, answer the questions on the lines provided.

② Reproduction

This parent albatross is sitting on its egg. Which type of fertilization resulted in this egg?

Internal fertilization

Why would external fertilization be difficult for albatrosses?

Albatrosses live on land, and the sperm and eggs might dry out on land.

① Courtship Behavior

Albatross courtship behavior involves calling and dancing. Why is it so important that these two albatrosses perform courtship behavior?

Courtship helps males and females of the same species find one another, so they can mate and reproduce.

278 Animal Reproduction and Behavior

Real-World Inquiry allows students to explore an animal in its environment and then to predict the animal's behaviors.

MY SCIENCE ONLINE .com ▶ Cyclic Behavior

Colony Life

How is this chick able to recognize and take food from its parent?

This chick has imprinted on its parent.

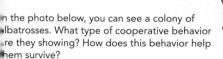

In the photo below, you can see a colony of albatrosses. What type of cooperative behavior are they showing? How does this behavior help them survive?

These albatrosses are living in a group. Living close to each other protects them from predators.

Do the Quick Lab Behavior Cycles.

🗝 Assess Your Understanding

2a. Review The regular, seasonal journey of an animal from one place to another and back again is called ((migration)/hibernation).

b. Compare and Contrast How are circadian rhythms and hibernation alike and different?

Both are cyclic behaviors, but circadian rhythms are a daily cycle and hibernation is a seasonal cycle.

c. CHALLENGE Why may building a road through a forest interfere with migration?

Sample: Some animals may not be able to cross the road safely.

d. ANSWER THE BIG Q How does an animal's behavior help it survive and reproduce?

Sample: Some behaviors, like courtship, establishing territory, and aggression, help animals find mates. Once they find a mate, they can reproduce and make more of their species.

got it? ....

○ **I get it!** Now I know that cyclic behaviors usually change over the course of a day or season.

○ I need extra help with See TE note.

Go to **MY SCIENCE COACH** *online for help with this subject.*

279

Elaborate

Explore the Big Q ? UbD

ANIMAL BEHAVIOR Review with students things that animals need to survive. Ask: **What are some examples of behaviors associated with getting food?** *(Samples: stalking, pouncing, hunting)* **What are some examples of behaviors associated with claiming and defending a territory?** *(Samples: making sounds, leaving scent marks, chasing invaders)* **What are some examples of behaviors associated with reproduction?** *(Samples: courtship displays, nest building, care of offspring)* **What are some ways in which cooperative behavior helps animals get food?** *(Samples: some predators hunt in packs, worker bees bring back food for the whole hive)*

Elaborate

Lab Resource: Quick Lab

L1 BEHAVIOR CYCLES Students will practice using their sense of smell to model how Pacific salmon guide themselves back to their home rivers to breed.

Evaluate

Assess Your Understanding

After students answer the questions, have them evaluate their understanding by completing the appropriate sentence.

Answer the Big Q ? UbD

To help students focus on the Big Question, lead a class discussion about how animals' behavior help them survive and reproduce.

RTI Response to Intervention

2a. If students need to review migration and hibernation, **then** work as a class to discuss one or two examples of each.

b. If students have difficulty comparing and contrasting circadian rhythms with hibernation, **then** compare events that happen each day with events that happen from one season to the next.

c. If students need help relating what they learned about migration to a new situation, **then** suggest they draw a picture to help them think about a road passing through an animal's environment.

d. If students need assistance answering the big question, **then** explain to students that reproduction is essential to the survival of a species.

MY SCIENCE COACH Have students go online for help in understanding cyclic behavior.

Differentiated Instruction

L1 Make Analogies Ask students to think of ways that human parental behavior is similar to the colony life of the albatrosses. *(Sample: Many parents may use a daycare center to provide childcare for their children so that the children have a safe, nurturing place to grow while parents gain resources* needed to help the child grow, such as food, clothing, and income to provide housing.)*

L3 Research Have students research the black-browed albatross, where it lives, what it eats, and why it is considered a threatened species.

Lab zone **After the Inquiry Warm-Up**

Patterns of Behavior

Inquiry Warm-Up, *Communicating Without Words*

In the Inquiry Warm-Up, you investigated how humans use facial expressions and body movements every day to communicate a wide range of emotions. Using what you learned from that activity, answer the questions below.

1. **COMPARE AND CONTRAST** Compare the sense or senses humans need to use to communicate by speaking with the sense or senses you and your partner needed to use in the lab to communicate with body language.

   _____

   _____

2. **USE PRIOR KNOWLEDGE** Do humans use any senses besides hearing and sight to communicate? If so, give an example.

   _____

   _____

   _____

3. **MAKE JUDGMENTS** Which senses, if any, are not consciously used by humans to communicate?

   _____

4. **USE PRIOR KNOWLEDGE** Do other animals use any senses to communicate that humans do not use to communicate? Explain.

   _____

   _____

   _____

Assess Your Understanding

Patterns of Behavior

What Are Three Ways That Animals Communicate?

gotit? ···

○ **I get it!** Now I know that animals communicate using _____

_____

○ **I need extra help with** _____

_____

What Are Examples of Competitive and Cooperative Behaviors?

1a. LIST What are two cooperative behaviors? _____

_____

b. EXPLAIN How are aggression and establishing a territory

related? _____

_____

_____

c. APPLY CONCEPTS Male red-winged blackbirds display red patches on
their shoulders to defend their territory. What would happen if these

red patches were dyed black? _____

_____

_____

gotit? ···

○ **I get it!** Now I know that examples of competitive and cooperative behavior are _____

_____

_____

○ **I need extra help with** _____

_____

Assess Your Understanding

Patterns of Behavior

┌─────────────────────────────────┐
│ **What Is Cyclic Behavior?** │
└─────────────────────────────────┘

2a. REVIEW The regular, seasonal journey of an animal from one place to another and back again is called (migration/hibernation).

b. COMPARE AND CONTRAST How are circadian rhythms and hibernation alike and different? _____

_____

_____

c. CHALLENGE Why may building a road through a forest interfere with migration? _____

_____

_____

d. ANSWER 🅱️ How does an animal's behavior help it survive and reproduce? _____

_____

_____

_____

got_it? ···

○ **I get it!** Now I know that cyclic behaviors _____

_____

○ **I need extra help with** _____

_____

Key Concept Summaries

Patterns of Behavior

What Are Three Ways That Animals Communicate?

Animals use sounds, scents, and body movements to communicate with one another. Animals may use sound to attract mates or to give warnings. Animals also communicate with chemical scents. A chemical released by one animal that affects the behavior of another animal of the same species is called a **pheromone.** A male cat that sprays a tree leaves a musky scent that advertises his presence to other cats in the neighborhood.

What Are Examples of Competitive and Cooperative Behaviors?

Animals compete with one another for limited resources, such as food, water, shelter, and mates. Competition can occur among different species of animals or within the same species. **Aggression** is a threatening behavior one animal uses to gain control over another. To control important resources, some animals establish a **territory,** an area that is occupied and defended by an animal or group of animals. **Courtship behavior** is any activity that prepares males and females of the same species for mating. These behaviors often involve competition for mates.

Not all animal behaviors are competitive. **Animals living in groups cooperate to survive.** Group members may protect one another or work together to find food. Some animals, such as honeybees and ants, live in societies. A **society** is a group of closely related animals of the same species that work together in a highly organized way.

What Is Cyclic Behavior?

Some animal behaviors, called cyclic behaviors, occur in regular patterns. **Cyclic behaviors usually change over the course of a day or a season. Circadian rhythms** are behavior cycles that occur over a period of about one day. Many animals are active either during the day or at night.

Other behavior cycles are related to seasons. Some animals hibernate. **Hibernation** is a state of greatly reduced body activity that occurs during the winter when food is scarce. During hibernation, all of an animal's body processes slow down, reducing the animal's need for food. **Migration** is the regular seasonal journey of an animal from one place to another and back again. Animals that migrate usually move twice a year to an area that provides a lot of food or a good environment for reproduction.

Think of the black bear. On a separate sheet of paper, give one example of a cyclic behavior and two examples of competitive behaviors the bear engages in. Also describe how the bear communicates during the competitive behaviors.

Review and Reinforce

Patterns of Behavior

Understanding Main Ideas
Answer the following questions on a separate sheet of paper.

1. What are the three ways that animals communicate?
2. For what do animals compete with one another?
3. What is a territory? List three ways an animal might mark and maintain its territory.
4. What is courtship behavior? Give an example.
5. What is cooperative behavior? Give an example.
6. What are cyclic behaviors? How often do they usually change?

Building Vocabulary
Match each term with its definition by writing the letter of the correct definition in the right column beside the term in the left column.

7. ___ pheromone

8. ___ aggression

9. ___ society

10. ___ circadian rhythm

11. ___ hibernation

12. ___ migration

a. behavior cycles that occur over a period of about one day

b. a threatening behavior one animal uses to gain control over another

c. a group of closely related animals of the same species that work together in a highly organized way

d. the seasonal journey of an animal from one place to another

e. a chemical released by one animal that affects another animal of the same species

f. a state of greatly reduced body activity

Enrich

Patterns of Behavior

Inside a hive, honeybees can communicate the direction, distance, and quality of food sources. Read the passage and study the figures at right. Then use a separate sheet of paper to answer the questions that follow.

The Language of Honeybees

When a honeybee returns home from a food source, she performs a "waggle-dance" that gives information about the food's location and quality. She repeatedly walks in the pattern of a squashed figure-8 on the wall of the honeycomb. In the middle of the figure-8, she makes a straight run, waggling her abdomen back and forth. The distance she walks while waggling tells her sisters how far away the food is. She waggles more vigorously if the food source is very good.

The dancing bee cannot point in the direction of the food, however. It is dark inside the hive, and the bee is dancing on a vertical surface. Instead, the angle between straight up and the direction of her straight run indicates the angle between the sun and the food source. For example, if the food were located in the direction of the sun, her straight run would be vertical. Armed with this information about the direction, distance, and quality of the food, other bees can then go to it.

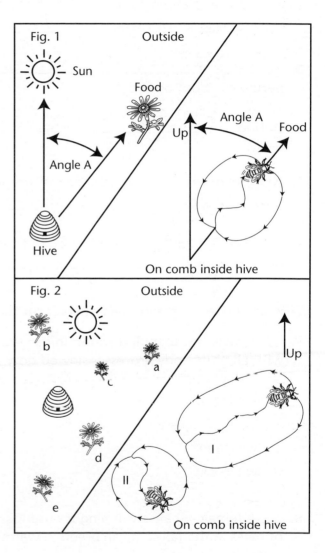

1. Figure 2 shows the location of several food sources (pictured as flowers), and the direction of the sun in relation to a beehive. Inside the hive, two bees are performing waggle-dances. Which food source is each one dancing about?

   a. Bee I:
   b. Bee II:

2. Based on the two bees' dances, which food source is closer?

3. Based on the two bees' dances, which is the better food source?

4. Which food source would you expect the other bees to fly to?

5. During the waggle-dance, what does the vertical direction stand for?

Lesson Quiz

Patterns of Behavior

Fill in the blank to complete each statement.

1. Animals compete with one another for _____ resources, such as food, water, shelter, and mates.

2. A chemical released by one animal that affects the behavior of another animal of the same species is called a(n) _____.

3. _____ are behavior cycles that occur over a period of about one day.

4. During _____, instead of eating, an animal lives off fat stored in its body.

5. A group of closely related animals of the same species that work together in a highly organized way is a(n) _____.

6. Animals that migrate usually move twice a year to an area that provides a lot of food or a good environment for _____.

Write the letter of the correct answer on the line at left.

7. ___ A male bat spending winter in its cave with all of its body processes slowed down is an example of

   A migration
   B courtship behavior
   C hibernation
   D aggression

8. ___ A female firefly responding to signals flashed by a male firefly is an example of

   A migration
   B courtship behavior
   C hibernation
   D cooperative behavior

9. ___ A female whale swimming thousands of miles in the fall so it can breed in warm water is an example of

   A migration
   B aggression
   C territorial behavior
   D hibernation

10. ___ A male cobra rearing up, flaring its hood, and hissing at another male cobra is an example of

   A migration
   B courtship behavior
   C cooperative behavior
   D aggression

Patterns of Behavior

Answer Key

After the Inquiry Warm-Up

1. To communicate by speaking, humans need to use hearing. To communicate with body language, my partner and I had to use sight.

2. Answers will vary. Sample: Humans also use touch to communicate. For example, a person might convey anger by hitting someone or convey caring by putting a hand on someone's shoulder.

3. smell and taste

4. Answers will vary. Sample: Yes, some animals use smell to communicate with each other. For example, a dog can tell a lot about other dogs in its neighborhood through its use of smell.

Key Concept Summaries

Sample: One cyclic behavior of a black bear is hibernation. In the winter when food is scarce, a bear goes into a state of greatly reduced body activity. One competitive behavior of a black bear is establishing a territory. To tell other animals and bears to stay away, a bear makes noise and marks its territory with its scent. Aggression is another competitive behavior of a black bear. If another bear enters its territory, the bear will rise up on its hind legs, bare its teeth, and make loud noises. The body language and sounds communicate, "Get away or I will hurt you!"

Review and Reinforce

1. sounds, scents, and body movements

2. limited resources, such as food, water, shelter, and mates

3. an area occupied and defended by an animal or group of animals; Accept any three: calls, aggression, scratches, droppings, or pheromones

4. Courtship behavior is any activity that prepares males and females of the same species for mating. Sample: A male cricket chirps to attract a female.

5. Cooperative behavior occurs when animals live in groups and help each other to survive. Sample: Lions hunt in a group to kill larger prey.

6. Cyclic behaviors are behaviors that occur in regular patterns. They usually change over the course of a day or a season.

7. e
8. b
9. c
10. a
11. f
12. d

Enrich

1. a. Bee I—source a
   b. Bee II—source d

2. Source d is closer.

3. Source d looks better because the bee is waggling more vigorously.

4. Source d makes sense. It's closer and better than source a.

5. The vertical stands for the direction to the sun.

Lesson Quiz

1. limited
2. pheromone
3. Circadian rhythms
4. hibernation
5. society
6. reproduction
7. C
8. B
9. A
10. D

Study Guide

Review the Big Q

Have students complete the statement at the top of the page. These Key Concepts support their understanding of the chapter's Big Question. Have students return to the chapter opener pages. What is different about how students view the image of the armadillos now that they have completed the chapter? Thinking about this will help them prepare for the *Apply the Big Q* activity in the Review and Assessment.

Partner Review

Have partners review definitions of vocabulary terms by using the Study Guide to quiz each other. Students could read the Key Concept statements and leave out words for their partner to fill in, or change a statement so that it is false and then ask their partner to correct it.

Class Activity: Concept Map

Have students develop a concept map to show how the information in this chapter is related. Have students brainstorm to identify Key Concepts, vocabulary, details, and examples, and then write each one on a sticky note and attach it at random on chart paper or on the board. Explain that the concept map will begin at the top with Key Concepts. Ask students to use the following questions to help them organize the information on the notes:
- How do animals reproduce?
- How do young animals develop?
- How do animals care for their young?
- What are the types and causes of animal behavior?
- How do animals communicate?
- What are competitive and cooperative behaviors?

My Science Coach allows students to complete the *Practice Test* online.

The Big Question allows students to complete the *Apply the Big Q* activity about how an animal's behavior helps it to survive and reproduce.

Vocab Flash Cards offer a way to review the chapter vocabulary words.

my science online .com ▶ Animal Reproduction & Behavior

REVIEW THE BIG Q

In __cooperative behavior__, animals live in groups to survive. Another type of behavior, called __courtship behavior__, leads to mating and reproduction.

LESSON 1 Animal Reproduction and Fertilization

🔑 Animals undergo either asexual or sexual reproduction to make more of their own kind or species.

🔑 External fertilization occurs outside of the female's body, and internal fertilization occurs inside the female's body.

Vocabulary
- larva • polyp • medusa
- external fertilization • internal fertilization
- gestation period

LESSON 2 Development and Growth

🔑 The growing offspring, or embryo, may develop outside or inside of the parent's body.

🔑 Young animals undergo changes in their bodies between birth and maturity.

🔑 Most amphibians and reptiles do not provide parental care. Most birds and mammals do.

Vocabulary
- amniotic egg • placenta • metamorphosis
- complete metamorphosis • pupa
- incomplete metamorphosis • nymph • tadpole

LESSON 3 What Is Behavior?

🔑 All animal behaviors are responses to stimuli.

🔑 The types of animal behavior are instincts and learned behaviors.

Vocabulary
- behavior • instinct • learning
- imprinting • conditioning
- trial-and-error learning
- insight learning

LESSON 4 Patterns of Behavior

🔑 Animals use sounds, scents, and body movements to communicate with one another.

🔑 Animals compete with one another for limited resources, such as food, water, space, shelter, and mates.

🔑 Animals living in groups cooperate to survive.

🔑 Cyclic behaviors usually change over the course of a day or a season.

Vocabulary
- pheromone • aggression • territory
- courtship behavior • society
- circadian rhythm • hibernation
- migration

(E)(L)(L) Support

4 Language Production

Divide the students into teams of four. Assign each member a number of 1, 2, 3, or 4. Ask the essential questions from the lessons in the chapter. Groups should work together to answer the question so that all can agree on the answer. Call out a number and have the corresponding member in each group answers.

Beginning

LOW/HIGH Allow students to answer with single words or short phrases.

Intermediate

LOW/HIGH Have students work cooperatively to answer the question aloud.

Advanced

LOW/HIGH Have students assist by acting as a coach for each team.

Review and Assessment

LESSON 1 Animal Reproduction and Fertilization

1. External fertilization is common for organisms that live in

  a. trees.   **(b.)** water.
  c. deserts.   **d.** open fields.

2. The _____larva_____ is an immature form of an organism that looks very different from the adult.

3. Classify Label each body form of the moon jelly. Then on the lines below identify whether each form represents an asexual or sexual stage.

Polyp   Medusa

The polyp is in the asexual stage. The medusa is in the sexual stage.

4. Infer All land animals undergo internal fertilization. Why do you think this method is an adaptation for life on land?

The egg and sperm may dry out on land. Internal fertilization prevents the egg and sperm from drying out.

5. **Write About It** Consider the following statement: _Organisms that reproduce asexually are at a higher risk of extinction than organisms that reproduce sexually._ Do you agree or disagree? Explain your answer.

See TE rubric.

LESSON 2 Development and Growth

6. Which of the following organisms lays amniotic eggs?

  a. fish   **b.** insect
  (c.) turtle   **d.** rabbit

7. Both ___birds___ and ___mammals___ care for their young.

8. Sequence Label each stage of complete metamorphosis. Then number each stage to put it in the correct order.

(2) Larva   (4) Adult

(1) Eggs   (3) Pupa

9. Compare and Contrast How is the development of an embryo in an amniotic egg and in a placental mammal different?

An embryo in an amniotic egg develops outside of the parent's body. Embryos in placental mammals develop inside the parent's body.

10. Make Generalizations Why is parental care so important for newborn birds and mammals?

Newborn birds and mammals are usually helpless and cannot care for themselves.

Review and Assessment

Assess Understanding

Have students complete the answers to the Review and Assessment questions. Have a class discussion about what students find confusing. Write Key Concepts on the board to reinforce knowledge.

RTI Response to Intervention

3. If students cannot label the body forms of the jellyfish, **then** have them review **Figure 5**.

8. If students need help with sequencing the stages of metamorphosis, **then** have them review the figure that accompanies the text on complete metamorphosis.

Alternate Assessment

L1 **DESIGN A GAME** Have students work in small groups to design a game about plants. Students can design a board game that requires players to answer questions in order to advance. Remind students to create rules, spinners, game pieces, and questions for their games. The questions for the game should include vocabulary terms and Key Concepts from the chapter. Students can exchange games with other groups or play their own game.

CHAPTER 7

Write About It Assess student's writing using this rubric.

SCORING RUBRIC	SCORE 4	SCORE 3	SCORE 2	SCORE 1
Explain whether organisms that reproduce asexually are at higher risk of extinction	Student agrees and explains that offspring from asexual reproduction have no genetic variation and may not survive changes in environment.	Student agrees with statement and provides limited support to explain position.	Student agrees with statement but does not offer any support to explain position.	Student disagrees with statement or does not offer a position.

Review and Assessment, Cont.

RTI Response to Intervention

13. If students have trouble drawing a conclusion about the effect of learning on an animal's chances for survival, **then** have them reread the text for the red heading *Learned Behaviors* and summarize the information.

16. If students cannot explain what courtship behavior is, **then** have them locate the highlighted term in the text and review the definition.

Apply the Big Q ? UbD

TRANSFER Students should be able to demonstrate understanding of how an animal's behavior helps it to survive and reproduce by answering this question. See the scoring rubric below.

Connect to the Big Idea ? UbD

BIG IDEA: Living things grow, change, and reproduce during their lifetimes.

Send students back to the Big Ideas of Science at the beginning of their student edition. Have them read what they wrote before they started the chapter. Lead a class discussion about how their thoughts have changed. If all chapters have been completed, have students fill in the bottom section for the Big Idea.

L3 WRITING IN SCIENCE Ask students to write an article that explains to readers how an animal's behavior helps it to survive and reproduce. Encourage students to discuss a variety of animals in their articles.

LESSON 3 What Is Behavior?

11. All animal behaviors are responses to
   a. pheromones.   b. learning.
   c. aggression.   (d.) stimuli.

12. A bird builds a nest correctly the first time it tries. This is an example of a(n) _instinct._

13. Draw Conclusions How does learning increase an animal's chance for survival?
   An animal may learn to avoid predators or to hunt for food more successfully.

14. **Write About It** Write about an example of learning in your own life. How did you or another organism use past knowledge to perform a new task?
   See TE rubric.

LESSON 4 Patterns of Behavior

15. Some cats mark their territory by spraying a chemical scent known as a
   a. courtship behavior.
   b. circadian rhythm.
   c. cooperative behavior.
   (d.) pheromone.

16. Animals use _courtship behavior_ to find a mate.

17. Make Generalizations How do migration and hibernation help animals to survive?
   Migration allows animals to move to favorable conditions as the seasons change. Hibernation slows down body processes, reducing the need for food when it is not available.

 How does an animal's behavior help it survive and reproduce?

18. This male giraffe, a mammal, uses its neck to fight a male competitor. Using at least four terms from this chapter, describe how this male giraffe's behavior helps it mate and reproduce.
   Sample: This male giraffe is competing with another male by showing aggression. He may also display courtship behavior to attract a female. Because he is a mammal, I know his offspring will be a result of internal fertilization. The female will give birth after a gestation period. See TE rubric.

Write About It Assess student's writing using this rubric.

SCORING RUBRIC	SCORE 4	SCORE 3	SCORE 2	SCORE 1
Explain how past knowledge can be used to perform new task	Student identifies an appropriate example and clearly explains how past knowledge was used to perform new task.	Student identifies an example and partially explains how past knowledge was used to perform new task.	Student identifies an example but offers a confusing explanation how past knowledge was used to perform new task.	Student does not identify an example or explain how past knowledge was used to perform new task.

? How does an animal's behavior help it survive and reproduce?
Assess student's response using this rubric.

SCORING RUBRIC	SCORE 4	SCORE 3	SCORE 2	SCORE 1
Describe how behavior helps a giraffe mate and reproduce using at least four terms from the chapter	Student clearly describes how behavior helps the giraffe mate and reproduce; and uses at least four terms.	Student fairly describes how behavior helps the giraffe mate and reproduce; and uses two or three terms.	Student partially describes how behavior helps a giraffe mate and reproduce; and uses one or two terms.	Student does not adequately describe how behavior helps the giraffe; and doesn't use terms from the chapter.

Standardized Test Prep

Multiple Choice

Circle the letter of the best answer.

1. The larval form of the frog shown in stage 3 is called a

A nymph.   B pupa.

Ⓒ tadpole.   D adult.

2. Circadian rhythms are cyclic behavior patterns that occur

Ⓐ daily.   B weekly.

C monthly.   D yearly.

3. An amniotic egg is the result of _____

and _____.

A asexual reproduction; external fertilization

B asexual reproduction; internal fertilization

C sexual reproduction; external fertilization

Ⓓ sexual reproduction; internal fertilization

4. A chimpanzee climbs on a box to reach a banana. When the banana is placed in a higher location, the chimpanzee stacks two boxes on top of each other to reach the banana. This is an example of

A trial-and-error learning.

Ⓑ insight learning.

C imprinting.

D conditioning.

5. Which of the following is an example of a competitive behavior?

A bees living together in a hive

B a school of fish escaping a predator

Ⓒ a bear defending a territory

D wolves hunting prey as a group

Constructed Response

Use the diagram below and your knowledge of science to help you answer Question 6. Write your answer on a separate piece of paper.

Guinea pig   Hydra

6. Identify what type of reproduction occurs in the guinea pig and the hydra. Then, compare and contrast the two types of reproduction.
See TE note.

283

Standardized Test Prep

Test-Taking Skills

INTERPRETING DIAGRAMS Tell students that when they answer questions like Question 1, which includes a diagram, they should make sure that they study all parts of the diagram carefully, including illustrations and labels. Urge students to get the diagram's information clear in their minds before they analyze how the diagram relates to the question as a whole. In this diagram, stage 3 shows the larva form of a frog, which is called a *tadpole*. The correct answer is C.

Constructed Response

6. The guinea pig reproduces sexually. The hydra reproduces asexually. Both types of reproduction make more of a species. But asexual reproduction only requires one parent, while sexual reproduction requires a male and a female parent. Offspring of asexual reproduction receive an exact copy of the parent's genetic material, or DNA. Offspring of sexual reproduction have a combination of their parents' genetic material. Sexual reproduction involves fertilization, while asexual reproduction does not.

Additional Assessment Resources

Chapter Test
ExamView® Computer Test Generator
Performance Assessment
Progress Monitoring Assessments
SuccessTracker™

ⒺⓁⓁ Support

5 Assess Understanding

Have ELLs complete the Alternate Assessment. Provide guidelines on the information it must cover, and a rubric for assessment. You may wish to have them complete the activity in small groups of varying language proficiencies.

Beginning

LOW/HIGH Allow students to work on designing the game board and game pieces.

Intermediate

LOW/HIGH Allow students to write the questions and answers.

Advanced

LOW/HIGH Allow students to write the instructions for playing and scoring the game.

Remediate If students have trouble with...

QUESTION	SEE LESSON	STANDARDS
1	2	
2	4	
3	2	
4	3	
5	4	
6	1	

Science Matters

Hot Science

Have students read *Special Delivery! Seahorse Reproduction.* Tell students that the dance-like routine seahorses go through is part of a ritual leading up to the mating process. Sometimes other seahorses will try to interfere with the couple to attract one of the partners away. Once a seahorse has a mate, they mate for life. Once the male has fertilized the eggs, the female visits him daily where they often repeat many of the activities they went through during their pre-mating dance. The males tend to stay in their own territory, within about one square meter of their habitat, while the females will swim in a range about a hundred times that size.

Tell students that the seahorse young are called *fry.* They have a very low survival rate; and very few of the infant seahorses survive to adulthood. Explain that because of this, incubation of the fertilized eggs is very important. Scientists think this might be why the males carry the eggs, though they have not proven it. Female seahorses need weeks to gather the nutrients necessary to develop a new set of eggs. Therefore, the male's body is more suited to incubating the eggs during that time. It may also explain the lifetime mating. The female forms a bond with her reliable egg-carrying partner during her daily visits, which is important, since a female seahorse will lose all her eggs if she cannot lay them within a few hours of when they are ready.

Ask: **How could the low survival rate of the newborns affect the mating of seahorses?** *(Sample: They are likely to mate often to maintain the population.)* **How do the mating "dance" and daily visits help seahorse reproduction?** *(They create a bond between the lifetime mating partners.)*

SCIENCE MATTERS

Hot Science

SPECIAL DELIVERY!
Seahorse Reproduction

In warm, coastal waters all over the world, just after sunrise every day, a dance-like scene takes place. Tails intertwined, pairs of seahorses spin and twirl under water. Some use their long tails to hold onto strands of seaweed. These long tails that are adapted for grabbing and holding things aren't seahorses' only unusual feature. Seahorses also have some unusual reproductive habits!

Seahorses practice sexual reproduction, like other fish do. Unlike fish—or any other vertebrate for that matter—it's the male seahorse that carries fertilized eggs, provides the eggs with oxygen and nutrients, and gives birth. The males can do this because they have pouches, called brood pouches, in their abdomens.

When mating, the female seahorse deposits about 2,000 eggs inside the male's pouch each time, and he does the rest. He fertilizes the eggs, which become embedded in his pouch wall, and carries them for several weeks. During this time, the eggs receive oxygen and nutrients through a network of tiny blood vessels.

In about three weeks, the male seahorse's brood pouch expands until it is almost spherical. It stays this way for several hours, until the seahorse suddenly gives birth to between eight and 200 baby seahorses. These tiny seahorses can swim and feed by themselves, although they will not be ready to mate with their own partners for many months. About an hour after giving birth, the male is ready to mate again.

▲ The male seahorse's brood pouch expands as the baby seahorses grow.

Design It Pipefish are another species with unusual reproductive habits. Find out about their reproductive cycles. Create a Venn diagram to compare and contrast the pipefish cycle and the seahorse cycle.

284 **Animal Reproduction and Behavior**

Quick Facts

Positive reinforcement is a kind of psychological technique called *behaviorism.* In psychology, reinforcement is using stimuli that increase the likelihood of a certain response. The opposite of positive reinforcement, used with guide dogs, is negative reinforcement, in which something negative is removed in response to a desired behavior. Another type of reinforcement is punishment. This involves adding something negative in response to an undesirable behavior. For example, cat owners spray cats with a spray bottle to teach them not to repeat certain behaviors. Extinction is a kind of reinforcement that involves removing something in order to decrease an undesirable behavior. Talk with the class about the kind of reinforcement they think is most effective in eliciting a desired behavior.

Teen GUIDE DOG Trainer

Wherever Lena Cole goes, a puppy named Davey goes with her—even to school. Davey is just one of the puppies Lena trains so that one day they can serve as guide dogs for blind people.

Lena began training guide dog puppies when she was 15. She cares for the puppies for the first two years of their lives. Lena says, "What I do is socialization, basic obedience, and getting Davey used to all the possible situations that might occur when he is a guide dog." Socialization involves helping a puppy learn appropriate behaviors for different settings. This can include taking the puppy to movie theaters, train stations, and other public areas. After two years with Lena, a dog is ready for more advanced training as a guide dog.

Praising Good Behaviors

Lena uses conditioning to train and socialize the dogs. First, she carefully observes a dog's behavior. She praises the dog for positive behaviors, such as waiting quietly in a busy environment. Through repetition, the dog learns to associate certain behaviors with praise and to stop repeating behaviors that do not earn praise.

Rewarding Work

Lena says that raising guide dog puppies is rewarding because the dogs go on to receive training as guide dogs. Eventually they serve as companions and helpers for blind people. Lena also enjoys the close bonds she forms with the puppies, even if it makes for difficult farewells. "It's hard to say goodbye, but this is what you raise the dog for," she says. "You hope that he will be able to go on and help someone else."

Write About It How might you use conditioning to teach a dog to stop and sit at a red light? Predict what methods might work best. Based on your prediction, write a how-to manual describing your training methods.

285

Kids Doing Science

Have students read *Teen Guide Dog Trainer.* Explain that guide dogs and their human partners work together. For example, the person decides where they want to go, and it is the dog's job to find a safe path. Another example is that the dog can lead a person to a street corner but the person must listen to judge when it is safe to cross. If the person makes an error and the dog can sense that it is unsafe, it will refuse to follow the command of its owner to proceed across a street. Tell students this is known as *intelligent disobedience.*

Tell students that one of the most difficult challenges is training a guide dog to help its owner avoid low overhanging objects that dogs would not encounter. Ideally, the trainers teach the dogs to avoid these obstacles through voice commands and repetition. If the owner does end up running into an overhanging object, the owner must rework the error with the dog repeatedly until the dog learns to guide its owner around the obstacle.

Tell students that the method of rewarding positive behavior with praise is known as *positive reinforcement.* This is one of many types of behavior modification techniques.

As students predict how to train dogs, have them research the methods and commands that are currently used in training guide dogs, and have them choose which they think will be effective.

Ask: **Why are sighted people used to train guide dogs?** *(They can see the things they need to train the dogs to avoid.)* **How does praise help the dogs to learn?** *(Dogs repeat behavior that earns praise.)*

Using a Microscope

The microscope is an essential tool in the study of life science. It allows you to see things that are too small to be seen with the unaided eye.

You will probably use a compound microscope like the one you see here. The compound microscope has more than one lens that magnifies the object you view.

Typically, a compound microscope has one lens in the eyepiece, the part you look through. The eyepiece lens usually magnifies 10×. Any object you view through this lens would appear 10 times larger than it is.

A compound microscope may contain one or two other lenses called objective lenses. If there are two, they are called the low-power and high-power objective lenses. The low-power objective lens usually magnifies 10×. The high-power objective lens usually magnifies 40×.

To calculate the total magnification with which you are viewing an object, multiply the magnification of the eyepiece lens by the magnification of the objective lens you are using. For example, the eyepiece's magnification of 10× multiplied by the low-power objective's magnification of 10× equals a total magnification of 100×.

Use the photo of the compound microscope to become familiar with the parts of the microscope and their functions.

The Parts of a Microscope

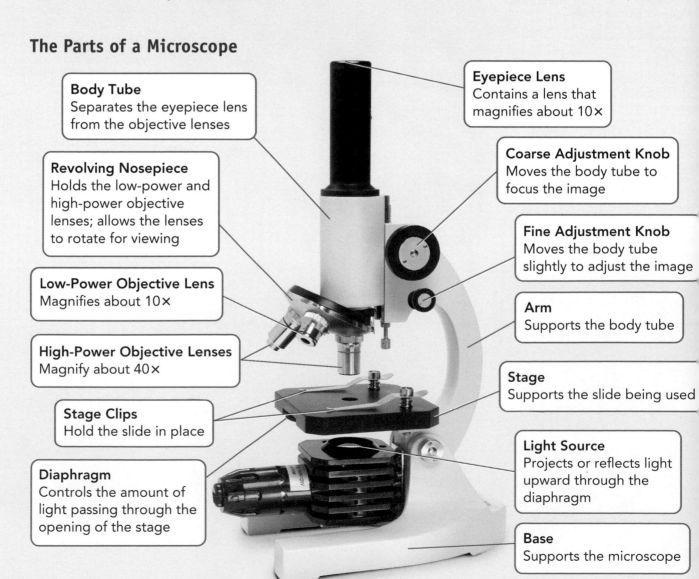

Body Tube
Separates the eyepiece lens from the objective lenses

Revolving Nosepiece
Holds the low-power and high-power objective lenses; allows the lenses to rotate for viewing

Low-Power Objective Lens
Magnifies about 10×

High-Power Objective Lenses
Magnify about 40×

Stage Clips
Hold the slide in place

Diaphragm
Controls the amount of light passing through the opening of the stage

Eyepiece Lens
Contains a lens that magnifies about 10×

Coarse Adjustment Knob
Moves the body tube to focus the image

Fine Adjustment Knob
Moves the body tube slightly to adjust the image

Arm
Supports the body tube

Stage
Supports the slide being used

Light Source
Projects or reflects light upward through the diaphragm

Base
Supports the microscope

Using the Microscope

Use the following procedures when you are working with a microscope.

1. To carry the microscope, grasp the microscope's arm with one hand. Place your other hand under the base.
2. Place the microscope on a table with the arm toward you.
3. Turn the coarse adjustment knob to raise the body tube.
4. Revolve the nosepiece until the low-power objective lens clicks into place.
5. Adjust the diaphragm. While looking through the eyepiece, also adjust the mirror until you see a bright white circle of light. **CAUTION:** *Never use direct sunlight as a light source.*
6. Place a slide on the stage. Center the specimen over the opening on the stage. Use the stage clips to hold the slide in place. **CAUTION:** *Glass slides are fragile.*
7. Look at the stage from the side. Carefully turn the coarse adjustment knob to lower the body tube until the low-power objective almost touches the slide.
8. Looking through the eyepiece, very slowly turn the coarse adjustment knob until the specimen comes into focus.
9. To switch to the high-power objective lens, look at the microscope from the side. Carefully revolve the nosepiece until the high-power objective lens clicks into place. Make sure the lens does not hit the slide.
10. Looking through the eyepiece, turn the fine adjustment knob until the specimen comes into focus.

Making a Wet-Mount Slide

Use the following procedures to make a wet-mount slide of a specimen.

1. Obtain a clean microscope slide and a coverslip. **CAUTION:** *Glass slides and coverslips are fragile.*
2. Place the specimen on the center of the slide. The specimen must be thin enough for light to pass through it.
3. Using a plastic dropper, place a drop of water on the specimen.
4. Gently place one edge of the coverslip against the slide so that it touches the edge of the water drop at a 45° angle. Slowly lower the coverslip over the specimen. If you see air bubbles trapped beneath the coverslip, tap the coverslip gently with the eraser end of a pencil.
5. Remove any excess water at the edge of the coverslip with a paper towel.

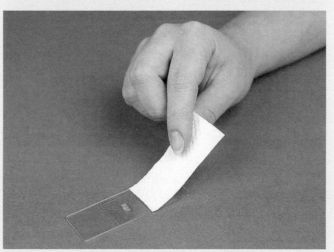

GLOSSARY

A

adaptation An inherited behavior or physical characteristic that helps an organism survive and reproduce in its environment. (139)
adaptación Comportamiento o característica física heredada que ayuda a que un organismo se reproduzca y sobreviva en su medio ambiente.

aggression A threatening behavior that one animal uses to gain control over another animal. (272)
agresión Comportamiento amenazador que un animal usa para controlar a otro.

algae Plantlike protists. (61)
algas Protistas con características vegetales.

amniotic egg An egg with a shell and internal membranes that keep the embryo moist; a major adaptation to life on land characteristic of reptiles, birds, and egg-laying mammals. (253)
huevo amniótico Huevo con cáscara y membranas internas que mantiene al embrión húmedo; adaptación principal a la vida en la tierra, característica de los reptiles, las aves y los mamíferos que ponen huevos.

amphibian A vertebrate whose body temperature is determined by the temperature of its environment, and that lives its early life in water and its adult life on land. (160)
anfibio Vertebrado cuya temperatura corporal es determinada por la temperatura de su medio ambiente, y que vive en el agua durante su infancia y en la tierra durante su adultez.

angiosperm A flowering plant that produces seeds enclosed in a protective fruit. (98)
angiosperma Planta con flores que produce semillas encerradas en una fruta protectora.

annual A flowering plant that completes its life cycle in one growing season. (111)
anual Planta con flores que completa su ciclo de vida en una sola temporada de crecimiento.

anus The opening at the end of an organism's digestive system (in humans, the rectum) through which waste material is eliminated from the body. (214)
ano Apertura en la porción final del sistema digestivo de un organismo (el recto en los seres humanos) a través del cual se eliminan los desechos del cuerpo.

arthropod An invertebrate that has an external skeleton, a segmented body, and jointed appendages. (152)
artrópodo Invertebrado que tiene un esqueleto externo, un cuerpo segmentado y apéndices articulados.

asexual reproduction A reproductive process that involves only one parent and produces offspring that are genetically identical to the parent. (7)
reproducción asexual Proceso reproductivo que consiste de un solo reproductor y que produce individuos que son genéticamente idénticos al reproductor.

atrium An upper chamber of the heart that receives blood. (228)
aurícula Cavidad superior del corazón que recibe la sangre.

autotroph An organism that is able to capture energy from sunlight or chemicals and use it to produce its own food. (11)
autótrofo Organismo capaz de capturar y usar la energía del Sol o de las sustancias químicas para producir su propio alimento.

auxin A plant hormone that speeds up the rate at which a plant's cells grow and controls a plant's response to light. (120)
auxina Hormona vegetal que acelera la velocidad del crecimiento de las células de una planta y que controla la respuesta de la planta a la luz.

B

bacteria Single-celled organisms that lack a nucleus; prokaryotes. (47)
bacteria Organismos unicelulares que no tienen un núcleo; procariotas.

behavior The manner in which an organism reacts to changes in its internal conditions or external environment. (262)
comportamiento Manera en la que un organismo reacciona a un cambio en sus condiciones internas o en su medio ambiente externo.

biennial A flowering plant that completes its life cycle in two years. (111)
bienal Planta con flores que completa su ciclo de vida en dos años.

bilateral symmetry A body plan in which a single imaginary line divides the body into left and right sides that are mirror images of each other. (144)
simetría bilateral Esquema del cuerpo en el que una línea imaginaria divide el cuerpo en dos partes, izquierda y derecha, que son el reflejo la una de la otra.

binary fission A form of asexual reproduction in which one cell divides, forming two identical cells. (51)
fisión binaria Forma de reproducción asexual en la que una célula se divide y forma dos células idénticas.

binomial nomenclature The classification system in which each organism is given a unique, two-part scientific name indicating its genus and species. (16)
nomenclatura binaria Sistema de clasificación en el que cada organismo tiene un nombre científico específico de dos partes que indica el género y la especie.

bird A vertebrate whose body temperature is regulated by its internal heat, lays eggs, and has feathers and a four-chambered heart. (162)
ave Vertebrado cuya temperatura corporal es regulada por su calor interno, que produce huevos y que tiene plumas y un corazón de cuatro cavidades.

brain **1.** An organized grouping of neurons in the head of an animal with bilateral symmetry. (183) **2.** The part of the central nervous system that is located in the skull and controls most functions in the body.
encéfalo **1.** Conjunto organizado de neuronas ubicado en la cabeza de animales con simetría bilateral. **2.** Parte del sistema nervioso ubicada en el cráneo y que controla la mayoría de las funciones del cuerpo.

branching tree diagram A diagram that shows probable evolutionary relationships among organisms and the order in which specific characteristics may have evolved. (27)
árbol ramificado Diagrama que muestra las relaciones evolucionarias probables entre los organismos y el orden en que ciertas características específicas podrían haber evolucionado.

budding A form of asexual reproduction in which a new organism grows out of the body of a parent. (68)
gemación Forma de reproducción asexual en la que una porción del cuerpo de un reproductor se separa y forma un nuevo organismo.

_____ **C** _____

cambium A layer of cells in a plant that produces new phloem and xylem cells. (102)
cámbium Una capa de células de una planta que produce nuevas células de floema y xilema.

capillary A tiny blood vessel where substances are exchanged between the blood and the body cells. (227)
capilar Vaso sanguíneo minúsculo donde se intercambian sustancias entre la sangre y las células del cuerpo.

carnivore A consumer that obtains energy by eating only animals. (207)
carnívoro Consumidor que come sólo animales para obtener energía.

cartilage A connective tissue that is more flexible than bone and that protects the ends of bones and keeps them from rubbing together. (159, 177)
cartílago Tejido conectivo que es más flexible que el hueso y que protege los extremos de los huesos y evita que se rocen.

cell The basic unit of structure and function in living things. (6)
célula Unidad básica de la estructura y función de los seres vivos.

cellular respiration The process that releases energy by breaking down glucose and other food molecules in the presence of oxygen. (50, 217)
respiración celular Proceso en el que se libera energía mediante la descomposición de glucosa y otras moléculas de los alimentos ante la presencia de oxígeno.

chlorophyll A green photosynthetic pigment found in the chloroplasts of plants, algae, and some bacteria. (85)
clorofila Pigmento fotosintético verde que se halla en los cloroplastos de plantas, algas y ciertas bacterias.

chloroplast An organelle in the cells of plants and some other organisms that captures energy from sunlight and changes it to an energy form that cells can use in making food. (86)
cloroplasto Orgánulo de las células vegetales y otros organismos que absorbe energía de la luz solar y la convierte en una forma de energía que las células pueden usar para producir alimentos.

chordate An animal that has a notochord, a nerve cord, and throat pouches at some point in its life. (155)
cordado Animal que tiene un notocordio, un cordón nervioso y bolsas en la garganta en determinada etapa de su vida.

cilia Tiny, hairlike projections on the outside of cells that move in a wavelike manner. (59)
cilios Pequeñas y finísimas proyecciones del exterior de una célula que se mueven formando ondas.

GLOSSARY

circadian rhythm A behavioral cycle that occurs over a period of about one day. (276)
ritmo circadiano Ciclo de comportamiento que ocurre durante el transcurso de aproximadamente un día.

circulatory system An organ system that transports needed materials to cells and removes wastes. (225)
sistema circulatorio Sistema de órganos que transporta los materiales que la célula necesita y elimina los desechos.

classification The process of grouping things based on their similarities. (15)
clasificación Proceso de agrupar cosas según sus semejanzas.

closed circulatory system A circulatory system in which blood moves only within a connected network of blood vessels and the heart. (227)
sistema circulatorio cerrado Sistema circulatorio en el que la sangre viaja sólo dentro de una red de vasos sanguíneos hacia el corazón.

cnidarian A radially symmetrical invertebrate that uses stinging cells to capture food and defend itself. (149)
cnidario Invertebrado de simetría radiada que usa células urticantes para obtener alimentos y defenderse.

complete metamorphosis A type of metamorphosis with four distinct stages: egg, larva, pupa, and adult. (256)
metamorfosis completa Tipo de metamorfosis de cuatro etapas: huevo, larva, pupa y adulto.

conditioning The process of learning to connect a stimulus or a response with a good or bad outcome. (267)
condicionamiento Proceso en el que se aprende a relacionar un estímulo o una respuesta con un resultado bueno o malo.

cone The reproductive structure of a gymnosperm. (114)
cono Estructura reproductora de una gimnosperma.

conjugation A form of sexual reproduction in which a unicellular organism transfers some of its genetic material to another unicellular organism. (51)
conjugación Forma de reproducción sexual en la que un organismo unicelular transfiere su material genético a otro organismo unicelular.

contractile vacuole The cell structure that collects extra water from the cytoplasm and then expels it from the cell. (58)
vacuola contráctil Estructura celular que recoge el agua sobrante del citoplasma y luego la expulsa de la célula.

controlled experiment An experiment in which only one variable is manipulated at a time. (9)
experimento controlado Experimento en el que se manipula sólo una variable a la vez.

convergent evolution The process by which unrelated organisms evolve similar characteristics. (29)
evolución convergente Proceso por el cual organismos no relacionados exhiben una evolución de características similares.

cotyledon A leaf produced by an embryo of a seed plant; sometimes stores food. (98)
cotiledón Hoja producida por el embrión de una planta fanerógama; a veces almacena alimentos.

courtship behavior The behavior in which males and females of the same species engage to prepare for mating. (273)
comportamiento de cortejo Comportamiento de los machos y las hembras de una especie en preparación del apareamiento.

critical night length The number of hours of darkness that determines whether or not a plant will flower. (121)
duración crítica de la noche El número de horas de oscuridad que determina si florecerá una planta o no.

crop An internal organ in some animals where food is softened and stored. (214)
buche Órgano interno de algunos animales en el que se ablandan y almacenan alimentos.

cuticle The waxy, waterproof layer that covers the leaves and stems of most plants. (88)
cutícula Capa cerosa e impermeable que cubre las hojas y los tallos de la mayoría de las plantas.

cytoplasm The thick fluid region of a cell located inside the cell membrane (in prokaryotes) or between the cell membrane and nucleus (in eukaryotes). (47)
citoplasma Región celular de líquido espeso ubicada dentro de la membrana celular (en las procariotas) o entre la membrana celular y el núcleo (en las eucariotas).

D

day-neutral plant A plant with a flowering cycle that is not sensitive to periods of light and dark. (121)
planta de día neutro Planta con un ciclo de floración que no es sensible a la luz o la oscuridad.

decomposer An organism that gets energy by breaking down wastes and dead organisms, and returns raw materials to the soil and water. (55)
descomponedor Organismo que obtiene energía mediante la descomposición de desechos y organismos muertos y que luego devuelve la materia resultante al suelo y al agua.

development The process of change that occurs during an organism's life to produce a more complex organism. (7)
desarrollo Proceso de cambio que ocurre durante la vida de un organismo, mediante el cual se crea un organismo más complejo.

dicot An angiosperm that has two seed leaves. (98)
dicotiledónea Angiosperma cuyas semillas tienen dos cotiledones.

diffusion The process by which molecules move from an area of higher concentration to an area of lower concentration. (218)
difusión Proceso por el cual las moléculas se mueven de un área de mayor concentración a otra de menor concentración.

digestion The process that breaks down complex molecules of food into smaller nutrient molecules. (212)
digestión Proceso que descompone las moléculas complejas de los alimentos en moléculas de nutrientes más pequeñas.

digestive system An organ system that has specialized structures for obtaining and digesting food. (213)
sistema digestivo Sistema de órganos que tiene estructuras especializadas para ingerir y digerir alimentos.

dormancy A period of time when an organism's growth or activity stops. (122)
latencia Período de tiempo durante el cual se detiene el crecimiento o la actividad de un organismo.

E

echinoderm A radially symmetrical marine invertebrate that has an internal skeleton and a system of fluid-filled tubes. (153)
equinodermo Invertebrado marino de simetría radiada que tiene un esqueleto interno y un sistema de apéndices en forma de tubos llenos de líquido.

ectotherm An animal whose body temperature is determined by the temperature of its environment. (157)
ectotermo Animal cuya temperatura corporal es determinada por la temperatura de su medio ambiente.

embryo **1.** The young organism that develops from a zygote. (106) **2.** A developing human during the first eight weeks after fertilization has occurred.
embrión **1.** Organismo joven que se desarrolla a partir del cigoto. **2.** Un ser humano en desarrollo durante las primeras ocho semanas después de llevarse a cabo la fertilización.

endoskeleton An internal skeleton; structural support system within the body of an animal. (153)
endoesqueleto Esqueleto interno; sistema estructural de soporte dentro del cuerpo de un animal.

endospore A structure produced by prokaryotes, such as bacteria, in unfavorable conditions; a thick wall encloses the DNA and some of the cytoplasm. (52)
endospora Estructura que las procariotas, como las bacterias, producen en condiciones desfavorables; capa gruesa que encierra al ADN y parte del citoplasma.

endotherm An animal whose body temperature is regulated by the internal heat the animal produces. (157)
endotermo Animal cuya temperatura corporal es regulada por el calor interno que produce.

esophagus A muscular tube that connects the mouth to the stomach. (214)
esófago Tubo muscular que conecta la boca con el estómago.

eukaryote An organism whose cells contain a nucleus. (24)
eucariota Organismo cuyas células contienen un núcleo.

evolution Change over time; the process by which modern organisms have descended from ancient organisms. (26)
evolución Cambios a través del tiempo; proceso por el cual los organismos modernos se originaron a partir de organismos antiguos.

excretory system An organ system that rids a body of nitrogen-containing wastes and excess salt and water. (231)
sistema excretor Sistema de órganos que elimina desechos que contienen nitrógeno, y excesos de sal y agua del cuerpo.

GLOSSARY

exoskeleton External skeleton; a tough, waterproof outer covering that protects, supports, and helps prevent evaporation of water from the body of many invertebrates. (152)
exoesqueleto Esqueleto exterior; una cobertura fuerte e impermeable que protege, soporta y ayuda a prevenir la evaporación del agua del cuerpo de muchos invertebrados.

external fertilization When eggs are fertilized outside of a female's body. (250)
fertilización externa Cuando los óvulos se fertilizan fuera del cuerpo de la hembra.

F

fertilization The process in sexual reproduction in which an egg cell and a sperm cell join to form a new cell. (112)
fertilización Proceso de la reproducción sexual en el que un óvulo y un espermatozoide se unen para formar una nueva célula.

filter feeder An animal that strains its food from water. (209)
comedores por suspensión Animal que filtra sus alimentos del agua.

fish A vertebrate whose body temperature is determined by the temperature of its environment, and that lives in the water and has fins. (159)
pez Vertebrado cuya temperatura corporal es determinada por la temperatura de su medio ambiente, que vive en el agua y que tiene aletas.

flagellum A long, whiplike structure that helps a cell to move. (47)
flagelo Estructura larga con forma de látigo, que ayuda a la célula a moverse.

flower The reproductive structure of an angiosperm. (108)
flor Estructura reproductora de una angiosperma.

frond The leaf of a fern plant. (94)
fronda Hoja de un helecho.

fruit The ripened ovary and other structures of an angiosperm that enclose one or more seeds. (117)
fruto Ovario maduro y otras estructuras de una angiosperma que encierran una o más semillas.

fruiting body The reproductive structure of a fungus that contains many hyphae and produces spores. (68)
órgano fructífero Estructura reproductora de un hongo, que contiene muchas hifas y produce esporas.

fungus A eukaryotic organism that has cell walls, uses spores to reproduce, and is a heterotroph that feeds by absorbing its food. (67)
hongo Organismo eucariótico que posee paredes celulares, usa esporas para reproducirse y es un heterótrofo que se alimenta absorbiendo sus alimentos.

G

gametophyte The stage in the life cycle of a plant in which the plant produces gametes, or sex cells. (110)
gametofito Etapa del ciclo vital de una planta en la que produce gametos, es decir, células sexuales.

genus A classification grouping that consists of a number of similar, closely related species. (16)
género Clase de agrupación que consiste de un número de especies similares y estrechamente relacionadas.

germination The sprouting of the embryo out of a seed; occurs when the embryo resumes its growth following dormancy. (107)
germinación Brotamiento del embrión a partir de la semilla; ocurre cuando el embrión reanuda su crecimiento tras el estado latente.

gestation period The length of time between fertilization and birth of a mammal. (251)
período de gestación Tiempo entre la fertilización y el nacimiento de un mamífero.

gill A feathery structure where gases are exchanged between water and blood. (219)
branquia Estructura filamentosa donde se realiza el intercambio de gases entre el agua y la sangre.

gizzard A muscular, thick-walled organ that squeezes and grinds partially digested food. (214)
molleja Órgano muscular y de paredes gruesas que exprime y tritura los alimentos parcialmente digeridos.

gymnosperm A plant that produces seeds directly on the scales of cones—not enclosed by a protective fruit. (96)
gimnosperma Planta que produce semillas directamente sobre las escamas de los conos—sin estar encerradas en un fruto protector.

H

heart A hollow, muscular organ that pumps blood throughout an organism's body. (225)
corazón Órgano muscular y hueco que bombea sangre a través del cuerpo de un organismo.

herbivore A consumer that obtains energy by eating only plants. (207)
herbívoro Consumidor que come sólo plantas para obtener energía.

heterotroph An organism that cannot make its own food and gets food by consuming other living things. (11)
heterótrofo Organismo que no puede producir sus propios alimentos y los consigue mediante el consumo de otros seres vivos.

hibernation An animal's state of greatly reduced activity that occurs during the winter. (276)
hibernación Estado de gran reducción de la actividad de un animal que ocurre en el invierno.

homeostasis The condition in which an organism's internal environment is kept stable in spite of changes in the external environment. (13, 139)
homeostasis Condición en la que el medio interno de un organismo se mantiene estable a pesar de cambios en el medio externo.

hormone 1. A chemical that affects growth and development. (120) **2.** The chemical product of an endocrine gland.
hormona 1. Sustancia química que afecta el crecimiento y el desarrollo. **2.** Producto químico de una glándula endocrina.

host An organism that a parasite lives with, in, or on, and provides a source of energy or a suitable environment for the parasite to live. (41)
huésped Organismo dentro del o sobre el cual vive un parásito y que provee una fuente de energía o un medio apropiado para la existencia del parásito.

hyphae The branching, threadlike tubes that make up the bodies of multicellular fungi. (67)
hifas Delgados tubos ramificados que forman el cuerpo de los hongos multicelulares.

I

imprinting A learned behavior in which newly hatched birds and newborn mammals follow the first moving object they see. (266)
impronta Comportamiento adquirido de las aves y los mamíferos recién nacidos que consiste en seguir al primer cuerpo en movimiento que ven.

impulse An electrical message that carries information in the nervous system. (182)
impulso Mensaje eléctrico que transporta información por el sistema nervioso.

incomplete metamorphosis A type of metamorphosis with three stages: egg, nymph, and adult. (257)
metamorfosis incompleta Tipo de metamorfosis de tres etapas: huevo, ninfa y adulto.

insight learning The process of learning how to solve a problem or do something new by applying what is already known. (269)
aprendizaje por discernimiento Proceso de aprendizaje de cómo resolver un problema o hacer algo nuevo aplicando lo que ya se sabe.

instinct An inborn behavior that an animal performs correctly the first time. (264)
instinto Comportamiento innato que un animal ejecuta correctamente en su primer intento.

internal fertilization When eggs are fertilized inside a female's body. (251)
fertilización interna Cuando los óvulos se fertilizan dentro del cuerpo de la hembra.

interneuron A neuron that carries nerve impulses from one neuron to another. (182)
interneurona Neurona que transporta los impulsos nerviosos de una neurona a otra.

intestine An organ where digestion is completed and food is absorbed. (214)
intestino Órgano donde se completa la digestión y se absorben los alimentos.

invertebrate An animal without a backbone. (140)
invertebrado Animal sin columna vertebral.

J

joint A place in the body where two bones come together. (178)
articulación Lugar en el cuerpo en donde se unen dos huesos.

K

kidney A major organ of the excretory system; removes urea and other wastes from the blood. (231)
riñón Órgano importante del sistema excretorio; elimina la urea y otros desechos de la sangre.

GLOSSARY

L

larva The immature form of an animal that looks very different from the adult. (248)
larva Forma inmadura de un animal que luce muy distinta al adulto.

learning The process that leads to changes in behavior based on practice or experience. (265)
aprendizaje Proceso que conduce a cambios de comportamiento basados en la práctica o la experiencia.

lichen The combination of a fungus and either an alga or an autotrophic bacterium that live together in a relationship that benefits both organisms. (73)
liquen Combinación de un hongo y una alga o bacteria autotrópica que viven juntos en una relación mutuamente beneficiosa.

long-day plant A plant that flowers when the nights are shorter than the plant's critical night length. (121)
planta de día largo Planta que florece cuando la duración de la noche es más corta que la duración crítica.

lung **1.** An organ found in air-breathing vertebrates that exchanges oxygen and carbon dioxide with the blood. (219) **2.** In humans, one of two main organs of the respiratory system.
pulmón **1.** Órgano de los vertebrados que respiran aire, responsable del intercambio de oxígeno y dióxido de carbono en la sangre. **2.** En los seres humanos, uno de los dos órganos principales del sistema respiratorio.

M

mammal A vertebrate whose body temperature is regulated by its internal heat, and that has skin covered with hair or fur and glands that produce milk to feed its young. (163)
mamífero Vertebrado cuya temperatura corporal es regulada por su calor interno, cuya piel está cubierta de pelo o pelaje y que tiene glándulas que producen leche para alimentar a sus crías.

mammary gland An organ in female mammals that produces milk for the mammal's young. (163)
glándula mamaria Órgano de los mamíferos hembra que produce leche para alimentar a sus crías.

marsupial A mammal whose young are born at an early stage of development, and which usually continue to develop in a pouch on their mother's body. (163)
marsupial Mamífero cuyas crías nacen en una etapa muy temprana del desarrollo, y que normalmente continúan el desarrollo en una bolsa del cuerpo de la madre.

medusa A cnidarian body form characterized by an open umbrella shape and adapted for a free-swimming life. (248)
medusa Cnidario con cuerpo que tiene la forma de una sombrilla abierta y que está adaptado para nadar libremente.

metabolism The combination of chemical reactions through which an organism builds up or breaks down materials. (6)
metabolismo Combinación de reacciones químicas mediante las cuales un organismo compone o descompone la materia.

metamorphosis A process in which an animal's body undergoes major changes in shape and form during its life cycle. (255)
metamorfosis Proceso por el cual el cuerpo de un animal cambia de forma radicalmente durante su ciclo vital.

migration The regular, seasonal journey of an animal from one environment to another and back again for the purpose of feeding or reproduction. (276)
migración Viaje estacional y regular, de ida y vuelta, que hace un animal de un medio ambiente a otro con el propósito de alimentarse y reproducirse.

mollusk An invertebrate with a soft, unsegmented body; most are protected by a hard outer shell. (151)
molusco Invertebrado con cuerpo blando y sin segmentos; la mayoría tienen una concha exterior dura que les sirve de protección.

molting The process of shedding an outgrown exoskeleton. (176)
muda de cubierta Proceso de cambiar un exoesqueleto viejo por uno nuevo.

monocot An angiosperm that has only one seed leaf. (98)
monocotiledónea Angiosperma cuyas semillas tienen un solo cotiledón.

monotreme A mammal that lays eggs. (163)
monotrema Mamífero que pone huevos.

motor neuron A neuron that sends an impulse to a muscle or gland, causing the muscle or gland to react. (182)
neurona motora Neurona que envía un impulso a un músculo o glándula, haciendo que el músculo o la glándula reaccione.

multicellular Consisting of many cells. (6)
multicelular Que se compone de muchas células.

muscle A tissue that contracts or relaxes to create movement. (179)
músculo Tejido que se contrae o relaja para crear movimiento.

— N —

nervous system An organ system that receives information from the environment and coordinates a response. (181)
sistema nervioso Sistema de órganos que recibe información del medio ambiente y coordina una respuesta.

neuron A cell that carries information through the nervous system. (182)
neurona Célula que transporta información a través del sistema nervioso.

nonvascular plant A low-growing plant that lacks true vascular tissue for transporting materials. (90)
planta no vascular Planta de crecimiento lento que carece de tejido vascular verdadero para el transporte de materiales.

notochord A flexible rod that supports a chordate's back just below the nerve cord. (155)
notocordio Cilindro flexible que sostiene la columna de un cordado, debajo del cordón nervioso.

nucleus 1. In cells, a large oval organelle that contains the cell's genetic material in the form of DNA and controls many of the cell's activities. (23) **2.** The central core of an atom which contains protons and neutrons. **3.** The solid core of a comet.
núcleo 1. En las células, orgánulo grande y ovalado que contiene el material genético de la célula en forma de ADN y que controla muchas de las funciones celulares. **2.** Parte central del átomo que contiene los protones y los neutrones. **3.** Centro sólido de un cometa.

nymph A stage of incomplete metamorphosis that usually resembles the adult insect. (257)
ninfa Estado de la metamorfosis incompleta que generalmente se asemeja al insecto adulto.

— O —

omnivore A consumer that obtains energy by eating both plants and animals. (207)
omnívoro Consumidor que come plantas y animales para obtener energía.

open circulatory system A circulatory system in which the heart pumps blood into open spaces in the body and blood is not confined to blood vessels. (226)
sistema circulatorio abierto Sistema circulatorio en el que el corazón bombea la sangre a espacios abiertos del cuerpo y ésta no se limita a los vasos sanguíneos.

organ A body structure that is composed of different kinds of tissues that work together. (143)
órgano Estructura del cuerpo formada por distintos tipos de tejidos que actúan conjuntamente.

organism A living thing. (5)
organismo Un ser vivo.

ovary 1. A flower structure that encloses and protects ovules and seeds as they develop. (109) **2.** Organ of the female reproductive system in which eggs and estrogen are produced.
ovario 1. Estructura floral que encierra y protege a los óvulos y las semillas mientras se desarrollan. **2.** Órgano del sistema reproductivo femenino en el que se producen los óvulos y el estrógeno.

ovule A plant structure in seed plants that produces the female gametophyte; contains an egg cell. (114)
óvulo Estructura vegetal de las plantas de semilla que produce el gametofito femenino; contiene una célula reproductora femenina.

— P —

parasite An organism that benefits by living with, on, or in a host in a parasitism interaction. (41)
parásito Organismo que vive dentro de o sobre otro organismo y que se alimenta de él.

pasteurization A process of heating food to a temperature that is high enough to kill most harmful bacteria without changing the taste of the food. (54)
pasteurización Proceso de calentamiento de los alimentos a una temperatura suficientemente alta como para matar la mayoría de las bacterias dañinas sin que cambie el sabor.

peat Compressed layers of dead sphagnum mosses that accumulate in bogs. (126)
turba Capas comprimidas de musgos esfagnáceos muertos que se acumulan en las marismas.

GLOSSARY

perennial A flowering plant that lives for more than two years. (111)
perenne Planta con flores que vive más de dos años.

petal A colorful, leaflike structure of some flowers. (108)
pétalo Estructura de color brillante, similar a una hoja, que algunas flores poseen.

pheromone A chemical released by one animal that affects the behavior of another animal of the same species. (271)
feromona Sustancia química que produce un animal y que afecta el comportamiento de otro animal de la misma especie.

phloem The vascular tissue through which food moves in some plants. (93)
floema Tejido vascular de algunas plantas por el que circulan los alimentos.

photoperiodism A plant's response to seasonal changes in the length of night and day. (121)
fotoperiodicidad Respuesta de una planta a los cambios estacionales del día y de la noche.

photosynthesis The process by which plants and other autotrophs capture and use light energy to make food from carbon dioxide and water. (85)
fotosíntesis Proceso por el cual las plantas y otros autótrofos absorben la energía de la luz para producir alimentos a partir del dióxido de carbono y el agua.

pigment 1. A colored chemical compound that absorbs light. **2.** A colored substance used to color other materials. (61)
pigmento 1. Compuesto químico que absorbe luz. **2.** Sustancia de color que se usa para teñir otros materiales.

pistil The female reproductive part of a flower. (109)
pistilo Parte reproductora femenina de una flor.

placenta An organ in most pregnant mammals, including humans, that links the mother and the developing embryo and allows for the passage of materials between them. (163)
placenta Órgano de la mayoría de los mamíferos preñados, incluyendo a los seres humanos, que conecta a la madre con el embrión en desarrollo y que permite el intercambio de materiales entre ellos.

placental mammal A mammal that develops inside its mother's body until its body systems can function independently. (163)
mamífero placentario Mamífero que se desarrolla dentro del cuerpo de la madre hasta que sus sistemas puedan funcionar por sí solos.

pollen Tiny structure (male gametophyte) produced by seed plants that contain the cell that later becomes a sperm cell. (96)
polen Diminuta estructura (gametofito masculino) producida por las plantas de semilla que contiene la célula que más adelante se convertirá en un espermatozoide.

pollination The transfer of pollen from male reproductive structures to female reproductive structures in plants. (108)
polinización Transferencia del polen de las estructuras reproductoras masculinas de una planta las estructuras reproductoras femeninas.

polyp A cnidarian body form characterized by an upright vase shape and usually adapted for a life attached to an underwater surface. (248)
pólipo Cnidario con cuerpo de forma tubular y que está adaptado para vivir fijo en un fondo acuático.

prokaryote A unicellular organism that lacks a nucleus and some other cell structures. (23)
procariota Organismo unicelular que carece de un núcleo y otras estructuras celulares.

protist A eukaryotic organism that cannot be classified as an animal, plant, or fungus. (57)
protista Organismo eucariótico que no se puede clasificar como animal, planta ni hongo.

protozoan A unicellular, animal-like protist. (57)
protozoario Protista unicelular con características animales.

pseudopod A "false foot" or temporary bulge of cytoplasm used for feeding and movement in some protozoans. (58)
seudópodo "Pie falso" o abultamiento temporal del citoplasma que algunos protozoarios usan para alimentarse o desplazarse.

pupa The third stage of complete metamorphosis, in which a larva develops into an adult insect. (256)
pupa Tercera etapa de la metamorfosis completa, e la que la larva se convierte en insecto adulto.

—————————— R ——————————

radial symmetry A body plan in which any number of imaginary lines that all pass through a central point divide the animal into two mirror images. (144)
simetría radiada Esquema del cuerpo en el que cualquier número de líneas imaginarias que atraviesan un punto central dividen a un animal en dos partes que son el reflejo la una de la otra.

radula A flexible ribbon of tiny teeth in mollusks. (210)
rádula Hilera flexible de minúsculos dientes de los moluscos.

reptile A vertebrate whose temperature is determined by the temperature of its environment, that has lungs and scaly skin, and that lays eggs on land. (161)
reptil Vertebrado cuya temperatura corporal es determinada por la temperatura de su medio ambiente, que tiene pulmones y piel escamosa y que pone huevos en la tierra.

respiratory system An organ system that enables organisms to exchange gases with their surroundings. (219)
sistema respiratorio Sistema de órganos que permite al organismo intercambiar gases con su entorno.

response An action or change in behavior that occurs as a result of a stimulus. (7, 181)
respuesta Acción o cambio del comportamiento que ocurre como resultado de un estímulo.

rhizoid A thin, rootlike structure that anchors a moss and absorbs water and nutrients for the plant. (91)
rizoide Estructura fina parecida a una raíz que sujeta un musgo al suelo, y que absorbe el agua y los nutrientes para la planta.

ribosome A small grain-shaped organelle in the cytoplasm of a cell that produces proteins. (47)
ribosoma Orgánulo pequeño y en forma de grano del citoplasma celular que produce proteínas.

root cap A structure that covers the tip of a root, protecting the root from injury as the root grows through soil. (101)
cofia Estructura que cubre la punta de una raíz y la protege de cualquier daño mientras crece en la tierra.

—————————— S ——————————

seed The plant structure that contains a young plant and a food supply inside a protective covering. (96)
semilla Estructura vegetal que contiene una planta joven y una fuente alimenticia encerradas en una cubierta protectora.

sensory neuron A neuron that picks up stimuli from the internal or external environment and converts each stimulus into a nerve impulse. (182)
neurona sensorial Neurona que recibe estímulos de un medio interno o externo y que convierte a cada estímulo en un impulso nervioso.

sepal A leaflike structure that encloses and protects the bud of a flower. (108)
sépalo Estructura similar a una hoja que encierra y protege el capullo de una flor.

sexual reproduction A reproductive process that involves two parents that combine their genetic material to produce a new organism which differs from both parents. (7)
reproducción sexual Proceso de reproducción que involucra a dos reproductores que combinan su material genético para producir un nuevo organismo que es distinto a los dos reproductores.

shared derived characteristic A characteristic or trait, such as fur, that the common ancestor of a group had and passed on to its descendants. (27)
característica derivada compartida Característica o rasgo, como el pelaje, del ancestro común de un grupo que éste pasa a sus descendientes.

short-day plant A plant that flowers when the nights are longer than the plant's critical night length. (121)
planta de día corto Planta que florece cuando la duración de la noche es más larga que la duración crítica.

society A group of closely related animals of the same species that work together in a highly organized way for the benefit of the group. (275)
sociedad Grupo de animales de la misma especie y estrechamente vinculados que trabajan conjuntmente de manera organizada para el beneficio del grupo.

species A group of similar organisms that can mate with each other and produce offspring that can also mate and reproduce. (16)
especie Grupo de organismos similares que pueden aparearse entre sí y producir crías que también pueden aparearse y reproducirse.

spontaneous generation The mistaken idea that living things arise from nonliving sources. (8)
generación espontánea Idea equivocada de que los seres vivos surgen de fuentes inertes.

spore In bacteria, protists, and fungi, a thick-walled, tiny cell capable of surviving unfavorable conditions and then growing into a new organism. (64)
espora En las bacterias, los protistas y los hongos, una minúscula célula de paredes gruesas capaz de sobrevivir condiciones desfavorables y crecer hasta convertirse en un organismo.

sporophyte The stage in the life cycle of a plant in which the plant produces spores. (110)
esporofito Etapa del ciclo vital de una planta en la que produce esporas.

stamen The male reproductive part of a flower. (108)
estambre Parte reproductora masculina de una flor.

stimulus Any change or signal in the environment that can make an organism react in some way. (7, 181)
estímulo Cualquier cambio o señal en el medio ambiente que puede hacer que un organismo reaccione de alguna manera.

stomach An organ in the form of a muscular pouch where food is broken down, located in the abdomen. (214)
estómago Órgano en forma de bolsa muscular donde se descomponen los alimentos; ubicado en el abdomen.

stoma A small opening on the underside of a leaf through which oxygen, water, and carbon dioxide can move. (104)
estomas Pequeños orificios en la superficie inferior de la hoja a través de los cuales ocurre el intercambio de oxígeno y dióxido de carbono.

swim bladder An internal gas-filled organ that helps a bony fish stabilize its body at different water depths. (188)
vejiga natatoria Órgano interno lleno de gas que ayuda a un pez con esqueleto a estabilizar su cuerpo a distintas profundidades.

T
---

tadpole The larval form of a frog or toad. (258)
renacuajo Estado de larva de una rana o un sapo.

taxonomy The scientific study of how living things are classified. (15)
taxonomía Estudio científico de cómo se clasifican los seres vivos.

territory An area that is occupied and defended by an animal or group of animals. (272)
territorio Área ocupada y defendida por un animal o grupo de animales.

tissue A group of similar cells that perform a specific function. (86, 143)
tejido Grupo de células semejantes que realizan una función específica.

transpiration The process by which water is lost through a plant's leaves. (105)
transpiración Proceso por el cual las hojas de una planta pierden agua.

trial-and-error learning A type of learned behavior in which an animal learns to behave in a certain way through repeated practice, to receive a reward or avoid punishment. (268)
aprendizaje por ensayo y error Tipo de comportamiento aprendido en el que un animal aprende cierta conducta por repetición, para obtener recompensa o evitar castigo.

tropism The response of a plant toward or away from a stimulus. (119)
tropismo Respuesta de una planta acercándose o apartándose del estímulo.

U
---

unicellular Made of a single cell. (6)
unicelular Compuesto por una sola célula.

urine A watery fluid produced by the kidneys that contains urea and other wastes. (231)
orina Fluido acuoso producido por los riñones que contiene urea y otros materiales de desecho.

V
---

vaccine A substance used in a vaccination that consists of pathogens that have been weakened or killed but can still trigger the body to produce chemicals that destroy the pathogens. (44)
vacuna Sustancia usada en la vacunación y que consiste de patógenos que se han debilitado o matado, pero que aún pueden provocar que el cuerpo produzca sustancias químicas para destruir a los patógenos.

vacuole A sac-like organelle that stores water, food, and other materials. (86)
vacuola Orgánulo en forma de bolsa que almacena agua, alimentos y otros materiales.

vascular plant A plant that has true vascular tissue for transporting materials. (93)
planta vascular Planta que tiene tejido vascular verdadero para el transporte de materiales.

vascular tissue The internal transporting tissue in some plants that is made up of tubelike structures that carry water, food, and minerals. (88)
tejido vascular Tejido interno de algunas plantas compuesto de estructuras tubulares que transportan agua, alimentos y minerales.

ventricle A lower chamber of the heart that pumps blood out to the lungs or body. (228)
ventrículo Cavidad inferior del corazón que bombea sangre a los pulmones o el cuerpo.

vertebrae The bones that make up the backbone of an organism. In humans, one of the 26 bones that make up the backbone. (156)
vértebras Huesos que componen la columna de un organismo. En los seres humanos, cada uno de los 26 huesos que componen la columna vertebral.

vertebrate An animal with a backbone. (140)
vertebrado Animal con columna vertebral.

virus A tiny, nonliving particle that enters and then reproduces inside a living cell. (40)
virus Partícula diminuta inerte que entra en una célula viva y luego se reproduce dentro de ella.

W

---

water vascular system A system of fluid-filled tubes in an echinoderm's body. (188)
sistema vascular de agua Sistema de vasos llenos de líquido en el cuerpo de un equinodermo.

X

---

xylem The vascular tissue through which water and minerals move in some plants. (93)
xilema Tejido vascular de algunas plantas por el que circulan agua y nutrientes.

Z

---

zygote A fertilized egg, produced by the joining of a sperm cell and an egg cell. (112)
cigoto Óvulo fertilizado, producido por la unión de un espermatozoide y un óvulo.

INDEX

Page numbers for key terms are printed in **boldface** type. Red indicates Teacher's Edition entries.

INDEX

INDEX

Page numbers for key terms are printed in **boldface** type. Red indicates Teacher's Edition entries.

INDEX

Page numbers for key terms are printed in **boldface** type. Red indicates Teacher's Edition entries.

ACKNOWLEDGMENTS

ACKNOWLEDGMENTS

Staff Credits
The people who made up the ***Interactive Science*** team—representing composition services, core design digital and multimedia production services, digital product development, editorial, editorial services, manufacturing, and production—are listed below.
Jan Van Aarsen, Samah Abadir, Ernie Albanese, Bridget Binstock, Suzanne Biron, MJ Black, Nancy Bolsover, Stacy Boyd, Jim Brady, Katherine Bryant, Michael Burstein, Pradeep Byram, Jessica Chase, Jonathan Cheney, Arthur Ciccone, Allison Cook-Bellistri, Rebecca Cottingham, AnnMarie Coyne, Bob Craton, Chris Deliee, Paul Delsignore, Michael Di Maria, Diane Dougherty, Kristen Ellis, Theresa Eugenio, Amanda Ferguson, Jorgensen Fernandez, Kathryn Fobert, Julia Gecha, Mark Geyer, Steve Gobbell, Paula Gogan-Porter, Jeffrey Gong, Sandra Graff, Adam Groffman, Lynette Haggard, Christian Henry, Karen Holtzman, Susan Hutchinson, Sharon Inglis, Marian Jones, Sumy Joy, Sheila Kanitsch, Courtenay Kelley, Chris Kennedy, Toby Klang, Greg Lam, Russ Lappa, Margaret LaRaia, Ben Leveillee, Thea Limpus, Dotti Marshall, Kathy Martin, Robyn Matzke, John McClure, Mary Beth McDaniel, Krista McDonald, Tim McDonald, Rich McMahon, Cara McNally, Melinda Medina, Angelina Mendez, Maria Milczarek, Claudi Mimo, Mike Napieralski, Deborah Nicholls, Dave Nichols, William Oppenheimer, Jodi O'Rourke, Ameer Padshah, Lorie Park, Celio Pedrosa, Jonathan Penyack, Linda Zust Reddy, Jennifer Reichlin, Stephen Rider, Charlene Rimsa, Stephanie Rogers, Marcy Rose, Rashid Ross, Anne Rowsey, Logan Schmidt, Amanda Seldera, Laurel Smith, Nancy Smith, Ted Smykal, Emily Soltanoff, Cindy Strowman, Dee Sunday, Barry Tomack, Patricia Valencia, Ana Sofia Villaveces, Stephanie Wallace, Christine Whitney, Brad Wiatr, Heidi Wilson, Heather Wright, Rachel Youdelman

Photography
All uncredited photos copyright © 2011 Pearson Education.

Cover, Front and Back
David Doubilet/National Geographic Stock.

Front matter
Page vi, Chris Newbert/Minden Pictures; **vii,** Marevision Marevision/Photolibrary New York; **viii,** BIOS Bios-Auteurs Lafranchis Tristan/Peter Arnold; **ix,** Thomas Marent/Minden Pictures/National Geographic Stock; **x,** Michael Durham/Minden Pictures; **xi,** Michael & Patricia Fogden/Minden Pictures; **xii,** Konrad Wothe/Minden Pictures; **xiii t,** iStockphoto.com; **xiii m1,** iStockphoto.com; **xiii b,** iStockphoto.com; **xiii m2,** iStockphoto.com; **xxii bl,** Mark Turner/Garden Picture Library/Photolibrary New York; **xxii,** Imagebroker/Alamy; **xxiii,** Riccardo Savi/The Image Bank/Getty Images.

Chapter 1
Pages xxiv–1 spread, Chris Newbert/Minden Pictures; **1 br inset,** Gerry Ellis/Minden Pictures; **3 t,** Mau Horng/Shutterstock; **3 m,** Rod Williams/Nature Picture Library; **3 b,** Eye of Science/Photo Researchers, Inc.; **4,** George Steinmetz/Corbis; **5 tl,** Paroli Galperti/Photolibrary New York; **5 tm,** Mau Horng/Shutterstock; **5 tr,** Matt Meadows/Peter Arnold; **5 b,** Kjell Sandved/Photolibrary New York; **6 tl,** Biophoto Associates/Photo Researchers, Inc.; **6 tr,** Kerstin Hinze/Nature Picture Library; **6 b,** Science Photo Library/Photolibrary New York; **7 t,** John Kaprielian/Photo Researchers, Inc.; **7 m both,** Ingo Arndt/Nature Picture Library; **7 b,** David Tipling/NPL/Minden Pictures; **8 t,** Jürgen and Christine Sohns/Photolibrary New York; **8 b,** Dan Duchars/Photolibrary New York; **9,** Breck P. Kent/Animals Animals/Earth Scenes; **11,** Anup Shah/NPL/Minden Pictures; **12 t,** Pichugin Dmitry/Shutterstock; **12 b,** Jose Fuste Raga/age Fotostock/Photolibrary New York; **13 l,** Steve Maslowski/Visuals Unlimited/Alamy; **13 r,** Steve Byland/Shutterstock; **14,** Chip Clark; **15,** Ilian Animal/Alamy; **16 t,** Darren Bennett/Animals Animals/Earth Scenes; **16 bl,** Eric Isselée/Shutterstock; **16 br,** Rod Williams/Nature Picture Library; **17,** Alan Gleichman/Shutterstock; **18,** FloridaStock/Shutterstock; **20,** Visuals Unlimited/Corbis; **21 tl,** Armando Frazao/iStockphoto.com; **21 tm,** WizData, Inc./Shutterstock; **21 tr,** Eric Isselée/Shutterstock; **21 bl,** Hemera Technologies/JupiterUnlimited; **21 bm,** Kim Taylor/Nature Picture Library; **21 br,** Joseph Calev/Shutterstock; **22,** Michael Durham/Minden Pictures; **23 t bacteria,** SciMAT/Photo Researchers, Inc.; **23 b archaea,** Visuals Unlimited/Getty Images; **24 l inset,** Dennis Kunkel; **24 r inset,** Eye of Science/Photo Researchers, Inc.; **24–25 bkgrnd,** Niels Kooyman/Foto Natura/Minden Pictures; **25 inset,** Otto Plantema/Foto Natura/Minden Pictures; **26,** Dave Watts/Nature Picture Library; **28 t inset,** Photo courtesy of *Research in Review,* Florida State University/U. Treesucon, David Redfield Expedition. Used by permission; **28 b inset,** Tim Laman/Nature Picture Library; **28–29 bkgrnd,** Frans Lanting/Corbis; **29 lemur,** Nick Garbutt/Nature Picture Library; **29 camera,** Jasmina007/Shutterstock; **30 t,** Biophoto Associates/Photo Researchers, Inc.; **30 m,** Alan Gleichman/Shutterstock; **30 b,** Dennis Kunkel; **32,** Virgin Galactic.

Interchapter Feature
Page 34 bkgrnd, Explorer/Photo Researchers, Inc.; **35 br,** Rebecca Ellis/iStockphoto.com.

Chapter 2
Pages 36–37 spread, Topic Photo Agency IN/age Fotostock; **39 t,** Marevision Marevision/Photolibrary New York; **39 b,** Visuals Unlimited/Getty Images; **40,** Biosphoto/Heuclin Daniel/Peter Arnold, Inc.; **44,** Yoav Levy/Phototake; **46,** Index Stock Imagery/Photolibrary; **47,** Brian J. Ford; **48 l,** VEM/Photo Researchers, Inc.; **48 m,** Chris Bjornberg/Photo Researchers, Inc.; **48 r,** Dennis Kunkel; **49 tl,** Thermal Biology Institute; **49 bl,** From *Seen and Unseen* by Kathy B. Sheehan, David J. Patterson, Brett Leigh Dicks, and Joan M. Henson. Copyright © 2005. Photo by David J. Patterson. Used by permission of Globe Pequot Press; **49 m,** Dennis Kunkel; **49 r,** Rob Whitrow/GPL/Photolibrary New York; **50 tl,** Dennis Kunkel; **50 tr,** Science Photo Library/Photo Researchers, Inc.; **50 b,** Comstock Images/age Fotostock; **51,** Dennis Kunkel/Phototake; **53,** Stuart Westmorland/Getty Images; **54 t,** Dennis Kunkel/Phototake; **54–55,** Dennis Kunkel; **56 inset,** Gioiaphotography.com; **56 bkgrnd,** Copyright © John Rae 2008/Malaria No More; **57 l,** Eye of Science/Photo Researchers, Inc.; **57 m,** Visuals Unlimited/Getty Images; **57 r,** Dennis Kunkel; **59,** Larry West/Photo Researchers, Inc.; **61 t,** Visuals Unlimited/Getty Images; **61 b,** Steve Gschmeissner/Photo Researchers, Inc.; **62 tl,** David McCarthy/

ACKNOWLEDGMENTS

Photo Researchers, Inc.; **62 tr,** Steve Gschmeissner/Photo Researchers, Inc.; **62 m,** Marevision Marevision/Photolibrary New York; **62 b,** marinethemes.com/Kelvin Aitken/ImageQuest 3-D; **63 tl,** Marevision Marevision/age Fotostock/Photolibrary New York; **63 tr,** David McCarthy/Photo Researchers, Inc.; **63 bl,** Steve Gschmeissner/Photo Researchers, Inc.; **63 bm,** Lawrence Naylor/Photo Researchers, Inc.; **63 br,** Getty Images/Visuals Unlimited; **64,** Masana Izawa/Nature Production/Minden Pictures; **65,** AgStock Images/Corbis; **66,** Scott Camazine/Photo Researchers, Inc.; **68 l,** Visuals Unlimited/Getty Images; **68 r,** Ed Reschke/Peter Arnold, Inc.; **69 l,** Michael Lander/Getty Images; **69 inset,** Oxford Scientific/Photolibrary New York; **70–71,** Gary Meszaros/Photo Researchers, Inc.; **72 tl,** Emilio Ereza/age Fotostock; **72 tr,** Maximilian Stock/StockFood America; **72 bl,** Scanpix/Photolibrary New York; **73 t,** Jeffrey L. Rotman/Corbis; **73 b,** Photolibrary New York; **74,** Yoav Levy/Phototake; **75 l,** Chris Bjornberg/Photo Researchers, Inc.; **75 r,** VEM/Photo Researchers, Inc.

Interchapter Feature
Page 78 cartoon faces, Dean Murray/iStockphoto.com; **79 b,** Michel Viard/Jacana/Photo Researchers, Inc.; **79 t,** Science Photo Library/Alamy.

Chapter 3
Pages 80–81 spread, Laurent Bouvet/age Fotostock; **83 t,** Howard Rice/Dorling Kindersley; **83 b,** Nigel Bean/Nature Picture Library; **85 l,** iStockphoto.com; **85 r,** Albert Lleal/Minden Pictures; **86 t,** ZTS/Shutterstock; **86 b,** Perennou Nuridsany/Photo Researchers, Inc.; **88,** Kjell B. Sandved/Photo Researchers, Inc.; **90,** Francesca Yorke/Garden Picture Library/Photolibrary New York; **91 bkgrnd,** Neil Lucas/NPL/Minden Pictures; **91 inset,** John Serrao/Photo Researchers, Inc.; **92 t,** Adrian Davies/Nature Picture Library; **92 b,** Daniel Vega/Photolibrary New York; **93 bkgrnd,** Howard Rice/Photolibrary New York; **93 inset,** David T. Webb/University of Hawaii; **95 l,** Philippe Clement/Nature Picture Library; **95 r,** Albert Aanensen/Nature Picture Library; **97 t,** Christine M. Douglas/Dorling Kindersley; **97 m1,** Peter Anderson/Dorling Kindersley; **97 m2,** Joanna Pecha/iStockphoto.com; **97 b,** M. Philip Kahl/Photo Researchers, Inc.; **98 t,** K. Kaplin/Shutterstock; **98 m,** Howard Rice/Dorling Kindersley; **98 b,** Anna Subbotina/Shutterstock; **100,** Fletcher & Baylis/Photo Researchers, Inc.; **101 l,** Runk Schoenberger/Grant Heilman; **101 r,** Derek Croucher/Alamy; **102 l,** Peter Hestbaek/Shutterstock; **102–103,** Manfred Kage/Peter Arnold, Inc.; **104–105,** Pakhnyushcha/Shutterstock; **108 tl,** Kim Taylor/Nature Picture Library; **108 tm,** Tom Vezo/Minden Pictures, Inc.; **108 tr,** Barry Mansell/Nature Picture Library; **108 bl,** Barry Mansell/Nature Picture Library; **108 bm,** Niall Benvie/Nature Picture Library; **108 br,** Simon Williams/Nature Picture Library; **110,** Tom Bean/Corbis; **112,** Ed Reschke/Peter Arnold, Inc.; **113 t,** Tristan Lafranchis/Bios/Peter Arnold, Inc.; **113 b,** Christine M. Douglas/Dorling Kindersley; **114–115,** Andrew Browne/Ecoscene/Corbis; **115 t,** Breck P. Kent/Animals Animals/Earth Scenes; **115 m,** Breck P. Kent; **115 b,** Patti Murray/Animals Animals/Earth Scenes; **116 l,** Medio Images/Photodisc/Photolibrary New York; **116 seedling,** Dwight Kuhn; **117 berry bush,** Nigel Bean/Nature Picture Library; **117 tm, tr, bm, and br,** Peter Chadwick/Dorling Kindersley; **118,** Courtesy Dr. Kerry-Ann Nakrieko and Dr. Alison Smith, Department of Plant Sciences, University of Cambridge; **120,** Maryann Frazier/Photo Researchers, Inc.; **121,** Mark Turner/Garden Picture Library/Photolibrary New York; **122,** Carole Drake/Garden Picture Library/Photolibrary New York; **124 bkgrnd,** Gary K. Smith/Nature Picture Library; **125,** Albinger/age Fotostock; **126,** David Tipling/Nature Picture Library; **127,** Tom Mayes/Cal Sport Media/Zuma Press; **128 t,** Kjell B. Sandved/Photo Researchers, Inc.; **128 b,** David Tipling/Nature Picture Library.

Interchapter Feature
Page 132 br, Susumu Nishinaga/Photo Researchers, Inc.; **133,** Ames/NASA; **132 ml,** sgame/iStockphoto.com; **132 tl and bl,** Tim Messick/iStockphoto.com.

Chapter 4
Pages 134–135 spread, age Fotostock/SuperStock; **137 t,** Bruce Davidson/Nature Picture Library; **137 m1,** Michael & Patricia Fogden/Minden Pictures/National Geographic Stock; **137 m2,** Andrew J. Martinez/Photo Researchers, Inc.; **137 b,** Fritz Polking/Peter Arnold, Inc.; **138 inset,** Bruce Davidson/Nature Picture Library; **138–139 bkgrnd,** DLILLC/Corbis; **139 tl inset,** Pixtal/SuperStock; **139 tr inset,** SGM/Stock Connection; **139 bl inset,** Jason Edwards/National Geographic Stock; **139 br inset,** Tom Vezo/Minden Pictures; **141 tl,** Don Hammond/Design Pics/Corbis; **141 tr,** Connie Coleman/Photographer's Choice/Getty Images; **141 br,** Gerard Lacz/Animals Animals/Earth Scenes; **141 bl,** Keith Leighton/Alamy; **142,** Comstock Images/JupiterUnlimited; **143,** Neil Fletcher/Oxford University/Museum of Natural History/Dorling Kindersley; **144 t,** Michael & Patricia Fogden/Minden Pictures/National Geographic Stock; **144 bl,** Andrew J. Martinez/Photo Researchers, Inc.; **144 bm,** Stephen Frink/Photographer's Choice/Getty Images; **144 br,** G. Mermet/Peter Arnold, Inc.; **144 br bkgrnd,** Bill Curtsinger/National Geographic Stock; **144–145 bkgrnd,** D. Hurst/Alamy; **145 t,** B.A.E., Inc./Alamy; **145 ml,** Image Source/SuperStock; **145 mr,** D. Hurst/Alamy; **145 bl,** Photodisc/Alamy; **145 br,** Tatiana Popova/iStockphoto.com; **146 l inset,** Kaz Chiba/Stockbyte/Getty Images; **146 r inset,** Norbert Wu/Minden Pictures; **146 bkgrnd,** Gray Hardel/Corbis; **147,** Purestock/Getty Images; **148,** Thomas Eisner and Daniel Aneshansley/Cornell University; **149 r inset,** Michael DeFreitas Underwater/Alamy; **149 l inset,** Patricia Danna/Animals Animals/Earth Scenes; **149 bkgrnd,** Norbert Wu/Minden Pictures/National Geographic Stock; **150 l inset,** E.R. Degginger/Photo Researchers, Inc.; **150 m inset,** M.I. (Spike) Walker/Alamy; **150 r inset,** Dr. Richard Kessel & Dr. Gene Shih/Getty Images; **150–151 bkgrnd,** Tim Gainey/Alamy; **151 m,** Andrew J. Martinez/Photo Researchers, Inc.; **151 r,** David Fleetham/Mira.com; **151 l,** Sebastian Duda/Shutterstock; **152 arachnid,** Thomas Marent/Minden Pictures/National Geographic Stock; **152 insect,** Dave King/Dorling Kindersley; **152 flower,** JupiterImages/Creatas/Alamy; **152 crustacean,** Dave King/Dorling Kindersley; **152–153 bkgrnd,** Grant Faint/Getty Images; **153 sea cucumber,** Frans Lanting/Corbis; **153 sea star,** Kaz Chiba/Stockbyte/Getty Images; **153 sea urchin,** Brandon D. Cole/Corbis; **153 brittle stars,** Brian Parker/Tom Stack & Associates, Inc.; **154 t inset,** Galen Rowell/Corbis; **154 b,** Konrad Wothe/Animals Animals/Earth Scenes; **155,** Heather Angel/Natural Visions;

156 t inset, Dave King/Dorling Kindersley; **156 bkgrnd,** David Peart/Dorling Kindersley; **157 tl,** Christian Bauer/Tips Images; **157 tr,** Alan & Sandy Carey/Photo Researchers, Inc.; **157 bl,** Fritz Polking/Peter Arnold, Inc.; **157 br,** John Cancalosi/age Fotostock; **158,** Richard Cummins/Corbis; **159 lamprey,** Zigmund Eszczynskii/Animals Animals/Earth Scenes; **159 lamprey mouth,** Heather Angel/Natural Visions/Alamy; **159 goldfish,** Robert Maier/Animals Animals/Earth Scenes; **159 bkgrnd,** Stephen Frink/Getty Images; **160 l inset,** Albert Lleal/Minden Pictures; **160 r inset,** Nick Garbutt/Nature Picture Library; **160–161 bkgrnd,** Alex L. Fradkin/Stockbyte/Getty; **161 t,** Karl Shone/Dorling Kindersley; **161 m inset,** Breck P. Kent/Animals Animals/Earth Scenes; **161 b inset,** Sarah Leen/National Geographic Stock; **162 tl inset,** Hermann Brehm/Nature Picture Library; **162 r inset,** Franco/Bonnard/Peter Arnold, Inc.; **162 bl inset,** Dave Watts/Tom Stack & Associates, Inc.; **162–163 bkgrnd,** Shunsuke Yamamoto Photography/Getty Images; **163 t,** Joe McDonald/Corbis; **163 bl,** Ingo Arndt/Nature Picture Library; **163 br,** Tom McHugh/Photo Researchers, Inc.; **164 t,** SGM/Stock Connection; **164 ml,** Andrew J. Martinez/Photo Researchers, Inc.; **164 mr,** David Fleetham/Mira.com; **164 bl,** Christian Bauer/Tips Images; **164 br,** Ingo Arndt/Nature Picture Library; **166,** JupiterImages; **167 l,** Geoff Brightling/Peter Minister, modelmaker/Dorling Kindersley; **167 m,** Jerry Young/Dorling Kindersley; **167 r,** Stephen Frink/Photographer's Choice/Getty Images.

Interchapter Feature
Page 168, Bart Nedobre/Alamy; **169 t bkgrnd,** Doug Steley C/Alamy; **169 t inset,** Tom McHugh/Photo Researchers, Inc.; **169 b bkgrnd,** Cornel Stefan Achirei/Alamy; **169 b inset,** Ed Reschke/Peter Arnold, Inc.

Chapter 5
Pages 170–171 spread, Michael Durham/Minden Pictures; **173 t,** Warren Photographic; **173 m1,** Piotr Naskrecki/Minden Pictures/National Geographic Stock; **173 m2,** Stephen Dalton/Minden Pictures; **173 b,** Will & Deni McIntyre/Corbis; **174 b,** Alan Carey/Corbis; **174 t,** David A. Northcott/Corbis; **175,** Gallo Images-Denny Allen/Getty Images; **176 t,** Warren Photographic; **176 earthworm,** Frank Greenaway/Dorling Kindersley; **176 shell,** Keith Leighton/Alamy; **176 cicada,** Barry L. Runk/Grant Heilman Photography; **176–177 b bkgrnd,** Vibrant Image Studio/Shutterstock; **178 l,** Piotr Naskrecki/Minden Pictures/National Geographic Stock; **178 r,** Steve Bloom Images/Alamy; **180,** Robert Marien/Corbis; **181,** Stephen Dalton/Minden Pictures; **184 inset,** Geoff Brightling/Dorling Kindersley; **184–185 bkgrnd,** Dave Watts/Nature Picture Library; **185 tr inset,** Michael Habicht/Animals Animals/Earth Scenes; **185 m inset,** Deco Images II/Alamy; **185 br inset,** OSF/Richard Herrmann/Animals Animals/Earth Scenes; **186 kite,** D. Hurst/Alamy; **186 beach,** Platinum GPics/Alamy; **187 m,** Steve Goodwin/iStockphoto.com; **187 r,** Peter Burian/Corbis; **187 l,** M. Delpho/Peter Arnold, Inc.; **189 sea star,** Will & Deni McIntyre/Corbis; **189 penguins,** Blickwinkel/Alamy; **189 frog,** Zigmund Leszczynski/Animals Animals/Earth Scenes; **189 squid,** Mark Conlin/Alamy; **190 t,** Charles Stirling (Diving)/Alamy; **190 m,** Michael Fogden/Animals Animals/Earth Scenes; **190 b inset,** Smaointe/Alamy; **190–191 spread,** Remi Benali/Corbis; **191 tl inset,** Juergen Hasenkopf/Alamy; **191 tr inset,** Stephen Dalton/Animals Animals/Earth Scenes; **191 b inset,** Gallo Images/Alamy; **192 t,** Gijs Bekenkamp/Alamy; **192 b,** Imagebroker/Alamy; **192–193,** PhotoLink/Getty Images; **193 tl inset,** Bob Jensen/Alamy; **193 m,** Idamini/Alamy; **193 butterfly,** Ellen McKnight/Alamy; **193 grass,** D. Hurst/Alamy; **193 tr,** Rolf Richardson/Alamy; **196 t,** Steve Bloom Images/Alamy; **196 m,** Michael Habicht/Animals Animals/Earth Scenes; **196 b,** Rolf Richardson/Alamy; **198,** Gallo Images/Alamy.

Interchapter Feature
Page 200, Stephen Frink/Digital Vision/Getty Images; **201 bkgrnd,** Niels Poulsen/Alamy.

Chapter 6
Pages 202–203 spread, Michael & Patricia Fogden/Minden Pictures; **205 alligator,** Warren Photographic; **205 elephant,** Photodisc; **206 t,** Eric Isselée/iStockphoto; **206 b,** Joel Sartore/National Geographic Stock; **207 caterpillar,** Nancy Nehring/iStock Exclusive/Getty Images; **207 elephant,** Photodisc; **207 raccoon,** Photodisc; **207 lion,** Keith Levit/Shutterstock; **207 bear,** Tom Brakefield/Digital Vision/Getty Images; **207 jellyfish,** Darren Greenwood/Design Pics/JupiterImages; **208 t,** Gregory G. Dimijian/Photo Researchers, Inc.; **208 m,** Mark Newman/Stock Connection; **208 bl,** Panoramic Images/Getty Images; **208 br,** Warren Photographic; **208–209 whale bkgrnd,** Blickwinkel/Alamy; **209 t inset,** Marevision Marevision/age Fotostock; **209 l inset,** Norbert Wu/Minden Pictures; **210 tl,** Steve Kaufman/Photolibrary New York; **210 tr,** Gary Lewis/Photolibrary New York/JupiterImages; **210 b,** Stuart Westmorland/Corbis; **210–211 snake,** Kim Taylor & Jane Burton/Dorling Kindersley; **211 tl,** Rich Reid/National Geographic Stock; **211 tr,** Jeff Rotman Photography; **211 m,** George Grall/National Geographic Stock; **216,** Zigmund Leszczynski/Animals Animals/Earth Scenes; **217,** Mike Kemp/Rubberball Productions/Getty Images; **218,** Mark J. Barrett/Alamy; **219 t,** Jurie Maree/Shutterstock; **219 bl,** Steve Noakes/Shutterstock; **219 br,** Igor Gorelchenkov/Shutterstock; **220 t,** Georgette Douwma/Nature Picture Library; **220 bl,** Rico/Shutterstock; **220 br,** David Fleetham/Visuals Unlimited/Getty Images; **221 t,** Dreamstime.com; **221 m,** George Grall/National Geographic Stock; **221 b,** Lukáš Hejtman/iStockphoto.com; **222 l,** Karen Givens/Shutterstock; **222 r,** Jeffrey Oonk/Minden Pictures; **222 m,** Karen H. Johnson/iStockphoto.com; **223,** Linn Currie/Shutterstock; **224,** Dave Fleetham/Pacific Stock; **225,** Sapsiwai/Shutterstock; **226 t,** Jeff Lepore/Photographer's Choice/Getty Images; **226 b,** Dwight Nadig/iStockphoto.com; **228–229,** Reinhard Dirscherl/Visuals Unlimited/Getty Images; **230,** Eric Isselée/iStockphoto.com; **231,** Robert Stewart/Animals Animals/Earth Scenes; **232–233,** Riccardo Savi/The Image Bank/Getty Images; **234 t,** Stuart Westmorland/Corbis; **234 m,** Igor Gorelchenkov/Shutterstock; **234 b,** Eric Isselée/iStockphoto.com; **235,** Steve Noakes/Shutterstock; **236,** George Grall/National Geographic Stock.

Interchapter Feature
Page 239, Geoff Brightling/Dorling Kindersley; **238,** Natural Visions/Alamy; **238 crab illustration,** Jill Hartley/iStockphoto.com.

ACKNOWLEDGMENTS

Chapter 7
Pages 240–241 spread, Heidi & Hans-Juergen Koch/Minden Pictures; **243 t,** O.S.F./Animals Animals/Earth Scenes; **243 tm,** Juniors Bildarchiv/Photolibrary New York; **243 bm,** Ingo Arndt/Minden Pictures; **243 b,** Stan Osolinski/Corbis; **244 both,** Kathy Keatley Garvey/University of California at Davis Department of Entomology; **245,** Colin Milkins/Photolibrary New York; **246 b,** Paul Bricknell/Dorling Kindersley; **246 t,** Konrad Wothe/Minden Pictures; **247 t,** K.L. Kohn/Shutterstock; **247 b,** Stephen Dalton/Minden Pictures; **250–251,** O.S.F./Animals Animals/Earth Scenes; **252,** David G. Knowles; **253,** Juniors Bildarchiv/Photolibrary New York; **255 inset r,** Alistair Dove/Alamy; **255 bkgrnd,** Andrew J. Martinez/Photo Researchers, Inc.; **255 inset l,** George D. Lepp/Corbis; **256 r,** Ingo Arndt/Minden Pictures; **256 l,** Gladden Williams Willis/Animals Animals/Earth Scenes; **256 m,** SF Photo/Shutterstock; **257 r,** Ingo Arndt/Minden Pictures; **257 l,** Michael Durham/Minden Pictures; **259,** Zigmund Leszczynski/Animals Animals/Earth Scenes; **260–261 t,** WizData, Inc./Shutterstock; **260–261 b,** Robert Sabin/Animals Animals/Earth Scenes; **262 r,** Jesse Kunerth/Shutterstock; **262 l,** Brian Weed/Shutterstock; **263 t,** Cathy Keifer/Shutterstock; **263 b,** Joe Mercier/Shutterstock; **264–265,** Ingo Arndt/Minden Pictures; **265,** Anup Shah/NPL/Minden Pictures; **266–267,** Nina Leen/Getty Images; **268 t,** John Cancalosi/Peter Arnold, Inc.; **268 b,** Tony Wear/Shutterstock; **270,** Ron Cohn/Knight Ridder/Newscom; **271,** Piotr Naskrecki/Minden Pictures; **272,** Linda Freshwaters Arndt/Photo Researchers, Inc.; **272–273,** Mark Turner/Photolibrary New York; **273 tl,** Robert Muth/Shutterstock; **273 b,** Stan Osolinski/Corbis; **273 tr,** Mark Raycroft/Minden Pictures; **274,** Fred Bavendam/Minden Pictures; **276,** Jean-Paul Ferrero/Auscape/Minden Pictures **276–277,** Mark Carwardine/Nature Picture Library; **278 b,** Martin Withers/FLPA/Minden Pictures; **278 t,** Doug Allan/Nature Picture Library; **278–279,** Kevin Schafer/Photolibrary New York; **279,** T.J. Rich/Nature Picture Library; **280 t,** Paul Bricknell/Dorling Kindersley; **280 tm,** Cathy Keifer/Shutterstock; **280 bm,** Joe Mercier/Shutterstock; **280 b,** Piotr Naskrecki/Minden Pictures; **282,** Terry Andrewartha/NPL/Minden Pictures.

Interchapter Feature
Page 284, Mark Conlin/Alamy; **285,** Boris Djuranovic/iStockphoto.com.